The Biochemistry of Copper

The Biochemistry of Copper

Proceedings of the Symposium on

Copper in Biological Systems

Held at Arden House, Harriman, New York,

September 8–10, 1965

Edited by

Jack Peisach

Departments of Pharmacology and Molecular Biology
Albert Einstein College of Medicine
Yeshiva University · Bronx, New York

Philip Aisen

IBM Watson Laboratory · New York, New York
Albert Einstein College of Medicine
Yeshiva University · Bronx, New York

William E. Blumberg

Bell Telephone Laboratories
New York, New York

Academic Press

New York and London   1966

95811

574.1921 B10

0125502508

ACADEMIC PRESS INC.
111 Fifth Avenue, New York, New York 10003

United Kingdom Edition published by
ACADEMIC PRESS INC. (LONDON) LTD.
Berkeley Square House, London W.1

LIBRARY OF CONGRESS CATALOG CARD NUMBER: 66-17289

PRINTED IN THE UNITED STATES OF AMERICA

This book is dedicated to the memory of

John Maurice Nelson
(1876–1965)

A pioneer in the field of copper biochemistry

Contributors and Participants

Numbers in parentheses indicate the pages on which the authors' contributions begin. Those names with no listed numbers are participants only. Asterisk indicates Symposium Organizer.

*PHILIP AISEN, IBM Watson Laboratory, New York, New York, and Albert Einstein College of Medicine, Yeshiva University, Bronx, New York

JAMES O. ALBEN, Department of Physiological Chemistry, Ohio State University, College of Medicine, Columbus, Ohio

NORMAN ASPIN (503), Department of Medical Biophysics, University of Toronto and The Research Institute, The Hospital for Sick Children, Toronto, Canada

ALEXANDER G. BEARN (525), The Rockefeller University, New York, New York

*HELMUT BEINERT (213), Institute for Enzyme Research, University of Wisconsin, Madison, Wisconsin

GEORGE BEMSKI, Department of Medicine, Albert Einstein College of Medicine, Yeshiva University, Bronx, New York

RICHARD BERSOHN, Department of Chemistry, Columbia University, New York, New York

*W. E. BLUMBERG (49), Bell Telephone Laboratories, New York, New York

ESTHER BRESLOW (149), Department of Biochemistry, Cornell University Medical College, New York, New York

A. S. BRILL (67), Department of Molecular Biophysics, Yale University, New Haven, Connecticut

HANS BRINTZINGER, Randall Laboratory, University of Michigan, Ann Arbor, Michigan

LARS BROMAN, Biokemiska Institutionen, Uppsala, Sweden

DAVID W. BROOKS (343), Department of Chemistry, Columbia University, New York, New York

GRAEME F. BRYCE (115), Department of Biochemistry, Indiana University School of Medicine, Indianapolis, Indiana[1]

WINSLOW S. CAUGHEY, Department of Physiological Chemistry, Johns Hopkins University School of Medicine, Baltimore, Maryland

BRITTON CHANCE (293), Johnson Research Foundation, University of Pennsylvania, Philadelphia, Pennsylvania

GERALD COHEN, Department of Biochemistry, College of Physicians and Surgeons, Columbia University, New York, New York

LAWRENCE B. COHEN, Department of Zoology, Columbia University, New York, New York

LUCIEN J. COTE, Parkinson's Disease Information and Research Center, College of Physicians and Surgeons, Columbia University, New York, New York

W. A. CRAMP, Experimental Radiopathology Research Unit, Medical Research Council, Hammersmith Hospital, London, England

*J. N. CUMINGS (545), Department of Chemical Pathology, Institute of Neurology, The National Hospital, London, England

G. CURZON (545), Department of Chemical Pathology, Institute of Neurology, The National Hospital, London, England

*CHARLES R. DAWSON (305, 343), Department of Chemistry, Columbia University, New York, New York

HANS C. FREEMAN (77), School of Chemistry, University of Sydney, Sydney, Australia

EARL FRIEDEN (559), Department of

---

[1] Present address: Department of Molecular Biophysics, Yale University, New Haven, Connecticut.

Chemistry and the Institute of Molecular Biophysics, Florida State University, Tallahassee, Florida

QUENTIN H. GIBSON (235), Johnson Research Foundation, University of Pennsylvania, Philadelphia, Pennsylvania[2]

M. GOLDSTEIN (443), Department of Psychiatry and Neurology, Neurochemistry Laboratories, New York University School of Medicine, New York, New York

D. C. GOULD (35), Department of Biochemistry, University of Oregon Medical School, Portland, Oregon[3]

FRANK R. N. GURD (115), Department of Biochemistry, Indiana University School of Medicine, Indianapolis, Indiana

GORDON R. HAMILTON, Department of Chemistry, Princeton University, Princeton, New Jersey

DAISY I. M. HARRIS, The Research Institute, The Hospital for Sick Children, Toronto, Canada

PETER HEMMERICH (15), Institute for Inorganic Chemistry, University of Basel, Basel, Switzerland

NEIL A. HOLTZMAN, Departments of Biophysics and Pediatrics, Johns Hopkins University School of Medicine, Baltimore, Maryland

DONALD A. JOHNSON (559), Department of Chemistry and the Institute of Molecular Biophysics, Florida State University, Tallahassee, Florida

CHR. KLIXBULL JØRGENSEN (1), Cyanamid European Research Institute, Cologny (Geneva), Switzerland

S. KATOH (407), Charles F. Kettering Research Laboratory, Yellow Springs, Ohio

DENIS KERTESZ (359), Laboratoire de Biochimie Médicale, Faculté de Méde-

cine et de Pharmacie, Marseille, France

THEO P. A. KRUCK (183), Department of Pediatrics, Faculty of Medicine, University of Toronto and The Research Institute, The Hospital for Sick Children, Toronto, Canada

WALTER G. LEVINE (371), Department of Pharmacology, Albert Einstein College of Medicine, Yeshiva University, Bronx, New York

R. LONTIE (455), Laboratory of Biochemistry, University of Louvain, Louvain, Belgium

R. LØVSTAD (537), Institute for Medical Biochemistry, University of Oslo, Oslo, Norway

JAMES A. McDERMOTT (559), Department of Chemistry and the Institute of Molecular Biophysics, Florida State University, Tallahassee, Florida

CHARLES M. McEWEN, JR., Laboratory of Biochemical Pharmacology, National Institute of Arthritis and Metabolic Diseases, National Institutes of Health, Bethesda, Maryland

DAVID H. MacLENNAN (253), Institute for Enzyme Research, University of Wisconsin, Madison, Wisconsin

*BO G. MALMSTRÖM, Göteborgs Universitet, Institutionen för Biokemi, Göteborg, Sweden

*H. S. MASON (35, 339, 465), Department of Biochemistry, University of Oregon Medical School, Portland, Oregon

ANATOL G. MORELL, Department of Medicine, Albert Einstein College of Medicine, Yeshiva University, Bronx, New York

TAKAO NAKAMURA (389), Department of Biophysics and Biochemistry, Faculty of Science, University of Tokyo, Tokyo, Japan

---

[2] Present address: Department of Biochemistry, Cornell University, Ithaca, New York.

[3] Present address: Department of Biochemistry, The Nobel Medical Institute, Stockholm, Sweden.

SAKARI NARA (423), Department of Biochemistry and Biophysics, University of Hawaii, Honolulu, Hawaii[4]

WILLIAM NIEDERMEIER, University of Alabama Medical Center, Birmingham, Alabama

YASUYUKI OGURA (389), Department of Biophysics and Biochemistry, Faculty of Science, University of Tokyo, Tokyo, Japan

TSUNEO OMURA, The Rockefeller University, New York, New York

SHIGEMASA OSAKI (559), Department of Chemistry and the Institute of Molecular Biophysics, Florida State University, Tallahassee, Florida

GRAHAM PALMER, Biophysics Research Division, University of Michigan, Ann Arbor, Michigan

*JACK PEISACH (211), Departments of Pharmacology and Molecular Biology, Albert Einstein College of Medicine, Yeshiva University, Bronx, New York

H. G. PETERING (197), Biochemical Research Division, The Upjohn Company, Kalamazoo, Michigan

SIR RUDOLPH A. PETERS (175), Department of Biochemistry, University of Cambridge, Cambridge, England

WILLIAM N. POILLON (525), The Rockefeller University, New York, New York[5]

HUNTINGTON PORTER (159), Department of Neurology, New England Medical Center Hospitals, and Department of Medicine (Neurology), Tufts University School of Medicine, Boston, Massachusetts

ANTHONY SAN PIETRO (407), Charles F. Kettering Research Laboratory, Yellow Springs, Ohio

BIBUDHENDRA SARKAR (183), Department of Pediatrics, Faculty of Medicine, University of Toronto and The Research Institute, The Hospital for Sick Children, Toronto, Canada

ANDREW SASS-KORTSAK (503), Department of Pediatrics, University of Toronto and The Research Institute, The Hospital for Sick Children, Toronto, Canada

*I. HERBERT SCHEINBERG (513), Department of Medicine, Albert Einstein College of Medicine, Yeshiva University, and The Bronx Municipal Hospital Center, Bronx, New York

JACK SCHUBERT, Department of Occupational Health, Graduate School of Public Health, University of Pittsburgh, Pittsburgh, Pennsylvania

E. C. SLATER (245), Laboratory of Biochemistry, University of Amsterdam, Amsterdam, The Netherlands

IRMIN STERNLIEB, Department of Medicine, Albert Einstein College of Medicine, Yeshiva University, Bronx, New York

MAX R. TAYLOR, The Institute for Cancer Research, Philadelphia, Pennsylvania

ALEXANDER TZAGOLOFF (253), Institute for Enzyme Research, University of Wisconsin, Madison, Wisconsin

TORE VÄNNGÅRD, Fysiska Institutionen, Uppsalas Universitet, Uppsala, Sweden[6]

CORNELIUS VAN DEN HAMER, Department of Medicine, Albert Einstein College of Medicine, Yeshiva University, Bronx, New York

B. F. VAN GELDER (245), Laboratory of Biochemistry, University of Amsterdam, Amsterdam, The Netherlands

---

[4] Present address: Chemical Laboratory, Hokkaido Gakugei University, Hachimancho, Hakodate, Japan.

[5] Present address: Department of Medicine, College of Physicians and Surgeons, Columbia University, New York, New York.

[6] Present address: Göteborgs Universitet, Institutionen för Biokemi, Göteberg, Sweden.

G. J. VanGiessen (197), Biochemical Research Division, The Upjohn Company, Kalamazoo, Michigan

W. Vanneste (465), Department of Biochemistry, University of Oregon Medical School, Portland, Oregon[7]

J. H. Venable, Jr. (67), Department of Molecular Biophysics, Yale University, New Haven, Connecticut[8]

E. Walaas (537), Institute for Medical Biochemistry, University of Oslo, Oslo, Norway

O. Walaas (537), Institute for Medical Biochemistry, University of Oslo, Oslo, Norway

J. M. Walshe (475), Department of Experimental Medicine, University of Cambridge, Cambridge, England

David C. Wharton (235), Institute for Enzyme Research, University of Wisconsin, Madison, Wisconsin[9]

R. J. P. Williams (131), Wadham College and Inorganic Chemistry Laboratory, Oxford University, Oxford, England

R. Witters (455), Laboratory of Biochemistry, University of Louvain, Louvain, Belgium

T. Yamanaka (275), Department of Biology, Faculty of Science, University of Osaka, Osaka, Japan[10]

Kerry T. Yasunobu (423), Department of Biochemistry and Biophysics, University of Hawaii, Honolulu, Hawaii

Takashi Yonetani, Johnson Research Foundation, Department of Biophysics and Biochemistry, University of Pennsylvania, Philadelphia, Pennsylvania

Andreas D. Zuberbühler, Institute for Inorganic Chemistry, University of Basel, Basel, Switzerland

[7] Present address: University of Ghent, Ghent, Belgium.

[8] Present address: Department of Biophysics, King's College, University of London, London, England.

[9] Present address: Department of Biochemistry, University of Virginia, Charlottesville, Virginia.

[10] Present address: Department of Chemistry, University of California, San Diego, La Jolla, California.

Preface

"Why a meeting on the biochemistry of copper?" In the 15 years since the previous conference the direction of research has turned increasingly from the descriptive to the analytical. Perhaps few other areas have witnessed as productive a commingling of traditionally diverse disciplines. Questions generated by biologists catch the fancy of solid state physicists and physical chemists; clinicians and theoreticians find common grounds for discourse. With this rapid expansion of the compass of research in the biology of copper came the need for an exchange of information and views and an exposure of legitimate controversy.

A Symposium Sponsoring Committee was organized in 1964. Members were Drs. Helmut Beinert, J. N. Cumings, Charles R. Dawson, Bo G. Malmström, Howard S. Mason, Jack Peisach, and I. Herbert Scheinberg. The committee was responsible for selecting speakers and discussants. Funds for the attendance of foreign participants and for the operating expenses of the meeting were provided by the National Science Foundation. Arden House afforded a meeting site of great natural beauty, secluded yet reasonably accessible to the transportation terminals of New York City.

Six meeting sessions were held, each with its own chairman. Discussion was held after each paper except for the two series of directly related talks on ceruloplasmin and on cytochrome oxidase; at the close of these sessions general discussions were held.

In preparing this volume the editors have tried to maintain a consistent notation for symbols, abbreviations, and units. The most controversial choice involved the symbols to designate the different oxidation states of copper. Somewhat arbitrarily perhaps, and in cognizance that this violates the recommendations of the International Union of Pure and Applied Chemistry, Commission on Nomenclature, Cu^+ and Cu^{2+} were selected for cuprous and cupric forms, instead of $Cu(I)$ and $Cu(II)$ or Cu^I and Cu^{II}. This is in keeping with notations currently in more common use in biochemistry. These designations, of course, are not intended to suggest that the copper is ionized, and by themselves convey no information about the extent of covalent bonding of the metal to its ligands.

Standard abbreviations used throughout the book include the following:

BAL	Dimercaptopropanol
BCS	Bathocuproinesulfonate
p-CMB	p-Chloromercuribenzoate
p-CMS	p-Chloromercurisulfonate
DOPA	3,4-Dihydroxyphenylalanine
DPD	N,N-Dimethyl-p-phenylenediamine
EDTA	Ethylenediaminetetraacetate
EPR	Electron paramagnetic resonance
NADH	Reduced nicotinamide adenine dinucleotide
PPD	p-Phenylenediamine
Tris	Tris(hydroxymethyl)aminomethane

Finally, we would like to thank the National Science Foundation for financially sponsoring this symposium, Arden House for providing a symposium site especially conducive to the exchange of ideas, Mrs. Roslyn Rubinstein for able secretarial assistance, and Mr. Rudolph Cavalcante for redrawing many of the figures on short notice.

JACK PEISACH
PHILIP AISEN
WILLIAM E. BLUMBERG

April, 1966

Contents

PART 1.   *Chairman: Bo G. Malmström*

The Biochemistry of Copper

Symmetry and Chemical Bonding in Copper-Containing Chromophores

CHR. KLIXBULL JØRGENSEN

Cyanamid European Research Institute
Cologny (Geneva), Switzerland

I. Recent Developments in Ligand Field Theory

The interpretation of absorption spectra (and many other physical properties, say, paramagnetic resonance) of transition group complexes underwent an evolution between 1950 and 1965 similar to that of atomic spectroscopy from 1920 to 1930. It turned out in both cases that one can classify the energy levels by configurations, i.e., one may put zero, one, or two electrons in each of a series of suitably chosen orbitals and obtain agreement with respect to the symmetry types occurring (the quantum numbers parity, S, L, and J in spherical symmetry, for instance). Unfortunately, it is also completely clear that the actual wavefunctions of many-electron systems are not well-defined configurations to any great precision (1) and we do not yet understand why configurations nevertheless are so successful in predicting and classifying the energy levels.

In an isolated atom of spherical symmetry, each nl shell consists of $(2l + 1)$ orbitals having the same radial function. The angular functions of three such p orbitals, five d orbitals, or seven f orbitals are the same as for a one-electron system such as a hydrogen atom. Ligand field theory is essentially the description of weak perturbations of the neighboring atoms or molecules, the ligands, on the behavior of these sets of orbitals in a shell. It has very little to do with fields in the electrostatic sense, and it is an historical accident that the perturbations were represented by an electrostatic potential in most papers from 1929 to about 1955. It is now recognized that chemical bonding is much more important than electrostatic perturbations (for this purpose; not necessarily for the total binding energy) and specifically, those of the three p or five d orbitals directed toward the ligands have higher energy because they correspond to σ-antibonding molecular orbitals. In other words, it is not negative charge on the ligand atoms that repels the p or d electrons on the central atom; the orbitals get higher energy because they have to be orthogonal on the previously filled orbitals of the ligands. A simple description, somewhat related to the Hückel theory of conjugated molecules, is the angular overlap model (2, 3). An excellent introduction to ligand field theory was written by

Orgel (4). The failure of the electrostatic model and the assignment of many spectra are discussed in a book (5) and several reviews (6–9).

Since molecular orbital (MO) theory has been shown to be the appropriate instrument to classify energy levels of transition group complexes containing a partly filled d shell, it follows that the valence-bond treatment is open to some criticism. The fundamental hypothesis that one pair of electrons is responsible for each chemical bond is not very appealing to inorganic chemists. In particular, octahedral compounds such as SiF_6^{2-}, PCl_6^-, SF_6, $(Cr(H_2O)_6)^{3+}$, MnF_6^{2-}, $SnCl_6^{2-}$, and IrF_6 do not necessarily use six orbitals (e.g., Pauling's hybridization d^2sp^3) in order to form six bonds. The fractional delocalization of the molecular orbitals allows for fractional charge distribution on the atoms (i.e., for partly electrovalent bonding), and four of the central atom orbitals (sp^3) or even three (p^3) or one (s) may be the main contributors to the partly covalent bonding. The octet rule is mainly applicable to C, N, and O atoms, forming most of the organic compounds, but it seems to be based on the small atomic radii (allowing at most 4-coordination) to a higher extent than on electronic structure.

There is a certain similarity between the results of MO treatment and Pauling's hybridization theory if not too many d electrons occur in the central atom. Thus, the six σ-bonding orbitals do contain considerable admixtures of $4s$, $4p$, and $3d$ character in an octahedral complex of the first transition group. The three remaining d orbitals which are not involved in σ-bonding can accommodate at most six further electrons, producing low-spin d^6 systems such as $(Co(NH_3)_6)^{3+}$. The real troubles start if more than six d electrons are present. The two σ-antibonding orbitals of pronounced $3d$ character are neglected in the hybridization theory and this prevents a reasonable discussion of the lowest excited levels of $(Co(NH_3)_6)^{3+}$ as well as of $(Cr(H_2O)_6)^{3+}$. If octahedral Ni^{2+} complexes were ever to be covalent in Pauling's sense, the two superfluous electrons would have to be promoted to higher orbitals ($4d$, $5s$, or $5p$), suggesting ready oxidation of the complex to Ni^{4+}.

We use the word chromophore for the cluster consisting of the central atom and directly adjacent ligand atoms (10) and talk about CrO_6 and CoN_6 in the chromic and cobaltic examples. Quadratic cupric chromophores, CuX_4, are one of the main subdivisions of our subject. In Pauling's picture, the four σ-bonding orbitals involve one $4s$, two $4p$, and one $3d$ orbital, quite in agreement with MO theory. However, we do not have merely eight supplementary d electrons to fill in the four available orbitals (as is the case in low-spin quadratic complexes of Ni^{2+}) but nine. The last electron would be expected to go in a nonbonding $4p$ orbital perpendicular to the plane of the chromophore. However, it was found by EPR (11, 12) that the unpaired electron distinctly resides in a σ-antibonding MO containing $3d$ but no $4p$ contributions. It may of course be argued that the class of covalent Cu^{2+} complexes in Pauling's sense is empty, and that all cases studied so far are essentially ionic. However, this is not an easy position to maintain because the continuously variable delocalization of the σ-antibonding orbital suggested by MO theory actually seems to occur according to the physical measurements.

II. The Behavior of $3d^9$ in Distorted Octahedral Cu^{2+} Chromophores

Because only one electron is lacking in a complete $3d$ shell, certain phenomena caused by interelectronic repulsion effects cannot be studied in cupric complexes. This is unfortunate, because such effects supply some of the most direct evidence for the quantitative extent of partly covalent bonding (13). On the other hand, the behavior of the five d-orbital energies is far more variable as a function of the ligands and the external conditions than the behavior of typically octahedral chromophores. Thus, the absorption spectra of the $3d^8$ Ni^{2+} complexes are characterized mainly by the chromophore constitution such as NiO_6 or NiN_6, and the absorption bands of mixed Ni^{2+} complexes of the type $NiO_aN_{(6-a)}$ hardly show any splittings due to deviations from octahedral symmetry (14–22). Orgel and Dunitz (23, 24) pointed out that the local symmetry of Cu^{2+} in crystalline substances frequently is much lower than in similar compounds of the adjacent elements in the periodic table Mn^{2+}, Fe^{2+}, Co^{2+}, Ni^{2+}, and Zn^{2+}. This distortion usually consists of an octahedron CuX_4Y_2 with four unusually short Cu–X distances in a plane and two rather long Cu–Y distances perpendicular to this plane. It is not so surprising that the transmission or reflection spectra of such compounds show a considerable spreading of the five d-orbital energies. Far more surprising is the behavior of $(Cu(H_2O)_6)^{2+}$ and $(Cu(NH_3)_6)^{2+}$ in nearly cubic crystals; the absorption spectrum again gives the impression of strong tetragonal distortions, though not as much as in compounds of $(Cu(NH_3)_4)^{2+}$. The explanation is probably that the optical spectroscopist sees an instantaneous picture of $(Cu(H_2O)_6)^{2+}$, and that, at any given moment, its most probable nuclear positions correspond to four short and two long Cu–O distances. However, the choice of the "long" axis changes very rapidly, and the X-ray crystallographer has to apply extremely refined techniques in order to obtain finer details than the statistical average distribution of cubic symmetry. The positions and relaxation times of the EPR lines of salts of $(Cu(H_2O)_6)^{2+}$ vary in such a way that at some low temperature the choice of axes is "frozen in" and the gyromagnetic ratio g is strongly anisotropic, whereas at higher temperature the EPR experiment takes so many microseconds that a statistical average is observed (25, 26). The instantaneous optical anisotropy occurs even in rigid crystals such as small amounts of Cu^{2+} substituted in cubic MgO (27). The theoretical explanation of these effects is not very clear-cut at the moment; it is certain that it involves certain aspects of the Jahn-Teller effect (28, 29). However, it is doubtful whether numerical calculations of this effect are possible at the moment.

Empirically, the writer (30) proposed considering the ratio R between the total spreading of the five d-orbital energies (i.e., the wave number of the last absorption band due to internal transitions in $3d^9$) in a given Cu^{2+} complex and the energy difference between the two subshells in the corresponding octahedral Ni^{2+} complex with the same ligands. R (also called ν_{Cu}/ν_{Ni}) is rarely below 1.1 and is about 1.45 for Cu^{2+} complexes of six identical ligands such as $(Cu(H_2O)_6)^{2+}$ and $(Cu(NH_3)_6)^{2+}$. If the cupric chromophore CuN_4 occurs as in $(Cu(NH_3)_4)^{2+}$ or $(Cu(en)_2)^{2+}$,[1] R is as large as 1.7. Such species seem only to bind water or other solvent molecules very weakly perpendicular to the plane of four nitrogen atoms. The violet to purple colors of most CuN_4 chromophores correspond to large values of the tetragonality ratio R. The red color of certain solid salts of $(CuL_2)^{2+}$, L being an alkyl-substituted ethylenediamine, as well as the red tetrasuccinimidate (31), represents extreme values of R (31, 32). In these cases, there is really no perpendicular solvation on the quadratic CuN_4. Another typical case is $(Cu(NH_3)_4)(PtCl_4)$ (33). However, no example is known where R is beyond 2. The belief expressed by a few authors that Cu^{2+}-acetylacetonate has $R \sim 2.5$ was recently disproved by Piper and Belford (34). The comparison of different tetragonality for different ligands can be quite interesting (14, 35, 36).[2]

A comparison of formation constants for complexes of a large number of ligands, most frequently nitrogen- or oxygen-containing (37), nearly always confirms the order

$$Cr^{2+} \gg Mn^{2+} < Fe^{2+} < Co^{2+} < Ni^{2+} < Cu^{2+} \gg Zn^{2+} \tag{1}$$

first discussed by Irving and Williams and by Yatsimirskii. There are two rather different explanations of this series. Orgel (4) favors the ligand field stabilization being zero for Mn^{2+} and Zn^{2+} and maximum in octahedral chromophores of Ni^{2+} (14, 38, 39). The adaptation of this theory to Cu^{2+}

---

[1] The abbreviations used are en, ethylenediamine; den, diethylenediamine; tetren, tetraethylenepentamine; trien, triethylenetetramine; bip, 2,2'-bipyridine; phen, o-phenanthroline.

[2] It is sometimes possible to measure spectra of dichroic crystals in polarized light and find two (101) or sometimes all three (102) transitions expected in a quadratic cupric chromophore CuX_4. A similar resolution of solution spectra is much more difficult to perform in a well-defined fashion (11, 45, 103).

complexes necessitates an unusually large spreading of $3d$-orbital energies in tetragonal chromophores because the apparent values of the ligand field stabilization are 1.5 to 2 times larger for typical Cu^{2+} complexes than for the corresponding Ni^{2+} complexes, whereas they would be 0.5 times as large in octahedral symmetry. It might be argued that octahedral Ni^{2+} complexes contain two σ-antibonding electrons, 1.2 less than the "average value" $\frac{2}{5} \cdot 8$ for a nondirectional distribution of the d shell as found in Mn^{2+} and Zn^{2+}, whereas quadratic Cu^{2+} complexes contain only one σ-antibonding electron, 2.6 less than the "average value" $\frac{2}{5} \cdot 9$. However, this is a rather dangerous argument; it would leave open the question of why Zn^{2+} does not assume tetragonal symmetry, and the angular overlap model (3, 40) actually indicates that the total σ-antibonding effect is 1.67 rather than 1 for quadratic Cu^{2+}, as compared with 2 for Ni^{2+}, assuming the *same* internuclear distances. This is probably where the frog jumps; the Cu–O or Cu–N distances are considerably smaller in the plane of four strongly bound ligands, again connected with the Jahn–Teller effect, but our present excuses for this fact tend to go in vicious circles.

Williams (41) assumes that the high electron affinity, i.e., the relatively high electronegativity, of the $3d$ shell in Cu^{2+} is responsible for the stronger covalent bonding of most ligands other than water. This effect is absent in Zn^{2+} and is connected with the electron-transfer spectra in the visible region to be discussed in the next section. It is true, too, that the electron affinity of the gaseous ions $M^{2+} + e^- \rightarrow M^+$ follows the same sequence as Eq. (1); however, the discontinuity between Cr^{2+} and Mn^{2+} is caused by spin-pairing energy due to interelectronic repulsion and not to any variation of the one-electron energies. On the other hand, the Jahn–Teller effect of one σ-antibonding electron operates as well in Cr^{2+} as in Cu^{2+}. The same difficulty meets Williams' explanation that it is expected to be a rather minor correction relative to the different number of σ-antibonding electrons in Ni^{2+} and Cu^{2+}. The reason that sulfide shows a very strong apparent ligand field stabilization with Cu^{2+} (39) may be related either to Williams' ideas or to particularly weak restoring forces counteracting the Jahn–Teller distortion. We are not going to give a general discussion of complex chemistry here, but refer to four recent books (10, 42–44).

III. Mononuclear Cupric Chromophores of Other Symmetries

There is a persistent suspicion that Cu^{2+} in solution frequently forms 5-coordinated complexes with the copper central atom slightly above the plane of the four strongly bound ligand atoms and connected with a single ligand atom on the perpendicular axis. As early as 1932 Bjerrum studied the formation of $(Cu(NH_3)_5)^{2+}$ from $(Cu(NH_3)_4)^{2+}$ and strong aqueous ammonia. This problem was discussed on the basis of the electrostatic model of the ligand field theory in 1954 (45) but many of the inherent assumptions in this treatment are doubtful, as we saw above. At the moment, there is no compelling reason to believe that the pentammine is distorted octahedral $(Cu(NH_3)_5H_2O)^{2+}$.

The main argument for the absence of a center of inversion in these chromophores of tetragonal symmetry is the unusually high intensity of the internal transitions in the $3d^9$ shell. $(Cu(NH_3)_4)^{2+}$ is much darker blue than $(Ni(NH_3)_4(H_2O)_2)^{2+}$, which may, in part, be explained by the lower wave number of the electron-transfer bands in Cu^{2+} than in the corresponding Ni^{2+} complexes, making the vibronic mixing of forbidden and allowed transitions more effective. However, we are here touching upon the much more general question of under what circumstances a molecule adopts a lower symmetry than that potentially available to it, e.g., why H_2O is bent and not linear or why NH_3 is pyramidal and not planar. Gillespie and Nyholm (46, 47) had considerable success, regarding complexes outside of the transition groups, with the idea that lone pairs are somewhat more bulky than ordinary ligand atoms and, for some rather mysterious reason, tend to concentrate on one side of the central atom. There may be weak residual tendencies to similar (instantaneous) distortions in d-group complexes explaining the relatively high band intensities in $(Cu(NH_3)_4)^{2+}$ and $(Co(NH_3)_6)^{3+}$. However, there is no doubt that the pentammines and hexammines of Cu^{2+} show considerably larger intensities than the corresponding tetrammines. A comparison of the diethylenetriamine complexes $(Cu(den)_2)^{2+}$ and $(Cu(den)H_2O)^{2+}$ (14) or of the tetraethylenepentamine complex $(Cu(tetren))^{2+}$ (14)[3] with the triethylenetetramine complex $(Cu(trien))^{2+}$ (48) shows a close analogy with the phenomenon of much stronger bands for $(Cu(NH_3)_5)^{2+}$ than for $(Cu(NH_3)_4)^{2+}$. There are many instances known where the absorption spectra of mixtures of quadratic cupric complexes CuX_4 with another ligand Y are an exact linear combination of the original spectrum and one new spectrum (49, 50). This is not absolutely certain evidence for the presence of a single new species CuX_4Y because its spectrum might fall exactly between that of CuX_4 and CuX_4Y_2, though it is not very probable.

X-Ray crystallographic evidence for Cu^{2+} being out of the plane of the four strongly bound ligands is rather scarce. The cupric dialkyldithiocarbamates such as $Cu(S_2CN(C_2H_5)_2)_2$ seem to contain the square-pyramidal chromophore CuS_5, the fifth sulfur atom originating in another molecule (51, 52). There is also some evidence for trigonal-bipyramidic

---

[3] Cf. also Refs. (107) and (108).

complexes such as $(Cu(bip)_2I)^+$ involving CuN_4I (53). There is no doubt that aqueous solutions of Cu^{2+}–bipyridine and phenanthroline complexes do not exhibit the usual tendency toward quadratic CuN_4 though the actual structure is not yet certain (30, 35). This is a striking difference from octahedral Ni^{2+} complexes of aromatic diimines.

A few years ago, the general opinion was that tetrahedral Cu^{2+} complexes are exceedingly rare. Actually the tetrahalides such as $(CuCl_4)^{2-}$ and $(CuBr_4)^{2-}$ are fairly stable in aprotic organic solvents such as CH_3CN or CH_3NO_2 (54–60). They have some tendency to dissociate to trihalides which may either be $(CuX_3(solvent)_{1 or 2})^-$ or dimers $(X_2CuX_2CuX_2)^{2-}$. However, there is some evidence that the tetrahedra are not regular and really represent an intermediate form between tetrahedral and quadratic chromophores.[4] This is also true for Cu^{2+} complexes of complicated organic ligands designed for favoring tetrahedral coordination (61).

The most interesting information obtained from the halide complexes is the optical electronegativity x_{opt} of the central atom (1, 62). The filled, more or less nonbonding, $3d$ orbitals of Cu^{2+} have invariantly $x_{opt} = 2.3$ whereas the half-filled σ-antibonding orbital (to which the actual electron jump takes place) has $x_{opt} \sim 2.1$ in tetrahedral $(CuX_4)^{2+}$ and $x_{opt} \sim 1.8$ in quadratic and distorted octahedral chromophores. Thus, the strong band at 23,000 cm^{-1} of the analytically important dialkyldithiocarbamates, or the band at 26,000 cm^{-1} of the acetylacetonate (34, 63) is an electron-transfer band, as well as the broad band at 50,000 cm^{-1} of the aquo ion.

Aqueous chloride or bromide solutions containing Cu^{2+} produce electron-transfer bands at considerably larger wave number than $(CuCl_4)^{2-}$ and $(CuBr_4)^{2-}$ (64, 65). One might think that the central atom is more oxidizing, or has a higher x_{opt} in $(CuBr_4)^{2-}$ than in $(Cu(H_2O)_xBr)^+$. However, Barnes and Day (66) gave convincing arguments that the apparent shift of optical electronegativity by some 0.3 unit is due to a charge separation effect (1). It is possible to define anisotropic complexes (67) as an intermediate case between second sphere ion pairs separated by a solvent molecule such as $M(OH_2)X$ and normal complexes. Thus, if the bromide ligand is on an axis perpendicular to the plane of $(Cu(H_2O)_4)^{2+}$, there is no other atom separating Cu and Br, but the internuclear distance is anomalously long, increasing the energy necessary for the electron transfer. Actually, the ion pairs such as $(Cu(en)_2I)^+$, $Cu(en)_2(S_2O_3)$, and $Cu(en)_2(SO_3)$ have distinct new absorption bands in the near ultraviolet (68) and are, of course, in a certain sense 5-coordinated complexes. It is interesting to note that the ion pairs are preferentially formed with polarizable ligands, as if the central atom showed Chatt–Ahrland "type b"

---

[4] A light-yellow, planar $(CuCl_4)^{2-}$ has been reported in $(NH_4)_2CuCl_4$ (104). This species may also occur in $(Pt(NH_3)_4)(CuCl_4)$ (105).

behavior and was "soft" in Pearson's sense (69)[5] as pointed out by Larsson and Tobiason (70) in the case of halide ion pairs formed by $(Co(NH_3)_6)^{3+}$. This is confirmed by the crystal structure of $Cu(en)_2(SCN)_2$, rather different from $Ni(en)_2(NCS)_2$ (71).

IV. Mononuclear Cu³⁺ and Cu⁺ Complexes

The $3d^8$ system Cu^{3+} exists in high-spin octahedral chromophores such as $Cu^{3+}F_6$ and in low-spin quadratic chromophores $Cu^{3+}O_4$ in tellurate and periodate complexes (10) and in $Cu^{3+}S_4$ of certain sulfur-containing ligands (72). However, these species are so oxidizing that they are of little concern to the biochemist.

On the other hand, the low-lying electron-transfer levels of Cu^{2+} complexes of many reducing ligands clearly show that reduction to Cu^+ is an easy process, even retaining the ligands at their normal positions. This is not a trivial point; the stereochemistry of Cu^+ is very different from that of Cu^{2+} and does not involve quadratic chromophores but rather linear Cu^+X_2, trigonal (or pyramidal?) Cu^+X_3 and tetrahedral Cu^+X_4. Actually, Cu^+ is not a typical closed-shell ion such as Zn^{2+} and Ga^{3+}, which show almost no directional chemical bonding. Cu^+ is somewhat similar to Ag^+, Au^+, and Hg^{2+} and is extremely "soft" in Pearson's sense (69), more so than Cu^{2+}, though Cu^{2+} is distinctly the softest member of Eq. (1). Consequently, ligands such as I^- and CN^- tend to reduce Cu^{2+} to Cu^+. The stereochemistry was commented upon by Orgel (73) and produces equilibria of the type

$$(Cu(NH_3)_4)^{2+} + Cu(metal) \rightarrow 2\ (Cu(NH_3)_2)^+$$
$$(Cu(en)_2)^{2+} + Cu(metal) \leftarrow 2\ (Cu(en))^+$$

$$(2)$$

because the bidentate nature of ethylenediamine can be exploited by Cu^{2+} but not by Cu^+. The aquo ion is in an intermediate position; Cu^+ seems, like Ag^+, to bind water very weakly. Pyridine and its derivatives favor the formation of Cu^+ to a slightly larger extent than ammonia (74).

Unfortunately, the absorption spectra of Cu^+ are not well known. It is surprising that the ultraviolet spectra of the $(Cu(CN)_2)^-$, $(Cu(CN)_3)^{2-}$, and $(Cu(CN)_4)^{3-}$, which are all colorless, are so similar (75). Conjugated ligands having low-lying empty π^* orbitals frequently give strongly colored Cu^+ complexes. Thus, Williams (76) discussed the tetrahedral $(Cu(bip)_2)^+$ and $(Cu(phen)_2)^+$ and showed the direction of the "inverted" electron transfer by appropriate substitution in the phenanthroline molecule.

[5] A symposium on soft and hard Lewis acids and bases was held at the Cyanamid European Research Institute in May, 1965 (106).

Another aspect of the "soft" behavior of Cu^+ is the ability, at least with certain organic ligands, to combine with O_2. Frequently, only a very small stationary concentration of such an adduct can be detected (77) because it rapidly forms Cu^{2+}. One would expect such adducts to show electron-transfer bands due to formation of Cu^{2+} and O_2^- in the excited state, obeying the Franck–Condon principle by conserving the internuclear distances during the very short period of optical excitation. Incidentally, electron transfer in the opposite direction has been observed in solutions of O_2^- in pyridine (78) where the excited state probably involves an electron in a π^* orbital of pyridine and O_2.

Fe^{2+}, Fe^{3+} and Cu^+, Cu^{2+} are the two most common one-electron redox systems of biological importance. Many other transition group elements have a variety of oxidation states; some of them, such as vanadium and molybdenum, have been identified in organisms; others, such as ruthenium, rhenium, and iridium, have not yet been reported. Cu^{2+} forms stronger complexes with most ligands than other divalent metals studied, with the exception of Pd^{2+} and Hg^{2+} (37). In preparative organic chemistry, Cu is known to participate in many reactions (79). A final aspect to be discussed is the remarkable tendency of forming dinuclear Cu^+–Cu^{2+} or Cu^{2+}–Cu^{2+} complexes.

V. Dinuclear and Polynuclear Copper Complexes

A large number of crystal structures have been shown to contain two Cu^{2+} connected with one or two oxygen atoms from an organic ligand inducing a higher coordination number than expected from the chemical formula (80). Such compounds frequently have a lower magnetic susceptibility than mononuclear Cu^{2+} complexes because of antiferromagnetic interactions. Similar behavior is noted in many dihydroxy dimers of the type $L_2Cu(OH)_2CuL_2$ (81, 82) and in planar dimers $(Cl_2CuCl_2CuCl_2)^{2-}$ (83) and $L_2CuCl_2CuL_2$ (84) and may possibly occur in biological environments.

Dimers with direct Cu–Cu bonds were pointed out by Tsuchida and Yamada (85), who discovered a new absorption band at 27,000 cm^{-1} in Cu^{2+}-acetate and heavier alkanoates $Cu_2(O_2CR)_4(H_2O)_2$. It is difficult to know exactly how important the Cu–Cu bonding is for the total bonding energy of the molecule, because the four carboxylate groups each are connected to both Cu atoms, similarly to the basic beryllium acetate $OBe_4(O_2CCH_3)_6$. The most plausible model of the Cu–Cu bond is a weak antiferromagnetic interaction between the two half-filled δ orbitals (x^2-y^2) (86–88). Forster and Ballhausen's proposal of a stronger σ bond (89) is not probable because the concomitant full occupation of the $(x^2 - y^2)$ orbitals would be expected to modify to Cu–O distances (10, p. 172). Actually, these distances have their usual low values in $Cu_2(O_2CCH_3)_4(C_5H_5N)_2$ (90, 91).

Also Cu^+ compounds are frequently polymeric. Hesse (92) reports $((C_2H_5)_2NCS_2Cu)_4$ with a central tetrahedron consisting of four Cu^+ atoms, whereas the analogous Au^+ compound is dimeric. In phosphorescent compounds such as ZnS, the exact nature of Cu dimers is not yet known (93, 94). Glass makers have been familiar with many types of Cu-containing chromophores and of colloidal Cu metal (95). Though Nyholm (96) considers Cu as a sort of pseudohalogen, and indeed, the gaseous molecule Cu_2 has an unusually high dissociation energy and Cu and Au form many organometallic compounds, it is doubtful at present whether such intermetallic bonding may occur in biochemistry. On the other hand, mixed oxidation numbers may be of considerable interest. Salts of $(Cu_2Cl_9)^{6-}$, apparently containing Cu^+-Cu^{2+}, are dark colored (97, 98). The intensely violet $Cu^{2+}(RSCu^+)_4$ is not so paradoxical (99) when compared with other mercaptide-bridged complexes (100).

It seems indeed just and fit that the element deriving its name from the island of Aphrodite shows so unexpected and fascinating, even sometimes irritatingly complex, properties. Copper has the most complicated and varying stereochemistry among the $3d$-group elements, with the possible exception of vanadium (the name of which derives from Aphrodite's Scandinavian colleague). We have a very incomplete picture of how immensely much we do not yet know.

REFERENCES

1. Jørgensen, C. K., "Orbitals in atoms and molecules." Academic Press Inc., New York, 1962.
2. Jørgensen, C. K., Pappalardo, R., and Schmidtke, H. H., *J. Chem. Phys.*, **39**, 1422 (1963).
3. Schäffer, C. E., and Jørgensen, C. K., *Mol. Phys.*, **9**, 401 (1965).
4. Orgel, L. E. "An introduction to transition-metal chemistry." John Wiley and Sons, Inc., New York, 1960.
5. Jørgensen, C. K., "Absorption spectra and chemical bonding in complexes." Addison-Wesley (Pergamon), Reading, Mass., 1962.
6. Jørgensen, C. K., *Advan. Chem. Phys.*, **5**, 33 (1963).
7. Jørgensen, C. K., *Advan. Chem. Phys.*, **8**, 47 (1965).
8. Jørgensen, C. K. *Proc. Summer School in Milano*, 1963 (Director, M. Simonetta), Fondazione Donegani, Accademia Nazionale dei Lincei, Rome, 1965.
9. Jørgensen, C. K., *Z. Naturw. Mediz. Grundlagenforsch.*, **2**, 248 (1965).
10. Jørgensen, C. K., "Inorganic complexes." Academic Press Inc., New York, 1963.
11. Belford, R. L., Calvin, M., and Belford, G., *J. Chem. Phys.*, **26**, 1165 (1957).
12. Maki, A. H., and McGarvey, B. R., *J. Chem. Phys.*, **29**, 31, 35 (1958).

13. Jørgensen, C. K., *Progr. Inorg. Chem.*, **4,** 73 (1962).
14. Jørgensen, C. K., *Acta Chem. Scand.*, **10,** 887 (1956).
15. Bostrup, O., and Jørgensen, C. K., *Acta Chem. Scand.*, **11,** 1223 (1957).
16. Pelletier, S., *J. Chim. Phys.*, **57,** 287, 306 (1960).
17. Drago, R. S., Meek, D. W., Joesten, M. D., and LaRoche, L., *Inorg. Chem.*, **2,** 124 (1963).
18. Drago, R. S., Meek, D. W., Longhi, R., and Joesten, M. D., *Inorg. Chem.*, **2,** 1056 (1963).
19. Goodgame, D. M. L., and Venanzi, L. M., *J. Chem. Soc.*, pp. 616, 5909 (1963).
20. Lever, A. B. P., Lewis, J., and Nyholm, R. S., *J. Chem. Soc.*, p. 4761 (1964).
21. Ludwig, W., and Wittmann, G., *Helv. Chim. Acta*, **47,** 1265 (1964).
22. Nelson, S. M., and Shepherd, T. M., *J. Chem. Soc.*, p. 3276 (1965).
23. Orgel, L. E., and Dunitz, J. D., *Nature*, **179,** 462 (1957).
24. Dunitz, J. D., and Orgel, L. E., *Advan. Inorg. Chem. Radiochem.*, **2,** 1 (1960).
25. McClure, D. S., *Solid State Phys.*, **9,** 399 (1959).
26. Low, W., "Paramagnetic resonance in solids." Academic Press Inc., New York, 1960.
27. Schmitz-DuMont, O., and Fendel, H., *Monatsh.*, **96,** 495 (1965).
28. Opik, U., and Pryce, M. H. L., *Proc. Roy. Soc. (London), Ser. A.*, **238,** 425 (1957).
29. Lohr, L. L., and Lipscomb, W. N., *Inorg. Chem.*, **2,** 911 (1963).
30. Jørgensen, C. K., *Acta Chem. Scand.*, **9,** 1362 (1955).
31. Yamada, S., and Miki, S., *Bull. Chem. Soc. Japan*, **36,** 680 (1963).
32. Hatfield, W. E., Piper, T. S., and Klabunde, U., *Inorg. Chem.*, **2,** 629 (1963).
33. Day. P., Orchard, A. F., Thomson, A. J., and Williams, R. J. P., *J. Chem. Phys.*, **42,** 1973 (1965).
34. Piper, T. S., and Belford, R. L., *Mol. Phys.*, **5,** 169 (1962).
35. James, B. R., Parris, M., and Williams, R. J. P., *J. Chem. Soc.*, p. 4630 (1961).
36. Baillie, M. J., Brown, D. H., Moss, K. C., and Sharp, D. W. A., *Chem. Comm.*, p. 91 (1965).
37. Sillén, L. G., and Martell, A. E., *Chem. Soc. (London) Spec. Publ.* **17,** (1964).
38. Bjerrum, J., and Jørgensen, C. K., *Rec. Trav. Chim. Pays-Bas*, **75,** 658 (1956).
39. George, P., and McClure, D. S., *Progr. Inorg. Chem.*, **1,** 382 (1959).
40. Jørgensen, C. K., *J. Physique*, **26,** 825 (1965).
41. Williams, R. J. P., *Discuss. Faraday Soc.*, **26,** 123, 180 (1958).
42. Rossotti, F. J. C., and Rossotti, H., "The determination of stability constants and other equilibrium constants in solution." McGraw-Hill Book Company, Inc., New York, 1961.
43. Dwyer, F. P., and Mellor, D. P., (eds.) "Chelating agents and metal chelates." Academic Press Inc., New York, 1964.
44. Jones, M. M., "Elementary coordination chemistry." Prentice-Hall, Inc., Englewood Cliffs, New Jersey, 1964.
45. Bjerrum, J., Ballhausen, C. J., and Jørgensen, C. K., *Acta Chem. Scand.*, **8,** 1275 (1954).
46. Gillespie, R. J., and Nyholm, R. S., *Quart. Rev. (London)*, **11,** 339 (1957).
47. Gillespie, R. J., *J. Chem. Educ.*, **40,** 295 (1963).
48. House, D. A., and Curtis, N. F., *J. Chem. Soc.*, p. 3149 (1963).
49. Jørgensen, C. K., *Acta Chem. Scand.*, **8,** 175 (1954).
50. Gillard, R. D., and Wilkinson, G., *J. Chem. Soc.*, p. 5399 (1963).
51. Pignedou, A., and Peyronel, G., *Gazz. Chim. Ital.*, **92,** 745 (1962).
52. Bally, R., *Compt. Rend.*, **257,** 425 (1963).

53. Barclay, G. A., Hoskins, B. F., and Kennard, C. H. L., *J. Chem. Soc.*, p. 5691 (1963).
54. Gill, N. S., and Nyholm, R. S., *J. Chem. Soc.*, p. 3997 (1959).
55. Furlani, C., and Morpurgo, G., *Theor. Chim. Acta*, **1,** 102 (1963).
56. Schneider, W., and Zelewsky, A. V., *Helv. Chim. Acta*, **46,** 1848 (1963).
57. Barnes, J. C., and Hume, D. N., *Inorg. Chem.*, **2,** 445 (1963).
58. Ferguson, J., *J. Chem. Phys.*, **40,** 3406 (1964).
59. Morosin, B., and Lawson, K., *J. Mol. Spectr.*, **12,** 98 (1964).
60. Day, P., and Jørgensen, C. K., *J. Chem. Soc.*, p. 6226 (1964).
61. Cheeseman, T. P., Hall, F., and Waters, T. N., *Proc. Chem. Soc.*, p. 379 (1963).
62. Jørgensen, C. K., *Mol. Phys.*, **6,** 43 (1963).
63. Jørgensen, C. K., *Acta Chem. Scand.*, **16,** 2406 (1962).
64. Doehlemann, E., and Fromherz, H., *Z. Physik. Chem.*, **A171,** 371 (1934).
65. Bjerrum, J., *Mat. Fys. Medd. Dan. Vid. Selsk.*, **22,** No. 18 (1946).
66. Barnes, J. C., and Day, P., *J. Chem. Soc.*, p. 3886 (1964).
67. Jørgensen, C. K., Proc. Symp. Coordination Chemistry, Tihany, 1964, Hungarian Academy of Science, Budapest, 1965.
68. Yoneda, H., *Bull. Chem. Soc. Japan*, **29,** 68 (1956).
69. Pearson, R. G., *J. Am. Chem. Soc.*, **85,** 3533 (1963).
70. Larsson, R., and Tobiason, I., *Acta Chem. Scand.*, **16,** 1919 (1962).
71. Brown, B. W., and Lingafelter, E. C., *Acta Cryst.*, **17,** 254 (1964).
72. Shupack, S. I., Billig, E., Clark, R. J. H., Williams, R., and Gray, H. B., *J. Am. Chem. Soc.*, **86,** 4594 (1964).
73. Orgel, L. E., *J. Chem. Soc.*, p. 4186 (1958).
74. Hawkins, C. J., and Perrin, D. D., *J. Chem. Soc.*, p. 1351 (1962).
75. Simpson, E. A., and Waind, G. M., *J. Chem.*, p. 1746 (1958).
76. Williams, R. J. P., *J. Chem. Soc.*, p. 137 (1955).
77. Nord, H. *Acta Chem. Scand.*, **9,** 430,438,442 (1955).
78. Slough, W., *Chem. Comm.*, p. 184 (1965).
79. Bacon, R. G. R., and Hill, H. A. O., *Quart. Rev. (London)*, **19,** 95 (1965).
80. Kato, M., Jonassen, H. B., and Fanning, J. C., *Chem. Rev.*, **64,** 99 (1964).
81. Young, J. E., and Murmann, R. K., *J. Phys. Chem.*, **67,** 2647 (1963).
82. McWhinnie, W. R., *J. Chem. Soc.*, pp. 2959, 5165 (1964).
83. Willett, R. D., Dwiggins, C., Kruh, R. F., and Rundle, R. E., *J. Chem. Phys.*, **38,** 2429 (1963).
84. Willett, R. D., and Rundle, R. E., *J. Chem. Phys.*, **40,** 838 (1964).
85. Tsuchida, R., and Yamada, S., *Nature*, **176,** 1171 (1955).
86. Ross, I. G., *Trans. Faraday Soc.*, **55,** 1057 (1959).
87. Boudreaux, E. A., *Inorg. Chem.*, **3,** 506 (1964).
88. Tonnet, M. L., Yamada, S., and Ross, I. G., *Trans. Faraday Soc.*, **60,** 840 (1964).
89. Forster, L. S., and Ballhausen, C. J., *Acta Chem. Scand.*, **16,** 1385 (1962).
90. Barclay, G. A., and Kennard, C. H. L., *J. Chem. Soc.*, p. 5244 (1961).
91. Hanic, F., Stempelová, D., and Hanicová, K., *Acta Cryst.*, **17,** 633 (1964).
92. Hesse, R., *Arkiv Kemi.*, **20,** 481 (1963).
93. Kröger, F. A., *Ergeb. Exakt. Naturw.*, **29,** 61 (1956).
94. Blicks, H., Riehl, N., and Sizmann, R., *Z. Physik.*, **163,** 594 (1961).
95. Weyl, W. A., "Coloured glasses." Dawson, London, 1959.
96. Nyholm, R. S., *Proc. Chem. Soc.*, p. 273 (1961).
97. Mori, M., *Bull. Chem. Soc. Japan*, **33,** 985 (1960).
98. Culpin, D., Day, P., Edwards, P. R., and Williams, R. J. P., *Chem. Comm.*, p. 450 (1965).

99. Klotz, I. M., Czerlinski, G. H., and Fiess, H. A., *J. Am. Chem. Soc.*, **80**, 2920 (1958).
100. Jicha, D. C., and Busch, D. H., *Inorg. Chem.*, **1**, 872, 878 (1962).
101. Yamada, S., and Tsuchida, R., *Bull. Chem. Soc. Japan*, **29**, 289 (1956).
102. Chakravorty, A., and Basu, S., *J. Inorg. Nucl. Chem.*, **17**, 55 (1961).
103. Basu, G., and Basu, S., *Z. Physik. Chem. (Leipzig)*, **215**, 309 (1960).
104. Willett, R. D., *J. Chem. Phys.*, **41**, 2243 (1964).
105. Hatfield, W. E., and Piper, T. S., *Inorg. Chem.*, **3**, 841 (1964).
106. ——, *Chem. Eng. News*, 31 May, p. 90 (1965).
107. Paoletti, P., and Vacca, A., *J. Chem. Soc.*, p. 5051 (1964).
108. Sacconi, L., Paoletti, P., and Ciampolini, M., *J. Chem. Soc.*, p. 5046 (1964).

DISCUSSION

DR. MASON: May I ask what experimental methods are available to measure the extent of the vibration of the ligands away from the average position?

DR. JØRGENSEN: There would be a variety of plausible methods, but not any of them are extremely satisfactory. One of them, of course, is the appearance of abnormal overtones having too much intensity and displaced wave numbers in the infrared spectrum. A second one is an anisotropic vibrational temperature factor for the X-ray scattering.

It is surprising to what extent, for instance, copper dithiocarbamates and a variety of other species show the copper out of the plane of the four sulfurs in their crystal structures. Now, unfortunately, I must admit that all of these cases are really 5-coordinated. I don't think at present there is a case of a 4-coordinated complex where one is certain that the metal is out of the plane to any great extent.

DR. FREEMAN: I should like to comment on the question, to what extent a 4-coordinated Cu^{2+} atom can deviate from the plane of the four closest donor atoms. Table X of my paper in this volume contains the relevant data available from crystal structure analyses of five copper–amino acid and copper–peptide complexes. The deviations of the copper atoms from the best planes through the atoms of the coordination squares range from 0.05 to 0.25 Å; the deviations of the donor atoms lie between 0.001 and 0.16 Å. In only one of these five complexes, however, does the Cu^{2+} have coordination number 4 [formula (XIII), Freeman].

In nine other crystals the copper atoms (no matter what their total coordination numbers) are coplanar with their four closest neighbors. In all these cases they are *required to be coplanar* by the *reported crystallographic symmetry*. In fact, none of the copper atoms in amino acid complexes is strictly square-planar unless it lies at a center of symmetry. When a chelate ring is formed, how does the ligand know that its metal atom lies at a center of symmetry, so that the two donor atoms must be coplanar with two others on the other side of the metal? Very precise X-ray diffraction data would be required to distinguish between centrosymmetric (planar) and *almost* centrosymmetric (slightly distorted) structures in these complexes, and it is possible that some of them have been reported as having higher symmetries than they actually possess.

DR. OSAKI: In relation to this paper we want to present a convenient model (Fig. 1) of blue copper proteins: Cu-bisacetaldehydeoxalyldihydrazone.

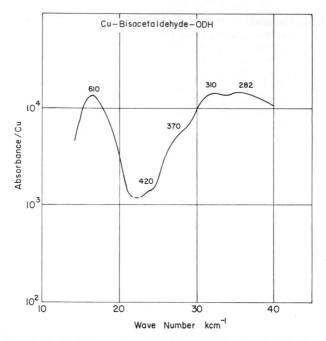

Fɪɢ. 1. Optical Absorption of Cu-bisacetaldehydeoxalyldihydrazone.

The optical absorption of this complex, as shown in the figure, has a striking similarity to the spectra of laccase and ceruloplasmin. This has bands at 610, 420, 370, 310, and 282 mµ. I think the absorptions in the visible region are due to charge transfer from the ligands to the copper. Also, it is very strange, but at 1 mM concentration this compound shows no copper EPR signal.

Dʀ. Jøʀɢᴇɴsᴇɴ: May I be permitted to say that the very high intensities of some copper complexes and blue copper proteins must correspond to an electron-transfer band, and hence not all blue copper complexes are blue because of the internal transitions in the d shell. Of course a very fascinating question is the situation of a cuprous complex where the ligands lack an electron. This has recently been described, for instance, by Gray in connection with sulfur-containing ligands conjugated to olefinic bonds. It also must be stressed that this delocalization only occurs in sulfur-containing *conjugated* systems. The dithiophosphates and dithiocarbamates are all completely "innocent" in the sense of allowing a well-defined oxidation state of the central atom. As to whether this hydrazone ligand could have the electron carrying the uncompensated spin completely delocalized, I'm not quite certain. I have a feeling that it is a normal copper compound having an electron-transfer band.

Model Studies on the Binding of Univalent and Redox-Active Copper in Proteins*

PETER HEMMERICH

Institute for Inorganic Chemistry,
University of Basel,
Basel, Switzerland

I. Introduction

It was not until EPR spectroscopy became available that copper could be demonstrated to participate directly in electron transfer catalyzed by copper proteins (1). On the other hand, the disappearance of the Cu^{2+} EPR signal upon reduction does not strictly prove that a change in copper valency has occurred; neither does the absence of EPR absorption disprove the active presence of Cu^{2+} at the redox-active site for two reasons:

(a)   Upon uptake of an electron by the protein, the Cu^{2+}-coordination sphere might be changed sufficiently to quench, broaden, or annihilate EPR absorption without alteration of the d^9 configuration at the metal, especially in the case of binuclear active units (2).

(b)   The valence of copper in certain copper proteins might be indeterminable (3).

Both cases are related since both imply the interaction of two copper nuclei or the cooperation of redox-active prosthetic groups of the protein. The first case means full localization; the second, partial localization of the extra electron at the redox-active ligand. In both cases, however, copper must be expected to be indispensable for the stabilization of the ligand redox system. The most obvious example of such a system is cytochrome *c* oxidase. The most recent data on its copper "site" may be summarized as follows, from the work of Beinert's group (1):

(a)   Oxidized enzyme shows about *one* EPR-active copper (per 2 heme units) per mole.
(b)   Reduced enzyme shows *no* EPR-active copper.
(c)   Urea-denatured enzyme (aerobic or anaerobic) shows *no* EPR-active copper.

* This program has been sponsored by the Swiss National Foundation for the Advancement of Scientific Research. Part of the work was done at the Institute for Enzyme Research, Madison, Wisconsin, during the author's stay as a visiting scientist in 1964, in cooperation with Dr. H. Beinert.

15

(d) Mercurial-pretreated, urea-denatured enzyme shows *two* EPR-active copper atoms.

Since cytochrome c oxidase is a four-electron acceptor system (as was established unequivocally by Slater and van Gelder (4)), one has to conclude that the second copper is "EPR inactive Cu^{2+}," or an "O_2 inert Cu^+," the electron being taken up by a ligand alone. The present contribution is devoted to studies that might clarify these points by comparison of the proteins with suitable, well-defined model complexes of copper and ligands that simulate the structure at the active site of proteins. In other words, we shall ask, What are the conditions that have to be fulfilled by the Cu-coordination sphere in order to establish redox activity in the physiological range? The answer will be:

(a) "O_2-inert Cu^+" seems to be confined to complexes with ligands providing empty orbitals of low energy and suitable symmetry to delocalize electrons from the d^{10} shell. The more electron-attracting the ligand, the more indeterminable is the actual valence of the metal.

(b) "EPR-inactive Cu^{2+}" seems to be confined to complexes with ligands providing filled orbitals of high energy and suitable symmetry to delocalize ligand electrons toward the d^9 shell. The more electron-donating the ligand, the more indeterminable is the actual valence of the metal.

Thus, in the borderline case, "EPR-inactive Cu^{2+}" and "O_2-inert Cu^+" will turn out to be the same, i.e., copper of indeterminable valence.

In cytochrome c oxidase, the second copper becomes EPR active upon denaturation in the presence of a mercaptide-blocking mercurial. Hence, if the native valence of this copper was 2, mercaptide must be suspected as an "EPR-inactivating" ligand of Cu^{2+}. If, however, the native valence was 1, an electron had to disappear "somewhere" upon denaturation. Consequently, under careful exclusion of air, the extra electron was to be found in the heme or in the protein. Therefore, experiments were done by this author with Dr. Beinert in order to assure that denaturation was not accompanied by reduction of heme and this was shown unequivocally by the unaltered reflection spectrum of oxidized heme a in the concentrated heat-denatured enzyme solution under aerobic as well as carefully anaerobic conditions with and without mercurial.

Thus, an eventual electron transfer has to occur with the protein. The only prosthetic protein group that might be "reduced" in that way is disulfide. Hence, disulfide was suspected as a ligand rendering Cu^+ inert toward oxygen.

Since disulfide is a two-electron redox system, whereas copper is a one-electron system, the metal valence would be indeterminable either if two copper nuclei should interact with one disulfide or if copper should stabilize disulfide as a one-electron acceptor, i.e., if it should stabilize "sulfur radical"

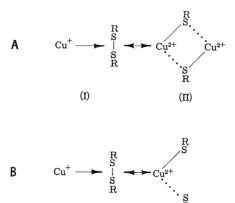

(I–IV), by what is called "valence mesomerism." The suspicion that a sulfur ligand is involved in the binding of redox-active copper in proteins dates from the investigations of Klotz *et al.* (5) on hemocyanin. Thinking along these lines was supported by the results of Malmström, who found many indications for the interaction of two differently bound copper atoms contained at one enzyme-active site (2).

II. The Basic Inorganic Facts

It is well known that cupric copper reacts with mercaptides to give cuprous copper and disulfide (6, 7). It is less well known that this reaction is reversible

$$Cu^{2+} + RS^- \rightleftarrows Cu^+ + \tfrac{1}{2} (RS)_2 \qquad (1)$$

and can only proceed toward the right if care is taken that the cuprous copper formed is stabilized by autoxidation or complexation with suitable ligands, the strongest of which is RS^- itself. Thus the full equation is (7), in the absence of air and *in the presence of excess RS⁻*,

$$Cu^{2+} + 2\,RS^- \rightleftarrows \tfrac{1}{2} (RS)_2 + CuSR \qquad (2)$$

If, on the other hand, Cu^{2+} is in excess, the reaction proceeds toward a very complicated equilibrium state involving the polynuclear products of the reaction $CuSR + Cu^{2+}$, which are not yet well established. Since CuSR exists in the form of a linear macromolecule involving $Cu–(RS)\cdots Cu$ bonds, the degree of (reversible) polymerization depends on many environmental factors (solubility, pH, buffer strength, and specificity). In any case, reaction (1) does not proceed to completion unless an additional Cu^+-specific agent is present in the environment. For example, at pH 5–6, the reaction appears to proceed through a state of indeterminable valence, Eq. (3), if Cu^{2+} is present in excess (see below).

$$2 Cu^{2+} + 2 RS^- \rightleftarrows (Cu_2(RS)_2)^{2+} \rightleftarrows (RS)_2 + 2 Cu^+ \qquad (3, 4)$$

The same state can be obtained from Cu^+ and disulfide, Eq. (4). Thus, the complex participates in two independent equilibria, one at the Cu^+, the other at the Cu^{2+} level. Addition of Cu^{2+}-specific agents (buffers) shifts Eq. (3) to the left, whereas Cu^+-specific agents shift Eq. (4) to the right. $Cu_2(RS)_2^{2+}$ has at least two more coordination positions to be occupied by buffer or solvent ligand or by additional functions contained in the residue R, which would contribute to the stability by their "valence specificity" but may contribute only to a minor extent to the color of the system.

III. Cu^+- and Cu^{2+}-Specific Agents

"Metal specificity" and "valence specificity" are two expressions widely misued in the literature, since kinetic, thermodynamic, and even analytical "specificity" are confused with each other. Thus, the valence specificity of 2,2'-bipyridine[1] for Fe^{2+} over Fe^{3+} is based on the fact that $(Fe(bip)_3)^{3+}$ formation is very slow (kinetic specificity). The specificity of bipyridine for Cu^+ (over Cu^{2+}) is merely an analytical specificity, because $(Cu(bip)_2)^+$ is a dull red complex, whereas $(Cu(bip)_2)^{2+}$ has no intense color. Clearly, specificity of that kind cannot be adapted to the study of equilibria or valence states in constituents of redox systems. Hence, the term "valence specificity" as used in this paper has a strictly thermodynamic meaning, i.e., a given "Cu^+-specific agent" should have no measurable thermodynamic affinity toward Cu^{2+} and vice versa, or there should be at least a difference of many orders of magnitude in the "valence affinities." The best criterion for valence specificity in the case of copper is based on Pearson's concept of "hard and soft acids and bases" (8), since Cu^{2+} is a (relatively) hard acid, whereas Cu^+ is a very soft one. Hence, valence specificity should be strongest among weak ligands, "weak-and-soft" ligands like thiourea, thioethers, disulfides, nitriles, and carboxylic imidates, all being Cu^+-specific, and "weak-and-hard" ligands like carboxylates, water, phenolates, and amino acids, which are Cu^{2+}-specific.

On the other hand, "strong-and-soft" ligands, like cyanide, iodide, and mercaptide will demonstrate their Cu^+ specificity by reducing Cu^{2+},

[1] The abbreviations used are: bip, 2,2'-bipyridine; ImH, imidazole.

whereas "strong-and-hard" ligands will show their Cu^{2+} specificity by causing disproportionation of Cu^+ as do aliphatic α-amino acids and 1,2-diamines (see below).

IV. The Cu Affinity of Functional Groups in Proteins

The Cu^{2+} affinities of functional groups in proteins are well known. The striking feature of Cu^{2+}-protein coordination is the high stability of five-membered chelate rings involving deprotonation of a peptide nitrogen as in (V) [e.g , Ref. (9)].

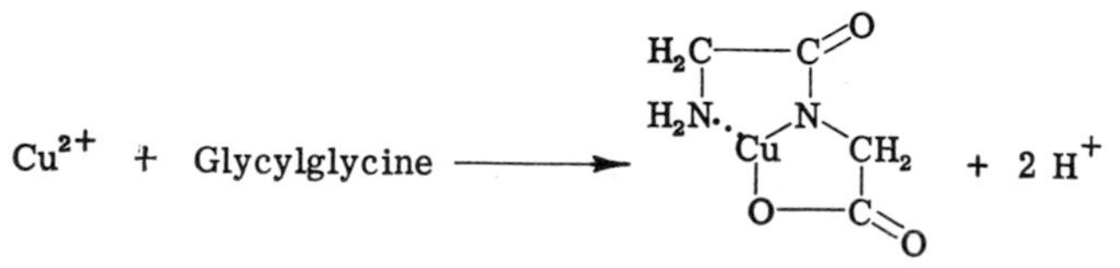

$$Cu^{2+} \; + \; Glycylglycine \longrightarrow \qquad\qquad + \; 2\,H^+$$

(V)

Attention should be paid, however, to the fact that a five-membered chelate ring involving deprotonation of two peptide NH groups, as in (VI), has no stability in itself, at least not under aqueous conditions,

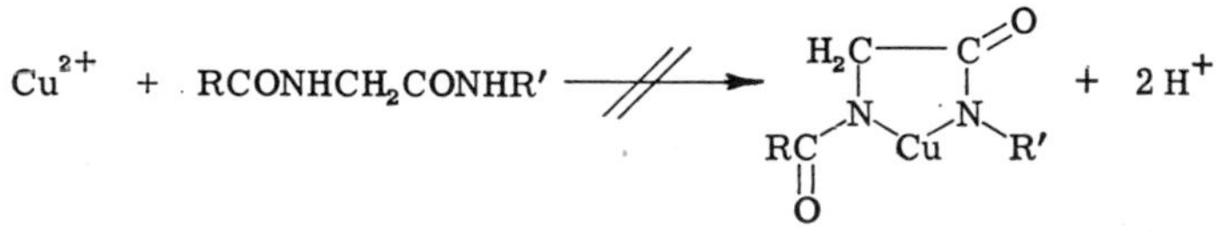

$$Cu^{2+} \; + \; RCONHCH_2CONHR' \longrightarrow\!\!\!/\!\!\!/ \qquad\qquad + \; 2\,H^+$$

(VI)

i.e., if water efficiently competes for coordination. Thus, in a multidentate Cu^{2+}-protein complex, formation of macrocyclic chelate rings may be the rule rather than the exception.

On the other hand, Cu affinities of protein prosthetic groups may be classified from what has been said above as follows:

(a) Cu^{2+}-specific:

—COO⁻, ArO⁻ (Tyr), RO⁻(Ser, Thr),

—NHC(NH)NH₂(Arg), —CONH—, —NH₂(Lys).

(b) Cu^+-specific: R_2S(Met), RSSR (cystine).

(c) Nonspecific: imidazole (His), RS⁻ (cysteine).

The classification of the amino group needs some further comment: Its Cu^{2+} specificity depends on its participation in five- and six-membered chelates, which are generally unstable for Cu^+ (see below). In the absence of a chelate effect, —NH_2 is a relatively poor ligand for Cu^{2+} as well as for Cu^+ because of its high proton affinity, in contrast to imidazole, which exists as the free base at physiological pH. This helps to decide which ligands have to be cosnidered for redox-active copper in proteins: Electron transfer to and from copper in any "valence-specific" environment would imply either nonphysiological potentials or infringement of the Franck–Condon principle, i.e., ligand displacement occurring as rapidly as electron uptake or donation. Hence, the effective constituents of a redox-active Cu-coordination sphere are most likely "valence-nonspecific" imidazole and redox-active cyst(e)ine residues.

V. Study of Cu^+-Complex Formation in Homogeneous, Aqueous Solutions

The study of Cu^+-coordination reactions and Cu^+-complex structure in polar solution is hampered by the tendency of the hydrated Cu^+ to disproportionate to give Cu^{2+} and metallic copper. In other words, pure water is not a model environment suited for "copper in biology." Apparently the protein provides effective stabilization for Cu^+ and does not allow disproportionation, because it prevents uncontrolled statistical contact of copper centers with each other. In order to connect Cu^+-coordination chemistry—and, consequently, the biochemistry of Cu^+—with aqueous thermodynamics, an auxiliary weak, water-soluble, Cu^+-specific environmental factor is required. Furthermore, it should not exhibit measurable proton affinity or affect organic matter to any appreciable extent by its presence. We found acetonitrile to be such a factor (10). It is a water-soluble, H^+-inactive, absolutely Cu^+-specific ligand, but sufficiently weak to allow the study of substitution equilibria and their competition with hydrolysis, Eqs. (5) and (6):

$$Cu(CH_3CN)_2^+ + n\ L \rightleftarrows CuL_n^+ + 2\ CH_3CN \qquad (5)$$

$$Cu(CH_3CN)_2^+ + \tfrac{1}{2}\ (OH_2) \rightleftarrows \tfrac{1}{2}\ Cu_2O + H^+ + 2\ CH_3CN \qquad (6)$$

These reactions turned out to be nicely reversible within the time of measurement (aging of Cu_2O has to be avoided) when free CH_3CN is present in constant 10^2–10^3-fold excess, i.e., in a concentration range between 0.1 and 1 M in water. As follows from Eqs. (5) and (6), complex formation as well as hydrolysis depends on the concentration of free acetonitrile in the first power for the first ligand and in the second power for two and more ligands to be associated. Hence, for a given ligand L, the apparent stability constant depends on $[CH_3CN]$ for a monodentate L and on $[CH_3CN]^2$ for a bidentate L. Variation of $[CH_3CN]$ therefore gives a direct answer as to the first ligand being a chelator or not. CH_3CN concentration can be varied up to an environment containing as much as 50% CH_3CN, which suppresses hydrolysis completely below pH 12 and precludes substitution by all but the strongest ligands. Hence, in 50% aqueous CH_3CN only —SH protons can be liberated by Cu^+, whereas —NH_3^+, imidazole-H^+, and so on, are not attacked.

That our system can be effectively used to introduce copper as Cu^+ into proteins has in the meantime been demonstrated by Lontie *et al.* (11), who reincorporated Cu into apohemocyanin without damage to the protein. Furthermore, if the ligand itself liberates protons upon complex formation, as in Eq. (7),

$$Cu(CH_3CN)_2^+ + n \ LH^+ \rightleftarrows CuL_n^+ + 2 \ CH_3CN + n \ H^+ \tag{7}$$

the complex stability can be calculated acidimetrically after correction for the stability of the $Cu(CH_3CN)_2^+$ itself compared with the hypothetical aquo-Cu^+ complex, i.e., with $Cu^{2+}(aq)$ and metallic copper in the equilibrium of comproportionation. We have evaluated this constant as

$$\beta_2 = [Cu(CH_3CN)_2^+]/[Cu^+(aq)][CH_3CN]^2 = 10^{4.35}$$

polarographically (10).

VI. Water-Soluble Cu$^+$ Complexes and Their Structure

The stoichiometry and steric structure of the complexes formed and the kind of chemical bonds involved in metal fixation are more important for biology than thermodynamic stabilities.

I want to emphasize a few characteristic points in this context:

(a) Ligands involving only oxygen functions do not form complexes at all with Cu^+, be it mono- or polydentate, with the unique exception of oxide ion O^{2-}, which is at the same time the softest and strongest oxygen base.

(b) Nitrogenous monodentate ligands generally form no higher than 2:1 complexes in dilute solution. They may be subdivided into those complexes with pyramidal configuration at the nitrogen (ammonia) and those with trigonal configuration (pyridine). The latter are in general somewhat more stable than the former owing to the higher s character of the bonding ligand orbital whereby Cu^+ affinity is favored.

The most interesting and biologically most important N ligand is imidazole (ImH). It follows from the titration of free imidazole (Fig. 1) that no more than two imidazoles associate to one Cu^+ in dilute solution. At

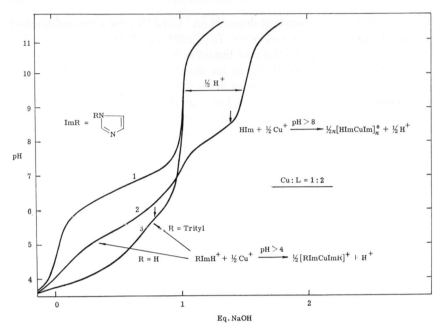

Fig. 1. pH Titration of imidazole (ImH). Curve 1: $c = 2 \times 10^{-3}$ M, W-E. Curve 2: $n = 0.25$ ml Cu$^+$ + 0.25 ml CH$_3$CN. Curve 3: N,N'-ditritylhistidinemethylester, $c = 2 \times 10^{-3}$ M, W-E, $n = 0.25$ ml Cu$^+$. The ligand alone gives the same curve as Curve 1.

General description of the titrations: pH titrations were done upon 25 ml of ligand solution, molar concentration c, at 25°, ionic strength maintained by 0.1 M NaClO$_4$, with 0.1 M NaOH, Metrohm XU 100 glass electrode, Metrohm Combititrator automatic titration unit, in either water (W), 1:1 water–ethanol (W-E), or 1:1 water–acetonitrile (W-A) as solvent. The W-E solvent prevents precipitation more easily, and W-A precludes any but SH-Cu interaction. Beginning of the eventual inhomogeneity of the systems is indicated by an arrow. Curve 1 always gives the titration of the ligand in the absence of metal. The starting pH was chosen about pH 3, by addition of the suitable amount of 1 M HClO$_4$ to the ligand stock solution. "Zero equivalents" on the abscissa indicates the point where neutralization of mineral acid begins. Approximate pK_a of the ligands may be read from the half-titrations points. Metal was added as n ml of a 0.1 M solution of pure, crystalline, absolutely colorless Cu(CH$_3$CN)$_4$ClO$_4$ in CH$_3$CN. This solution was nearly saturated at 25°. In one case a 0.2 M Cu$^+$ solution was used (Fig. 4) which had to be pipetted at 45°. Ligand-to-metal ratios are indicated on the figures. Eventually, free acetonitrile was also added, as indicated.

higher pH, however, one ImH proton is expelled from Cu(ImH)$_2^+$ and a neutral extremely insoluble polymer is formed, Eq. (8).

$$Cu^+ + \text{excess } ImH_2^+ \overset{pH4}{\rightleftharpoons} Cu(ImH)_2^+ + 2\ H^+$$

$$\overset{pH8}{\rightleftharpoons} 1/n\ (CuIm)_n + 3\ H^+ + ImH \qquad (8)$$

Thus at pH > 7, imidazole acts quite generally on Cu^+ as a bidentate (nonchelating) ligand or, in other words, as a unit of coordination number 2—as does mercaptide (see below). The second step is not observed with monoalkylated imidazole (ImR). If, however, ImH bears a charged residue like in histamine and histidine (Fig. 2), the polymer remains dissolved, but the shape of complex formation is the same as with unsubstituted imidazole.

$$2\,n\,(Cu^+ + \text{Histamine}) \rightleftharpoons \left[\begin{array}{c} \end{array} \right]_n \quad (9)$$

(VII)

Apparently, the amino group of histamine and histidine does not compete for coordination at Cu to form a six-membered chelate; in the $(CuIm)_n$ polymer obtained from histamine or histidine, the pK_a of $-NH_3^+$ is increased owing to the presence of the saturated metal coordination sphere.

(c) Chelate ligands do not form more than monodentate complexes with Cu^+, except for such chelators which allow extensive delocalization of d electrons toward low-lying empty antibonding d or π orbitals of the ligand (π_{dd} or π_{dp} back-donation). Such ligand systems are oxinate, bipyridine, phenanthroline, and, in particular, ligands that exhibit redox activity in themselves, like aza-o-quinones (most prominent example: riboflavin) (12), 1,2-dioximes, and (di)sulfides having a second ligand group like cystine, cystamine, etc. (see below).

1,4-Bidentate ligands such as ethylenediamine and glycine are exceptional in that they cause immediate disproportionation (and no hydrolysis) of Cu^+, Eq. (10), (VIII and IX), as soon as the second function is deprotonated and therefore ready for coordination. The same is not

$$[Cu(CH_3CN)_2]^+ + 2\,\overset{+}{H_3}NCH_2CH_2\overset{+}{NH_3} \rightleftharpoons \overset{+}{H_3}N(CH_2)_2NH_2Cu^+H_2N(CH_2)_2\overset{+}{NH_3} + 2\,H^+$$

$$\longrightarrow \left[\begin{array}{c} \end{array} \right] + 2\,H^+ \xrightarrow{Cu^+} \begin{array}{c} \end{array} + Cu^0 \quad (10)$$

Unstable
(VIII)   (IX)

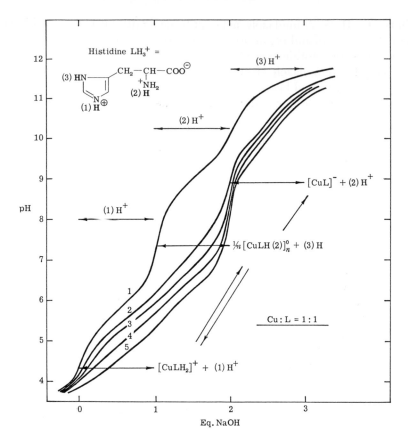

FIG. 2. pH Titration of histidine. Curve 1: $c = 10^{-3} M$, W-E. Curve 2: $n = 0.25$ ml $Cu^+ + 1.75$ ml CH_3CN. Curve 3: $n = 0.25$ ml $Cu^+ + 0.75$ ml CH_3CN. Curve 4: $n = 0.25$ ml $Cu^+ + 0.25$ ml CH_3CN. Curve 5: $n = 0.25$ ml Cu^+. See Fig. 1 for general description of titrations.

true for 1,5-bidentate ligands like 1,3-diaminopropane and β-alanine, where at first monodentate coordination and, at higher pH, hydrolysis occur, but no disproportionation. This reflects the characteristic stability of five-membered Cu^{2+} chelates, which falls off, in general, for two orders of magnitude in the six-membered analogs (13).

All this shows convincingly that chelate formation with Cu^+ can only occur if at least some reduction of d-electron density on the Cu atom is brought about at the same time. This explains also why in certain cases Cu^+ forms trigonal and tetrahedral complexes more easily, i.e., with cyanide, though also in this case there is a sudden strong increase in the apparent pK_a of $Cu^+(CN^-)_nH$ for $n > 2$ (14). Furthermore small-size chelates should be unstable in Cu^+ proteins unless sulfur is involved.

(d) Reactions of Cu^+ with S-containing ligands show a very complicated behavior. Differentiation of S bonding in the free ligand should be made carefully:

In all cases where no π bonding between sulfur and ligand residue occurs we find a coordination number of 3 for the Cu^+-coordinated sulfur.

A. Linear Sulfur

(a) No π bonds in the ligand: Mercaptide ion, RS^-. Linear Cu–S(R)$\cdots$Cu coordination is strictly preferred over formation of chelate rings. If RS^- is in excess, the highest L:Cu ratio is 1.5; hence Eq. (11) leads to a binuclear unit, but no mononuclear unit $Cu(RS)_2^-$ is observed.

$$\text{Cu}^+ + \text{excess RSH} \rightleftharpoons \overset{\text{R}\qquad\text{R}\quad\text{R}}{[\text{S–Cu}\cdots\text{S–Cu–S}]^-} + 1\tfrac{1}{2}\,\text{H}^+ \text{ per Cu} \qquad (11)$$

Equimolar quantities form a colorless linear polymer $(RSCu)_n$, which is very insoluble, if no ionic groups are contained in the residues R. On the other hand, if Cu^+ is in excess, the reaction depends again very strongly on the environment (cf. above). Principally, the reaction takes the form of Eq. (12).

$$\frac{1}{n}\,\overset{\text{R}}{(\text{SCu})_n} + \text{excess Cu}^+ \rightleftharpoons \overset{\text{R}}{\text{CuSCu}^+} \qquad (12)$$

Now, if R contains a Cu^{2+}-specific function (e.g., $-COO^-$ in thioglycolate), the system will tend to disproportionate toward a violet mixed valence state, $Cu^+(RS)Cu^{2+}$. If no second function is present in R the system will partially hydrolyze in water. If, however, a Cu^+-specific environment such as CH_3CN prevents hydrolysis, $RSCu^{2+}$ will be stable under anaerobic conditions. This is borne out by the titration of cysteamine (Fig. 3), where addition of Cu^+ to polymeric $H_3N^+CH_2CH_2SCu$ results in deprotonation of NH_3^+ with an apparent pK_a of 6.3, although direct coordination of the amino group is not possible in the chosen environment of 50% aqueous CH_3CN.

(b) π Bonds in the ligand: e.g., thiourea, thiosemicarbazones. This case depends on the availability of a dissociable proton. If a full charge can be generated at the sulfur, the system must behave like RS^-, e.g., Eq. (13).

$$\overset{\overset{\text{NH}_2}{|}}{\text{RCH=N–NH–C=S}} + \text{Cu}^+ \rightleftharpoons \frac{1}{n}\; \overset{\text{H}_2\text{N}\diagdown}{\underset{\diagup}{}} \text{C=N–N=CHR} + \text{H}^+ \qquad (13)$$
$$(\text{CuS})_n$$

This complex has been described by Gingras and Sirianni (15) but has been

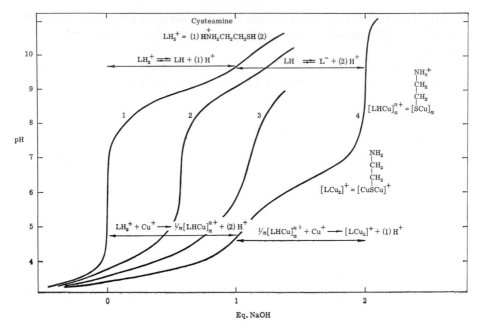

FIG. 3. pH Titration of cysteamine. Curve 1: $c = 2 \times 10^{-3}\,M$, W-A. Curve 2: $n = 0.2$ ml Cu^+. Curve 3: $n = 0.4$ ml Cu^+. Curve 4: $n = 1.0$ ml Cu^+. See Fig. 1 for general description of titrations.

mistaken for a chelate, although the authors primarily assumed a macro-molecular structure.

If no dissociable proton is available, as in thiourea, up to four ligands may coordinate to Cu^+, thanks to the acceptor qualities of the thioamide system, as was correctly established by Laitinen (16) polarographically.

B. Digonal Sulfur

Stable digonal sulfur occurs only in thioethers. Their Cu^+ affinity is remarkable in view of their low proton affinity, but this is in agreement with the concept of hard and soft acids and bases. Hence, methionine and S-alkylcysteine behave quite unlike glycine toward Cu^+, forming rather stable $S \cdots Cu \cdots S$ complexes (Fig. 4). If additional negative charges are present in the ligand, as in thiodiglycolate $S(CH_2COO^-)_2$, hydrolysis of the CuL_2^{3-} does not occur below pH 6.

If, however, the ligand R_2S contains an additional amino group, like methionine and S-benzylcysteine, hydrolysis as well as disproportionation is suppressed up to very high pH if a metal-to-ligand ratio of 1:2 is ensured. This and the fact that S-benzylcysteine-Cu^+ (five-membered chelate) is

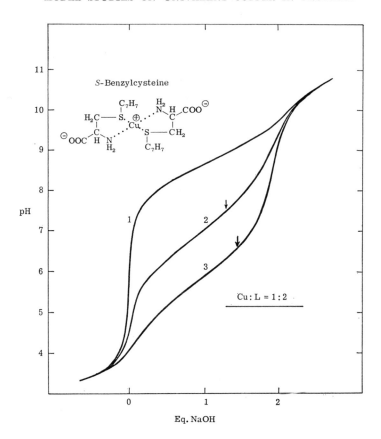

FIG. 4. pH Titration of S-benzyl-L-cysteine. Curve 1: $c = 2 \times 10^{-3}\ M$, W. Curve 3: $+$ 0.125 ml of 0.2 M Cu$^+$ solution; Curve 2: $n = 0.25$ ml Cu$^+$ + 1 ml CH$_3$CN. See Fig. 1 for general description of titrations.

at least one order of magnitude more stable than methionine-Cu$^+$ (six-membered chelate) support the chelate structures (Fig. 4) and not the monodentate ones. It should be noted that analogous Cu^{2+} chelates are unstable, since digonal sulfur has no Cu^{2+} affinity at all.

C. Disulfide

A special class of digonal sulfur is present in disulfides, RSSR. As has been stated above, in a complex of general formula $(R_2S_2Cu_2)^{2+}$ Cu$^+$-disulfide and Cu^{2+}-mercaptide structure would be indistinguishable. Valence mesomerism seems to play a fundamental role in biological complexes of the redox-active ions of iron [heme-Fe–O$_2$ and $-$O$_2$H$_2$ (17), nonheme Fe–S$_2$R$_2$

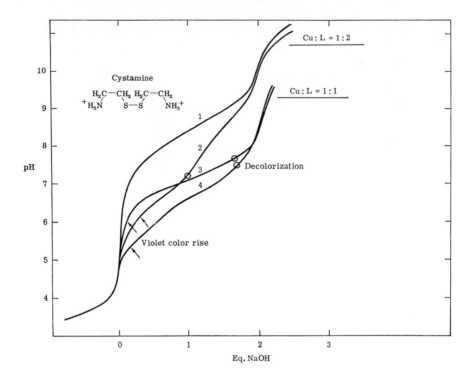

FIG. 5. pH Titration of cystamine. Curve 1: $c = 10^{-3}$ M, W-E. Curve 2: $n = 0.125$ ml Cu$^+$ + 0.125 ml CH$_3$CN. Curve 3: $n = 0.25$ ml Cu$^+$ + 0.75 ml CH$_3$CN. Curve 4: $n = 0.25$ ml Cu$^+$. See Fig. 1 for general description of titrations.

(18)], molybdenum [RS–Mo–flavin (12)], and copper. Copper is the most obvious example for this phenomenon, because of its low coordination numbers. To ensure complex formation of disulfide and Cu$^+$ in dilute aqueous solution, the ligand RSSR must contain an additional, possibly chelating, group as was the case for ligands RSR. Hence, dibenzyldisulfide does not show any reaction with Cu(CH$_3$CN)$_2$$^+$, nor does lipoic acid, whereas cystamine, H$_2$NCH$_2$CH$_2$–S–S–CH$_2$CH$_2$NH$_2$, reacts readily with Cu(CH$_3$CN)$_2$$^+$. The carefully anaerobic titration (Fig. 5) goes through a violet form, which arises with beginning —NH$_3$$^+$ deprotonation and fades out with increasing pH. At the equivalence point of —NH$_3$$^+$ deprotonation, the solution is again colorless, if Cu:L = 1, whereas the violet color persists at higher ratio.

The violet complex reacts only slowly with air once it is formed, whereas it is immediately decolorized by reducing agents. These reactions are reversible, though a slight hysteresis might be obtained on back-titration with acid, indicating slow equilibration and, therefore, polymer complexation. The equilibria to be considered are the following:

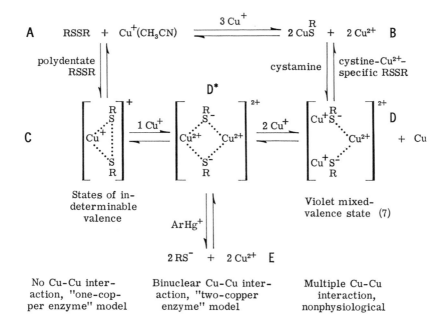

The spectrum of the violet chromophore is not very specific, showing a very broad band with a molar extinction of about 10^3 centered at 520 mμ, stretching far out toward the infrared. The entire system can be equilibrated starting from one of three levels: Cu^{2+} + mercaptide (7), Cu^+ + disulfide, or by autoxidation of preformed cuprous mercaptide. Since $Cu(CH_3CN)_2^+$ is O_2 inert, as well as disulfide, the second way is preferred in this paper and seems the safest. State E may generally be neglected because it does not contribute essentially to the equilibrium. The same is true for state A if a "polydentate disulfide" is considered. This is best shown from the titration of excess cystine with Cu^+ (Fig. 6), where exactly one H^+ per Cu^+ is liberated reversibly below pH 7 without disproportionation or formation of any colored "mixed-valence" species, to give state C. The reaction A $\rightarrow$ B, however, liberates only $\frac{1}{2}H^+$ per Cu in the case of cysteine. Upon addition of more Cu^+, the cystine system acquires only slight violet color due to state D, whereas direct shift toward B is highly favored owing to the Cu^{2+} specificity of the α-amino acid bidentate residues. However, in the dark violet cystamine system, state D is favored over B, if 2 Cu per RSSR are present. At still higher Cu-to-RSSR ratios, the cystamine system is also decolorized.

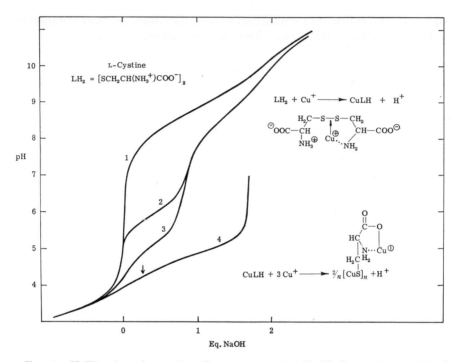

FIG. 6. pH Titration of L-cystine. Curve 1: $c = 10^{-3}\,M$, W. Curve 2: $n = 0.2$ ml $Cu^+ + 1.8$ ml CH_3CN. Curve 3: $n = 0.2$ ml $Cu^+ + 0.8$ ml CH_3CN. Curve 4: $n = 5$ ml Cu^+. See Fig. 1 for general description of titrations.

It has to be noted that states B, D, D*, E imply Cu–Cu interaction, whereas A and C do not. In enzymes, therefore, state C is of general relevance, whereas D* might have to be considered in "two-copper enzymes" solely. The structure of the intermediate D* complex is tentative, but explains our results best. Auxiliary protein ligands might keep the system D in a comproportionated state D*.

Clearly, the whole system will be shifted rapidly toward E by mercurial, toward A by acetonitrile, toward B by glycine, etc. Thus, complete information about these equilibria can only be obtained by physical means, i.e., applying acidimetry (and no buffers!) for constant pH, EPR for Cu^{2+}, optical spectroscopy for the mixed valence state, and polarography for Cu^+—all at the same time, as we have done.

We have analyzed spectrophotometrically the stoichiometry of the violet state by continuous variation starting from $Cu(CH_3CN)_2^+$ and dithiodiglycolate $(SCH_2COO^-)_2$ at pH 5 and constant concentrations of free CH_3CN under careful exclusion of air. The spectral shape does not alter within the visible range of the spectrum, i.e., the presence of only one coloring species might be anticipated. The maximum of the complex formation clearly is obtained at a ratio of $Cu:S = 2:1$, in agreement with the structure of Klotz et al. (7), $((RS^-Cu^+)_4Cu^{2+})^{2+}$ (state D). This structure seems to be preferred if no ternary ligands of sufficient strength are present. The strong color, however, might be found in any $Cu^{2+}(RS^-)Cu^+$ system. The "mixed-valence" state D implies change of center coordination upon reduction, whereas C and D* should be able to undergo change in oxidation number without drastic change in σ structure.

Preliminary experiments with EPR, done in cooperation with Beinert,[2] indicate that the violet state obtained from cystamine is EPR inactive. In addition, Cu^{2+} is seen to be formed according to the reaction $C \rightarrow D$. Upon addition of mercurial, practically all the copper is set free as Cu^{2+}. This Cu^{2+} from state E is different in its EPR absorption from the Cu^{2+} in state D, as might be expected.

Thus the $Cu(CH_3CN)_2^+$ method provides a means for studying Cu^+ in biological systems. Earlier assumptions (19) on Cu^+-imidazole and Cu^+-SR_2 coordination can be verified more safely. With the aid of this tool more elaborate information on polynuclear Cu^+ complexes as well as differentiation of "mixed-valence" and "indeterminable valence" states might become available.

VII. Summary

O-, N-, and S-containing ligands, in particular those occurring as prosthetic groups in proteins, have been scanned for their affinity toward univalent copper by a new method which allows handling of Cu^+ in homogeneous, dilute aqueous solution in the absence of Cu^{2+}. The copper valence specificity of ligands and the structure of complexes in the univalent and "mixed valence" states are discussed and correlated with biochemical data in order to establish what the structural demands of redox-active copper in proteins are.

ACKNOWLEDGMENTS

I am deeply indebted to Dr. H. Beinert for invaluable aid and encouragement in this work. Furthermore, thanks are due to Dr. B. G. Malmström, Dr. B. F. van Gelder, and Dr. S. Fallab for discussions, and to Mr. C. Sigwart and Miss E. Rommel for experimental assistance and Miss L. Nebel for help in preparing the manuscript.

REFERENCES

1. Beinert, H., and Palmer, G., *J. Biol. Chem.*, **239,** 1221 (1964).
2. Malmström, B. G., in T. E. King, H. S. Mason, and M. Morrison (eds.), "Oxidases and related redox systems," John Wiley and Sons, Inc., New York, 1965, p. 207.

[2] Unpublished observations.

3. Hemmerich, P., *in* T. E. King, H. S. Mason, and M. Morrison (eds.), "Oxidases and related redox systems," John Wiley and Sons, Inc., New York, 1965, p. 157.
4. van Gelder, B. F., and Slater, E. C., *Biochim. Biophys. Acta*, **73**, 663 (1963).
5. Klotz, I. M., Urquhart, J. M., and Fiess, H. A., *J. Am. Chem. Soc.*, **80**, 553 (1952).
6. Kolthoff, I. M., and Stricks, W., *J. Am. Chem. Soc.*, **73**, 1728 (1951).
7. Klotz, I. M., Czerlinski, G. H., and Fiess, H. A., *J. Am. Chem. Soc.*, **80**, 2920 (1958).
8. Pearson, R. G., *J. Am. Chem. Soc.*, **85**, 3533 (1963); cf. also *Chem. Eng. News*, **43**, 90 (1965).
9. Freeman, H. C., this symposium.
10. Hemmerich, P., and Sigwart, C., *Experientia*, **19**, 488 (1963).
11. Lontie, R., Blaton, V., Albert, M., and Peeters, B., *Arch. Intern. Physiol. Biochim.*, **73**, 150 (1965).
12. Hemmerich, P., and Spence, J., *in* E. C. Slater (ed.), "Flavins and flavoproteins," Elsevier, Amsterdam (in press).
13. Zuberbühler, A., Ph.D. thesis, Basel (1965).
14. Sillén, L. G., and Martell, A. B., *Chem. Soc. (London) Spec. Publ.*, **17** (1964).
15. Gingras, B. A., and Sirianni, A. F., *Can. J. Chem.*, **42**, 17 (1964).
16. Onstott, E. I., and Laitinen, H. A., *J. Am. Chem. Soc.*, **72**, 4724 (1950).
17. Ehrenberg, A., *Z. Grundlagenforsch.*, **3**, 203 (1965).
18. Hemmerich, P., *Z. Grundlagenforsch.*, **3**, 230 (1965).
19. James, B. R., and Williams, R. J. P., *J. Chem. Soc.*, p. 2007 (1961).

DISCUSSION

DR. BLUMBERG: I want to amplify some remarks that Dr. Hemmerich made concerning EPR-detectable and EPR-nondetectable copper. Table I may clarify some of the conditions under which some characteristics of EPR spectra that exhibit cupric-cupric exchange can be observed.

TABLE I

CHARACTERISTICS OF AN EPR SPECTRUM OF EXCHANGE-COUPLED PAIRS OF Cu^{2+} IONS

Magnitude	Characteristics of spectrum
Large, negative	No signal at room temperature or below
Large, positive	Four-thirds full signal intensity, large dipolar splitting, 7 hyperfine lines (no cases yet observed)
Moderate, either sign	Large temperature dependence of intensity, dipolar splitting, 7 hyperfine lines
Small, either sign	No temperature dependence of intensity, dipolar splitting, 7 hyperfine lines, no loss of signal strength at any temperature

Table II gives possible explanations for copper EPR not observed at full strength (i.e., integrated absorption as compared with a standard). First, one might have a

TABLE II

Conditions under Which Cu^{2+} EPR Is Not Observed at Full Intensity

---

1. Heterogeneous system, some normal cupric signal plus:
    A. Large negative exchange between cupric ion pairs.
    B. Large negative exchange between a cupric ion and a free radical.
    C. Large negative exchange between a cupric ion and another paramagnetic metal ion.
2. Homogeneous system (only one Cu-binding site present): Moderate exchange between cupric ion pairs (this signal will always have a large temperature dependence)

---

heterogeneous system; that is, a normal copper giving the full strength EPR, plus some other kind of copper, e.g., a large negative exchange in cupric pairs. That is one of the cases mentioned in Dr. Hemmerich's paper. There could also be a large negative exchange between a cupric ion and a free radical, which is one of the other cases mentioned by Dr. Hemmerich. One may have a large negative exchange between a cupric ion and another metal ion. This has never been observed in biology—but why not? It is observed in solid state physics.

If one is absolutely sure he has a homogeneous system (i.e., there is only one kind of copper-binding site present) and if he doesn't have the full EPR strength, there must be moderate exchange between cupric pairs. One can always tell this because the EPR signal will have a large temperature dependence.

DR. PEISACH: Dr. Hemmerich, would you please elucidate the Pearson notation of soft and hard ligands?

DR. HEMMERICH: A hard ligand is just a ligand whose action upon metals can be adequately described by an electrostatic interaction or by a σ covalent interaction which does not disturb the preponderant electron configuration of the ligand. For example, water is a rather hard ligand, and becomes softer as soon as it is deprotonated. Water forms stable complexes with Cu^{2+}, but it does not with Cu^+. The only oxygen ligand that forms stable complexes with Cu^+ is O^{2-} in cuprous oxide.

If we look at complexes containing soft ligands, we see extensive delocalization of electrons, which means additional binding might take place by π bonds; $(d, p)\pi$ bonding or $(d, d)\pi$ bonding. The metal always contributes d orbitals, whereas the ligand contributes p orbitals or, in the case of sulfur, d orbitals that are empty. If the ligand is a more complicated molecular system, it may contain π orbitals that are empty and into which electrons can be delocalized from the metal.

If we consider only prosthetic groups of proteins, we can say hard ligands are NH_2, COO^-, and carbonamide.

Soft ligands are not to be confused with weak ligands. Weak and strong notation is a matter of basicity, hard and soft concerns electron delocalization or orbital polarizability of ligands.

Soft ligands include thioethers, e.g., methionine or ethionine, which form stable complexes with cuprous copper. Mercaptide is the softest of all possible ligands in proteins. Disulfide is a very soft and "noninnocent" ligand, as Dr. Jørgensen calls it, in that it, too, can accommodate donated electrons. It may be stable with one or two extra electrons added because the disulfide can assume mecaptide configuration.

DR. JØRGENSEN: I completely agree with Dr. Hemmerich's description of these hard and soft ligands, but there is one fascinating thing that normally escapes solution chemists' attention. It is true that heavy atoms, such as sulfur, also tend to form π bonds, but this is not the only condition for softness or even the only source of it. The hydrides are among the softest ligands we have. Hydrides also form only σ bonds, so softness is a queer mixture of π-bonding capability and polarizability.

DR. WILLIAMS: Why don't you keep the names "polarizable" and "nonpolarizable"?

DR. JØRGENSEN: There are many different reasons for that. One is that Cs^+ is more polarizable than Ag^+ in the physical sense, but in the chemical sense it is not. Another thing may be that the Tl^{3+} is remarkably soft in the chemical sense, but has tremendously high ionization energy.

DR. WILLIAMS: The advantage of "polarizable" and "nonpolarizable" is that they have meaning and can be measured, whereas "soft" and "hard" have no meanings whatsoever.

DR. JØRGENSEN: I agree completely that polarizability can be measured, but it is not the same thing.

DR. GURD: Could someone confirm or deny my impression that imidazole would belong in the soft list?

DR. HEMMERICH: It is only moderately soft but its effect seems mostly due to its basicity. It is a ligand that is just deprotonated in the physiological range. No other ligand among protein prosthetic groups generally does that. This means that the free base is present in rather high concentrations, which is not the case with amino nitrogen. But imidazole is certainly softer than amino nitrogen.

DR. PEISACH: What is the spatial configuration of cuprous benzylcysteine?

DR. HEMMERICH: I think it is a tetrahedron.

DR. CAUGHEY: I wasn't quite clear about the concentration range of acetonitrile that was used.

DR. HEMMERICH: It depends on the complexing strength of the ligand one wants to investigate. If one wants to exclude any other interaction but mercaptide, which is a very soft ligand, then he can go up to 50% acetonitrile; but for normal thermodynamic measurements the range is 0.1 to 1.0 M. These are concentrations which do not affect the activity of hydrogen ions in water.

An EPR Study of Cupric Glycylglycinate and Its Ethyl Ester*

D. C. GOULD† AND H. S. MASON

Department of Biochemistry,
University of Oregon Medical School,
Portland, Oregon

Although the structure of copper-containing enzymes has been the subject of much study, no single ligand of copper in any such protein has been identified (1). The problem is more complex than the case of heme proteins because four of the six ligands of iron are very stable and are automatically identified upon isolation and characterization of the heme, whereas in copper proteins each copper atom may have three, four, five, or six labile ligands supplied by the protein. EPR spectroscopy has offered some promise for identification of these ligands by analysis of hyperfine splittings in the cupric states (2). The results of this approach have not, however, been very useful because of the relatively featureless spectra obtained from naturally occurring copper proteins (2, 3). Some exhibit unusually narrow hyperfine splittings in the $g_{||}$ region of the spectra, the meaning of which is not settled.

In an effort to understand features of the EPR spectrum of the *Pseudomonas* blue copper protein (4) and other copper proteins, we have undertaken a systematic study of the EPR spectra of certain cupric amino acid and peptide complexes. This report is concerned with copper glycylglycinate and its ethyl ester. The spectra have been determined as a function of pH, of temperature between 110° and 350°K, and of using ^{14}N and ^{15}N in the terminal NH_2 and in the peptide bond. It appears that the best explanation of our results is that the nitrogen atom of the peptide bond acts as a ligand toward copper.

I. Experimental Procedures

EPR spectra were obtained with a Varian model V-4500 EPR spectrometer equipped with Fieldial sweep control. All spectra were obtained at 100 Kc/sec field modulation. The Varian V-4547 accessory for variable temperature measurements was utilized, which, in these experiments,

* This study was supported by grants from the American Cancer Society and the National Institutes of Health, for which we express our thanks.

† Predoctoral Fellow, National Institutes of Health. Present address: Department of Biochemistry, The Nobel Medical Institute, Stockholm, Sweden.

provided a temperature control of ±0.5°. Field modulation amplitudes of from 0.4 to 10 Gauss and microwave power levels from 0.25 to 250 milli-Watts were utilized.

The EPR results are presented as the first derivative of the absorption curves. The samples were placed in quartz tubes of 3 mm inside diameter and wall thickness of 0.5 mm for the EPR measurements at 110°K. For the spectra at temperatures above 258°K, three types of cells were utilized. Best sensitivity was obtained with a flat quartz cell but this cell was unsuitable for measurements at variable temperatures. For these, a cell consisting of a quartz tube of 3 mm internal diameter and 0.5 mm wall thickness filled with benzene or n-hexane and containing a capillary of 0.8 mm internal diameter was used. The aqueous sample was placed in the inner capillary for measurement. A quartz tube of 3.5 mm outside diameter containing 2 holes each 0.8 mm in diameter was also utilized. Because of the variability in the internal diameters of the sample tubes, no conclusions should be drawn from apparent quantitative differences in the curves.

The potentiometric titrations of the copper-glycylglycine solutions were carried out with 0.1 and 1 M NaOH upon 5 and 10 mM CuCl$_2$-ligand mixtures, using Cu^{2+}-to-glycylglycine ratios of 1:1, 1:2, and 1:4. These conditions duplicate those used by Dobbie and Kermack (5) and by Koltun et al. (6).

The u^{14}N- and u^{15}N-glycylglycine were synthesized by mixed anhydride procedures (7). The titration curves for equimolar glycylglycine and Cu^{2+} and equimolar glycylglycine ethyl ester and Cu^{2+} were the same, as were the EPR spectra, for the mixtures at pH 7 and pH 10, 110°K, and at all temperatures above 258°K. The ethyl ester form of glycylglycine was used in the label experiments, where material was limiting. Starting materials for the glycylglycine ethyl ester synthesis were carbobenzoxy-^{14}N-glycine from Aldrich Chemical Company; ^{15}N-glycine of 96 atomic percent-^{15}N from Bio-Rad Laboratories; and ^{14}N-glycine from Matheson, Coleman, & Bell.

II. Results of the EPR Experiments

The EPR spectra, measured at 110°K, of 10 mM CuCl$_2$ in the presence of equimolar glycylglycine at pH 3.7, 6.9, 10.7, and 11.5 and an ionic strength of 0.16 are shown in Fig. 1. NaCl was used to adjust the ionic strength. The EPR spectra, at 110°K, of 10 mM CuCl$_2$ equimolar with glycylglycine at pH 10 and NaCl concentrations of from 0 to 2.5 M are shown in Fig. 2. The curves obtained under similar conditions but at pH values down to pH 6 were of essentially the same shape.

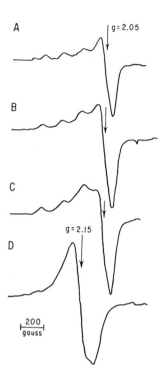

FIG. 1. EPR spectra of 10 mM glycylglycine with 10 mM CuCl$_2$. Temperature, 110°K; ionic strength, 0.16. Curve A: equivalents of NaOH and pH 11.5. Curve B: 3 equivalents of NaOH and pH 10.7. Curve C: 2 equivalents of NaOH and pH 6.9. Curve D: 0 equivalent of NaOH and pH 3.7.

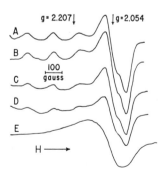

FIG. 2. EPR spectra of 10 mM glycylglycine and 10 mM CuCl$_2$ with 3 equivalents NaOH and pH 10.4. Temperature, 110°K. Curve A: 2.5 M in NaCl. Curve B: 1 M in NaCl. Curve C: 0.5 M in NaCl. Curve D: 0.2 M in NaCl. Curve E: 0 M in NaCl.

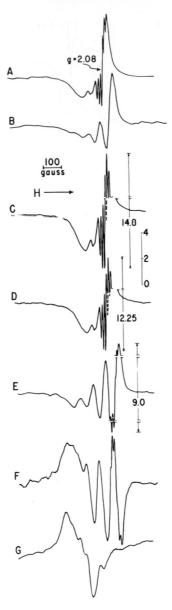

Fig. 3. EPR spectra of mixtures of glycylglycine (GG) and 10 mM CuCl$_2$. Temperature, 268°K. Curve A: 20 mM GG, 4 equivalents NaOH, pH 10.7. Curve B: 20 mM GG, 3 equivalents NaOH, pH 8.8. Curve C: 10 mM GG, 4 equivalents NaOH, pH 11.8 Curve D: 10 mM GG, 3 equivalents NaOH, pH 10. Curve E: 10 mM GG, 2 equivalents NaOH, pH 7. Curve F: 10 mM GG, 1 equivalent NaOH, pH 4.7. Curve G: 10 mM GG, 0 equivalent NaOH, pH 3.8.

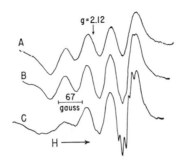

FIG. 4. EPR spectra of 10 mM glycylglycine ethyl ester and 10 mM CuCl$_2$ with 2 equivalents NaOH, pH 7.   Curve A: 333°K.   Curve B: 293°K.   Curve C: 273°K.

EPR spectra of 10 mM CuCl$_2$ (T = 273°K) at Cu-to-glycylglycine ratios and pH values, respectively, of 1:1 and 4, 1:1 and 4.8, 1:1 and 7, 1:1 and 10, 1:1 and 11.8, 1:2 and 8, and 1:2 and 10 are shown in Fig. 3.

The temperature dependence of the EPR absorption curve of a 10 mM solution of CuCl$_2$ in a 1:1 molar ratio with glycylglycine ethyl ester at pH 7 is shown in Fig. 4. This curve is the same as that observed with glycylglycine.

Figure 5 shows the EPR absorption curves of 10 mM CuCl$_2$ in the presence of 10 mM glycylglycine ethyl ester u^{14}N (D) and with 10 mM glycylglycine ethyl ester u^{15}N (A) at pH 10 and 273°K.

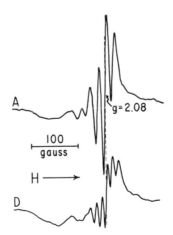

FIG. 5. EPR spectra of 10 mM glycylglycine ethyl ester and 10 mM CuCl$_2$ with 3 equivalents NaOH, pH 10. Temperature, 273°K.   Curve A: glycylglycine ethyl ester u^{15}N.   Curve D: glycylglycine ethyl ester u^{14}N.

III. Discussion

A. Equilibria of the Complexes

Cu^{2+} binding by glycylglycine has been extensively investigated by potentiometric methods (5, 6, 8–10). When an equimolar mixture of glycylglycine and Cu^{2+} is titrated with NaOH, the curve shown in Fig. 6 is obtained. Dobbie and Kermack have postulated that the following reactions occur when aqueous mixtures of glycylglycine (GG in the equations) and Cu^{2+} are titrated with NaOH:

$$Cu^{2+} + GG^- \rightleftharpoons CuGG^+$$

$$CuGG^+ \rightleftharpoons CuGG + H^+$$

$$CuGG + H_2O \rightleftharpoons CuGG(OH)^- + H^+$$

$$CuGG + GG^- \rightleftharpoons Cu(GG)_2^-$$

$$Cu(GG)_2^- \rightleftharpoons Cu(GG)_2^{2-} + H^+$$

Using methods first set forth by Bjerrum (11) and more fully developed by Albert (12), mathematical equations can be derived from which, utilizing

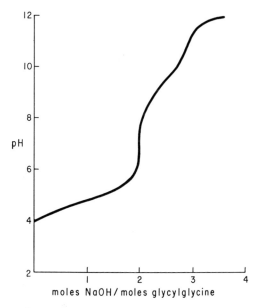

Fig. 6. Titration of 10 mM glycylglycine and 10 mM CuCl₂. Temperature 293°K.

potentiometric titration data, values for the following equilibrium constants were obtained:

$$K_1 = \frac{[\text{CuGG}^+]}{[\text{Cu}^{2+}][\text{GG}^-]} \qquad \log K_1 = 5.88$$

$$K_2 = \frac{[\text{Cu(GG)}_2^-]}{[\text{CuGG}][\text{GG}^-]} \qquad \log K_2 = 3.26$$

$$K_c = \frac{[\text{CuGG}][\text{H}^+]}{[\text{CuGG}^+]} \qquad pK_c = 4.25$$

$$K_c' = \frac{[\text{CuGG(OH)}^-][\text{H}^+]}{[\text{CuGG}]} \qquad pK_c' = 9.65$$

$$K_c'' = \frac{[\text{Cu(GG)}_2^{2-}][\text{H}^+]}{[\text{Cu(GG)}_2^-]} \qquad pK_c'' = 10.20$$

Koltun *et al.* (6) postulate the following reactions for the sequential reactions occurring in an equimolar mixture of glycylglycine and Cu^{2+}:

$$\text{Cu}^{2+} + \text{GG}^- \rightleftharpoons \text{CuGG}^+$$

$$\text{CuGG}^+ \rightleftharpoons \text{CuGG} + \text{H}^+$$

$$\text{CuGG} \rightleftharpoons \text{CuGGOH}^- + \text{H}^+$$

$$\text{CuGG} + \text{CuGGOH}^- \rightleftharpoons (\text{CuGG})_2\text{OH}^-$$

$$\text{CuGGOH}^- \rightleftharpoons \text{CuGG(OH)}_2^{2-} + \text{H}^+$$

They obtained the following values for the equilibrium constants:

$$K_{I^+} = \frac{[\text{CuGG}^+]}{[\text{GG}^-][\text{Cu}^{2+}]} \qquad \log K_{I^+} = 4.96$$

$$K_{I^0} = \frac{[\text{CuGG}][\text{H}^+]}{[\text{CuGG}^+]} \qquad pK_{I^0} = 3.90$$

$$K_{I^-} = \frac{[\text{CuGGOH}^-][\text{H}^+]}{[\text{CuGG}]} \qquad pK_{I^-} = 9.37$$

$$K_{2I^-} = \frac{[\text{Cu(GG)}_2\text{OH}^-]}{[\text{CuGG}][\text{CuGGOH}^-]} \qquad \log K_{2I^-} = 2.30$$

$$K_{I^{2-}} = \frac{[\text{CuGG(OH)}_2][\text{H}^+]}{[\text{CuGGOH}^-]} \qquad pK_{I^{2-}} = 12.2$$

Two conclusions can be drawn from the foregoing data. First, the fitting of the experimental data to the proposed successive reactions between the Cu^{2+} and glycylglycine is a necessary but not sufficient condition that the proposed reactions represent the actual reactions. Second, the nature of the binding of Cu^{2+} to glycylglycine cannot be deduced from these reactions alone.

The consumption of two equivalents of hydroxide in the pH range 4 to 7, in equimolar glycylglycine and Cu^{2+} mixtures, is accounted for by neutralization of the terminal ammonium group and by proton ionization from the peptide linkage (5, 13). The consumption of one additional equivalent of hydroxide in the pH range 7 to 10 is ascribed to hydroxyl ion association (5, 6).

The possibility that the peptide linkage can dissociate a proton and subsequently bind Cu^{2+} is supported by infrared data (14, 15) in which the absorption frequencies of the peptide carbonyl group shift, in the presence of Cu^{2+}, to lower frequencies, which is consistent with the displacement of a proton from the peptide nitrogen, resulting in the following resonance forms:

The interpretation cannot be made on this basis alone, since, as will be shown, the Cu^{2+} is covalently bound to the peptide nitrogen and would thus at least partially "replace" the ionized proton (assuming the proton does ionize).

Datta and Rabin (16) have shown that replacement of the peptide hydrogen atom in glycylglycine by a methyl group results in the consumption of only one equivalent of NaOH in the pH range 4 to 7. At pH 7 the Cu^{2+} is essentially quantitatively precipitated from solution as $Cu(OH)_2$.

There remain three points that are unsettled: (a) the form of the complex ions which exist at different pH values, and thus the equations which represent the reactions that occur in solution, (b) the nature of the binding of the Cu^{2+} to the glycylglycine, and (c) the direct confirmation of the ionization of a proton from the peptide bond. The EPR study which has now been made provides additional information about the first two of these.

B. Interpretation of the EPR Spectra

The 110°K EPR spectra in Figs. 1 and 2 (except for curve D, Fig. 1, and curve E, Fig. 2) have the general shape shown by a wide variety of Cu^{2+} complexes. These curves are generally interpreted in terms of the theoretical work of Sands (17) and Kneubühl (18). Sands' derivation assumes D_{4h} symmetry about the copper, so it would appear that the symmetry about the copper atom in the glycylglycine complex at 110°K is D_{4h}. However, the spectra are highly dependent on ionic strength of the medium (Fig. 2). On the other hand, at temperatures above 258°K, the shapes of the EPR spectra are identical over the whole range of ionic strengths. For this reason, there is a strong possibility that the structures of the complex at 110°K are different from that in a liquid phase at room temperature. From the point of view of application of EPR to structures of copper proteins, this emphasizes once again the dangers of extrapolating low-temperature results to the temperatures (and concentrations) at which the copper proteins are functional.

The EPR absorption curves for the aqueous solutions (Fig. 3), usually obtained above 258°K are much more revealing than the 110°K curves. Three distinct spectra can be seen as the pH is changed: (a) at no added equivalents of NaOH (curve G, pH 4), (b) at two equivalents of NaOH added to the 1:1 Cu:GG system (curve E, pH 7), and (c) at three equivalents of NaOH added to the 1:1 Cu:GG system (curve D, pH 10). Curve G is virtually the same as that seen for an aqueous solution of $CuCl_2$. While a complete analysis has not been made, it seems certain that curves other than the three mentioned above are the result of overlapping of these three spectra. It can be seen from these spectra that in GG-to-Cu^{2+} ratios greater than 1, if one adds 3 equivalents NaOH per Cu^{2+} and then 1 equivalent of OH^- for each glycylglycine in excess of the $[Cu^{2+}]$ the same curve results. Above three equivalents NaOH, further addition of NaOH does not alter the spectra. This holds true up to GG:Cu = 4, so we feel certain that we are dealing with a 1:1 complex. Thus, there seem to be two EPR-distinct complex species, namely, at pH 7 (2 equivalents NaOH) and at pH 10 (3 equivalents NaOH). These would correspond, in the notation of Koltun et al. (6), to the forms CuGG and CuGG(OH)$^-$. However, as is shown in the work of Dobbie and Kermack, the complex form CuGG$^+$ is never in very high concentration ($< 10\%$) and would thus be difficult to detect by EPR.

The EPR absorption curve for the pH 7 complex in aqueous solution (Fig. 4) resembles that seen for various other paramagnetic copper complexes at room temperature (18–20). The temperature dependence of the absorption is indicated in the figure. The four absorption lines with a spacing of approximately 80 Gauss result from an unpaired electron interacting with the Cu nucleus with a spin $I = \frac{3}{2}$. Additional hyperfine structure is evident on the $m = -\frac{3}{2}$ and $m = -\frac{1}{2}$ lines of the Cu spectrum, and this additional hyperfine splitting appears to consist of five lines with a spacing of 12.9 Gauss. It is also evident that this hyperfine structure of spacing 12.9 Gauss is most clearly resolved in the 273°K spectrum and, as can be seen from curve D, Fig. 3, in the pH 10 complex. For this reason, the EPR results for the copper ^{14}N- and ^{15}N-glycylglycine complexes are given for the pH 10 complex at 273°K.

Two explanations for the asymmetry of the curves as represented by the curve C of Fig. 4, and for the approach to symmetry upon increasing the temperature, are (a) that of McConnell (19) in which the relaxation time, T_2, depends on I_z of the copper nucleus and (b) that of Rivkind (20) in which the asymmetry is thought to result from incomplete averaging of the anisotropic components of the hyperfine structure. Experiments and calculations are under way to determine which mechanism is operative.

Finally, the nature of the binding of the copper to glycylglycine may be considered. As mentioned previously, the hyperfine structure with a spacing of 12.9 Gauss is most clearly resolved at 273°K and pH 10. For this reason, the following discussion is concerned with this form of the complex only. No generalizations to other forms will be made at this time.

Figure 5, curve D, representing the EPR spectrum of equimolar Cu^{2+} and glycylglycine at pH 10, clearly depicts hyperfine structure consisting of five lines separated by 12.9 Gauss. The existence of five lines is consistent with an interaction between two equivalent ^{14}N nuclei and an unpaired electron. The splittings of 12.9 Gauss are of the same order as those observed by Maki and McGarvey, 11.1 Gauss, due to nitrogen atoms, in the copper-bissalicylaldehydeimine complex.

If the anisotropies in the hyperfine splittings are averaged out, then the splittings should be proportional to the square of the wavefunction at the nucleus giving rise to the splittings. This would be expected to alter very little in replacing ^{14}N with ^{15}N. Then, if the splittings arise only from the Fermi contact term, the splitting a^N should be proportional to μ/I (21). Thus, by replacing ^{14}N with ^{15}N, we should see $a^{15N} = -1.40\, a^{14N}$. Hence, if the 12.9 Gauss hyperfine splitting is due to complexing of Cu^{2+} with 2 equivalent nitrogen atoms (as ^{14}N), then replacement of these two nitrogen atoms with ^{15}N-labeled atoms should result in three lines with a spacing of 18 Gauss. As can be seen from Fig. 5A, three lines separated by 17.6 Gauss are actually observed.

The situation is not this straightforward, as the EPR spectra of copper glycylglycinate containing mixed isotopes, ^{14}N and ^{15}N, are not entirely consistent with the above observations. These spectra will be published elsewhere, but it may be noted here that while the EPR data for ^{14}N-glyclyglycine and ^{15}N-glycylglycine are consistent with the assumed equivalence of the nitrogen atoms, this assumption does not explain the results for the mixed ^{14}N, ^{15}N peptide. The equivalence of the nitrogens is, if the anisotropies are averaged out, an equivalence of Fermi contact terms for the terminal ammonium and peptide nitrogens. This would imply that the bonds between these atoms and copper are, qualitatively and quantitatively, the same. The apparent equivalence of the two nitrogen atoms, while still not rigorously proven, must certainly be investigated more fully. Two troublesome points must be considered. The first is that from X-ray determination of the crystal structure of copper-glycylglycine (22) it was found that the peptide nitrogen–Cu bond length was 1.87 Å whereas the terminal amino nitrogen–Cu bond length was 2.02 Å. This is a difference of 8%. Second, the bonding of the two nitrogen atoms would seem to be basically different: while the terminal amino nitrogen atom is involved in σ bonds only (excluding metal bonds), the peptide nitrogen atom is probably bound through π bonds as well (22). It seems reasonable that the 8% difference in bond lengths would not be seen in room temperature EPR. The question of the exact bonding (σ and π) of the nitrogen atoms remains to be resolved.

Calculations have been made for paramagnetic copper complexes (23–25) in order to determine the covalent character of the copper-ligand bonds. The starting point for such calculations has been the assumption of symmetry about the Cu nucleus. For the calculations mentioned above, the symmetry was assumed to be D_{4h}. Such an assumption for the copper-glycylglycine complex is not justified, as Courtauld models and structural calculations have shown (26).

The results indicate that both the peptide nitrogen and the terminal amino nitrogen are covalently bound to the copper and that the degree of covalency is quite large. No proof of proton ionization from the peptide nitrogen is given by these results, and the justification for such an assumption remains to be given.

IV. Summary

(a) The form or structure of the complex that is formed when glycylglycine reacts with Cu^{2+} is highly pH dependent. The structure of the complex is not the same in frozen solution (110°K) as it is at 300°K (liquid).

(b) EPR detects two definite forms of 1:1 Cu:glycylglycine, one occurring at pH 7 and one at pH 10. This indicates that only two EPR-distinct complexes of Cu^{2+}-glycylglycine exist under these conditions.

(c) EPR gives conclusive evidence that the bonding between the Cu^{2+} and the glycylglycine involves covalent bonds between the Cu and the peptide and terminal amino nitrogen atoms. It is indicated that the two bonds may be essentially equivalent.

ACKNOWLEDGMENT

We gratefully acknowledge the insight and advice provided by Dr. T. Shiga during many discussions.

REFERENCES

1. Malmström, B. G., and Neilands, J., *Ann. Rev. Biochem.*, **33**, 331 (1964).
2. Malmström, B. G., and Vänngård, T., *J. Mol. Biol.*, **2**, 118 (1960).
3. Beinert, H., and Palmer, G., *J. Biol. Chem.*, **239**, 1221 (1964).
4. Mason, H. S., *Biochem. Biophys. Res. Communs.*, **10**, 11 (1963).
5. Dobbie, H., and Kermack, W. O., *Biochem. J.*, **59**, 246 (1955).
6. Koltun, W. L., Roth, F. H., and Gurd, F. R. N., *J. Biol. Chem.*, **238**, 124 (1963).
7. Izumiya, N., and Greenstein, J. P., *Arch. Biochem. Biophys.*, **52**, 203 (1951).
8. Manyak, A. F., Murphy, C. B., and Martell, A. E., *Arch. Biochem. Biophys.*, **59**, 373 (1955).
9. Murphy, C. B., and Martell, A. E., *J. Biol. Chem.*, **226**, 37 (1957).
10. Datta, S. P., Leberman, R., and Rabin, B. R., *Trans. Faraday Soc.*, **55**, 2141 (1959).
11. Bjerrum, J., *Chem. Rev.*, **46**, 381 (1950).
12. Albert, A., *Biochem. J.*, **47**, 531 (1950).
13. Rising, M. M., Parker, R. M., and Gaston, D. R., *J. Am. Chem. Soc.*, **56**, 1178 (1934).
14. Chouteau, J., and Lenormant, H., *Compt. Rend.*, **232**, 1479 (1951).
15. Kim, M. K., and Martell, A. E., *Biochemistry*, **3**, 1169 (1964).
16. Datta, S. P., and Rabin, B. R., *Trans. Faraday Soc.*, **52**, 1123 (1956).
17. Sands, R. H., *Phys. Rev.*, **99**, 1222 (1955).
18. Kneubühl, F. K., *J. Chem. Phys.*, **33**, 1074 (1960).
19. McConnell, H. M., *J. Chem. Phys.*, **25**, 709 (1955).
20. Rivkind, A. E., *Zhur. Fiz. Khim.*, **35**, 2099 (1961).
21. Ultee, C. J., *J. Chem. Phys.*, **43**, 1080 (1965).
22. Strandberg, B., Lindquist, I., and Rosenstein, R., *Z. Krist.*, **116**, 266 (1961).
23. McGarvey, B. R., *J. Phys. Chem.*, **60**, 71 (1956).
24. Gersmann, H. R., and Swalen, J. D., *J. Chem. Phys.*, **36**, 3221 (1962).
25. Wiersema, A. K., and Windle, J. J., *J. Phys. Chem.*, **68**, 2316 (1964).
26. Gould, D. C., thesis, Univ. of Oregon Medical School (1965).

DISCUSSION

Dr. Gurd: Did you imply in your paper that there were some complexes that the rest of us have seen that you couldn't see?

Mr. Gould: Yes. It seems that Dobbie and Kermack (5) postulated a 2:1 glycylglycine-to-Cu^{2+} complex, and from data given by them we should see a large percentage of this complex in, say, a 3:1 glycylglycine-to-Cu^{2+} mixture at pH 10.

The curve that we see in that case is identical with the curve we see in the 1:1 glycylglycine-to- Cu^{2+} mixture.

DR. GURD: I think that is not too surprising, because at that pH the hydroxide-bearing stage, the last thing you were talking about, would probably compete very successfully with the process of putting the second glycylglycine on. We do know that the second glycylglycine can't go on with both of its nitrogens. So it is probably not a very effective competitor at that pH. In order to work out these equilibria you would want to do the study at a lower pH, which you very wisely avoided doing. Here you would have risked forming the dimerization complex that was discussed, where the hydroxide-bearing complex tends to react with another copper glycylglycine complex without an hydroxyl ion on it. You wisely went to a pH where you couldn't get tangled up in that problem. I think this all fits together.

MR. GOULD: We have seen little indication of the reaction that you have proposed, the formation of the dicupric-diglycylglycine complex. It would seem that a complex of that sort would have a very broad EPR signal and perhaps would not be detected.

DR. GURD: Yes, and it is rather hard to get a lot of it. Martell has confirmed the titration results that we have. It just is not a very easy thing to study in your system.

MR. GOULD: The same is true for the complex formed if just one equivalent of hydroxide is consumed. That complex also is in very low concentration, and we see no EPR evidence for its existence.

DR. SARKAR: Recently Kim and Martell [*Biochem.*, **3**, 1169 (1964)] have shown by simultaneous pH titration and infrared spectra measurements in D_2O that the structure of copper-glycylglycine complex at about pH 10 has a 2:1 peptide-to-copper ratio, with copper having a coordination number of 6. Do you agree with this structure proposed by them?

MR. GOULD: No.

Some Aspects of Models of Copper Complexes

W. E. BLUMBERG

Bell Telephone Laboratories,
New York, New York

I. The Possibility of Constructing Models from Physical Measurements

Physical measurements have been made on transition metal ion complexes for many years. Some of these complexes have been of biological interest. Biochemists often ask why such a large body of physical information cannot be used to calculate a physical structure for a specific complex under study. Indeed if perhaps 100 distinct, meaningful physical measurements were to be made on a single transition metal ion complex and if a comprehensive physical theory were in existence to relate these measurements to the physical structure of the complex, a very meaningful picture of the complex could be computed. However, such is not the case. There are rarely more than 10 or 20 physical measurements which are related to structure by sound physical theory and which can be made on any given transition metal ion complex. Some of these are the magnetic susceptibility parameters, the spectroscopic splitting factors and hyperfine coupling constants of the EPR spectrum, the positions of the optical transitions and their strengths and optical rotatory dispersions, as well as perhaps their magnetooptical rotations, and, in certain cases where single crystals are available, measurements of optical dichroism. We shall try to see what kind of simplified model, if any, can result from some of these measurements. Cu^{2+} complexes are ideal for this study as almost all of these complexes can be represented as distortions of the classical square planar complex which exists so often in inorganic copper complexes. (See, for example, Ref. (1).)

Before proceeding, we must outline a number of assumptions that must be made:

(a) All calculations are to be done in the language of electrostatics even though nowadays this is to be regarded as a somewhat allegorical approach (cf. Ref. (2)). Positions of maxima in electrostatic potential are to be related to the positions of ligand atoms, and the value of the potential is to be related to the strength of the chemical bond.

(b) All copper complexes are to be considered as distortions of a square planar complex.

(c) Any p-electron mixing introduced by such distortions can be taken into account by invoking the principle of closure (3).

(d) Information will only be sought concerning the directions and bond strengths of the ligand atoms, along with a single over-all measure of covalency. No information can be obtained directly from these physical measurements about the kind of ligand atom involved or its distance from the copper ion or the degree of covalency of any one copper ligand bond.

First we decide on the following 12 physical measurements, all of which can be related to structure by physical theory, as being the most suitable for this study. We shall take these as the three spectroscopic splitting factors g_z, g_x, g_y of the EPR spectrum (4), the positions of the three d–d optical transitions highest in energy (5–8), and the oscillator strengths (9)

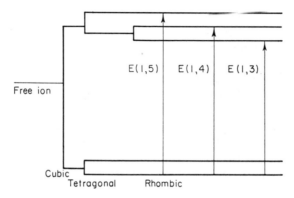

FIG. 1. Energy levels of Cu^{2+} in fields of various symmetries. The effects of spin-orbit coupling have been omitted. The levels are ordered for a d^1 hole, which occupies the bottom level. This is the state in which the EPR spectroscopic splitting factors g are measured. The optical transitions referred to in the text are shown by vertical arrows.

and optical rotatory dispersions (10, 11) of these three transitions.[1] The energy levels of a cupric ion in fields of various symmetries are shown in Fig. 1, where the unpaired electron has been considered as a d^1 hole. The g values are measured in the bottom or ground state, and the optical transitions referred to are shown by vertical arrows. We shall not here be concerned with the difficulty or impossibility of obtaining these physical measurements under certain circumstances but shall assume that these values exist, and, where there are temperature dependences, the values are appropriate to a temperature of absolute zero. That is to say, the physical measurements should be properties of the static configuration of the copper

---

[1] The magnetic susceptibility does not add significantly to the information provided by the g values; the hyperfine components are less rigorously related to structure in that they depend on both core polarization (12–14) and p-electron admixture (15–18) in ways which are not easy to calculate; and the magnetooptical rotation depends on triple sums over wavefunctions that are difficult to approximate in many cases.

complex and not represent averages of values which obtain in the different vibrational states of the complex (17–20).

II. Choice of Crystal Field Parameters

Having chosen 12 physical measurements, we are now allowed up to 12 parameters to describe the electrostatic potential around the copper ion. We use one of these parameters to describe the spin-orbit coupling constant,

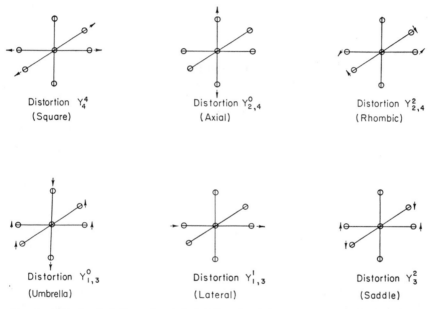

FIG. 2. The physical distortions of the ligands of Cu^{2+} from a square planar ligand field configuration. A geometrical representation of each of the distortions $Y_k{}^q$ is shown by the small arrows. The top three figures represent even-even distortions while the bottom three are odd.

which decreases from the free ion value (21) of 829 cm^{-1} as the covalency of the complex increases (22). Next we look at the possible distortions of the square planar geometry. These are shown in Fig. 2. The ligand atoms along the vertical or z axis are the axial or apical ligands and the other four form the square plane. It is important to the theory to distinguish between two classes of distortions, depending on symmetry.[2] The top three are of even-even symmetry, meaning that they are symmetrical in the plus

[2] The symmetry symbols used are the spherical harmonics $Y_k{}^q$. See, for example, Ref. (3) .

and minus z directions and under an inversion in the horizontal plane as well, e.g., the square distortion Y_4^4 represents a compression or extension in both the plus and minus x and y directions and no change in the z direction. The rhombic distortions can exist in two forms which are indistinguishable from considerations of the energies and g values alone. These forms are the rectangular (as shown) and the rhomboidal, in which the square plane is distorted into a rhombus instead of a rectangle. It will be assumed that any rhombic distortions are rectangular for the reason that only this type can permit optical rotatory dispersion to exist. Y_2^1, which represents a tilt of the z axis, has been omitted as it affects the selected physical measurements to a very small extent.

The bottom three distortions are odd, meaning that they are antisymmetrical under at least one type of inversion; e.g., Y_1^0 and Y_3^0 represent a compression in the plus z direction and an extension in the minus z direction (moving the copper ion slightly down from the plane as a result).

The distinction between the different kinds of distortions is important as only the even-even symmetries directly affect the g values and the energies of the optical transitions. The oscillator strengths of these optical transitions, however, depend on the combination of two odd distortions, and the optical rotatory dispersion only exists when both certain odd (Y_3^2) and even-even $(Y_2^2$ or $Y_4^2)$ distortions are present simultaneously. This separation of the effects of the fields of different symmetries, the assumption of a square planar configuration to start with, and the use of the principle of closure for the p-electron mixing make the following calculations economically feasible with 12 physical measurements to be fitted.

We take five of the seven mathematically distinguishable[3] even-even distortions and the five possible odd distortions[4] as the remaining adjustable parameters. We are now in a position to do the following calculation: Assume arbitrary values for the crystal field components leading to the square planar geometry (the coefficients of Y_2^0, Y_4^0, Y_4^4), add in any arbitrary amounts of the distortions shown in Fig. 2, and compute values for all 12 physical measurements that would have been obtained with such a hypothetical complex. Although we are in a position to proceed much farther, we will digress as such fictitious models may be of instructive value in themselves.

---

[3] Although Y_2^0 and Y_4^0 are physically indistinguishable distortions from square planar geometry, they are to be included separately in the calculations as they affect the Cu^{2+} wavefunction in different ways; similarly for Y_2^2 and Y_4^2, Y_1^0 and Y_3^0, Y_1^1 and Y_3^1.

[4] Note that the lateral distortions can be in either the x or the y direction. The directional effects are indistinguishable with the physical measurements to be used. The direction of any required lateral distortion must be decided upon by other means.

III. Conventions for Reduction of the Crystal Field to a Model

Now we have the problem of reducing the mathematical description of these crystal field parameters to two- or three-dimensional models which may be understood by those not well acquainted with the rather abstract mathematics of crystal field theory. To do this we need to have numerical representations of the Cu^{2+} d-electron wavefunctions for the purpose of plotting the spatial contrours of the electron density and for determining the average values of powers of the radius r ($\langle r^n \rangle$, $n = 1$ to 4), which are needed to give numerical values (in Volts per centimeter, etc.) to the crystal field potentials. Any of the numerical wavefunctions, such as the Hartree–Fock (23) or even the Slater orbitals (24, 25), should be adequate

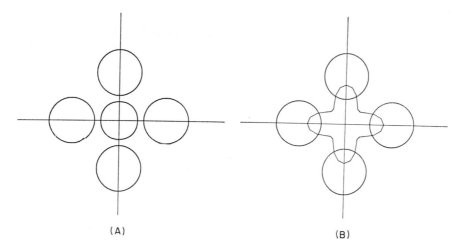

(A) (B)

FIG. 3. Cross section of Cu^{2+} ion and square planar ligands. The figure in the center is a contour of the Cu^{2+} electron density near its ionic radius. (a) As computed; (b) d-hole density treated as electron and enhanced by factor of 10 in accordance with text.

for this purpose. If the electron density of the Cu^{2+} ion is now plotted, two surprises may be registered: first, the electron density variation due to the d-electron distribution is very small compared with the total electron density and, second, the electron density in the direction of the ligand atoms is *less* than in other directions (see Fig. 3a). To conform more to intuition, we adopt the following convention: the d-hole density is plotted as if it were an electron, i.e., pointing outward instead of inward, and for emphasis is plotted 10 times as pronounced as it actually is. This gives a contour cross section in the ligand plane such as is seen in Fig. 3b, where it may be seen that the lobes of the Cu^{2+} "wavefunction" are very prominent and point in the direction of the ligand atoms.

We must also make some arbitrary decisions about plotting the electrostatic potential. Since spatial contours of the various crystal field potentials would have little meaning to the biochemist, we adopt this convention: in the direction of each of the six maxima in potential and at a constant distance, say 2 Å, we construct a sphere representing a ligand atom or molecule. The radius of the sphere is to correspond to the strength of the ligand field at that point. Thus water molecules, which give rise to weak ligand fields, should show up as small spheres while sulfur and imino nitrogen, which contribute strong ligand fields, should appear as large spheres. These spheres are not meant to represent the physical size or shape of the ligands or their distance away, merely the ligand field strengths they contribute and their directions.

IV. Models of Arbitrary Complexes of Various Symmetries

Figures 4–7 are illustrations of models made by computer for Cu^{2+} in ligand fields of several symmetries. These have been constructed in sections perpendicular to the z axis separated by approximately 0.2 Å. Figure 4 is the classical square planar configuration having no distortions. It has no g-value anisotropy in the horizontal plane and no oscillator strengths or optical rotatory dispersion. Any slight color such a complex may exhibit must be obtained by means of vibrationally assisted optical transitions as in $NiSO_4 \cdot 7H_2O$ (26). Figure 5 shows a complex which is rectangular in the

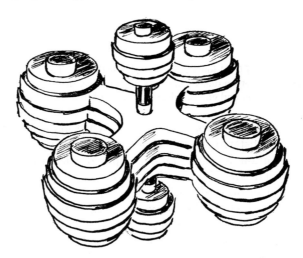

Fig. 4. Model of square planar Cu^{2+} complex stylized according to text. Note Cu^{2+} "wavefunction" contours pointing in direction of square planar ligands represented by large spheres. Apical ligands are represented by the smaller spheres.

Fig. 5. Model of Cu^{2+} complex with rectangular distortion made by the addition of Y_2^2 or Y_4^2 to the square planar ligand field. This complex would have $g_x \neq g_y$ but would not be highly colored or possess optical rotatory dispersion.

horizontal plane and thus may have two distinct values of g_x and g_y but still has no intense optical absorptions or rotatory dispersion. Optical absorption only becomes allowed as distortions giving rise to odd fields, such as that shown in Fig. 6, are introduced. This laterally distorted complex would have no anisotropy in the g values in the horizontal plane but

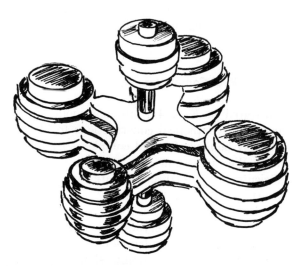

Fig. 6. Model of Cu^{2+} complex laterally distorted by the addition of Y_1^1 to the square planar ligand field. This complex would have $g_x = g_y$ but would be strongly colored. No optical rotatory dispersion would be observed.

Fig. 7. Model of Cu^{2+} complex with rectangular, saddle, and lateral distortions produced by the addition of $Y_2{}^2$ or $Y_4{}^2$, $Y_3{}^2$, and $Y_1{}^1$ to the square planar ligand field. This complex would have $g_x \neq g_y$, strong optical absorptions, and optical rotatory dispersion.

would possess strong optical absorptions. These absorptions would, however, not give rise to any optical rotatory dispersion. Last we show in Fig. 7 an example of a Cu^{2+} chromophoric complex having all the physical properties mentioned: $g_x \neq g_y$, strong optical absorptions, and strong rotatory dispersions.

V. Models of Two Real Complexes

The models illustrated in Figs. 4–7 are not models of specific Cu^{2+} complexes but are only hypothetical constructions to illustrate the principle. Such models may be made for real complexes by following a fitting procedure as follows. We can assume any values of the crystal field parameters (the coefficients of the $Y_k{}^q$) as an initial guess and calculate the physical measurements as before. We can use these values, when compared with the physical measurements of a real complex of interest, to give partially corrected values for all the crystal field parameters and the spin-orbit coupling energy, which tells the degree of covalency. This process is then repeated many times. If branch points should occur, it is assumed that the path is to be taken which represents the least distortion from square planar geometry. If this process should converge to an acceptable degree of accuracy, we would now have a hypothetical electrostatic potential such that a Cu^{2+} ion in this potential, and having sufficient covalency to give the correctly reduced spin-orbit coupling, would possess all the 12 selected physical properties of the real Cu^{2+} complex of interest. What then is the relation between the hypothetical model and the real complex? We may hope that the directions and magnitudes of the maxima of the hypothetical crystal field potential correspond to the directions and bond strengths of the real ligands. For a completely ionic complex this is rigorously true, but for covalent complexes it would be expected to correspond only approximately.

Now we return to our main goal, that of constructing models of specific real copper complexes. We shall illustrate the technique with two selected cases, one a particularly simple case in which the structure is already well known by other methods and the other a more complicated case where no previous information about structure was available.

A. The Cupric Ion Sites in $CuSO_4 \cdot 5H_2O$

First we shall consider the two nearly identical complexes of copper that occur in the crystalline state of $CuSO_4 \cdot 5H_2O$, the structure of which has been determined by X-ray crystallography (27). As the copper sites in this crystal are very symmetrical with only a minimal amount of distortion from our starting point of a perfect square planar complex, the oscillator strengths of the optical absorptions and the optical rotations are very small and we may take these, for the purposes of this calculation, to be zero. The parameters that we shall use as input data for the fitting pro-

TABLE I

EXPERIMENTAL AND CALCULATED VALUES FOR PHYSICAL MEASUREMENTS ON THE CUPRIC IONS IN $CuSO_4 \cdot 5H_2O$

Measurement	Experimental[a]	Calculated
g_z	2.37	2.373
g_x	2.08	2.074
g_y	2.08	2.072
$E(1, 3)$	10,500 cm^{-1}	10,991 cm^{-1}
$E(1, 4)$	13,000 cm^{-1}	13,020 cm^{-1}
$E(1, 5)$	14,500 cm^{-1}	14,177 cm^{-1}

[a] The experimental g values are from Ref. (28). The experimental energies (E) of optical transitions are from Ref. (26).

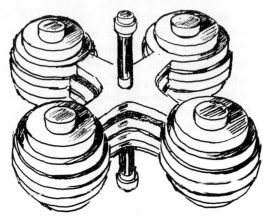

FIG. 8. Model of the Cu^{2+} sites in $CuSO_4 \cdot 5H_2O$. The complex appears square planar within the accuracy of the model. The weak apical ligands show up as very small spheres.

cedure are the g values and the energies of the optical absorptions as shown in the first column of Table I. The best fit using only even-even fields in the calculation is shown in the second column. It is to be seen that the values of the physical parameters of the cupric ion can be reproduced quite well by this procedure. The model which results from this calculation is shown in Fig. 8. A consideration of this model leads us to expect that there will be four moderately strong and two very weak ligands to the copper ion and that the four stronger ligands will be in a square planar configuration with very little, if any, rhombic distortion. We should compare these results with Fig. 9, which shows a model made by the same technique from the structure as determined by X-ray crystallography, where the near-neighbor oxygen atoms are shown at their correct distances and orientations from the copper and are constructed as spheres of the same arbitrary size. Note these two features. The nearest oxygens, belonging to water molecules, are in intimate contact with the copper, whereas the apical oxygens, belonging to SO_4^{2-}, are much farther away and affect the copper ion minimally. This minimal effect is reflected in Fig. 8 by the smallness of the apical spheres. Also, in the crystal there is a tilt in the axis of the apical ligands from the normal of the square plane. As this tilt does not appreciably affect any of the physical measurements used in this study, no attempt has been made to include it. Therefore, it of course does not appear in the computed model shown in Fig. 8. Estimates of the tilt, if it proves to be important in certain cases, must be made by other methods. The "square planes" of Figs. 8 and 9 contain small rhombic distortions which are not observable in the models. The value of the spin-orbit coupling constant as returned by the fitting procedure is 683 cm^{-1}, which is 82%

FIG. 9. Model of the near neighbors to Cu^{2+} in $CuSO_4 \cdot 5H_2O$ as determined by X-ray crystallography. All neighboring atoms are oxygen, the nearest ones belonging to H_2O and the farther two belonging to $SO_4{}^{2-}$. The oxygen atoms are constructed to be the same arbitrary size.

of the free ion value. This indicates that the complex is approximately 36% covalent,[5] not an unreasonable value for this principally ionic crystal.

B. The Cupric Ion Sites in Ceruloplasmin

Having had a moderate degree of success in a simple case, we attack a much more complicated structure, the cupric ion sites in the copper protein ceruloplasmin. Here we must bring into play all the crystal field parameters at our disposal. First the even-even field fitting was carried out to give the values shown in the first six lines of Table II. Next the odd fields were added in to produce the values given in the last six lines. It can be seen that the best fit is not perfect, but the principal features of ceruloplasmin seem to be reproduced adequately for our purposes. Three important assumptions must be noted before a model can be constructed. (a) The rhombic dis-

[5] When the unpaired spin is shared equally between the Cu^{2+} and the ligands, the spin-orbit coupling will be reduced by 50%. In a manner of speaking, this case may be called 100% covalent.

TABLE II

EXPERIMENTAL AND CALCULATED VALUES FOR PHYSICAL MEASUREMENTS ON THE
CUPRIC IONS IN CERULOPLASMIN

Measurement	Experimental[a]	Calculated
g_z	2.214	2.2177
g_x	2.048	2.0339
g_y	2.048	2.0359
$E(1, 3)$	12,600 cm^{-1}	12,634 cm^{-1}
$E(1, 4)$	16,400 cm^{-1}	16,389 cm^{-1}
$E(1, 5)$	21,800 cm^{-1}	21,790 cm^{-1}
$f(1, 3)$	0.007	0.011
$f(1, 4)$	0.051	0.045
$f(1, 5)$	0.006	0.010
$R(1, 3)$	75 deg M^{-1} cm^{-1}	75.3 deg M^{-1} cm^{-1}
$R(1, 4)$	-34 deg M^{-1} cm^{-1}	-42.8 deg M^{-1} cm^{-1}
$R(1, 5)$	45 deg M^{-1} cm^{-1}	11.7 deg M^{-1} cm^{-1}

[a] The experimental g values are from Ref. (29). The experimental energies (E) and oscillator strengths (f) are from Ref. (30). The experimental optical rotatory strengths (R) are unpublished observations, where $R(1, n)$ is the coefficient of

$$\left(\frac{\nu - E(1, n)}{\Delta \nu} \right) \exp \left[- \left(\frac{\nu - E(1, n)}{\Delta \nu} \right)^2 \right]$$

which best fits the data. The widths $\Delta \nu$ are from Ref. (30).

tortion was considered to be only rectangular in form although there might be some rhomboidal distortion as well. (b) The lateral distortion was assumed to be in the direction toward the gap produced by one of the longer ligand-ligand distances, as this is the energetically most favorable direction for such a distortion. (c) There was assumed to be no tilt in the axis of the apical ligands. With the results of the fitting procedure and these assumptions, the model for the cupric ion sites in ceruloplasmin shown in Fig. 10 was constructed.

The reader is urged to review the conventions for the construction of such models before trying to draw any inferences from Fig. 10. It is not postulated that the cupric ion in ceruloplasmin has this configuration, but merely that if it did have such an environment produced by electrostatic fields, it would have the physical properties listed in the second column of Table II, which are nearly the same as those for ceruloplasmin. The apical ligands, as depicted by the small spheres on the model, are very weak. Thus it is

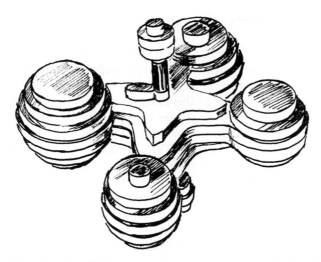

Fig. 10. Model of the Cu^{2+} sites in the copper protein ceruloplasmin. The apical ligands depicted by the small spheres are very weak. The four "square planar" ligands have rectangular and three types of odd distortions as discussed in the text.

likely that one or both of them are water molecules. It is known that the solvent water molecules can reach the vicinity of the cupric ions in ceruloplasmin (30). The other ligands consist of two types, suggesting that perhaps the ligands occur in pairs, such as two amine and two imine nitrogen atoms, or two nitrogen and two sulfur atoms, etc. No direct inferences may be drawn concerning the descriptions of these ligands—only their relative bonding strengths. The over-all degree of covalency may be estimated from the spin-orbit coupling constant, 550 cm^{-1}, which gives the best fit. Thus the average covalency as defined above is about 68%. As expected, this is considerably more than the covalency observed for $CuSO_4 \cdot 5H_2O$.

Three types of odd distortions are evident. (a) The copper ion is slightly above the average position of the four strongest ligands. (b) There is a strong lateral push as there are two ligands on one side which are stronger that the other. (c) There is a small amount of Y_3^2 (saddle) distortion, which makes the four strongest ligands attempt to take up tetrahedral positions.

Several unusual configurations for the cupric sites in ceruloplasmin have been suggested to account for their physical properties (30). Among these were the neighboring position of an aromatic amino acid or a bridge to a cuprous ion. While these special ligands may indeed contribute to the over-all crystal field of the cupric ions, their invocation is not necessary. The properties of ceruloplasmin can be explained by sufficiently strong distortions from the more usual square planar configuration.

VI. Some Speculations

It is hoped that such models, while they cannot be taken at face value, will lead to speculations about the structure of cupric complexes which will, in turn, lead to theories of reaction mechanisms amenable to experimental confirmation. It is appropriate at this symposium to make two speculations which may stimulate such ideas among the participants. It is known that the Cu^{2+} ion in ceruloplasmin can be reduced to Cu^+ without being freed from its binding site in the protein (31). As has been pointed out (32), a rigid square planar cupric complex will not allow this. Perhaps, on reduction, the four strongest ligands, which have an incipient tetrahedral configuration in the cupric complex, move in that direction enabling the Cu^+ complex to be stable. In this case the apical ligands, which are very weakly bound anyway, would be disengaged. Another possibility is that, on reduction, all four of the weakest ligands become disengaged, and the Cu^+ is held by the two remaining strongest ligands in either a linear or digonal bonding configuration. Such a configuration has the advantage that it would allow plenty of room for the approach of substrate or oxygen molecules to the cuprous ion. It must be again emphasized, however, that neither of these speculations follows directly from the work presented in this paper.

It is hoped that, when such models are constructed for a variety of the more complicated structures involving Cu^{2+}, the experience gained will allow more definite conclusions to be drawn and that, in the future, such stylized models may be useful to the biochemist in trying to understand possible enzyme mechanisms and active site structures.

VII. Summary

(a) Some rather stylized models have been used to illustrate what kinds of distortions from square planar geometry lead to certain physical properties: g-value anisotropy, enhanced optical transitions, and optical rotatory dispersion.

(b) How to construct such models of specific Cu^{2+} complexes of interest such that a hypothetical Cu^{2+} ion in the potential of such a complex would exhibit some of the same physical properties as the real complex has been outlined.

(c) Illustrations of the technique have been carried out for the structures of the Cu^{2+} sites in crystalline $CuSO_4 \cdot 5H_2O$, which had been previously studied by X-ray crystallography, and in ceruloplasmin, a copper protein, for which no structural information was previously available.

(d) The purpose of these fictitious models is to encourage new lines of thought on the mechanism of action of cupric enzymes and the configuration of the cupric ion in such enzymes.

ACKNOWLEDGMENTS

These calculations were facilitated by the use of a computer program written by Dr. A. Kiel for rare-earth ions in crystals and adapted for Cu^{2+} by Dr. Kiel. The results would not have been possible without the tireless efforts of Dr. Kiel in finding the errors in the special programs written for these calculations. The fitting procedure was adapted from a program used to fit data from satellites, which was compiled for general use by Dr. C. S. Roberts. Special thanks are due Mr. David Zuckerman, who assembled the computer-generated models, and to Mr. Paul Hamlin, who made the illustrations of them.

REFERENCES

1. Wells, A. F., "Structural inorganic chemistry," Oxford Univ. Press, London and New York, 1950, 2nd Ed., pp. 618 ff.
2. Jørgensen, C. K., this symposium.
3. Condon, E. U., and Shortley, G. H., "The theory of atomic spectra," 2nd Ed., Cambridge Univ. Press, London and New York, 1953.
4. Abragam, A., and Pryce, M. H. L., *Proc. Roy. Soc. (London)*, Ser. A, **206**, 164 (1951).
5. Bethe, H. A., *Ann. Physik*, **3**, 133 (1929).
6. Johrdahl, O. M., *Phys. Rev.*, **45**, 87 (1934).
7. Polder, D., *Physica*, **9**, 709 (1942).
8. Bleaney, B., and Stevens, K. W. H., *Rept. Progr. Phys.*, **16**, 108 (1953).
9. Mulliken, R. S., and Rieke, C. A., *Rept. Progr. Phys.*, **8**, 231 (1941).
10. Condon, E. U., *Rev. Mod. Phys.*, **9**, 432 (1937).
11. Moffitt, W., *J. Chem. Phys.*, **25**, 1189 (1956).
12. Heine, V., *Phys. Rev.*, **107**, 1002 (1957).
13. Wood, J. H., and Pratt, G. W., Jr., *Phys. Rev.*, **107**, 995 (1957).
14. Watson, R. E., and Freeman, A. J., *Phys. Rev.*, **123**, 2027 (1961).
15. Koide, S., and Pryce, M. H. L., *Phil. Mag.*, **3**, 607 (1959).
16. Koide, S., *Phil. Mag.*, **4**, 243 (1959).
17. Tanabe, Y., *Progr. Theoret. Phys. (Kyoto)*, Suppl. **14**, p. 17 (1960).
18. Sugano, S., *Progr. Theoret. Phys. (Kyoto)*, Suppl. **14**, 66 (1960).
19. Van Vleck, J. H., *J. Phys. Chem.*, **41**, 67 (1937).
20. Liehr, A. D., and Ballhausen, C. J., *Phys. Rev.*, **106**, 1161 (1957).
21. Moore, C. E., *Natl. Bur. Std. Circ.* **467**, (1949).
22. Stevens, K. W. H., *Proc. Roy. Soc. (London)*, Ser. A, **219**, 542 (1953).
23. Hartree, D. R., "The calculation of atomic structures," John Wiley and Sons, New York, 1957.
24. Slater, J. C., *Phys. Rev.* **36**, 57 (1930).
25. Brown, D. A., *J. Chem. Phys.*, **28**, 67 (1958).
26. Holmes, O. G., and McClure, D. S., *J. Chem. Phys.*, **26**, 1686 (1957).
27. Beevers, C. A., and Lipson, H., *Proc. Roy. Soc. (London)*, Ser. A, **146**, 570 (1934).
28. Bagguley, D. M. S., and Griffiths, J. H. E., *Proc. Roy. Soc. (London)*, Ser. A, **201**, 366 (1950).

29. Malmström, B. G., and Vänngård, T., *J. Mol. Biol.*, **2**, 118 (1960).
30. Blumberg, W. E., Eisinger, J., Aisen, P., Morell, A. G., and Scheinberg, I. H., *J. Biol. Chem.*, **238**, 1675 (1963).
31. Holmberg, C. G., and Laurell, C.-B., *Acta Chem. Scand.*, **2**, 550 (1948).
32. Hemmerich, P., this symposium.

DISCUSSION

DR. MASON: Dr. Blumberg, am I splitting hairs or being unduly naive concerning your usage of the expression *"the* structure" or "the *real* structure"? Biochemists have traditionally taken as their field the relationship of structure to function. I wonder just what is the meaning of the expression "structure." Isn't it true that there is no absolute structure? Especially in the light of Dr. Jørgensen's comment that in aqueous solution at room temperature there is a probability distribution of nuclei, and that there is a probability distribution of electrons, the "real" structure can only be described as having a range of probabilities.

DR. BLUMBERG: That is certainly true, but I think that the range over which the probabilities may vary is rather restricted, except in certain particularly flexible cases. The range of thermal vibrations in a molecule such as ceruloplasmin, for example, is small compared with the static distortion which must be there already in order to give it its properties. One way to determine how much statistical fluctuations in structure determine the physical properties (relative to the static distortions of structure) is to measure the temperature dependence of these various physical parameters. In particular, the measurements that I have made on ceruloplasmin, or taken from other papers, don't have much temperature dependence in the region in which the measurements were made. I would say that these physical properties are principally a property of the static configuration of ceruloplasmin. Of course it must be slightly flexible around that, but I have done the calculations for what I would call the "average configuration."

Certainly nothing like that inversion which occurs in the ammonia molecule can happen. It is not possible that ceruloplasmin can turn around and exist half the time in an inverted configuration and half the time back in the original. Such violent motions are just not possible when it possesses these temperature-independent properties.

DR. JØRGENSEN: Claus Schäffer and I have just published a paper [*Mat. fys. Medd. Dan. Vid. Selsk.*, **34**, No. 13 (1965)] concerning orthoaxial chromophores, having all six ligands on Cartesian coordinate axes, but possibly having all six different. Our results agree essentially with yours—with a quarter of a percent of the amount of calculation. It is extremely interesting to compare the two.

You were talking about p-orbital mixing. I think Ballhausen and Liehr made an original error by thinking it was the d^8p configuration that was responsible for the intensity of the d^9 transitions. I wonder whether you have considered the $d^{10}p^{-1}$ mixing, because, at this occasion, I am going to swallow the argument that the electron transfer spectra might be represented as $d^{10}p^{-1}$.

DR. BLUMBERG: I think both contingencies are taken care of in the calculations. One must put in different energy denominators for those two things, and I put in very arbitrarily an energy denominator of 125,000 cm^{-1} for the p electron, which is perhaps too high for the $d^{10}p^{-1}$ that you have mentioned, but, I think, is about right for the d^8p.

DR. JØRGENSEN: I see. You have considered both effects at the same time?

DR. BLUMBERG: Yes.

DR. SCHEINBERG: Considering that we are forgetting the four or five cuprous atoms that are around, which of the three or four cupric atoms in ceruloplasmin does this apply to?

DR. BLUMBERG: Since you haven't been able to give me a sample in which I can distinguish between any of the cupric atoms in the native material, I say it is *the* site.

DR. SCHEINBERG: The proton relaxation rate showed different types of cupric sites.

DR. BLUMBERG: That is a way that we made a kind of distinction between two different classes of cupric atoms in ceruloplasmin. Some are more accessible and some are less accessible to the solvent water molecules, but they don't seem to have any different chromophoric or EPR properties, so they probably are roughly in the same ligand configuration. Some just happen to be deeper in the molecule than others. If you can separate these from one another so that they have different physical properties, I will construct a model for both of them.

DR. SCHEINBERG: Could you do it by having someone else make your 12 measurements on partially decolorized material?

DR. BLUMBERG: I'm willing, as long as I don't have to make the measurements.

The Cupric Ion and a Trigonal Field: Cupric Insulin*

A. S. BRILL AND J. H. VENABLE, JR.†

Department of Molecular Biophysics,
Yale University,
New Haven, Connecticut

The most complete picture presently available of the cupric ion in a protein environment is provided by studies of cupric insulin crystals. We shall present here parts of this picture which may be of general interest, paying particular attention to the principles involved in arriving at these features.

I. Cupric Ion EPR in Nonprotein Trigonal Complexes

A cupric complex of true trigonal symmetry would have an orbitally degenerate ground state. According to the Jahn–Teller theorem, such a complex would be unstable and would distort to a lower symmetry, thereby removing the degeneracy. The cupric ion has been studied by EPR in several inorganic trigonal lattices of known structure, such as $ZnSiF_6 \cdot 6H_2O$ (1, 2). In all these complexes the copper is coordinated to a nearly regular octahedron of six water molecules or chloride ions. At temperatures above $90°K$ the EPR spectra show an isotropic g value. At lower temperatures the spectra become similar to those of tetragonal copper, but there are three mutually perpendicular directions of g_{max} which make equal angles with the trigonal axis (Fig. 1). That is, there appear to be three distinct sites for copper in the crystal. Spectra of the chloride complex, $(CuCl_6)^{4-}$ in $CdCl_2$, show hyperfine structure due to the ligands, but the splittings are explained by an interaction with four equivalent Cl^- atoms rather than the expected six.

These data have been successfully explained in terms of the Jahn–Teller theorem (3, 4). At low temperatures each molecule is trapped into one of three equivalent distortions which produce a tetragonal field about the copper. Each of the three g_{max} directions corresponds to the tetragonal axis of one of the three distorted complexes. The distortion is an elongation so that two of the ligands are more distant from the metal than the other four. This explains the four-Cl^- hyperfine pattern. At elevated temperatures

* The U. S. Public Health Service supported this work through research grant GM-09256 from the Division of General Medical Sciences.

† Not at meeting. Present address: Department of Biophysics, King's College, University of London, London, England.

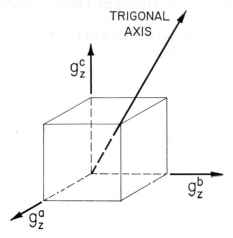

FIG. 1. Relations among the directions of g_{max} and the symmetry axis for the cupric ion and a trigonal field.

the vibrational energy exceeds the trapping energy and the complex resonates among the three distorted forms. This results in an isotropic g value.

Recently *tris* complexes of the cupric ion with the bidentate ligands 1,10-*o*-phenanthroline and 2,2′-bipyridine have been studied by EPR (5). Unfortunately, the crystal structures of these compounds are not known. Furthermore, single crystals of sufficient size were not available, and polycrystalline samples were used for the EPR measurements. Geometrical relationships of the type described above for the inorganic complexes were thus not experimentally determinable. However, two important features of these bulky *tris* organic complexes were established:

(a) The spectra show a transition from isotropic to anisotropic magnetic parameters just as do the inorganic crystal spectra, but this behavior occurs at much higher temperatures—from about −50° to +50° in the case of the *o*-phenanthroline complex.

(b) Although the metal ion is bound to six nitrogens, a four-nitrogen ligand hyperfine structure is seen in the low-temperature spectra.

Before describing how the behavior of the cupric ion in insulin crystals is a natural extension of the properties discussed above, we shall present pertinent properties of this well-studied protein-metal complex.

II. Some Facts about Insulin Crystals

Pig insulin crystallizes in citrate buffer, pH 6.0–6.2, in the presence of Zn^{2+}, Cu^{2+}, and other divalent metal ions of the $3d$ group. The crystals from the various metals are all rhombohedral in shape, and X-ray diffraction patterns show them to be isomorphic (6, 7). The first crystallization yields about two metal ions per 36,000 mol. wt. unit cell (6 Sanger units). Similarly, further crystallizations (no metal added) require that sufficient metal be present for the incorporation of about two ions per unit cell, or else crystals do not form. The significance of two metal ions per six Sanger units also appears in solutions measurements: osmotic pressure (8); dialyzability and sedimentation (9); electrophoretic mobility (7, 9). Metal ions can be bound in excess of two per 36,000 mol. wt., but these ions interact more weakly with the protein.

Detailed X-ray diffraction studies of zinc insulin crystals have been made (10, 11). These crystals belong to the space group R3 which has only threefold rotation and threefold screw axes. Recently the existence of three noncrystallographic twofold axes relating members of each asymmetric unit (12,000 mol. wt.) has been reported (12). These axes are perpendicular to the threefold crystallographic axis.

The unit cell is thus seen to have a trigonal axis, with two metal ions bound to six Sanger units. This suggests a trigonal environment, provided by three Sanger units, for each metal ion. One is curious to see how the EPR spectrum of cupric insulin bears upon this picture.

III. Relevant Features of the EPR Spectra of Cupric Insulin Crystals

Our technique for EPR spectroscopy of protein single crystals has been sketched in a preliminary report of the spectra from cupric insulin (13). Further details of this work and the computational methods employed will be published elsewhere (14). We shall summarize here the pertinent features of the magnetic spectra:

(a) There are six magnetic sites per unit cell, two sets of three, the members of each set being related by the trigonal axis. While the two sets do have the same g components (within experimental error), and the directions of the g_{max} make the same angle with the trigonal axis (59°), there is no simple relationship between the (rhombic) g tensors of the two sets.

(b) Spectra taken at room temperature differ only in line width from those at low temperatures; the magnetic parameters are anisotropic between 18° and 298°K.

(c) In certain directions the high-field absorption is observed to be modulated by five subpeaks. This is the interaction of the cupric ion with two magnetically equivalent nitrogen atoms.

Thus the environment of the cupric ion in this otherwise trigonal protein crystal suffers distortions which are geometrically analogous to those found in the inorganic trigonal crystals previously discussed. Apparently the transition temperature has been elevated beyond that of the tris-o-phenanthroline and $2,2'$-bipyridine complexes, but the existence of a transition cannot be checked since it would lie above the denaturation temperature of the protein. The identification of two nitrogens in the coordination sphere of the cupric ion when three are expected parallels the four versus six behavior of the hexachloride and organic complexes.

It should be emphasized that these distortions are a property of the cupric ion. In zinc insulin, for example, the environment will be symmetrical, and bonding to the three nitrogens will be equivalent. It is interesting to note that the EPR spectrum is at least as sensitive to bond differences as X-ray diffraction data. For a protein crystal where diffraction data are limited, the EPR method is clearly more sensitive. The diffraction patterns of cupric and zinc insulin are not significantly different (14).

One would like to be able to confirm or deny the above picture of the strong metal-binding site in insulin by consideration of completely independent data, and, if possible, identify the source of the coordinating nitrogens. We describe below how the hydrogen ion titration curve of the zinc insulin complex serves these purposes, verifying the trigonal site hypothesis and indicating that the nitrogens may belong to α-amino groups. For other considerations, the reader is referred to the work of Marcker (15) on substituted insulins, which rules out glycine N-terminal nitrogens, and to the thoughtful analysis of Marcker and Graae (16) in which a binding site of three phenylalanine N-terminal nitrogens is proposed.

IV. Hydrogen Ion Titration Curve Arising from a Trigonal Site

The differences between the titration curves of zinc-free and zinc insulin have been attributed, on the acid side, to the promoted displacement of protons by complex formation between the metal ions and weak nitrogenous bases on the protein; and on the alkaline side, to dissociation of protons from water molecules in the hydration sphere of the zinc (17, 18). The striking changes in slope in the region from pH 3 to pH 6.5 are a critical test of any quantitative treatment, but no attempt to compute a matching curve was described along with the presentation of these titration data. It was possible at the time to match the titration curves of zinc insulin which had been altered by exposure to acid or base. The model employed for this purpose involved the binding of a zinc ion to a site consisting of two imidazole groups on the same insulin dimer (12,000 mol. wt.). The authors suggested that this situation applied as well to normal zinc insulin, but

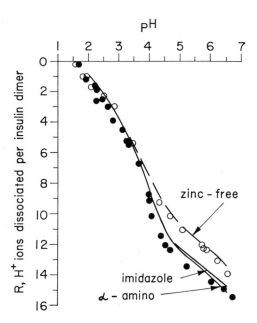

FIG. 2. Hydrogen ion titration data and computed curves: ○, zinc-free insulin data points (17); ●, zinc insulin data points (18); – – –, computed curve for zinc-free insulin; ——, computed curves for zinc insulin.

that crystallization in the region of pH 4 to 8 interfered with the titration experiment. Evidence for a trigonal site was, of course, not available at the time.

In Fig. 2 are presented hydrogen ion titration data for zinc-free and crystalline zinc insulin, a computed curve for the zinc-free case, and curves which have been computed[1] on the basis of two trigonal zinc-binding sites per three dimers. The curves are calculated from the intrinsic pK values for the ionizable groups of insulin and the electrostatic correction parameter (as a function of the molecular charge) given by Tanford and Epstein (17). For the curve labeled "imidazole," the trigonal site was taken to consist of three imidazole groups (pK 6.40); and for the curve "α-amino," the site consists of three α-amino groups (pK 7.45). The equilibrium between zinc and a trigonal site is characterized by an intrinsic association constant, K, which has been adjusted in each case to match the shape of the computed to the experimental curve. The two computed functions do not differ significantly from each other,[2] but the association constant for the imidazole

[1] We thank Patricia H. Brill for programming these computations.
[2] As suggested by Dr. Brintzinger, the computed curves are being extended beyond pH 6.5 where differences between the two cases appear. When the computer studies are completed, a detailed report will be published.

curve, $10^{10.5}$, is somewhat large. Stability constants for a single zinc-imidazole interaction are typically under 10^3, and one would expect K to be about 10^9 for the complex with three imidazoles. Since the N-terminal glycines are not involved, the α-amino groups of the N-terminal phenylalanines are clearly implicated. For zinc–α-amino interactions which have been studied, the association constants average $10^{4.5}$ per complexing group. The α-amino curve of Fig. 2 was computed with $\log K = 13.5$, a reasonable figure for this site.

Independently of whether the nitrogens belong to imidazole or to α-amino groups, the outstanding features of the titration curve arise from a trigonal site.

V. Relation of Cupric Insulin to Other Copper Proteins

Upon integrating the features discussed above, one sees the cupric ion in insulin crystals bound to three identical nitrogens belonging to α-amino groups of N-terminal phenylalanines or to imidazole groups. The complex is distorted so that two of the bonds are equivalent and the third is weaker

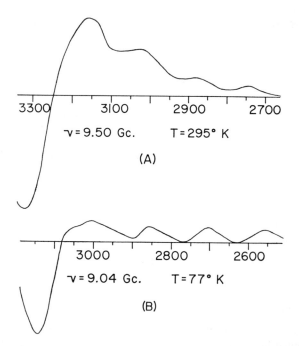

Fig. 3. Observed spectra from cupric insulin, polycrystalline samples in liquid of negligible copper content. (A) 295°K; (B) 77°K.

and longer. The remaining coordination positions are occupied by molecules of water, or possibly citrate, when present.

This detailed picture of the cupric ion in one particular environment will not serve as a model for the binding of the cupric ion to proteins in which the metal is an integral part of the structure. The cupric ion in the insulin complex is readily exchanged for other divalent ions of the $3d$ group, and such exchange results in very little change in the three-dimensional structure of the protein. The g values are markedly rhombic and indicate that there should be at least one energy level difference corresponding to an optical transition centered in or near the visible region, but wet insulin crystals have *no* color at all. The polycrystalline EPR spectrum (Fig. 3) is unlike that of other cuproproteins. The copper-insulin interaction is one in which the binding site on the protein generally conforms to the geometrical requirements of the metal, rather than one in which the final configuration is a compromise between demands of the protein and the metal ion.

VI. Summary

Single-crystal EPR spectroscopy of the cupric ion has been used as a probe of environmental symmetry to establish the strong metal-binding sites in insulin as trigonal. The magnetic spectra show that three ligands are nitrogenous bases. Titration data strongly support this picture.

ACKNOWLEDGMENTS

We are pleased to thank Dr. Jørgen Schlichtkrull, Director of Research, Novo Research Institute, Copenhagen, and Professor Dorothy Crowfoot Hodgkin, Chemical Crystallography Laboratory, Oxford, for their assistance in this investigation.

REFERENCES

1. Bleaney, B., Bowers, K. D., and Trenam, R. S., *Proc. Roy. Soc. (London), Ser. A* **228,** 157 (1955).
2. Thornley, J. H. M., Mangum, B. W., Griffiths, J. H. E., and Owen, J., *Proc. Phys. Soc. (London),* **78,** 1263 (1961).
3. Liehr, A. D., and Ballhausen, C. J., *Ann. Phys.,* **3,** 304 (1958).
4. Abragam, A., and Pryce, M. H. L., *Proc. Roy. Soc. (London), Ser. A,* **63,** 409 (1950).
5. Allen, H. C., Kokoszka, G. F., and Inskeep, R. G., *J. Am. Chem. Soc.,* **86,** 1023 (1964).
6. Schlichtkrull, J., *Acta Chem. Scand.,* **10,** 1455 (1956).
7. Schlichtkrull, J., thesis, Univ. of Copenhagen (1958).
8. Marcker, K., *Acta Chem. Scand.,* **14,** 194 (1960).
9. Cunningham, L. W., Fischer, R. L., and Vestling, C. S., *J. Am. Chem. Soc.,* **77,** 5703 (1955).
10. Crowfoot, D., *Nature,* **135,** 591 (1935).

11. Crowfoot, D., and Riley, D., *Nature*, **144**, 1011 (1939).
12. Dodson, E., Harding, M. M., Hodgkin, D. C., and Rossmann, M. G., *J. Mol. Biol.*, **16**, 227 (1966).
13. Brill, A. S., and Venable, J. H., Jr., *Nature*, **203**, 752 (1964).
14. Venable, J. H., Jr., Ph.D. thesis, Yale Univ. (1965).
15. Marcker, K., *Acta Chem. Scand.*, **14**, 2071 (1960).
16. Marcker, K., and Graae, J., *Acta Chem. Scand.*, **16**, 41 (1962).
17. Tanford, C., and Epstein, J., *J. Am. Chem. Soc.*, **76**, 2163 (1954).
18. Tanford, C., and Epstein, J., *J. Am. Chem. Soc.*, **76**, 2170 (1954).

DISCUSSION

DR. BLUMBERG: The facts that the site appears to be quite rhombic and yet is not colored are not inconsistent, because rhombic distortions have an even-even field that does not tend to introduce any oscillator strengths. These are produced by odd fields, and perhaps here copper gets itself into a site that has no odd field. This is not easy to do in this crystal, but copper is very good at this sort of thing where it has free rein to rearrange the electrons and the ligands in its neighborhood. Of course, there might not be any transitions in the visible region at all.

I would like to offer an explanation as to why the temperature dependence of the copper EPR in insulin crystals is different from the temperature dependence of the inorganic ones you have mentioned. It does not seem to me very likely that the Jahn–Teller energy obtained by distortion in the insulin crystals is so much larger than in the inorganic crystals. What may be more likely is that the rapid reorientation of the axes of the g tensor is blocked in insulin crystals by an interstitial water molecule, which you probably wouldn't pick up at all in the X-ray structural determination. Assume we are looking along a trigonal axis in Fig. 1 and we see the edges of three insulin molecules (the large arcs) each of which contributes one N atom to the copper-binding site. Suppose two N atoms are to be bound strongly, as

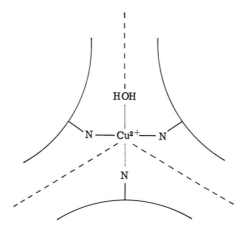

FIG. 1. Proposed site of Cu^{2+} on trigonal axis of insulin crystal.

indicated by the solid lines, and the third is to be bound weakly, as shown by the dotted line. Then the copper will pick up, on crystallization from solution, one water molecule on the opposite side to help balance the ligand field so that the odd field components are canceled out. Then it sits in only a rhombic field. Since the position of the water molecule is random with respect to the three insulin molecules, there would be three equivalent g tensors, as observed. This water molecule would, however, block reorientation at room temperature.

DR. BRILL: The titration data on zinc insulin indicate that there are three water molecules in the coordination sphere of the metal ion. The same is probably true in cupric insulin.

DR. BLUMBERG: The other two water molecules are apical, above and below the plane.

DR. BRILL: In the cupric insulin crystal, I think the three nitrogens are probably in a triangle and the three waters also in a triangle on the opposite side.

DR. MASON: Does the EPR spectrum have a pH dependence?

DR. BRILL: Crystallization was carried out at pH 6.2 for all the crystals used in our experiments. Schlichtkrull (7) has shown that such crystals can be grown in the pH range 5.5 to 7.0. Metal-free insulin crystals form in acid solution.

Crystal Structure Studies of Cupric–Peptide Complexes[*]

HANS C. FREEMAN

School of Chemistry,
University of Sydney,
Sydney, Australia

I. Introduction

This paper deals with 14 complexes of cupric copper with peptides and amino acids plus one with imidazole, whose structures are now known from X-ray diffraction studies. Fifteen crystal structure analyses can contain such a mass of individual numerical details that the time seems to be ripe for an evaluation of the information that is available. Most of this information has been compiled into 13 tables. This is a somewhat prosaic approach, in which the biochemically relevant and irrelevant will appear side by side. Dramatic presentation has intentionally been sacrificed in the interests of comprehensiveness. The structures to be discussed are listed in Table I.

II. Precision of Crystal Structure Analyses

The 15 structures listed in Table I have been determined over a period of more than 20 years and are accordingly known to widely differing degrees of precision. Some published clues as to the precision of each structure analysis are contained in Table II. The significance of this table, column by column, is as follows:

"Refinement": the process of systematically adjusting the positions and vibrational parameters of the atoms until the diffraction data that *would* be obtained from them (F_{calc}) resemble as closely as possible the diffraction data that have actually been recorded (F_{obs}).

"Two-/three-dimensional": two ways of sampling the electron density in the crystal (corresponding to two specific ways of sampling the available diffraction data). A "two-dimensional" structure analysis yields a view of the structure only in projection; two or three projections along different crystal axes must be combined to give a picture of the structure in depth.

"Isotropic/anisotropic least-squares": least-squares fitting of the atomic parameters to the diffraction data, a method frequently used in three-

[*] This work was supported by a grant, GM–10867, from the Institute of General Medical Sciences, United States Public Health Service.

TABLE I

CUPRIC COMPLEXES OF AMINO ACIDS, BIURET, AND PEPTIDES

Ligand	Complex formula	Complex abbreviation	Formula no.	Ref.
α-Amino acids				
Glycine	$Cu(NH_2-CH_2-COO)_2 \cdot H_2O$	$Cu(gly)_2 \cdot H_2O$	(I)	(1, 2)
DL-α-Amino-n-butyric acid	$Cu[NH_2-CH(CH_2CH_3)-COO]_2$	$Cu(\alpha-NH_2but)_2$	(II)	(3)
1-Aminocyclo-pentanecar-boxylic acid	$Cu(NH_2-\overset{\displaystyle}{\underset{\displaystyle}{C}}-COO)_2$	$Cu(pen)_2$	(III)	(4)
Proline	$Cu(\overset{H}{N}-CH-COO)_2 \cdot 2H_2O$	$Cu(pro)_2 \cdot 2H_2O$	(IV)	(5)
Glutamic acid	$Cu[NH_2-CH(CH_2CH_2COO)-COO] \cdot 2H_2O$	$Cu(glu) \cdot 2H_2O$	(V)	(6, 7)
β-Amino acids				
β-Alanine	$Cu(NH_2CH_2CH_2COO)_2 \cdot 6H_2O$	$Cu(ala)_2 \cdot 6H_2O$	(VI)	(8)
β-Amino-n-butyric acid	$Cu[NH_2-CH(CH_3)-CH_2COO]_2 \cdot 2H_2O$	$Cu(\beta-NH_2but)_2 \cdot 2H_2O$	(VII)	(9)

Peptides and biuret

Biuret	$[Cu(NH_2CONHCONH_2)_2]Cl_2$	$Cu(biu)_2Cl_2$	(VIII)	(10, 11)
	$K_2[Cu(NHCONHCONH)_2]\cdot 4\,H_2O$	$K_2Cu(biu)_2\cdot 4\,H_2O$	(IX)	(10, 12)
Glycylglycine	$Cu(NH_2CH_2CONCH_2COO)\cdot 3\,H_2O$	$Cu(gg)\cdot 3\,H_2O$	(X)	(13, 14)
Glycylglycylglycine	$Cu[H(NHCH_2CO)_3O]Cl\cdot 1\frac{1}{2}\,H_2O$	$Cu(ggg)Cl\cdot 1\frac{1}{2}\,H_2O$	(XI)	(15, 16)
Glycylglycylglycine	$Na[Cu(NH_2(CH_2CON)_2CH_2COO)]\cdot H_2O$	$NaCu(ggg)\cdot H_2O$	(XII)	(15, 17)
Glycylglycylglycylglycine	$Na_3[Cu(NH_2(CH_2CON)_3CH_2COO)]\cdot 10\,H_2O$	$Na_2Cu(gggg)\cdot 10\,H_2O$	(XIII)	(18)
β-Alanyl-L-histidine (carnosine)	$Cu(NH_2CH_2CH_2CON\!\!-\!\!CH\!\!-\!\!COO)\cdot 2\,H_2O$ $CH_2(C_3H_3N_2)$	$Cu(ala\!-\!his)\cdot 2\,H_2O$	(XIV)	(19)

Imidazole

Imidazole	$Cu(C_3H_3N_2)_2$	$Cu(im)_2$	(XV)	(20, 21)

TABLE II

DETAILS OF STRUCTURE ANALYSES[a]

Formula no.	Complex	Ref.	3D/2D[b]	Method[c]	No. of F_{obs}	No. of F_{unobs}	Final R
(I)	$Cu(gly)_2 \cdot H_2O$	(2)	3D	FM ALS	809	68	0.091
(II)	$Cu(\alpha\text{-}NH_2but)_2$	(3)	$1 \times 2D$	ED P	109	17	—
(III)	$Cu(pen)_2$	(4)	3D	FM ALS	781	—	0.13
(IV)	$Cu(pro)_2 \cdot 2 H_2O$	(5)	$3 \times 2D$	ED P	223	89	0.165
(V)	$Cu(glu) \cdot 2 H_2O$	(7)	3D	FM ALS	NA[d]	NA[d]	0.04
(VI)	$Cu(ala)_2 \cdot 6 H_2O$	(8)	$2 \times 2D$	ED P	257	—	0.19, 0.22
(VII)	$Cu(\beta\text{-}NH_2but)_2 \cdot 2 H_2O$	(9)	$3 \times 2D$	FM ILS	415	—	0.11
(VIII)	$Cu(biu)_2Cl_2$	(11)	3D	FM ALS	710	60	0.091
(IX)	$K_2Cu(biu)_2 \cdot 4 H_2O$	(12)	3D	FM ALS	929	331	0.079
(X)	$Cu(gg) \cdot 3 H_2O$	(14)	3D	FM ALS	1818	—	0.119
(XI)	$Cu(ggg)Cl \cdot 1\frac{1}{2} H_2O$	(16)	3D	FM ALS	1747	632	0.119
(XII)	$NaCu(ggg) \cdot H_2O$	(17)	3D	FM ALS	1502	598	0.132
(XIII)	$Na_2Cu(gggg) \cdot 10 H_2O$	(18)	3D	FM ALS	3690	629	0.092
(XIV)	$Cu(ala\text{-}his) \cdot 2 H_2O$	(19)	3D	FM ALS	1184	135	—
(XV)	$Cu(im)_2$	(21)	3D	LS	1448	1448	0.115

dimensional structure analyses. Individual atoms may be assigned parameters to represent (an)isotropic thermal vibrations.

"F_{obs}, F_{unobs}": the measured intensities of the X-ray reflections are converted into "structure amplitudes", F_{obs}. Reflections which are too weak to be recorded can be given statistically valid values, F_{unobs}, and appropriate statistical weights. Since the random errors in the measurements of X-ray reflections from a crystal are commonly as high as 10%, a precise solution of a crystal structure is possible only if there are many more observations than there are parameters to be fitted to them. The number of F_{obs} per parameter, the inclusion or exclusion of the F_{unobs}, and the ratio of the

TABLE II (*Continued*)

DETAILS OF STRUCTURE ANALYSES

Formula no.	Centric (C) or noncentric (N/C)	Average final standard deviations						
		Atomic coords. (Å)		Bond lengths (Å)		Bond angles (deg)		
		Cu	Light atoms, L	d_{Cu-L}	d_{L-L}	θ_{L-Cu-L}	θ_{Cu-L-L}	θ_{L-L-L}
(I)	N/C	0.002	0.012	0.012	0.017	0.5	1.0	1.2
(II)	C	—	—	—	—	—	—	—
(III)	C	—	0.012	0.012	0.02	0.5	0.9	1.2
(IV)	C	—	0.03	0.03	0.04	1.2	2.4	3
(V)	N/C	0.0004	0.003	0.004	0.005	0.2^e	0.25^e	0.3^e
(VI)	C	—	0.03	0.03^e	0.05^e	1.2^e	2.4^e	3^e
(VII)	C	—	0.02	0.015	0.03	0.8^e	1.6^e	2
(VIII)	C	—	0.004	0.003	0.006	0.2	0.3	0.4
(IX)	C	—	0.007	0.007	0.012	0.3	0.6	0.7
(X)	C	0.002	0.011	0.011	0.015	0.5	0.9	1.1
(XI)	C	0.001_3	0.008	0.008	0.012	0.3	0.6	0.8
(XII)	C	0.001_2	0.008	0.008	0.012	0.3	0.6	0.8
(XIII)	C	0.001	0.004	0.004	0.007	0.2	0.3	0.4
(XIV)	N/C	NA^d	NA^d	NA^d	NA^d	NA^d	NA^d	NA^d
(XV)	C	NA^d	NA^d	NA^d	NA^d	NA^d	NA^d	NA^d

[a] See text, section II, for detailed explanation.

[b] $n \times 2D = n$ two-dimensional electron-density projections.

[c] Abbreviations: ED P, electron density projections; FM ILS, full-matrix least-squares, isotropic atomic thermal parameters; FM ALS, full-matrix least-squares, anisotropic atomic thermal parameters.

[d] NA, information not available at time of writing.

[e] Figures adjusted for this review from published values or calculated from other information supplied by authors.

number of F_{obs} to the number of F_{unobs} are thus guides to the precision of a refinement.

"*Reliability index*":

$$R = \frac{\sum ||F_{obs}| - |F_{calc}||}{\sum |F_{obs}|}$$

a qualitative measure both of the quality of the F_{obs} and of the success with which the structure has been fitted to the observations. Ideally, refinement of the parameters should produce their "true" values, and the F_{calc} calculated from them should then differ from the observations F_{obs} only because the latter contain random errors of measurement.

"*Centric or noncentric*": given the same number of data to refine two structures of equal complexity, one of whose unit cells has a center of symmetry while the other does not, the same reliability index R will tend to correspond to a more precise determination of the parameters in the centric structure.

"*Standard deviations*": estimated from the statistical agreement between the F_{obs} and F_{calc}. It is normal crystallographic practice to regard quantities as being "significantly different" only if their difference exceeds three standard deviations. Quantities whose difference lies between two and three standard deviations are considered to be "probably significantly different."

III. Brief Descriptions of the Structures

The structural formulas (I) to (XIV) represent the bonding in the complexes. Some attempt has been made to indicate the spatial relationships between the atoms surrounding the copper in each complex while abandoning any attempt to show the true orientations of other parts of the molecules or of surrounding complexes. In the following descriptions, the term "coordination square" will refer to the four closest ligand atoms, usually occurring at about 2 Å from the copper. The terms "octahedral" and "apical" will refer to the positions of the more distant ligands which complete the tetragonally distorted octahedral coordination.

The ligands in complexes (I) to (V) are α-amino acids and in (VI) to (VII) β-amino acids, functioning as bidentate chelates through their amino and carboxylic acid groups.

(I) Bisglycinato copper(II) hydrate.[1] This complex is unique among the

(I)   (II)

[1] The complexes are named in accordance with the nomenclature of the International Union of Pure and Applied Chemistry, even where these names differ from those used by the original authors.

bisamino acid complexes of transition metals because it is the only one in whose crystal structure the two glycine residues are *cis* with respect to each other. A second Cu^{2+} complex, believed to be *trans* (22), and *cis* complexes of a number of other transition metals are known, but their structures have not been determined and the evidence for their geometries is partly chemical and partly spectroscopic.

The four ligand atoms of the two glycine molecules lie at the corners of an approximately square figure. The distorted octahedral environment of the copper atom is completed by a water molecule and a carboxylic oxygen atom of a neighboring complex. The four closest neighbors are only approximately coplanar, and the copper is displaced from their plane by 0.05 Å in the direction of the water molecule. The chelate rings are not planar. In one ring, the copper and the nitrogen atoms lie 0.006 and −0.103 Å out of the plane of the –C–CO–O⁻ group, respectively. In the other ring, the deviations are −0.126 and −0.162 Å.

(II) Bis(DL-α-aminobutyrato) copper(II). The structure of this complex can be deduced from an incomplete crystal structure analysis in one projection. The environment of the copper atom appears to be square-planar and centrosymmetric, so that the bidentate chelate amino acid residues must be *trans*. The crystal is anhydrous although the spectrum of the complex in solution suggests that two water molecules become attached to the copper to complete an octahedral environment (23).

(III) Bis(1-aminocyclopentanecarboxylato) copper(II). As does Cu(α-NH₂but₂), this complex forms anhydrous crystals in which the copper atom has coordination number 4. The next nearest neighbors of the copper

(III)   (IV)

are carboxylic oxygens at distances of 3.17 Å. The visible absorption spectrum of the crystals differs significantly from that of the solution (23). In both (II) and (III), 4-coordination of copper in the solid state seems to arise from packing considerations.

(IV) Bisprolinato copper(II) dihydrate. The structure of this complex in the crystal resembles more closely than any of the other compounds (I) to (V) the structure which is expected for bisamino acid chelates of

Cu^{2+} in solution. The environment of the copper atom is tetragonally distorted octahedral, with two water molecules lying along the normal to the square of the four closest ligand atoms. The two amino acid molecules are *trans* to each other. The amino nitrogen atoms lie 0.21 Å out of the plane of the carboxyl groups. The pyrrolidine rings naturally do not lie in the planes of the amino acid skeletons; in each pyrrolidine ring, the methylene carbon opposite the N–C bond lies 0.6 Å away from the plane of the other four atoms.

(V) Glutamato copper(II) dihydrate. The structure analysis of this complex is the first study of a complex between Cu^{2+} and an amino acid with a functional side chain. Each glutamate residue is bonded to three different copper atoms, so that each copper atom links three different

(V)

glutamate residues. With respect to one copper, the glutamate acts as a normal bidentate α-amino acid chelate. The second oxygen atom of the chelating carboxyl group lies in one of the octahedral positions with respect to a second copper atom. The side chain carboxyl group of the glutamate molecule is coordinated to yet a third copper atom. The third corner of the coordination square around each copper is thus occupied by a side chain carboxyl oxygen. A water molecule is bound at the fourth corner. These four nearest neighbors are coplanar to within 0.03 Å, but the copper is displaced by 0.15 Å from their plane in the direction of the fifth apical oxygen atom. In addition to the five bonds for which we have now accounted, the copper atom forms a sixth: the donor is the second oxygen atom of the side chain carboxyl group to which the same copper is already bound. This oxygen lies near the second of the octahedral coordinating positions. The geometry of the carboxyl group being, however, less susceptible to distortion than that of the coordination polyhedron of the metal atom, the second side chain carboxyl oxygen lies considerably away from the normal to the coordination square.

(VI) Bis-β-alaninato copper(II) hexahydrate[2] and (VII) bis(β-amino-n-butyrato) copper(II) dihydrate resemble each other in their amino acid

(VI)   (VII)

chelation and similar copper atom environments. The β-amino acids form six-membered chelate rings, and two water molecules complete a distorted octahedron about each copper. The angle between the planes containing, respectively, $CC_\alpha C_\beta$ and $C_\alpha C_\beta N$ is about 70° in (VI) and about 67° in (VII). As might be expected from the difference between the numbers of water molecules in the formula units, the hydrogen bond scheme in (VI) is much more extensive than in (VII).

The structures of complexes (VIII) to (XIV) have been studied as part of a program to explore the interaction between Cu^{2+} ions and peptide groups. All except (XIV) correspond to species whose existence in solution has been claimed on the basis of spectroscopic and potentiometric titration data (24–29).

(VIII) Bisbiuret copper(II) dichloride is a blue-green complex formed in neutral or mildly acid solutions. The biuret molecules act as bidentate chelates via their amide oxygen atoms, which have a square-planar arrangement around the copper atom. The complex as a whole is not planar: the mean planes of the biuret molecules are at 21° to the coordination

(VIII)   (IX)

[2] The atomic coordinates reported by Tomita (8) were not those from which the molecular dimensions in his paper had been calculated (Tomita, personal communication). The revised molecular geometry of bis-β-alaninato copper(II) hexahydrate quoted in this review is based on corrected atomic coordinates kindly supplied by Dr. Tomita.

square. Within each biuret molecule, the two —NHCONH$_2$ residues are not coplanar, the angle between their normals being about 6°. The chloride ions form electrostatic bonds with the copper atoms, and the crystal is held together by these ionic forces and by N—H⋯Cl$^-$ hydrogen bonds.

(IX) Dipotassium bisbiureto cuprate(II) tetrahydrate, violet-pink, is formed by the reaction of biuret and Cu^{2+} in alkaline solution. The amide nitrogens lose one proton each and become the metal-binding sites. Four amide nitrogen atoms of two biuret residues are bonded to each copper atom. In the direction perpendicular to the square of these four atoms the copper makes only van der Waals contacts (3.33 Å) with two copper-bonded nitrogen atoms of adjacent complexes, one on each side. The complex deviates from planarity in the same sense but not to the same extent as Cu(biu)$_2$Cl$_2$: the angles between the coordination square and the biuret residues are here 2.5°, and those between the —NHCONH— groups are 5°. In the crystalline state, the complexes are linked by hydrogen bonds via water molecules and by electrostatic interactions involving the K$^+$ ions.

(X) Glycylglycinato copper(II) trihydrate[3] (more correctly, diaquo-

3 For the refinement of the glycylglycinato copper(II) trihydrate structure Strandberg *et al.* (13) used the method of "3-dimensional backshift corrections" with only limited allowance for the thermal motions of individual atoms. The structure has recently been subjected to further refinement by full-matrix least-squares, using the original data and including parameters for anisotropic atomic vibrations (14). The revised dimensions have been used in this review. The asymmetric unit in this crystal structure contains two crystallographically distinct formula units; some apparent discrepancies between them have been removed by the further refinement.

glycylglycinato copper(II) hydrate). The asymmetric unit in this structure contains two crystallographically distinct complexes. Both have the same structure, with dimensions which are not significantly different except in the copper-ligand bond lengths (see below). The peptide molecule behaves as a tridentate chelate via its terminal amino group, peptide nitrogen atom, and carboxyl group.

The single peptide nitrogen is deprotonated, in complete agreement with the behavior stated to occur in solution on the basis of spectroscopic measurements and potentiometric titrations (24, 25, 27, 28). The copper atom has coordination number 5. The three peptide donor atoms and one water molecule form an approximate square. A tetragonal pyramid is completed by a second water molecule, characteristically situated at a slightly larger distance from the copper atom at a point along the normal to the center of the square of the closer ligand atoms. The copper is slightly displaced from the center of the square in the direction of the apical water molecule (0.16 Å in one complex, 0.25 Å in the other).

(XI) Glycylglycylglycinato copper(II) chloride sesquihydrate and (XII) sodium glycylglycylglycinato cuprate(II) hydrate have structures that reflect the pH's at which they are formed in solution in the same way as do the two biuret-copper complexes (see above). In the blue-green complex $Cu(ggg)Cl \cdot 1\frac{1}{2} H_2O$, a copper is bonded to the peptide molecule via the nitrogen and oxygen of the N-terminal amino acid residue. This mode of attachment is exactly that postulated by Rabin (30) to occur in copper-peptide solutions of low pH.[4] A second copper atom is attached at the C-terminal carboxyl group. There it is bound by *both* oxygen atoms, one of which is at one corner of the square of four close ligand atoms, and the second of which is constrained by the geometry of the carboxyl group to occupy a position to one side of the normal to the coordination square and 2.82 Å from the copper atom. This double carboxyl-copper interaction is almost identical with that in $Cu(glu) \cdot 2H_2O$ (V), where the corresponding Cu–O= distance is 2.59 Å. In the original description of the structure of $Cu(ggg)Cl \cdot 1\frac{1}{2} H_2O$, it was suggested (16) that the second carboxyl oxygen is forced into proximity with the copper and thereby prevents the approach of any other ligand in that direction. Subsequent comparison and correlation with other structures make it more probable that both in

[4] The structural evidence suggests that this type of complex will be formed as the first step in the N-terminal chelation of Cu^{2+} by other peptides. The planarity and hence the resonance energy of the peptide group are not sacrificed if the copper atom is bound at the peptide oxygen. For this reason, this structural type is preferable to that proposed by Kim and Martell (formula I in Ref. (27)). At a pH where the proton on the first peptide nitrogen atom is not dissociated, the formation of an additional bond from the peptide nitrogen to the copper atom would involve a change from trigonal to tetrahedral configuration and hybridization.

$Cu(glu) \cdot 2\ H_2O$ and $Cu(ggg)Cl \cdot 1\frac{1}{2}\ H_2O$ the second carboxyl oxygens are true ligands, though the orientations of their carboxyl groups prevent them from occupying the most favorable bond-forming positions.

(XII)   (XIII)

If the solution from which $Cu(ggg)Cl \cdot 1\frac{1}{2}\ H_2O$ crystallizes is made alkaline, the violet-pink complex $NaCu(ggg) \cdot H_2O$ is formed. In addition to the terminal amino and carboxyl groups, the two peptide nitrogen atoms become copper-binding sites with simultaneous dissociation of their protons. The surprising feature about the crystal structure of $NaCu(ggg) \cdot H_2O$ is that the complex turns out to be a dimer (XII). The three nitrogen atoms of the peptide molecule bind one copper atom, the carboxyl group another. The second copper atom is also attached to the three nitrogen atoms of a second peptide molecule, whose carboxylic oxygen occupies the fourth corner of the coordination square about the first copper atom. The third nitrogen of each peptide molecule, in addition to the strong bond that it forms with one copper, lies at a bonding distance of 2.57 Å from the other copper atom. This additional N–Cu bond is almost perpendicular to the plane containing the peptide group and the first copper atom: the angle Cu-N-Cu is 84°. The resultant configuration about the nitrogen is not tetrahedral, and the other bonds in which this atom takes part have atypical lengths (see Table III). As a result of this extra interaction, each copper of the dimer acquires a tetragonal-pyramidal environment of five ligand atoms. It is displaced slightly (0.115 Å) from the center of the base of the pyramid, toward the apical atom. As in $Cu(gg) \cdot 3\ H_2O$, there is a complete absence of any ligand in the potential sixth octahedral coordination position. Although the species $(Cu(ggg))^-$ has been identified in solution (24, 29), there is no evidence whether it exists there as a dimer.

(XIII) Disodium glycylglycylglycylglycylglycinato cuprate(II) decahydrate. This violet-pink complex is prepared under the same conditions of high pH as $K_2Cu(biu)_2 \cdot 4\ H_2O$ and $NaCu(ggg) \cdot H_2O$. All four nitrogen atoms of the peptide are bound to the metal, the three peptide nitrogens being deprotonated. The carboxyl group does not participate in metal binding. The copper atom has coordination number 4, the almost planar complexes being stacked on top of one another at van der Waals contact distances ($\geq$ 3.65 Å). In the crystal, layers of stacked complexes are separated by layers built up of Na$^+$-water octahedra.

(XIV) β-Alanyl-L-histidinato copper(II) dihydrate. The structure of this complex has not previously been described.[5] The blue-violet crystals are

(XIV)

prepared by dissolving freshly precipitated cupric hydroxide in a solution of β-alanyl-L-histidine (L-carnosine). The complex crystallizes out on evaporation and may be recrystallized from alkaline aqueous solution. The crystals belong to the noncentric trigonal space group $P3_12$. The following features of the crystal structure of the complex are represented by formula (XIV): (a) The complex is dimeric, the two halves of the dimer being related by a twofold axis. (b) Each copper is surrounded by five ligand atoms at the corners of a square pyramid. (c) At the apex of the pyramid is a water molecule. Three corners of the base are occupied by the terminal amino group, peptide nitrogen, and terminal carboxyl group of the peptide. The fourth ligand atom in the square is an imidazole nitrogen of the histidine side chain of the *other* peptide molecule of the dimer. (d) The first peptide molecule is likewise coordinated to the second copper atom via a ring nitrogen of its histidine side chain.

The structural formula does *not* correctly depict the geometry at the asymmetric carbon atom or the spatial relationship of the two halves of the dimer. In a model based on the partially refined structure, the planes of the coordination squares of the two copper atoms are parallel to within about 10°. The imidazole rings are pulled slightly out of these planes, partly by rotation about the C–N bonds, and partly by deflection of the Cu–N bonds.

(XV) Bisimidazolato copper(II). Although this is not a Cu^{2+}-peptide complex and will not be discussed further, it is described here on account of its relevance to the geometry of copper binding by the imidazole rings of

---

[5] At the time of writing (July 1965), this structure has been solved and partly refined.

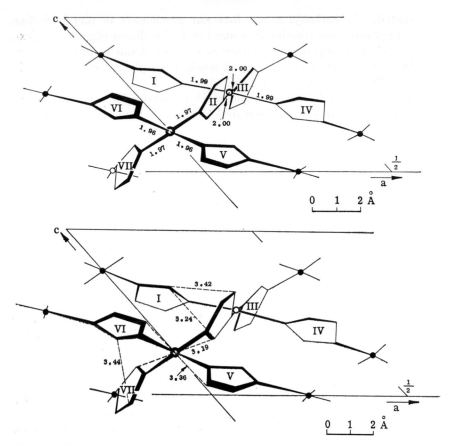

FIG. 1. (Upper) Projection of bisimidazolato copper(II) down y axis, showing Cu–N bond lengths. (Lower) Similar projection, showing intermolecular contact distances.

histidine residues. Figure 1 is based on hitherto unpublished information.[6] The structure may be described in terms of two systems of kinked chains of the type -Cu-imidazole-Cu-imidazole- running almost parallel to the xz plane. The two systems are cross linked at the copper atoms. The imidazole rings belong to two nonequivalent sets (Fig. 2), but in each type of chain all the rings are crystallographically equivalent (i.e., symmetry related). The copper atoms also belong to two nonequivalent sets.

Square-planar coordination around each copper atom with a coplanar

[6] The essentials of this structure were reported by Jarvis and Wells at the Cambridge Meeting of the International Union of Crystallography (20). The author is indebted to Dr. Wells for a list of atomic coordinates from which Fig. 1 and other details quoted in this review have been deduced. The unit cell whose projection is shown in Fig. 1 has dimensions $a = 15.51$ Å, $b = 14.07$ Å, $c = 8.77$ Å, $\beta = 131.3°$, in spacegroup $C2/c$. It is obtained by a transformation of the published cell (20).

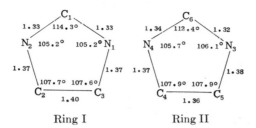

Ring I   Ring II

FIG. 2. Dimensions of the two nonequivalent types of imidazole rings in bisimidazolato copper(II).

arrangement of the four imidazole rings is sterically impossible. It would lead to carbon-carbon contacts of 2.48 Å between adjacent imidazole rings, quite apart from the need to accommodate the hydrogen atoms of the heterocycles. The two types of copper atoms accommodate the resultant steric strains in different ways. In both cases, satisfactory contacts between adjacent imidazole rings are established (Fig. 1, lower structure).

The coordination around the first type is nearly square-planar with N-Cu-N angles of $90 \pm 1°$. Two imidazole rings (rings I, IV in Fig. 1) make angles of 46° with the coordination plane while the other two (rings II, III) lie at angles of 81° from it.

The coordination around the second type of copper (rings II, V, VI, VII) is considerably distorted from square-planar toward tetrahedral. If the donor atoms are subscripted with the numerals of their imidazole rings, the angles N_V-Cu-N_{VII} and N_{II}-Cu-N_{VI} are 140°, and the other N-Cu-N angles $97 \pm 1°$. With respect to a least-squares plane fitted to the four donor atoms, rings V and VI are rotated by 53° and rings II and VII by 78°. The rings of each of these pairs are related by a twofold axis and rings V and VII are rotated about the Cu-N bonds in opposite senses.

The copper atoms are not coplanar with any of the imidazole rings. The N–Cu bonds are bent out of the imidazole planes by 6° to 16°.

IV. Geometry of Copper-Peptide Binding

A. Dimensions of the Ligand Molecules

In Tables III and IV, the bond lengths and bond angles in the complexed amino acid and peptide molecules are listed, together with their averages.[7]

[7] It will be noted that in Table IV the mean bond lengths ($\bar{d} = \sum_i d_i/n$) are not significantly different from the weighted mean bond lengths ($\bar{d}_w = \sum_i d_i\sigma_i^{-1}/\sum_i\sigma_i^{-1}$, where σ_i = standard deviation of ith value). This implies that the less reliable values are randomly scattered about the more reliable values. In Table IV and subsequent tables, the "standard deviation of the mean," e.g., $[\sum_i (\bar{d} - d_i)^2/n(n-1)]^{\frac{1}{2}}$, is included as a more realistic estimate of the spread of values in each sample than is given by the "range" (effectively, the difference between the extreme values in the sample).

TABLE III

Bond Lengths in Ligand Molecules (Å)

Formula no.	Complex	$H_2N{-}CH_2$	$H_2C{-}CH_2$	$H_2C{-}CO$ (peptide)	$C{=}O$ (peptide)	$OC{-}N{<}$ (peptide)	$>H_2C{-}N$ (peptide)	$H_2C{-}CO$ (carboxyl)	$C{=}O$ (carboxyl)	$C{-}O$ (carboxyl)
(I)	$Cu(gly)_2 \cdot H_2O$	1.47						1.50	1.23	1.28
		1.48						1.54	1.24	1.29
(III)	$Cu(pen)_2$	1.49						1.49	1.21	1.33
(IV)	$Cu(pro)_2 \cdot 2\,H_2O$	1.52						1.50	1.24	1.24
(V)	$Cu(glu) \cdot 2\,H_2O$	1.48	1.53					1.53	1.23	1.28
			1.51					1.51	1.24	1.30
(VI)	$Cu(ala)_2 \cdot 6\,H_2O$	1.51	1.58					1.54	1.22	1.28
(VII)	$Cu(\beta\text{-}NH_2but)_2 \cdot 2\,H_2O$	1.44	1.49					1.49	1.22	1.30
(X)	$Cu(gg) \cdot 3\,H_2O$	1.51		1.53	1.28	1.30	1.46	1.52	1.24	1.28
		1.49		1.51	1.27	1.30	1.48	1.53	1.25	1.26
(XI)	$Cu(ggg)Cl \cdot 1\tfrac{1}{2}\,H_2O$	1.44		1.54	1.23[a]	1.30	1.45	1.51	1.21	1.31
				1.54	1.19[a]	1.31	1.47			
(XII)	$NaCu(ggg) \cdot H_2O$	1.49		1.57	1.23	1.29	1.44	1.53	1.23	1.28
				1.53	1.24	1.36[b]	1.43			
(XIII)	$Na_2Cu(gggg) \cdot 10\,H_2O$	1.49		1.527	1.276	1.290	1.458	1.527	1.246	1.268
				1.523	1.267	1.316	1.444			
				1.527	1.272	1.301	1.460			
	Mean	1.48_3	1.53	1.53	1.26	1.30	1.45_4	1.52	1.23	1.28_4
	Weighted mean	1.48_2	1.52	1.53_1	1.26_3	1.30_1	1.45_4	1.52_0	1.23_5	1.28_6
	S.D. of mean	0.007	0.02	0.006	0.007	0.004	0.006	0.005	0.005	0.007
	Range	1.44–1.52	1.49–1.58	1.51–1.57	1.19–1.28	1.29–1.32	1.43–1.48	1.49–1.53	1.21–1.25	1.24–1.33
	No. in sample	12	4	9	7	8	9	13	13	13

[a] Omitted from mean because adjacent peptide nitrogen *not* bonded to copper.

[b] Omitted from mean because peptide nitrogen has unusual (quasi-tetrahedral) configuration.

TABLE IV

Bond Angles in Ligand Molecules (Degrees)

Formula no.	Complex	Cu—N—CH$_2$ ∧	N—C—CH$_2$	N—C—CO	C—C—C	C—C=O (peptide)	C—CO—N<	O=C—N<	OC—N—C	OC—N—Cu	Cu—N—C |	C—C=O (carboxyl)	C—CO—O	O=C—O	OC—O—Cu
(I)	Cu(gly)$_2$·H$_2$O	109, 110		113, 111								118, 120	117, 118	124, 123	115, 116
(III)	Cu(pen)$_2$	108		108								125	116	119	115
(IV)	Cu(pro)$_2$·2 H$_2$O	112	115	108								118	120	122	116
(VI)	Cu(ala)$_2$·6 H$_2$O	115	114		117, 113							116	114	129	140
(VII)	Cu(β-NH$_2$but)$_2$·2 H$_2$O	117										123	121	117	126
(X)	Cu(gg)·3 H$_2$O	109		111, 111		118, 120, 121, 122	114, 114, 115, 113	128, 126, 123, 125	123, 122, 121, 121	120, 121	117, 117	119	118	123	115
(XI)	Cu(ggg)Cl·1½ H$_2$O	110, 111		108, 111, 111								118, 126	120, 113	122, 122	115, 114
(XII)	NaCu(ggg)·H$_2$O	110		110, 109, 116^a		118, 119	113, 116	128, 126	121, 116^a	121, 113^a	117, 127	119	120	121	125
(XIII)	Na$_2$Cu(gggg)·10 H$_2$O	109		112, 109, 109, 116		118, 120, 117	115, 114, 117	127, 126, 127	125, 126, 117	119, 119, 115	116, 115, 127	120	115	125	
	Mean	111	115	110	115	119	115	126	122	119	119	120	117.5	122.5	120
	Standard deviation	0.9	1.0	0.6	2.0	0.6	0.5	0.6	1.0	0.9	2.0	1.0	0.9	1.0	2.7
	Range	108–117	114–115	108–116	113–117	117–122	113–117	123–128	117–126	115–121	115–127	116–126	113–121	117–129	114–140
	No. in sample	11	2	15	2	9	9	9	8	6	7	11	11	11	10

^{a} Omitted from mean because peptide nitrogen has unusual configuration.

93

A few values deviate markedly from the means, but most of these exceptions look worse than they are: for instance, the terminal N–C bond in $Cu(\beta\text{-}NH_2but)_2 \cdot 2\ H_2O$ appears to be short (1.44 Å, Table III), but in terms of its standard deviation (0.03 Å, Table II) the bond length is not in fact significantly different from the mean for such bonds (1.48 Å). The corresponding bond length in $Cu(ggg)Cl \cdot 1\frac{1}{2}\ H_2O$ is also 1.44 Å. In this case the standard deviation is such (0.012 Å) that the difference from the mean is significant. This bond exhibits a real shortening, probably due to abnormal sp^2 character of the nitrogen atom, which is consistent with the latter's geometry (16).

In the above example, a significant deviation from the mean leads one to look for a reason. Two other groups of bonds in Tables III and IV (indicated by footnotes) so obviously refer to nonaverage situations that they have been excluded from the means altogether. (a) The two peptide C—O bonds in $Cu(ggg)Cl \cdot 1\frac{1}{2}\ H_2O$ are the only ones in the sample whose adjacent peptide nitrogen atoms are *not* copper binding. (b) At the second peptide nitrogen in $NaCu(ggg) \cdot H_2O$, the normal trigonal character is distorted by the additional weak bond to the second copper atom of the dimer. The length of the peptide C–N bond to this nitrogen and the bond angles about it thus have abnormal values.

When these special cases are excluded, the average dimensions found in the free *amino acid* ligands are preserved within the limits of significance when these molecules are chelated to copper. The bond lengths of the *peptide* group (31, 32) are, however, significantly disturbed when the hydrogen atom on the peptide nitrogen is replaced by copper. This is shown in Table V. The shortening of the C–N and lengthening of the C=O bonds have already been noted by Brill *et al.* (33) as the most significant

TABLE V

AVERAGE DIMENSIONS OF FREE AND COMPLEXED PEPTIDE GROUPS

Bond	Average length (Å)		Angle	Average angle (degrees)	
	Free peptides	Complexes		Free peptides	Complexes
C_α—C	1.53	1.53	C_α—C—N	114	115
C=O	1.24	1.26	C_α—C=O	121	119
C—N	1.32	1.30	O=C—N	125	126
N—C_α'	1.47	1.45	C—N—C_α'	123	122
			N—C_α'—C'	110	110

TABLE VI

BOND LENGTHS IN FREE AND CHELATED GLYCINE AND GLYCYLGLYCINE

Bond	Bond length (Å)			
	Glycine	Cu(gly)$_2$·H$_2$O	Glycylglycine	Cu(gg)·3H$_2$O
Peptide group				
NH$_2$—C	1.474	1.47, 1.48	1.497	1.51, 1.49
C—CO	—	—, —	1.528	1.53, 1.51
C=O	—	—, —	1.249	1.28, 1.27
OC—N	—	—, —	1.328	1.30, 1.30
N—C	—	—, —	1.462	1.46, 1.48
Carboxyl group				
C—CO	1.523	1.50, 1.54	1.516	1.52, 1.53
C=O	1.252	1.23, 1.24	1.239	1.24, 1.25
C—O	1.256	1.28, 1.29	1.262	1.28, 1.26

evidence that chelation causes increased double-bond character in the peptide C–N bond.

Instead of comparing averages, it would be preferable to make comparisons between the dimensions of individual ligands before and after complex formation. Unfortunately only two pairs of crystal structure analyses are available which are precise enough for effective comparison: these are the structures of glycine (34) and α-glycylglycine (35) and their cupric complexes. The asymmetric unit of Cu(gly)$_2$·H$_2$O contains two independent glycine ligands, while the asymmetric unit of Cu(gg)·3 H$_2$O contains two independent complexes. The resultant bond-length comparisons are shown in Table VI and support the generalizations stated above.

The remaining property generally ascribed to peptide groups is coplanarity of the atoms C$_\alpha$—CO—NH—C$_\alpha$'. Table VII shows that the coplanarity of C$_\alpha$—CO—N is preserved in copper-binding peptide groups, but that the bonded copper atom and C$_\alpha$' may lie significantly out of the planes of the groups. Amino acid chelate rings (not tabulated) are buckled, with both the copper and the amino nitrogen atoms lying out of the plane of the adjacent C—COO$^-$ group. Where data are available, they indicate that peptide chelate rings containing terminal amino groups are similarly deformed.

B. Lengths and Configurations of Cu^{2+}-Ligand Bonds

Tables VIII and IX show the lengths and interbond angles of the copper-ligand bonds. Since the bonds involving copper atoms are generally de-

TABLE VII

PLANARITY OF Cu–BONDED PEPTIDE GROUPS

Formula no.	Complex	Distances from planes of peptide groups[a] (Å)				
		Cu	>NH	C	O	N
(VIII)	$Cu(biu)_2Cl_2$	−0.427	+0.001	−0.002	0	+0.001
(IX)	$K_2Cu(biu)_2 \cdot 4 H_2O$	+0.090	−0.001	+0.005	−0.002	−0.002
		+0.129	+0.001	−0.002	+0.001	+0.001

Formula no.	Complex	Distances from planes of peptide groups[a] (Å)						
		Cu	NH_2	C_α	C	O	N	C_α'
(X)	$Cu(gg) \cdot 3 H_2O$	−0.079	+0.141	$+0.000_2$	-0.000_8	$+0.000_3$	$+0.000_3$	−0.048
		−0.063	+0.147	−0.008	+0.027	−0.010	−0.009	+0.067
(XII)	$NaCu(ggg) \cdot H_2O$	+0.188		−0.002	+0.006	−0.003	−0.002	+0.004
		−0.388		+0.001	−0.005	+0.002	+0.002	−0.156
(XIII)	$Na_2Cu(gggg) \cdot 10 H_2O$	−0.069		−0.015	+0.009	+0.002	+0.015	−0.012
		+0.004		0	−0.003	+0.002	+0.004	−0.002
		+0.124		+0.011	−0.011	−0.001	−0.012	+0.013

[a] Deviations of atoms included in calculation of each least-squares plane are shown in **bold face**.

TABLE VIII
Copper-Ligand Bond Lengths (Å)

Formula no.	Complex	Bonds to four nearest ligand atoms							Bonds perpendicular to coordination square	
		Cu—NH$_2$	Cu—N<	Cu—N<	Cu—O= (peptide)	Cu—O— (carboxyl)	Cu—OH$_2$	Cu—Cl	Cu—OH$_2$	Cu—O= (carboxyl)
(I)	$Cu(gly)_2 \cdot H_2O$	1.984, 2.021				1.96, 1.95			2.40	
(III)	$Cu(pen)_2$	1.98				1.91			2.52	
(IV)	$Cu(pro)_2 \cdot 2\,H_2O$	1.99				2.03			2.52	
(V)	$Cu(glu) \cdot 2\,H_2O$	2.01				1.99, 1.98	1.98			2.30, 2.59
(VI)	$Cu(ala)_2 \cdot 6\,H_2O$	2.01				2.04			2.52	
(VII)	$Cu(\beta\text{-}NH_2but)_2 \cdot 2\,H_2O$	1.99				2.00			2.45	
(VIII)	$Cu(biu)_2Cl_2$				1.935					
(IX)	$K_2Cu(biu)_2 \cdot 4\,H_2O$		1.94, 1.93							
(X)	$Cu(gg) \cdot 3\,H_2O$	2.00, 2.03	1.89, 1.89			1.97, 1.98	1.96, 1.96		2.40, 2.30	
(XI)	$Cu(ggg)Cl \cdot 1\tfrac{1}{2}\,H_2O$	1.99	1.89		1.987	1.93		2.24	2.30	2.82
(XII)	$NaCu(ggg) \cdot H_2O$	2.04		2.00		1.93				
(XIII)	$Na_2Cu(gggg) \cdot 10\,H_2O$	2.03	1.923, 1.912, 1.944							
Mean		2.00$_6$	1.92	2.00	1.96	1.97	1.97	2.24	2.41	2.57
Weighted mean		2.00$_8$	1.91$_7$		1.95	1.96$_6$	1.97		2.38	
Standard deviation		0.007	0.008	0.008	0.025	0.012	0.01	0.003	0.04	
Range		1.98–2.04	1.88–1.94	2.00	1.94–1.99	1.91–2.04	1.96–1.98	2.24	2.30–2.52	2.30–2.82
No. in sample		12	8	1	2	12	3	1	7	3

termined with lower standard deviations than bonds between light atoms alone, deviations from the mean are liable to have greater significance in these tables than in Tables III and IV. On the other hand, each metal-ligand bond is influenced by the ligand field of all the ligand atoms attached to the metal, as well as by the strain of the particular chelate ring or rings of which it is a part. While each significant deviation from the mean has an explanation, there are so many special situations that Table VIII has only four columns where it is meaningful to compute averages at all. These are the columns for Cu—NH_2, Cu—N(peptide), Cu—O(carboxyl), and Cu—OH_2.

Cu–NH_2 bonds: These bonds should really be divided into two sets according to whether the adjacent bond in the chelate ring is Cu—N (peptide) or Cu—O(carboxyl or peptide). The average of four determinations in the first group (complexes (X), (XII), and (XIII)) is 2.02_5 Å (S.D. = 0.009) and the average of the eight other values is 1.99_6 Å (S.D. = 0.005). The difference is part of the slightly different chelate ring geometries.

Cu–N(peptide) bonds: There are two reasons that these bonds are systematically shorter (mean, 1.91 Å) than Cu–NH_2 bonds (2.01 Å). The covalent radius of sp^2-hybridized (trigonal) nitrogen is smaller than that of sp^3-hybridized (tetrahedral) nitrogen. In addition, these bonds may be considered to be formed between copper and a deprotonated nitrogen bearing a formal negative charge. An exception is the bond to the distorted second peptide nitrogen in NaCu(ggg)·H_2O, whose length is 2.00 Å.

Cu–O(carboxyl) bonds: The deviations on the high side of the mean all occur in the less precisely determined structures. Three deviations on the low side have high statistical significance and can be understood in detail.

The short Cu–O bond in Cu(pen)$_2$, (III), is consistent with the total covalency of 4 of the copper atom in the crystal. In solution this complex almost certainly has two additional donors (H_2O) bonded to the copper atom. Apparently owing to more efficient packing, the complex crystallizes without these water molecules. This leaves the copper atom with unsatisfied bonding capacity, which manifests itself by drawing the carboxylic donor oxygen closer to the metal. This in turn produces a stronger ligand field at the copper, causing the absorption maximum to shift to a shorter wavelength (λ_{max} = 510, 590 mμ (23)).

The other two short Cu–O bonds both occur in complexes where these bonds are not members of normal amino acid chelate rings. In Cu(ggg)Cl· $1\frac{1}{2}$ H_2O (XI) the carboxyl group forms its own four-membered chelate ring, if the interaction between the copper and the second carboxyl oxygen is taken into account. In NaCu(ggg)·H_2O (XII), the carboxyl group is

TABLE IX

BOND ANGLES (DEGREES) AT COPPER ATOMS

Formula no.	Complex	Between Cu—NH₂ and				Between Cu—N(peptide) and			Between Cu—OH₂ and	Between "vertical" Cu—OH₂ and					Between "vertical" Cu—O=(carboxyl) and	
		Cu—N peptide	Cu—O carboxyl	Cu—O= peptide	Cu—OH₂	Cu—N peptide	Cu—O carboxyl	Cu—OH₂	Cu—O carboxyl	Cu—NH₂	Cu—N peptide	Cu—O carboxyl	Cu—OH₂	Cu—O= carboxyl	Cu—NH₂	Cu—O carboxyl
(I)	Cu(gly)₂·H₂O		85							96		92		171[b]	93	91
			85							90		89			87	83
(III)	Cu(pen)₂		85													
(IV)	Cu(pro)₂·2 H₂O		82							93		79				
(VI)	Cu(ala)₂·6 H₂O		91							90		88				
(VII)	Cu(β-NH₂but)₂·2 H₂O		92							87		87				
(X)	Cu(gg)·3 H₂O	85	168[a]		100		83	162[a]	92	92	112	92	85			
			163[a]		98		83	163[a]	93	100	104	94	92			
(XI)	Cu(ggg)Cl·1½ H₂O	83	175[b]	84			95[b]			91		91			126	51
							173[a]									
(XII)	NaCu(ggg)·H₂O	83	97[b]			84										
		166[a]														
(XIII)	Na₂Cu(gggg)·10 H₂O	84				83										
		110[b]				84										

Angles between bonds to four closest ligand atoms — *Angles involving bonds to more distant ligand atoms*

[a] Angle between bonds to atoms at opposite sides of central copper atom.

[b] Angle between bonds which are not part of a chelate ring.

part of a chelate ring distorted from its normal geometry by the long, weak copper-nitrogen interaction.

Other Cu–O bonds: No comments seem necessary concerning Cu–OH$_2$ bonds in the coordination square. The Cu–O(amide) bonds which occur in Cu(biu)$_2$Cl$_2$ and in Cu(ggg)Cl·1$\frac{1}{2}$ H$_2$O have distinctive environments. For this reason they have been listed separately in Table VIII, although their lengths fall in the range for Cu–O(carboxyl) bonds.

Table IX contains a selection from the bond angles occurring at the copper atoms. Most angles between bonds of which there is only one example (e.g., O-Cu-O in Cu(biu)$_2$Cl$_2$) have been omitted. The best-characterized angles are those involving Cu–N and Cu–O bonds in the chelate rings. All the angles N-Cu-N and N-Cu-O between bonds to the closer ligands are 83°–84° if the chelate rings are five membered, and 92° if the rings are six-membered (i.e., in the case of β-amino acids).

TABLE X

Deviations from Planes of Four Closest Ligand Atoms

Complex	Formula no.	Deviations of ligand atoms from plane (Å)[a]				
Cu(gly)$_2$·H$_2$O	I	NH$_2$	O$^-$	NH$_2$	O$^-$	Cu
		−0.03	**+0.02**	**+0.04**	**−0.03**	+0.05
Cu(gg)·3 H$_2$O	X	NH$_2$	N	O$^-$	OH$_2$	Cu
		+0.125	**−0.148**	**+0.137**	**−0.114**	+0.156
		NH$_2$	N	O$^-$	OH$_2$	Cu
		+0.029	**−0.033**	**+0.030**	**−0.026**	+0.244
Cu(ggg)Cl·1$\frac{1}{2}$ H$_2$O	XI	NH$_2$	O =	O$^-$	Cl	Cu
		+0.109	**−0.191**	**+0.100**	**−0.160**	+0.142
NaCu(ggg)·H$_2$O	XII	NH$_2$	N	N	O$^-$	Cu
		−0.001	**+0.001**	**−0.001**	**+0.001**	+0.115
Na$_2$Cu(gggg)·10 H$_2$O	XIII	NH$_2$	N	N	N	Cu
		−0.046	**+0.048**	**−0.040**	**+0.039**	**+0.029**

[a] Deviations of atoms included in least-squares planes calculations are shown in **bold face**.

These values are independent of whether the nitrogen is in an amino or peptide group, and of whether the oxygen is carboxylic or peptidic.

Angles between bonds on opposite sides of the central metal, and angles with bonds to single donor atoms, show a much greater spread. On the whole, the angle between a bond to one of the closer donors and a bond to one of the more distant (octahedral) donors tends to be larger than 90° if the closer donor is nitrogen, and smaller than 90° if the closer donor is oxygen. Individual values, however, are sensitive to the environments of the particular donor atoms.

It is obvious from the values of the bond angles in the coordination square that the coordination around the copper atom is not rigorously square-planar. There are two kinds of deviation from planarity (Table X). A copper atom may be displaced from the plane of its four nearest neighbors, generally in the direction of a more loosely bonded donor atom; and the four nearest neighbors themselves may deviate from their plane of best fit, their arrangement becoming a very flattened tetrahedron. It is, indeed, remarkable that the only truly planar arrangements of four ligand atoms occur in crystals where they are *demanded* by crystallographic symmetry (i.e., where the copper atom lies at a symmetry center).

The results of the preceding section are summarized in Fig. 3. At first sight it is disappointing that the information in ten tables can be distilled

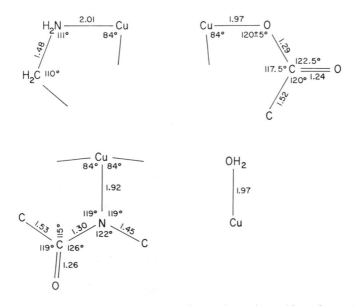

FIG. 3. Average dimensions in cupric complexes of α-amino acids and α-amino acid peptides. The water molecule is assumed to be one of the four close ligand atoms.

into such a small diagram. This, however, is precisely the purpose for which this paper was written.

For stability of the five-membered chelate rings that are characteristic of these structures, only small variations from the averages shown in Fig. 3 (or from the corresponding averages for the six-membered rings in the cases of β-amino acids) seem to be permitted. The geometry of a stable chelate ring which includes a copper atom in the *cupric* state is therefore incompatible with the near-tetrahedral angle which would be required at the copper atom if it were reduced to the *cuprous* state. This suggests an "ejection" mechanism for substrate molecules from reactive sites. If, as has been proposed (36), the substrate molecules in some oxidases form bidentate chelates with Cu^{2+} which become reduced to Cu^+, it is geometrically most unlikely that the chelate rings would survive the consequent change from square-planar to tetrahedral coordination.

V. Ligand Fields and Coordination Numbers in Cupric-Peptide Complexes

A. Ligand Field Differences

The complexes in Table I have colors which range from blue-green through blue to violet-pink, corresponding to a range of λ_{max} from 700 to 505 mμ. Unfortunately very few of the absorptions of these complexes have as yet been measured in the crystalline state, though the colors of the crystals generally appear to be the same as those of the solutions.

It is tempting to seek a connection between color and coordination, and this idea is anything but new. In 1916, Kober and Haw (37) divided copper-peptide complexes into three classes: blue, purple, and red, corresponding to $\lambda_{max} = 630$ mμ (two N ligands), $\lambda_{max} = 540$ mμ (three N ligands), and $\lambda_{max} = 505$ mμ (four N ligands), respectively. (It is humbling to speculate on the equipment with which these absorption spectra were recorded!) Restatements of this correlation have been made in the light of additional spectroscopic data (38). Brill *et al.* (33) have classified the visible bands of cupric–peptide complexes as *d-d* transitions. The spectral shifts to shorter λ_{max} then correspond to increases in the ligand field as donor oxygen atoms of carbonyl groups or water molecules are replaced by negatively charged donor nitrogen atoms of deprotonated peptide groups: "The appearance of the biuret color in most cupric interactions with proteins is probably associated with hydrogen ionizations from at least three and at most four peptide bonds. Cupric biuret reactions are now seen to be really nothing more than a gradual shift of the ligand field band to lower wavelength as C=N— replaces oxygen donor groups ⋯. The

TABLE XI

ENVIRONMENT OF THE COPPER ATOMS: LIGAND FIELDS AND COORDINATION NUMBERS

Formula no.	Complex	4 Closest ligand atoms	Next-nearest ligand atoms (distances in Å)	Coordination number of Cu	Color (crystals)	λ_{max} (mμ) (solution)	Ref. for λ_{max}
(VIII)	$Cu(biu)_2Cl_2$	O=, O=, O=, O=	2 Cl⁻ (2.96)	6	Blue-green	—	(29)
(XI)	$Cu(gggg)Cl \cdot 1\frac{1}{2} H_2O$	NH₂, O=, O⁻, Cl⁻	OH₂ (2.30), O= (2.82)	$5\frac{3}{4}$	Blue-green	730	(29)
(V)	$Cu(glu) \cdot 2 H_2O$	NH₂, O⁻, O⁻, OH₂	O= (2.30), O= (2.59)	$5\frac{3}{4}$	Blue	620	(23)
(I)	$Cu(gly)_2 \cdot H_2O$	NH₂, NH₂, O⁻, O⁻	OH₂ (2.41), O= (2.74)	$5\frac{1}{2}$	Blue	630	(23)
(IV)	$Cu(pro)_2 \cdot 2 H_2O$	NHR, NHR, O⁻, O⁻	2 OH₂ (2.52)	$5\frac{1}{2}$	Blue	610	(23)
(VI)	$Cu(ala)_2 \cdot 6 H_2O$	NH₂, NH₂, O⁻, O⁻	2 OH₂ (2.53)	$5\frac{1}{2}$	Blue		
(VII)	$Cu(\beta\text{-}NH_2but)_2 \cdot 2 H_2O$	NH₂, NH₂, O⁻, O⁻	2 OH₂ (2.45)	$5\frac{1}{2}$	Blue		
(X)	$Cu(gg) \cdot 3 H_2O$	NH₂, N, O⁻, OH₂	OH₂ (2.3, 2.4)	5	Blue	635	(29)
(XII)	$NaCu(ggg) \cdot H_2O$	NH₂, N, N, O⁻	N (2.57)	$4\frac{1}{2}$	Violet	555	(29)
(IX)	$K_2Cu(biu) \cdot 4 H_2O$	NH, NH, NH, NH	—	4	Violet-pink	505	(39,40)
(XIII)	$Na_2Cu(gggg) \cdot 10 H_2O$	NH₂, N, N, N	—	4	Violet-pink	520	(29)

103

rather high extinction coefficients of these complexes, $E = 50$–200 (variable), are due to the lack of symmetry of the complex." (33).

If we now look at the cupric–peptide complexes whose crystal structures are known, we find that the oxygens which are replaced by nitrogen donors are always in the coordinating positions close to the copper, i.e., at the corners of the "coordination square." It follows that if we leave out any octahedral ligand atoms and arrange the complexes in an order where the four closest ligand atoms are $4 O : 3 O + N : 2 O + 2 N : O + 3 N : 4 N$, then the complexes should also be in the order of decreasing λ_{max}. Table XI, which includes the amino acid and biuret complexes, shows that this is substantially the case.[8] This shows that it is the nature of the *donor atoms in the coordination square* that primarily determines differences in the ligand field.

B. Ligand Fields and Coordination Numbers

Adjacent to the column listing the four closest neighbors of each copper atom, Table XI also lists the additional ligands. With two exceptions, these are all water molecules or carboxylic oxygens. (The two exceptions are the chloride ions in $Cu(biu)_2Cl_2$ and the weakly bound peptide nitrogen in the dimeric $NaCu(ggg)\cdot H_2O$). It is unlikely that the interactions between carboxyl oxygens and copper atoms of adjacent complexes survive when the crystals are dissolved in water; in these cases, the complexes will exist in solution with an equivalent number of water molecules loosely bonded to the copper.

The copper atoms in the listed peptide complexes do not, however, all have two additional donor atoms in the octahedral positions. The structures (I) to (XIV) include examples of Cu^{2+} with coordination numbers 6, 5, and 4. Copper has six nearest neighbors in all the octahedral complexes, some of which show gross angular distortions in addition to the normal Jahn–Teller effect. In $Cu(gg)\cdot 3 H_2O$ and $NaCu(ggg)\cdot H_2O$, there is no doubt that the copper atoms have five nearest neighbors arranged square-pyramidally at bonding distances, and not six. Square-planar coordination by four nitrogen atoms occurs in $K_2Cu(biu)_2\cdot 4 H_2O$ and $Na_2Cu(gggg)\cdot 10 H_2O$.

In this context, the conventional "coordination number" is merely the number of nearest neighbors of a central atom and does not tell us whether the nearest neighbors are close or distant, strongly or weakly bound. For

[8] The complexes $Cu(\alpha$-$NH_2but)_2$ (II) and $Cu(pen)_2$ (III) have been omitted from Table XI because the environments of their copper atoms in the crystals are demonstrably different from those in solution (4, 23).

the purposes of the present study we shall therefore use the word "co-ordination number" for the sum of rather arbitrary bond numbers which do take into account the differences between strong and weak bonds.

A bond may be lengthened (a) because it lies in a direction where the apparent radius of the copper atom is increased by the Jahn–Teller effect, or (b) because the copper cannot bind the donor more strongly, or (c) because the donor atom is sterically forced into a position that is unfavorable for bonding.

Accordingly, in Table XI,

(a) It has been assumed that the bonds to the four closest ligands are equivalent and have bond number 1.

(b) It has been assumed that the lower limit, 2.3 Å, of the Cu–O bond lengths recorded perpendicular to the coordination square represents the length of a full single bond after allowing for Jahn–Teller distortion. Cu–O and Cu–N bonds in this direction have been assigned bond number 1 if the bond distance is 2.3–2.4 Å; $\frac{3}{4}$, if it is 2.5–2.6 Å; and $\frac{1}{2}$, if it is 2.7–2.8 Å.

(c) Where copper atoms are bonded to both oxygens of a single carboxyl group, the Cu–O bonds which are not in the coordination squares are assigned bond number $\frac{3}{4}$. In these two cases the geometry of the carboxyl group predetermines the closest approach and the orientation of the oxygen with respect to the copper.

(d) Ionic Cu^{2+}–Cl^- bonds in $Cu(biu)_2Cl_2$ are assigned bond number 1 since they have lengths predicted for ionic bonds in this direction (11).

The coordination numbers calculated on the basis of these assignments decrease as the ligand fields of the donors in the coordination squares increase. There is a logical basis for this relationship. The ligand field depends partly on the polarizabilities of the ligands. The higher their polarizabilities, the greater also is the charge they will transfer to the metal. In accordance with the Pauling electroneutrality principle, a metal takes up such a number of ligands as will reduce its charge to nearly zero. It follows that the higher the polarizabilities of the ligands are (and the stronger therefore their ligand field), the smaller will be the metal's ability to bind additional ligands (41). If we combine this rule with the observations that a cupric atom always has at least four ligand atoms and that these lie at the corners of a square, then we can conclude that it is the ligand field of these four atoms that determines the strength and number of any additional bonds which the copper may form.

An example of this balance between the ligand field of four close donor atoms and the strength of the bond to a fifth occurs in $Cu(gg) \cdot 3\ H_2O$.

Although closely similar, the two independent complexes in the asymmetric unit have *systematically* different copper-ligand bond lengths. The complex (upper line in Table III) with the *shorter* bonds to the donors in the coordination square has the *longer* bond (2.4 Å) to the loosely bound water molecule and (Table X) a smaller displacement of the copper atom from the plane of the coordination square.

C. Biochemical Implications

This idea may have biochemical implications. Assuming that the reaction of a metal-activated enzyme proceeds via a protein-metal-substrate complex, it is necessary that (a) the complex have sufficient stability to keep the substrate in position while something happens to it, and (b) a mechanism exists whereby this stability can be upset so that the substrate is released. Especially the second condition seems to be met ideally by cupric complexes in which the ligand field of the four strongly bound donor atoms favors a total coordination number near 5.

Let us imagine that three or four of the ligand atoms in the coordination square belong to peptide or side chain groups of the enzyme protein. From Table XI we can deduce that the copper atom will have coordination number 5 if two or three of these ligand atoms are nitrogen and one or two are oxygen atoms. One of the latter may come from a water molecule. The structural evidence suggests that the fifth bond will be contributed by a single donor, that this donor will most likely be an oxygen atom of a water molecule or a nearby carboxyl group, and that it will lie at the closest bond distance permitted by the Jahn–Teller distortion of the copper environment. If a substrate molecule now approaches the copper atom from the direction opposite that of the fifth ligand, the metal may temporarily form bonds with both donors—the sixth arriving and the fifth departing—until the original fifth ligand has been displaced. The release of the new ligand will follow a similar path, its bond to the copper being weakened and broken by the collision of a water or fresh substrate molecule. It is obvious that, once a substrate molecule has formed one bond with the metal, it may form a second bond by displacing a second ligand atom if this is necessary for the reaction.

Displacement reactions in octahedral and square-planar complexes are equally well known, and no novelty is claimed for the above proposal. It is mentioned here only because the occurrence of coordination number 5 in cupric–peptide complexes is now well authenticated from structural analyses, and because this configuration offers reaction sites of ideal lability and accessibility.

VI. Peptide-Peptide Interactions

A. Peptide-Cu-Peptide Links

The copper atoms in five of the 14 complexes considered here interact with the ligands attached to another copper atom. In $Cu(gly)_2 \cdot H_2O$, there is a weak bond (2.74 Å) between the copper atom of one complex and one of the free carboxyl oxygen atoms of an adjacent complex. The same kind of interaction occurs in $Cu(glu) \cdot 2 H_2O$ (where this Cu–O distance is 2.30 Å). In $Cu(ggg)Cl \cdot 1\frac{1}{2} H_2O$ the copper atoms link the peptide molecules in infinite chains, being attached to the terminal NH_2 and first C=O groups of one peptide, and to the terminal carboxyl group of another. A similar linkage occurs in $Cu(glu) \cdot 2 H_2O$ (with the substitution of carboxylic for peptide C=O); as mentioned previously, the interaction of the copper with *both* oxygen atoms of the terminal carboxyl group in this complex is almost identical with that in $Cu(ggg)Cl \cdot 1\frac{1}{2} H_2O$. A third type of peptide-Cu-peptide linkage occurs in the dimeric $NaCu(ggg) \cdot H_2O$, where each copper atom forms bonds to three nitrogen atoms of one peptide and to the carboxyl group and one peptide nitrogen of the other. One consequence of this particular configuration is that the $N-CH_2-COO^-$ residues of two peptides are brought into close contact ($O \cdots N$, 2.9 Å; $O \cdots C$, 3.1 Å). The most recent addition to this list of interactions is the copper–imidazole bond in $Cu(ala-his) \cdot 2 H_2O$, which joins the histidine side chain of one peptide to a copper atom already chelated by another.

B. Peptide-Cu-OH₂-Peptide Links

It is much more common to find that a copper atom is linked to a neighboring peptide molecule via a coordinated water molecule. Excluding the incompletely analyzed structure of $Cu(ala-his) \cdot 2 H_2O$, there are 15 known cases of peptide$-Cu-OH_2 \cdots$peptide bridges. These involve nine of the eleven copper-bonded water molecules which are distributed among eight of these crystals. The two exceptional $Cu-OH_2$ groups are linked only to other water molecules, and are found in $Cu(ala)_2 \cdot 6 H_2O$ (where there is a $Cu-NH_2 \cdots O-Cu$ bridge) and in $Cu(glu) \cdot 2 H_2O$ (where each copper is bonded to three different amino acid residues in any case). There is thus a high probability that if a copper atom is bonded to one amino acid or peptide molecule, it will be separated from a neighboring ligand by not more than one hydrogen-bonded donor atom.

C. Survey of Hydrogen Bonds

In order to determine whether there is any pattern in the hydrogen-bonding behavior of these complexes, all the sites at which hydrogen

TABLE XII

Frequency of Hydrogen Bonding in Metal-Peptide Complexes

H-bonding sites[a]	No. of examples	No. of H bonds	H bonds per site	Frequency of H bonds[a]:
Cu-bonded groups				
Cu—**NH₂**	11	19	1.7	With **C=O**(carboxyl), 8; Cu—**O**—, 5; **H₂O**, 3; Cu—**OH₂**^{p}, 2; Cu=**O**(peptide), 1
Cu—**NH**—	2[b]	2	1	With **H₂O**, 2
Cu—O=(peptide)	2[c]	0	0	
Cu—**O**—(carboxyl)	11	9	1.2	With Cu—**NH₂**, 5; Cu—**OH₂**^{p}, 2; **H₂O**, 2
Cu—**Cl**	1	1	1	With >**NH**, 1
Cu—**OH₂**^{s}	3	6	2	With **H₂O**, 4; **C=O**(peptide), 1; **C=O**(carboxyl), 1
Cu—**OH₂**^{p}	6	17	2.8	With **C=O**(carboxyl), 6; **H₂O**, 4; **C=O**(peptide), 3; Cu—**NH₂**, 2; Cu—**O**—, 2
Nonchelating groups				
—**NH₂**	1[c]	1	1	With **Cl**⁻, 1
>**NH**	4[b,c]	3	0.8	With Cu—**Cl**, 1; **H₂O**, 1; **Cl**⁻, 1
C=O(peptide)	10[b]	17	1.7	With **H₂O**, 12; Cu—**OH₂**^{p}, 3; Cu—**NH₂**, 1; Cu—**OH₂**^{s}, 1
C=O(carboxyl)	12	23	1.9	With Cu—**NH₂**, 8; **H₂O**, 8; Cu—**OH₂**^{p}, 6; Cu—**OH₂**^{s}, 1
C—O⁻(carboxyl)	1	2	2	With **H₂O**, 2
H₂O	19	55	2.9	With **H₂O**, 18; **C=O**(peptide), 12; **C=O**(carboxyl), 8; Cu—**OH₂**^{p}, 4; Cu—**OH₂**^{s}, 4; Cu—**NH₂**, 3; Cu—**NH**—, 2; Cu—**O**—, 2; **C—O**—, 2
Cl⁻	1[c]	3	3	With Cu—**NH₂**, 2; Cu—**NH**, 1

[a] Atoms connected by hydrogen bonds are shown in **bold face**. Superscript p indicates that H₂O is on perpendicular to square of four closest ligand atoms; s, that H₂O is in square of four closest ligand atoms.
[b] Includes K₂Cu(biu)₂·4 H₂O.
[c] Includes Cu(biu)₂Cl₂.

TABLE XIII

BOND ANGLES AT HYDROGEN-BONDING ATOMS

Hydrogen-bonding site[a]	Angle	Average value [b]	Range[b]	No. in sample
	Cu—N—C	111	108-117	10
	Cu⋯N⋯A / Cu—N⋯B	118	97-134	12
Cu—N⋯B (with A and C)	C—N⋯A / C—N⋯B	106	81-120	13
	A⋯N⋯B	99	91-108	3
	Cu—O—C	121	114-140	6
Cu—O (with A and C)	Cu—O⋯A	111	102-120	5
	C—O⋯A	114	100-134	6
	Cu—OH_2⋯A / Cu—OH_2⋯B / Cu—OH_2⋯D	116	89-143	18
Cu—OH_2⋯B (with A and D)	A⋯OH_2⋯B / A⋯OH_2⋯D / B⋯OH_2⋯D	108	82-154	12
Peptide C=O (with A and B)	C=O⋯A / C=O⋯B	135	95-152	17
	A⋯O⋯B	99	76-113	9
Carboxyl C=O⋯B (with A and D)	C=O⋯A / C=O⋯B / C=O⋯D	122	107-143	15
	A⋯O⋯B / A⋯O⋯D / B⋯O⋯D	98	73-129	9
Peptide C—N (with A and C)	OC—N—C_α	123	121-127	3
	OC—N⋯A	116	113-117	3
	C_α—N⋯A	120	116-126	3

[a] The maximum number of hydrogen bonds is shown, although examples with fewer hydrogen bonds are included in the sample.

[b] In degrees.

bonding can occur have been summarized in Table XII. No quantitative significance can be attached to the numbers of "H-bonds per site," though it is clear that the groups most likely to participate in hydrogen bonding are copper-bonded amino groups and water molecules, and free carbonyl and carboxyl groups. The high hydrogen bond frequency of noncoordinated water molecules is only to be expected. Copper-bonded terminal amino groups emerge from this treatment not only as the ligand sites with the highest proportion of hydrogen bonds, but also as the groups whose hydrogen bonds most often link them directly to other ligand (as distinct from water) molecules. In fact, *all* such bonds involve $Cu-NH_2$ groups, among whose total of 19 hydrogen bonds there are

eight $Cu-NH_2 \cdots O=C$(carboxyl) links,

five $Cu-NH_2 \cdots O-Cu$(carboxyl) links,

one $Cu-NH_2 \cdots O=C$(peptide) link.

In compiling Table XII, the hydrogen bond assignments of the original authors of the structural analyses have generally been accepted. The ranges and averages of the published intervector angles at hydrogen-bonded peptide and amino acid atoms are shown in Table XIII. The extreme values in some ranges probably involve close contacts rather than hydrogen bonds, but there are not enough of these to invalidate the comments made in the preceding section.

VII. Conclusions

(1) The solution chemistry of cupric–peptide systems has shown that at low pH the copper atoms are bound by terminal $-NH_2$ and by oxygen donors. As the pH is increased, oxygen ligands are progressively replaced by peptide nitrogen donors, which lose protons in the process. The structural evidence supports the proposed mechanism by providing examples in the solid state of the species which are postulated to exist in solution.

(2) There is as yet no structural evidence for the existence of species in which peptide nitrogens bind copper atoms *without* loss of their attached protons.

(3) The results of structural analyses confirm that changes of the d-d absorption bands of the complexes in solution correspond to changes in the coordination of the metal. Implicit in this statement is the assumption that the ligand atom types that are observed in the crystalline state are the ones which bind the metal in solution.

(4) As the ligand field of the four closest ligands increases (usually, in

this series of structures, by the replacement of an oxygen by a nitrogen donor atom), the absorption moves to shorter λ_{max} and the capacity of the copper atom to bond additional ligands is decreased.

(5) There is little variation among the angles between the copper-ligand bonds in peptide or amino acid chelate rings. These angles appear to be insensitive to the nature and number of the other donor atoms attached to the metal.

(6) Within the significance limits of the available structural analyses, chelation of α- and β-amino acids leaves the bond lengths in the ligand molecules unchanged.

(7) Binding of Cu^{2+} at peptide nitrogen atoms is accompanied by appreciable changes in the peptide C=O and C—N bond lengths, corresponding to increased double-bond character of the C—N bond and therefore an increased contribution of the resonance form

(8) The planarity of the peptide groups is maintained in their cupric complexes, with the reservation that the copper atoms (and hence the N–Cu bonds) may lie significantly out of the peptide planes.

(9) Direct peptide-peptide (or amino acid–amino acid) hydrogen bonding is relatively infrequent in Cu^{2+} complexes, and all recorded examples of it involve copper-bonded amino groups. Hydrogen-bonded links between complexes are usually made via one or more water molecules. The copper atoms themselves provide junctions between adjacent ligand molecules in a number of structures.

VIII. Summary

The results of the single-crystal X-ray structural analyses of 14 cupric complexes with amino acids and peptides, and one with imidazole, are tabulated and evaluated. The geometries both of the ligand molecules and of the metal-ligand coordination polyhedra are discussed. Chelation does not affect the dimensions of amino acid molecules but does change the bond lengths in peptide groups to whose nitrogen atom copper is bonded. The ligand field of the four ligands that are closest to the copper atom determines λ_{max} of a complex (corresponding to the d-d transition in the Cu^{2+} spectrum) as well as the total bond-forming ability of the copper atom.

ACKNOWLEDGMENTS

The author gratefully acknowledges the permission of Dr. C. Gramaccioli, Dr. E. W Hughes, Dr. R. E. Marsh, Dr. K. Tomita, and Dr. A. F. Wells to quote their unpublished results, and the assistance of Mr. J. D. Bell and Dr. J. T. Szymanski in making some of the calculations for this paper.

REFERENCES

1. Tomita, K., and Nitta, I., *Bull. Chem. Soc. Japan*, **34**, 286 (1961).
2. Freeman, H. C., Snow, M. R., Nitta, I., and Tomita, K., *Acta Cryst.*, **17**, 1463 (1964).
3. Stosick, A. J., *J. Am. Chem. Soc.*, **67**, 362 (1945).
4. Barclay, G. A., and Stephens, F. S., *J. Chem. Soc.*, p. 2027 (1963).
5. Mathieson, A. McL., and Welsh, H. K., *Acta Cryst.*, **5**, 599 (1952).
6. Gramaccioli, C. M., *Acta Cryst.*, **16**, 65A (1963).
7. Gramaccioli, C. M., and Marsh, R. E., unpublished work.
8. Tomita, K., *Bull. Chem. Soc. Japan*, **34**, 397 (1961).
9. Bryan, B. R., Poljak, R. J., and Tomita, K., *Acta Cryst.*, **14**, 1125 (1961).
10. Freeman, H. C., Smith, J. E. W. L., and Taylor, J. C., *Nature*, **184**, 707 (1959).
11. Freeman, H. C., and Smith, J. E. W. L., *Acta Cryst.*, in press.
12. Freeman, H. C., Smith, J. E. W. L., and Taylor, J. C., *Acta Cryst.*, **14**, 407 (1961).
13. Strandberg, B., Lindqvist, I., and Rosenstein, R., *Z. Krist.*, **116**, 266 (1961).
14. Freeman, H. C., Hudson, P., and Strandberg, B., unpublished observations.
15. Cooper, T., Freeman, H. C., Robinson, G., and Schoone, J. C., *Nature*, **194**, 1237 (1962).
16. Freeman, H. C., Robinson, G., and Schoone, J. C., *Acta Cryst.*, **17**, 714 (1964).
17. Freeman, H. C., Schoone, J. C., and Sime, J. G., *Acta Cryst.*, **18**, 381 (1965).
18. Freeman, H. C., and Taylor, M. R., *Acta Cryst.*, **18**, 939 (1965).
19. Freeman, H. C., and Szymanski, J. T., *Acta Cryst.*, in press.
20. Jarvis, J. A. J., and Wells, A. F., *Acta Cryst.*, **13**, 1028 (1960).
21. Jarvis, J. A. J., and Wells, A. F., unpublished observations.
22. Tomita, K., *Bull. Chem. Soc. Japan*, **34**, 280 (1961)
23. Graddon, D. P., and Munday, L., *J. Inorg. Nucl. Chem.*, **23**, 231 (1961).
24. Dobbie, H., and Kermack, W. O., *Biochem. J.*, **59**, 246, 257 (1955).
25. Manyak, A. R., Murphy, C. B., and Martell, A. E., *Arch. Biochem. Biophys.*, **59**, 273 (1955).
26. Murphy, C. B., and Martell, A. E., *J. Biol. Chem.*, **226**, 37 (1957).
27. Kim, M. M., and Martell, A. E., *Biochemistry*, **3**, 1169 (1964).
28. Koltun, W. L., Fried, M., and Gurd, F. R. N., *J. Am. Chem. Soc.*, **82**, 233 (1960).
29. Koltun, W. L., Roth, R. H., and Gurd, F. R. N., *J. Biol. Chem.*, **238**, 124 (1963).
30. Rabin, B. R., *in* Crook, E. M., (ed.), "Metals and enzyme activity," Cambridge University Press, London and New York, 1958, p. 21.
31. Corey, R. B., and Pauling, L., *Proc. Roy. Soc. (London)*, Ser. B, **141**, 10 (1953).
32. Hahn, T., *Z. Krist.*, **109**, 438 (1957).
33. Brill, A. S., Martin, R. B., and Williams, R. J. P., *in* B. Pullman (ed.), "Electronic aspects of biochemistry," Academic Press Inc., New York, 1964, p. 519.
34. Marsh, R. E., *Acta Cryst.*, **11**, 654 (1958).
35. Hughes, E. W., unpublished observations.
36. Martell, A. E., and Calvin, M., *in* "Chemistry of the metal chelate compounds," Prentice-Hall, New York, 1952, p. 387.

37. Kober, P. A., and Haw, A. B., *J. Am. Chem. Soc.*, **38**, 457 (1916).
38. Plekhan, M. I., *Zhur. Obshch. Khim.*, **22**, 1633 (1952).
39. Kato, M., *Z. Phys. Chem.*, **23**, 391 (1960).
40. Ferguson, J., personal communication, quoted in Ref. (12).
41. Gill, N. S., Nyholm, R. S., Barclay, G. A., Christie, T. I., and Pauling, P. J., *J. Inorg. Nucl. Chem.*, **18**, 88 (1961).

DISCUSSION

DR. JØRGENSEN: I think formula (II) shows something very interesting. There has been much discussion of why Ni^{2+} complexes of highly alkyl-substituted ethylenediamines are low spin and the similar complexes without *C*-alkyl groups high spin, and I suspect what is going on is not, as an organic chemist might think, an inductive effect, but may simply be due to the fact that when there are a lot of alkyl groups close to the nitrogen, the dielectric constant is much lower. Consequently, the nickel-nitrogen distances tend to be shorter, and the complexes tend to become low spin. In the cases of Cu^{2+}, compounds tend to become pink, and there are some old observations about alkyl substitution producing pink rather than violet colors. I completely subscribe to your point. [See Jørgensen, Refs. (31) and (32).]

DR. CAUGHEY: Dr. Freeman's remarks about the philosophy of interpretations of the uniqueness of these structures in regard to complexes in solution reminded me of the fact that different conformations of tetraphenylporphin are found for different crystal forms [Hoard, J. L., Hamor, M. J., and Hamor, T. A., *J. Am. Chem. Soc.*, **85**, 2334 (1963); Hamor, M. J., Hamor, T. A., and Hoard, J. L., *ibid.*, **86**, 1938 (1964); Silvers, S., and Tulinsky, A., *ibid.*, **86**, 927 (1964); Hamor, T. A., Caughey, W. S., and Hoard, J. L., *ibid.*, **87**, 2305 (1965).]. Thus the same molecule can show quite different conformations in different crystals—presumably as a result of differences in crystal-packing forces. I am therefore wondering if among the copper complexes described here, there are also examples of different crystal forms giving rise to different conformations or arrangements of ligands about the copper atom.

DR. FREEMAN: Yes, there are examples of differences of both configuration and conformation. Bisglycinato copper(II) can be crystallized as a *cis* complex monohydrate and as a *trans* complex dihydrate [Tomita, K. *Bull. Chem. Soc. Japan*, **34**, 280 (1961)]. Only the crystals of the *cis* complex [Freeman, formula (I)] have been suitable for X-ray crystal structure analysis. In solution, the two forms must be in equilibrium, the conditions of crystallization determining which separates out.

In the crystals of the copper-carnosine complex [Freeman, formula (XIV)] the β-alanine chelate ring makes no close nonbonded contacts. The atoms of the ring can be located only approximately in the electron density maps—they look as though they are vibrating wildly. In reality, the smeared-out electron density corresponds to the average of two or more conformations.

Any configuration or conformation which is confirmed by crystal structure analysis is the best for that particular group of atoms under those conditions. What I have tried to say in my paper is that some structural features turn up so often that they must be, if not essential, at least *geometrically particularly favorable*.

Interaction of Cupric Ion with Histidine Peptides and Sperm Whale Metmyoglobin[*]

FRANK R. N. GURD AND GRAEME F. BRYCE[†]

Department of Biochemistry,
Indiana University School of Medicine,
Indianapolis, Indiana

I. Introduction

Three years ago one of us summarized the prospects for interpreting the interactions of Cu^{2+} and Zn^{2+} ions with sperm whale myoglobin in terms of interactions with model peptides (2). The amino acid sequence (3) and three-dimensional structure of this protein in the crystalline state (4) are known. The protein is small enough that a fairly detailed comparison with peptides representing segments of its amino acid sequence is feasible. It is large enough to present problems that may be widely significant in metal-protein interactions. The present report brings the analysis of the prospects in this study up to date.

The sequence of amino acid residues in sperm whale myoglobin (3) is listed in Table I. The residues are referred to the three-dimensional structure by naming according to their position in a given helix or between given helical regions. A single prefix letter and number, e.g., A10, denotes that the residue is in a helical segment, in this case the tenth residue in the first helical segment. Two prefix letters denote that the residue is in a nonhelical region between the helical segments denoted by the letters. The relations between the helical and nonhelical segments are diagrammed in Fig. 1 (5). The first two residues, NA1 and NA2, were not recognized at the time the figure was prepared. They should lie in the diagram above and slightly to the right of A1 (lower left).[1]

Given the complete amino acid sequence of myoglobin we should be able to correlate the observed behavior of myoglobin toward Cu^{2+} ions with the nature and number of certain residues in the protein. The correlation requires the synthesis of a series of peptide models. For example, com-

[*] This is the 18th paper in a series dealing with coordination complexes and catalytic properties of proteins and related substances; see Ref. (1). This work was supported by United States Public Health Service Research Grants HE–05556 and HE–06308.

[†] Not at meeting. Present address: Department of Molecular Biophysics, Yale University, New Haven, Connecticut.

[1] We wish to thank Dr. J. C. Kendrew and Dr. H. C. Watson for making available prior to publication the atomic coordinates of sperm whale metmyoglobin.

TABLE I

AMINO ACID SEQUENCE OF MYOGLOBIN[a]

Symbol		Amino acid	Symbol		Amino acid
NA	1	Valine		3	Arginine
	2	Leucine		4	Phenylalanine
A	1	Serine		5	Lysine
	2	Glutamic acid		6	Histidine
	3	Glycine		7	Leucine
	4	Glutamic acid		8	Lysine
	5	Tryptophan	D	1	Threonine
	6	Glutamine		2	Glutamic acid
	7	Leucine		3	Alanine
	8	Valine		4	Glutamic acid
	9	Leucine		5	Methionine
	10	Histidine		6	Lysine
	11	Valine		7	Alanine
	12	Tryptophan	E	1	Serine
	13	Alanine		2	Glutamic acid
	14	Lysine		3	Aspartic acid
	15	Valine		4	Leucine
	16	Glutamic acid		5	Lysine
AB	1	Alanine		6	Lysine
B	1	Aspartic acid		7	Histidine
	2	Valine		8	Glycine
	3	Alanine		9	Valine
	4	Glycine		10	Threonine
	5	Histidine		11	Valine
	6	Glycine		12	Leucine
	7	Glutamine		13	Threonine
	8	Aspartic acid		14	Alanine
	9	Isoleucine		15	Leucine
	10	Leucine		16	Glycine
	11	Isoleucine		17	Alanine
	12	Arginine		18	Isoleucine
	13	Leucine		19	Leucine
	14	Phenylalanine		20	Lysine
	15	Lysine	EF	1	Lysine
	16	Serine		2	Lysine
C	1	Histidine		3	Glycine
	2	Proline		4	Histidine
	3	Glutamic acid		5	Histidine
	4	Threonine		6	Glutamic acid
	5	Leucine		7	Alanine
	6	Glutamic acid		8	Glutamic acid
	7	Lysine	F	1	Leucine
CD	1	Phenylalanine		2	Lysine
	82	Aspartic acid		3	Proline

TABLE I (*Continued*)

AMINO ACID SEQUENCE OF MYOGLOBIN[a]

Symbol		Amino acid	Symbol		Amino acid
	4	Leucine		4	Asparagine
	5	Alanine		5	Phenylalanine
	6	Glutamine		6	Glycine
	7	Serine	H	1	Alanine
	8	Histidine		2	Aspartic acid
	9	Alanine		3	Alanine
FG	1	Threonine		4	Glutamine
	2	Lysine		5	Glycine
	3	Histidine		6	Alanine
	4	Lysine		7	Methionine
	5	Isoleucine		8	Asparagine
G	1	Proline		9	Lysine
	2	Isoleucine		10	Alanine
	3	Lysine		11	Leucine
	4	Tyrosine		12	Glutamic acid
	5	Leucine		13	Leucine
	6	Glutamic acid		14	Phenylalanine
	7	Phenylalanine		15	Arginine
	8	Isoleucine		16	Lysine
	9	Serine		17	Aspartic acid
	10	Glutamic acid		18	Isoleucine
	11	Alanine		19	Alanine
	12	Isoleucine		20	Alanine
	13	Isoleucine		21	Lysine
	14	Histidine		22	Tyrosine
	15	Valine		23	Lysine
	16	Leucine		24	Glutamic acid
	17	Histidine	HC	1	Leucine
	18	Serine		2	Glycine
	19	Arginine		3	Tyrosine
GH	1	Histidine		4	Glutamine
	2	Proline		5	Glycine
	3	Glycine			

[a] After Edmundson (3).

parison (6, 7) of titration curves in the presence and absence of Cu^{2+} has indicated that histidine residues react with Cu^{2+}. The same study further showed that more protons were displaced by Cu^{2+} binding than could be accounted for by simple binding to imidazole groups (6). For these reasons we planned the synthesis of a series of histidine-containing peptides to explore the possibility of concurrent binding to both imidazole groups and peptide bonds (1, 2, 8, 9).

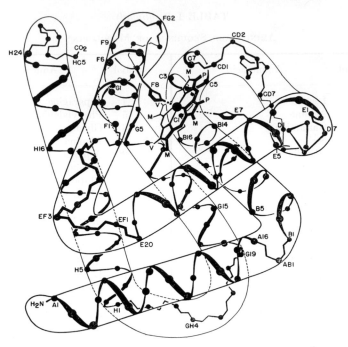

Fig. 1. α-Carbon diagram of myoglobin molecule obtained from 2 Å analysis. For identification of residues see text and Table I. Stretches of α-helix are represented by smooth helix with exaggerated perspective, numbered as described in text. The nonhelical segments, numbered as described in the text, are represented by three-segment zigzag lines between α-carbon atoms. Fainter parallel lines outline high-density region as revealed by 6 Å analysis. Heme group framework is sketched in forced perspective, with side groups identified as follows: M = methyl, V = vinyl, P = propionic acid. Five-membered rings at F8 and E7 represent histidines associated with heme group. After Dickerson (5).

II. Model Studies with Histidine Peptides

A. The Copper-Ligand Equilibrium

The type of peptide model that will probably prove to be most useful is illustrated by the structure of acetylglycylglycyl-L-histidylglycine.[2] The anionic form of this is shown as (I). Nitrogen atoms that are potential ligands for Cu^{2+} are numbered 1–6. The principal ligand atoms that combine with Cu^{2+} during the titration with alkali of a 1:1 mixture of metal ion and peptide are nitrogens 1, 2, 3, and 4. On the basis of comparison of (I) with acetylglycylglycyl-L-histidine, in which nitrogen 6 is missing, it

[2] G. F. Bryce, R. W. Roeske, and F. R. N. Gurd (in preparation).

(I)

appears that nitrogen 6 is not involved in the predominant chelate formation (9). On the basis of comparison of acetylglycyl-L-histidylglycine with acetylglycyl-L-(3)-iminobenzylhistidylglycine it is clear that nitrogen 5, the 3 nitrogen of the imidazole ring, is not involved (9).

The stepwise formation of complexes is described as follows:

$$Cu^{2+} + L^- \rightleftharpoons CuL^+ \qquad K_1 = \frac{[CuL^+]}{[Cu^{2+}][L^-]} \qquad (1)$$

$$CuL^+ + L^- \rightleftharpoons CuL_2 \qquad K_2 = \frac{[CuL_2]}{[CuL^+][L^-]} \qquad (2)$$

$$CuL^+ \rightleftharpoons CuL + H^+ \qquad K_c = \frac{[CuL][H^+]}{[CuL^+]} \qquad (3)$$

$$CuL \rightleftharpoons CuL^- + H^+ \qquad K_c' = \frac{[CuL^-][H^+]}{[CuL]} \qquad (4)$$

$$CuL^- \rightleftharpoons CuL^{2-} + H^+ \qquad K_c'' = \frac{[CuL^{2-}][H^+]}{[CuL^-]} \qquad (5)$$

The complex CuL$^+$ represents an initial 1:1 product, and CuL$_2$ the product of adding a second ligand. In the 1:1 mixtures studied CuL$_2$ is formed only in the early stages of the titration with alkali; later dissociations of amide hydrogens stabilize the 1:1 complexes. The products of these dissociations are CuL (II), CuL$^-$ (III), and CuL^{2-} (IV) (1).

The complex formation between Cu^{2+} and the series of peptides of the form acetyl(glylcyl)n-L-histidine or acetyl(glycyl)n-L-histidylglycine has been followed by titration (9), by measurement of absorption spectra, and by measurement of ORD (1). Measurement of circular dichroism is under way.

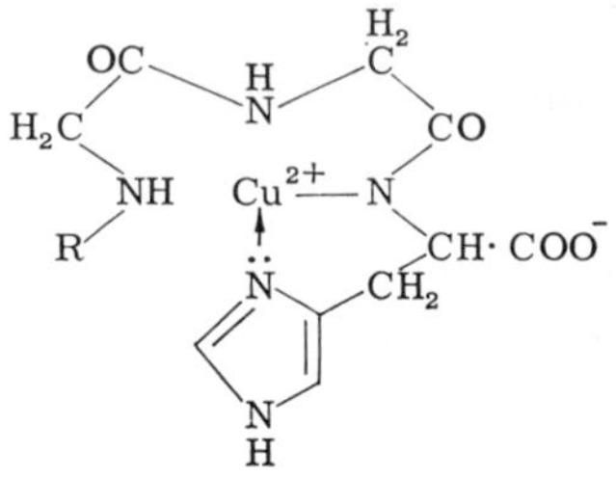

CuL, (II)

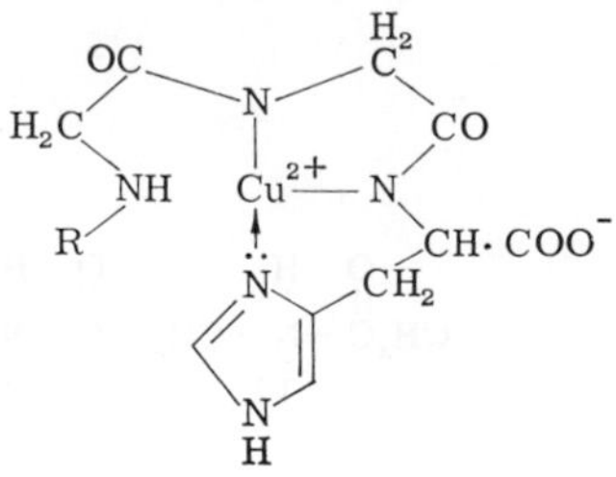

CuL$^-$, (III)

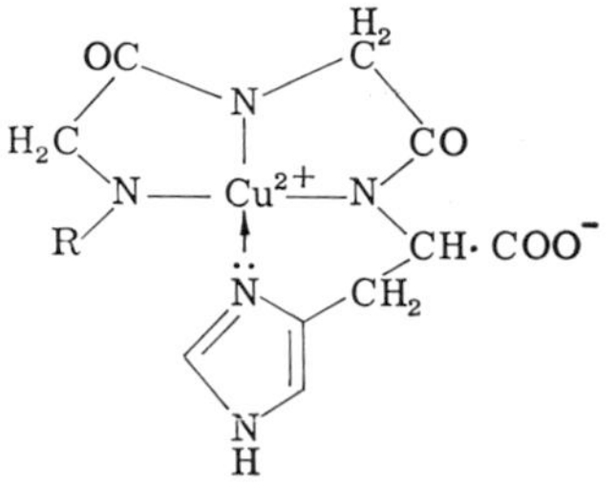

CuL^{2-}, (IV)

Representative values for the equilibrium constants are those for Cu^{2+} complexes of acetylglycylglycyl-L-histidine: $\log K_1 = 4.24$, $\log K_2 = 3.68$, $pK_c = 6.50$, $pK_c' = 7.35$, and $pK_c'' = 9.25$ (9). The values of $\log K_1$ and $\log K_2$ are in the expected range for Cu^{2+}-imidazole complexes (10, 11). The values of $\log K_1$ for complexes of this type have been found to vary linearly with the pK of the imidazole group. The values of pK_c and pK_c' are somewhat higher than for simple peptides containing a free α-amino group and no histidyl residue (12–14). Results for a number of peptides are shown in Table II (9).

B. Spectra

As the degree of complex formation proceeds the wavelength of maximal absorption in the visible range decreases. For CuL$^+$ it is 765–770 mμ, for CuL it is 675–685 mμ, for CuL$^-$ about 590 mμ, and for CuL^{2-} about 545 mμ, in the system Cu^{2+}-acetylglycylglycyl-L-histidine (1). In the Cu^{2+}-triglycylglycine system the corresponding values are 730, 660, 590, and 520 mμ (12). The relative effectiveness of ligands in contributing to the ligand field appears to be in the order α-amino N > peptide N > imidazole N. Results for a number of peptides are shown in Table III (1).

TABLE II

FORMATION AND IONIZATION CONSTANTS FOR Cu^{2+} COMPLEXES OF L-HISTIDINE-CONTAINING PEPTIDES AT $25°$ AND 0.16 IONIC STRENGTH[a,b]

Peptide	pK_{COOH}	pK_{Im}	pK_{NH_2}	$\log K_1$	$\log K_2$	pK_c	pK_c'	pK_3''
Glycyl-L-histidine	2.66	6.77	8.24	ND	ND	4.00	4.50	9.25
Glycylglycyl-L-histidine	2.84	6.87	8.22	ND	ND	4.75	4.90	5.00
Glycylglycylglycyl-L-histidine	3.02	6.85	8.11	ND	ND	6.35	7.10	8.70
Acetylglycylglycyl-L-histidine	3.08	7.18	—	4.24	3.68	6.50	7.35	9.25
Acetylglycylglycylglycyl-L-histidine	3.16	7.21	—	4.40	3.52	6.50	7.35	8.80
Acetylglycyl-L-histidylglycine	3.25	6.86	—	3.84	3.68	6.35	6.90	11.4
Acetylglycyl-L-iminobenzylhistidylglycine	3.30	6.37	—	3.06	3.27	5.95	6.90	11.5

[a] After Bryce, Roeske, and Gurd (9).
[b] ND = Not determined.

TABLE III

VISIBLE ABSORPTION CHARACTERISTICS OF 1:1 COMPLEXES OF Cu^{2+} WITH ACETYLGLYCYLGLYCYLGLYCYL-L-HISTIDINE AND ACETYLGLYCYLGLYCYLGLYCYLGLYCYL-L-HISTIDINE[a,b]

Peptide	CuL⁺		CuL		CuL⁻		CuL²⁻	
	λ_{max} (mμ)	ϵ_{max} ($M^{-1}cm^{-1}$)	λ_{max} (mμ)	ϵ_{max} ($M^{-1}cm^{-1}$)	λ_{max} (mμ)	ϵ_{max} ($M^{-1}cm^{-1}$)	λ_{max} (mμ)	ϵ_{max} ($M^{-1}cm^{-1}$)
Acetylglycylglycyl-L-histidine	765	22	685	35	590	95	545	97
Acetylglycylglycylglycyl-L-histidine	770	23	675	35	590	84	545	98
Acetylglycyl-L-histidylglycine	ND	ND	ND	ND	590	68	555	84
Acetylglycyl-L-iminobenzyl-histidylglycine	770	38	660	63	590	65	560	128

[a] Computed from the observed spectra of solutions of various compositions and the equilibrium constants defined in Eqs. (1–5).
[b] ND = Not determined because of precipitation.

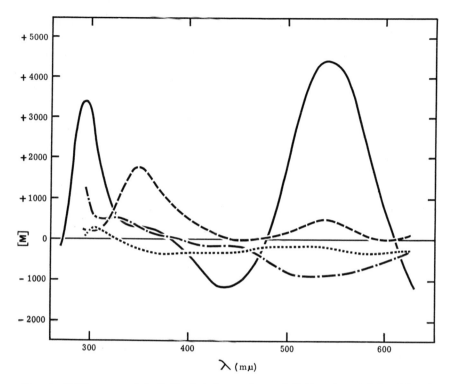

FIG. 2. ORD curves of individual 1:1 complexes of Cu^{2+} and acetylglycylglycyl-L-histidine. The solid curve represents the CuL^{2-} species; dashed curve, CuL^- species; dot-dashed curve, CuL species; and the dotted curve, CuL^+ species. After Bryce, Roeske, and Gurd.[2]

C. Optical Rotatory Dispersion

Measurements of ORD of the complexes of Cu^{2+} with the histidine-containing peptides show evidence of two Cotton effects in the visible range (1). These are illustrated in Fig. 2 for Cu^{2+}-acetylglycylglycyl-L-histidine. By far the greatest anomalous dispersion is observed for the complex CuL^{2-} (IV) representing the most highly chelated form. The ORD in the visible range appears to be the resultant of two overlapping Cotton effects: a negative one centered at about 600 mμ and a positive one centered at about 480 mμ. The positive extrema overlap extensively. The fine structure implied in the absorption spectrum is not discernible in the broad absorption peak. Measurements of circular dichroism support the interpretation of the ORD.

The Cotton effects at 480 and 600 mμ observed with the most highly chelated form suggest a considerable distortion from a square planar distribution for the four nitrogens around the Cu^{2+} (IV). The difference, 4100 cm^{-1}, may be useful in assessing the degree of distortion from square planar symmetry. The chelate ring in structure (IV) that contains the α- and β-carbon atoms of the L-histidyl residue is necessarily puckered. The existence of optical activity associated with d-d transitions suggests that one of the two puckered forms is favored. The carbonyl oxygen of the L-histidyl residue can approach an apical position with respect to the Cu^{2+} over the approximate plane of the four nitrogens. In that case it is axial to the chelate ring containing the L-histidyl residue. It will not approach the Cu^{2+} if it is arranged equatorially. Other influences controlling the puckering of the ring may operate with other peptides. With fewer chelate rings the complexes that precede the final stage exhibit much less, but significant, anomalous dispersion in the visible region (Fig. 2).

Also evident from Fig. 2 are Cotton effects in the near ultraviolet below 350 mμ. These may be related to low-energy charge-transfer bands that are not obvious in the absorption spectrum.

III. Correlation with Myoglobin Complexes

Table IV shows a measure of correlation between metmyoglobin and apomyoglobin on the one hand and two histidine-containing peptides on the other with respect to the number of protons displaced per Cu^{2+} bound ($-\Delta\bar{\nu}_H/\bar{\nu}_M$), at various pH values (9). Values for the proteins are estimated from previous studies (6, 7). The values for the peptides were computed by taking as the starting point the anionic form of the peptide in which the imidazole group is unprotonated. At pH 7.50 and above the correlations are reasonably good. At pH 6.50 and 7.00 the correlations are weakened in part by arbitrary choice of reference conditions, which stems from the

TABLE IV

VALUES OF $(-\Delta\bar{\nu}_H/\bar{\nu}_M)$ AS A FUNCTION OF pH FOR THE Cu^{2+} COMPLEXES OF METMYOGLOBIN, APOMYOGLOBIN, AND ACETYLATED HISTIDINE PEPTIDES[a]

Compound	pH 6.50	pH 7.00	pH 7.50	pH 8.50	pH 9.20	pH 10.00	pH 11.00
Metmyoglobin	1.25	1.50	1.56	2.12	2.48	2.50	3.15
Apomyoglobin	1.38	1.44	1.56	2.17	2.60	2.86	3.47
Acetylglycylglycylglycylglycyl-L-histidine	0.56	1.09	1.53	2.32	2.69	2.94	3.00
Acetylglycylglycylglycyl-L-histidine	0.50	1.08	1.56	2.07	2.46	2.85	2.98

[a] See text for explanation.

difficulty of defining the internal comparisons for the proteins, but almost certainly are related as well to the choice of model peptides that have rather higher values of pK_c than appear to apply to the proteins.

The correlation of absorption spectra and ORD between the protein and peptide complexes is being assessed at the present time, and is reported in more detail elsewhere.[2] The value for λ_{max} for the 4:1 Cu^{2+}-apomyoglobin complex above pH 10 is 530 mμ (7).[2] This value falls between that for the histidine peptides (1), Table II, and that for simple tetrapeptides (1, 12), an observation that has led us to explore the possibility that the amino terminus of the polypeptide chain of myoglobin may act as one binding site. Qualitatively this explanation seems compatible with ORD and circular dichroism measurements of the peptide and protein complexes. Furthermore, correlations of this sort appear to extend to the Ni^{2+} complexes.[2]

IV. Special Problems of Correlation with Binding Properties of the Whole Protein

The peptides that have been studied up to the present give promise of allowing a correlation with many of the characteristics of the Cu^{2+}-myoglobin interaction. Presumably the precision of the correlation could be increased indefinitely by the choice of peptides for study that match precisely the histidine-containing sequences in myoglobin (Table I). In this way the influence of composition on pK_c, absorption spectra, and optical rotatory properties could be assessed. For example, side chain substitutions may well affect each of these properties to some extent. The steric properties of the neighboring chains may affect the degree of predominance of one puckered chelate ring form over another, thereby moderating the net values for the optical rotatory parameters.

A. Amino Acid Sequences

The study of the actual amino acid sequences presented in myoglobin will be necessary to explain the behavior of the protein more completely. Although the model peptides studied so far form complexes with many of the properties of the Cu^{2+}-myoglobin complexes, the very promise of generality in this correlation perhaps leaves us unprepared to learn that the total number of strong Cu^{2+}-binding sites in myoglobin seems distinctly less than the total number of histidine residues. Myoglobin contains 12 histidine residues, whereas in the pH range up to 6 or 7 the binding of only six or perhaps seven Cu^{2+} ions is as strong as one would expect from the model peptide studies (6, 7). The validity of the comparisons presented here has depended on making them in terms of the first four or six Cu^{2+} ions to be bound to the protein.

The amino acid sequence given in Table I presents certain possibilities for explaining the apparent upper limit on the number of Cu^{2+} bound. First, the two adjacent histidine residues, EF4 and EF5, would probably share one Cu^{2+} except possibly at quite high concentrations of metal ion. This type of explanation probably does not apply more widely since it did not emerge from the original binding studies (6, 7) and, furthermore, would require the formation of some enormous chelate rings (Fig. 1). Second, two histidine residues, C1 and GH1, are each followed in the sequence by a proline residue that may interfere with the wrapping up of the peptide chain around the metal ion. Third, the residues G14, G17, and GH1 are separated from each other in the sequence only by four residues occurring as two pairs (G15, G16 and G18, G19). The development of an appropriate chelate involving each histidine residue with one or two more peptide groups may be prevented sterically in such a segment of amino acid sequence. Fourth, other interactions within the protein may stabilize potential components of the chelate sites in other conformations incompatible with the formation of the metal chelates. Segments of the peptide sequence are being prepared synthetically to test these various possibilities.

B. Changes in Structure

Up to the last point mentioned, the foregoing discussion has tacitly assumed that the protein may be considered as a flexible polypeptide chain able to accommodate to the demands of complex formation somewhat as a smaller chelating agent might. To some extent this assumption accords with the observed fact that Cu^{2+} causes a drastic change in the structure of myoglobin. The change was first detected by observations on the absorption spectrum and solubility of the complexes (6), and later confirmed by measurements of optical rotation (15). There is evidence that the first Cu^{2+} ion to bind does not cause drastic changes in the structure of the protein (6). Even with as many as six Cu^{2+} bound, at which point solubility and heme spectrum are fully altered, the ORD properties show that an appreciable amount of helical structure remains in the polypeptide chain. It is therefore quite reasonable to look for stabilizing interactions, for example, constraints on hydrophobic side chains, that act to reduce the stability of potential chelate sites.

The disruption of the native structure by Cu^{2+} shows an activation energy (15) comparable with that by Zn^{2+} (16) and with the heat of denaturation by hydrogen ion (17). The recovery in the presence of excess chelating agent is rapid (15). A detailed study of the three-dimensional crystalline structure,[1] not discernible in Fig. 1, shows that hardly any histidine residue is so arranged that a Cu^{2+} ion could bind concurrently to the imidazole group and amide nitrogen without disturbing the conformation of the peptide chain; cf. structure (II), above. The involvement of a second peptide nitrogen (cf. structure (III), above) would in all cases have to be accompanied by an extensive disturbance of the peptide chain (15). Independent evidence points to quite a close similarity between the crystalline structure and the predominant structure in solution (18–21).

C. Crystallographic Analysis

The indications from the studies in solution that the first Cu^{2+} bound does not cause disruption of the structure accord with an elegant crystallographic study of Banaszak et al. (22). They found by the technique of difference Fourier analysis that the isomorphous crystal structure containing not more than one site having a high degree of Cu^{2+} occupancy showed such occupancy at the correct position to bind to N-3 of histidine residue A10. Other ligands that could be involved were the ϵ-amino group of lysine A14 and the carboxamide group of asparagine GH4. Peptide backbone involvement was not indicated. When the concentration of Cu^{2+} was further increased in an attempt to detect occupancy of other sites, the crystals were observed to disintegrate. Somewhat parallel observations were made with Zn^{2+}, except that in that case the histidine residue GH1 was found to be involved in the binding site. It is quite conceivable that the sites involved in the binding to the native structure do not survive to function as before once the conformational changes are induced by reaction with larger numbers of Cu^{2+} or Zn^{2+} ions.

The results of the crystallographic analysis of the binding site for Cu^{2+} in the native, crystalline protein point up to the fact that the structure of the protein is too complex for many potential binding sites to be explored in model form. The search for potential binding sites in a protein whose crystalline structure is known will depend on direct experience of the stereochemistry of such binding (22) and on experience with the stereochemistry of the relatively manageable peptide complexes discussed here. It is to be hoped that crystallographic analysis of Cu^{2+}-peptide complexes, discussed elsewhere in this volume by Freeman, will be extended to cases as complicated as the histidine-containing tetrapeptides, for example. The various puckered conformations may be observed. Spectrometric correlations between the known crystalline peptide complexes and protein complexes then should be capable of much refinement. The obvious objection to reliance on crystal structures, that the lattice energy may stabilize a conformation that is not important in solution, should not be taken too seriously for two reasons. First, the more completely the chelating peptide satisfies the coordination potentialities of the metal ion the greater the possibility that interactions between complexes in the lattice are confined to hydrogen bonds and van der Waals contacts. Second, the spectrum of structures differing in details of puckering and distortion that may result from lattice energy effects is probably quite comparable with the spectrum of variations in structures that occur in the protein complexes, where comparable forces are probably at work.

V. Summary

The correlation between cupric ion interactions with synthetic histidine-containing peptides and with sperm whale metmyoglobin is discussed. Model studies with the peptides show that a cupric ion can form a chelate with N-1 of the imidazole ring, the peptide N of the L-histidine residue, and the peptide nitrogens of the two residues preceding the histidine residue in the amino-terminal direction. The steps in the formation of the complex are described in terms of successive equilibrium constants and are correlated with optical absorption and rotation spectra. By the same means correlations are made with the behavior of cupric ions toward metmyoglobin and apomyoglobin. Special problems involved in any such correlation are discussed.

ACKNOWLEDGMENTS

The advice and encouragement of Dr. E. Breslow, K. D. Hardman, and Dr. T. S. Piper are gratefully acknowledged.

REFERENCES

1. Bryce, G. F., and Gurd, F. R. N., *J. Biol. Chem.* **241,** 122 (1966).
2. Gurd, F. R. N., *Pure Appl. Chem.*, **6,** 49 (1963).
3. Edmundson, A. B., *Nature*, **205,** 883 (1965).
4. Kendrew, J. C., *Science*, **139,** 1259 (1963).
5. Dickerson, R. E., *in* H. Neurath (ed.), "The proteins," 2nd ed., Vol. II, Academic Press Inc., New York, 1964, p. 603.
6. Breslow, E., and Gurd, F. R. N., *J. Biol. Chem.*, **237,** 371 (1962).
7. Breslow, E., *J. Biol. Chem.*, **239,** 3252 (1964).
8. Bryce, G. F., Pinkerton, J. M. H., Steinrauf, L. K., and Gurd, F. R. N., *J. Biol. Chem.*, **240,** 3829 (1965).
9. Bryce, G. F., Roeske, R. W., and Gurd, F. R. N., *J. Biol. Chem.*, **240,** 3837 (1965).
10. Koltun, W. L., Dexter, R. N., Clark, R. E., and Gurd, F. R. N., *J. Am. Chem. Soc.*, **80,** 4188 (1958).
11. Nozaki, Y., Gurd, F. R. N., Chen, R. F., and Edsall, J. T., *J. Am. Chem. Soc.*, **79,** 2123 (1957).
12. Koltun, W. L., Roth, R. H., and Gurd, F. R. N., *J. Biol. Chem.*, **238,** 124 (1963).

13. Dobbie, H., and Kermack, W. O., *Biochem. J.*, **59**, 246 (1955).
14. Datta, S P., Leberman, R., and Rabin, B R., *Trans. Faraday Soc.*, **55**, 2141 (1959).
15. Hardman, K. D., Ph. D. thesis, Indiana University (1965).
16. Cann, J. R., *Proc. Nat. Acad. Sci. U. S.*, **50**, 368 (1963).
17. Hermans, J., Jr., and Rialdi, G., *Biochemistry*, **4**, 1277 (1965).
18. Sztankay, Z. G., Anderegg, J. W., and Beeman, W. W., *Abstr. Biophys. Soc. Meeting, San Francisco*, 1965, p. 145.
19. Krigbaum, W. R., and Brienne, R. T., *Nature*, **206**, 396 (1965).
20. Banaszak, L. J., Andrews, P. A., Burgner, J. W., Eylar, E. H., and Gurd, F. R. N., *J. Biol. Chem.*, **238**, 3307 (1963).
21. Banaszak, L. J., and Gurd, F. R. N., *J. Biol. Chem.*, **239**, 1836 (1964).
22. Banaszak, L. J., Watson, H. C., and Kendrew, J. C., *J. Mol. Biol.*, **12**, 130 (1965).

DISCUSSION

DR. MASON: I have recently been looking with EPR at copper bovine serum albumin systems, and I observed that there is a very profound change of EPR spectrum with pH, very consistent with the results reported by Dr. Breslow. There is no hyperfine structure at all, and so it's not possible from these studies to tell just what the ligands are. In other words, the changes are consistent with the titrimetric data, but there is no information in the spectrum to prove that the postulated ligands in this case at the high pH are imidazole and peptide nitrogens.

DR. BRESLOW: I postulated that the first copper which goes onto serum albumin binds to the α-amino and to the peptide nitrogen, and subsequent coppers at high pH were postulated to bind to imidazole and to peptide nitrogen.

DR. GURD: There is one interesting further aspect here for the protein chemists. I mentioned that the tertiary structure of metmyoglobin is seriously disrupted by the copper, but not fatally; it can recover. We have very recently been looking at a 24-membered peptide which was chopped out of ribonuclease by Shearer working with Brown at Wayne State. It was put into a helical conformation to a fair degree with a mixture of water and trifluoroethanol. If one adds copper to that, the helix is destroyed, as observed in the ultraviolet ORD curves, and is regained quantitatively by putting EDTA back in and pulling copper off. The effects in myoglobin match very closely the effects we have seen in these small models.

DR. BRESLOW: I would just like to comment on what appears to me to be a rather interesting difference between myoglobin and ribonuclease on the one hand, and serum albumin on the other. We have been looking at the interaction of Cu^{2+} ions with ribonuclease, and so far it appears to us that at neutral pH, Cu^{2+} ions interact with histidine side chains and peptide nitrogen atoms, as seems to occur also in myoglobin and the small peptides that Dr. Gurd is studying. With serum albumin, on the other hand, at neutral pH the first copper interacts with the α-amino and several peptide nitrogens, as we have published, but subsequent Cu^{2+} ions do not seem to show any involvement with peptide nitrogen atoms at neutral pH [Breslow, E., *J. Biol. Chem.*, **239**, 3252 (1964)]. This difference is rather puzzling to us, and if anyone has any comments on it, I would appreciate it, especially since albumin appears to be in many respects one of the more flexible proteins.

DR. GURD: Oh, heavens! One could bring up the point about limitations on motility of the chain, but it doesn't solve the problem.

DR. SARKAR: Dr. Breslow, I read your paper [*J. Biol. Chem.*, **239**, 3252 (1964)] very carefully and failed to see any mention of the extent of contamination of your albumin sample by copper. Thus, when you refer to the first binding of copper with albumin, I would like to know whether or not you have established your albumin sample to be free from copper prior to the addition of copper for the study of successive bindings. Even our purest sample of albumin has a certain amount of copper.

DR. BRESLOW: Well, if it was there, it should have shown up in the spectrum.

DR. MASON: On this point I have seen a small amount of copper contamination in high-purity bovine serum albumin using EPR, but it represents less than 20% of the first copper bound.

Electron Transport and Copper Proteins

R. J. P. WILLIAMS

Wadham College and Inorganic Chemistry Laboratory,
Oxford University,
Oxford, England

I. Organized Units in Biological Systems

The attention of biologists and biochemists is being drawn away from the function of individual active centers in enzymes to that of the interaction between such centers. In this connection it is interesting to consider the effects of metal ions, here of copper, on electron transport in organized biological units. Such copper-containing units are not uncommon. Chloroplasts, which contain plastocyanin, and the cytochrome chain unit, which contains copper in cytochrome c oxidase, are examples. However, as many so-called copper enzymes are of large molecular weight and contain many atoms of copper, they too can be thought of as organized units of active centers. These units can be compared with the organized units of iron atoms in systems such as are listed in Table I. It seems to me that it is the duty of the chemist to show what properties can arise from this organization of copper-containing units but would be absent from a single unit.

TABLE I

NONDIFFUSING REDOX COUPLES IN BIOLOGICAL SYSTEMS

System	Couple	Ligands
Cytochrome chain	Fe^{2+}–Fe^{3+}	Porphyrin^{2-}
	Fe^{2+}–Cu^{2+}	
Succinoxidase	Fe^{2+}–Fe^{3+}	RS_2^- (?)
Xanthine oxidase	Fe^{2+}–Fe^{3+}	RS_2^- (?)
	Mo^{5+}–Mo^{6+}	(?)
Ferredoxin	Fe^{2+}–Fe^{3+}	RS_2^- (?)
Ceruloplasmin	Cu^+–Cu^{2+}	Special ligand (?)
Ascorbic acid oxidase	Cu^+–Cu^{2+}	Special ligand (?)
Laccase	Cu^+–Cu^{2+}	Special ligand (?)
Plastocyanins	Cu^+–Cu^{2+} and connected to other metals of chloroplast?	Special ligand (?)
Chloroplasts	General connection between metal centers? (Fe, Mn, Cu).	Special ligand (?)

Transport of electrons or atoms in a particular sequence is one possibility. In a previous paper (1) we have shown how electron transport has been studied recently in iron-containing systems. The same approach will be used here in the discussion of the copper systems. The main methods are the examination of (a) charge-transfer spectra in complexes and solids, (b) electrical conductivity in solids, and (c) photoconductivity in solids. The solid state physics of materials that contain inorganic complex ions is almost an untouched field.

II. Spectra of Charge-Transfer Complexes

First, a few remarks will be made about charge-transfer interactions in units containing single copper atoms. Details will be found in a number of papers (cf. Ref. (2)). Cuprous complexes have intense charge-transfer bands at long wavelength when the ligand combined with the copper is a good acceptor, i.e., strongly oxidizing. Examples are given in Table II.

TABLE II

CHARGE-TRANSFER BANDS IN Cu^+ COMPLEXES

Ligand	Absorption maximum (mμ)
(a) Model Compounds	
2, 2'-Bipyridine	450
o-Phenanthroline	450
Dimethylglyoximate	~425
Nitric oxide (NO^+–Cu^+)	~600
(b) Proteins	
Hemocyanin	375
	600 (with O_2)

Cupric complexes have intense charge-transfer bands at long wavelength when in combination with good donors, i.e., reducing ligands. Examples are given in Table III. These *localized* excitations will not of themselves lead to electron transport However, it is a general experience that the more delocalized an electron, or a hole, at its own exciton[1] center the higher the mobility of this electron or hole. Thus charge-transfer excited states of com-

---

[1] An exciton is a region of excitation characterized by the separation of positive and negative charges by a small distance. The exciton may or may not be free to move from molecule to molecule.

TABLE III

Charge-Transfer Bands of Cu^{2+} Complexes

Ligand	Absorption maximum (mμ)
(a) Model Compounds	
(2,9-dimethyl-o-phenanthroline)Cl$_2$	350
(2,9-dimethyl-o-phenanthroline)Br$_2$	400
Dithiocarbamate	500
Thiols	450 (?)
Thiocyanate	375
Azide	370
Benzimidazole anion	400
(b) Proteins	
Ascorbic acid oxidase	606
Ceruloplasmin	605
Laccase	615
Pseudomonas aeruginosa blue protein	630
Rhus vernicifera blue protein	605
Plastocyanin	597
Bordetella blue protein	625

plexes should lead to electron transport more readily than do their ground states. The extent to which the electron transport possibilities enter into the ground state will depend on the mixing of the charge transfer states into the ground state, which is an inverse function of the energy of the excited state. Electron transport phenomena are there best sought in copper complexes which show low lying excited states and in which electrons are delocalized, e.g., by ligands such as imine nitrogen (low-lying π or π^* orbitals) and RS (low-lying d orbitals).

A further possibility, charge transfer to next nearest neighbors, arises when both a reduced metal ion and its oxidized form are present in the same compound, e.g., Fe$_3$O$_4$ contains Fe^{2+} and Fe^{3+} as next nearest neighbors. Several examples are known in inorganic systems. One of these, (CuCl$_5$)$_x^{3-}$(CuCl$_4$)$_{1-x}^{3-}$(Co(NH$_3$)$_6$)$^{3+}$, where x is the ratio of Cu^{2+} to total Cu, has been studied by us in detail.

The spectra of the compounds with $x = 0.0, 0.5$, and 1.0 are shown in Fig. 1. There are d-d bands due to (Co(NH$_3$)$_6$)$^{3+}$ at 360 mμ and (CuCl$_5$)$^{3-}$ above 1,000 mμ, and there is the internal charge-transfer band of (CuCl$_5$)$^{3-}$ below 400 mμ. In addition, in the $x = 0.5$ compound, there is strong ab-

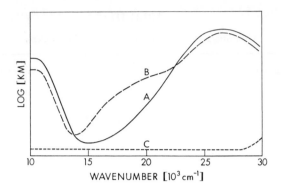

FIG. 1. (A) The optical absorption spectrum of $(CuCl_5)^{3-}(Co(NH_3)_6)^{3+}$. (B) The optical absorption spectrum of $(CuCl_5)_{0.5}{}^{3-}(CuCl_4)_{0.5}{}^{3-}(Co(NH_3)_6)^{3+}$. (C) The absorption spectrum of Cs_3CuCl_4.

sorption at $\sim$450–600 mμ. This absorption depends on x as shown in Fig. 2. That it is due to $Cu^+ \rightarrow Cu^{2+}$ electron jumps is shown by plotting the logarithm of the Kubelka–Munk function, which is proportional to the absorption intensity, against x, the mole fraction of Cu^{2+}. The Kubelka–Munk function, KM, is defined as $(1 - R)^2/2R$, where R is the reflection coefficient. Similar charge transfer bands arise in a number of solids containing copper (or other metals) in two valence states.

Apart from making references to model compounds in Tables II and III,

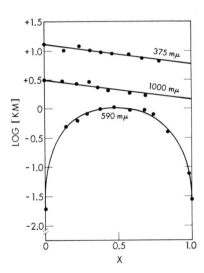

FIG. 2. The relationship between the absorbance, expressed by the Kubelka–Munk function (KM), and x, the fraction of Cu^+ in $(CuCl_5)_x^{3-}$ $(CuCl_4)_{1-x}^{3-}$ $(Co(NH_3)_6)^{3+}$.

we have attempted to indicate there the origin of the main absorption bands in copper proteins. None appear to be due to $Cu^+ \rightarrow Cu^{2+}$ charge transfer despite the fact that several contain both Cu^+ and Cu^{2+}. On this basis it seems improbable that the copper atoms are *very* close together, i.e., the Cu^+-to-Cu^{2+} distance must be greater than 5 Å.

In the next two sections we describe some observations on electron transport in solids before returning to the biological systems. The first section is devoted to thermally activated electron transport and the second to photoactivated transport. In the discussion of thermally activated electron transport we shall divide observations according to the divisions usually discussed in solution electron-transfer reactions. We then have as possible transport mechanisms,

(a) $M \rightarrow M$, electron jump.
(b) $(M - X) \rightarrow (Y - M)$, outer-sphere transport.
(c) $(M - X) \rightarrow M$, inner-sphere transport.
(d) $(M - X) \cdots (Z)_n \cdots (Y - M)$, long-range transport.

Examples of direct electron exchange in copper systems are very rare. Possible cases arise in such lattices as oxygen-deficient Cu_2O, which is a good semiconductor. The M-M electron transfer is between the copper atoms of the two different nets, one shaded, the other open, in Fig. 3.

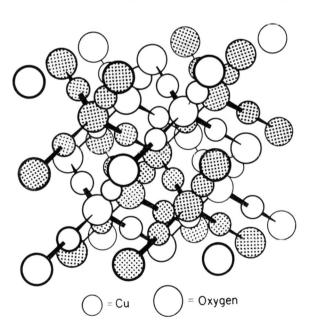

$\bigcirc$ = Cu $\bigcirc$ = Oxygen

Fig. 3. The structure of Cu_2O showing the two nets.

III. Thermally-Activated Electron Transfer

A. Inner-Sphere Electron Transfer

There are only one or two examples of the study of inner-sphere transport involving Cu^{2+} ions. We have examined (3) conduction in cubic $KCu^{2+}(Co(CN)_6)^{3-}$, and we and others have studied copper phthalocyanin (Fig. 4) (4). In the first case excitation to Cu^{3+} and $(Co(CN)_6)^{4-}$ is the most likely cause of conduction, and the very high activation energy ($\sim$35 Kcal) of the conductivity of $KCu(Co(CN)_6)$ is undoubtedly caused by the very high energy of this excitation. In the second case dispropor-

```
        Cu
        ⋮
N———N—Cu—N———N
        ⋮       ⋮
        N———N—Cu—N———N
                        ⋮
                        Cu
```

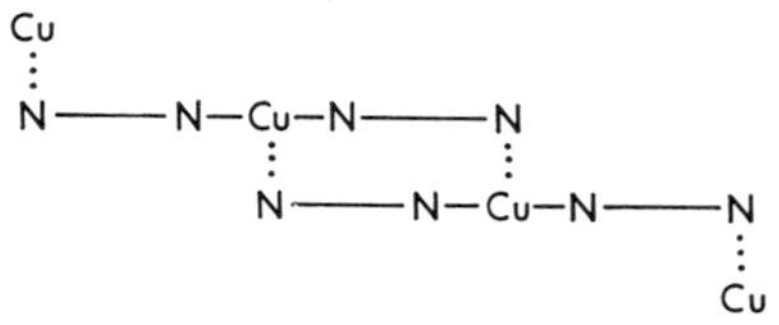

Fig. 4. An outline structure of Cu^{2+} phthalocyanin. The central nitrogen atoms of one organic molecule are coordinated to each copper which has two more distant nitrogen atoms which are *meso*-bridge groups.

tionation is required of $2Cu^{2+}$ to $Cu^{+} + Cu^{3+}$. These states can be given alternative formulation as phthalocyanin radical ions. Again this excitation is of very high energy and presumably causes the high activation energy of conduction, $\sim$30 Kcal. In order to lower the activation energy a more polarizable ligand system adjacent to the Cu^{2+} ion is required, but so far we have not found a good system to study. Alternatively the Cu^{+} ion could be crystallized in a lattice with a good oxidizing agent as anion; cf. $Tl_3(Fe(CN)_6)$, which is a good semiconductor (3).

B. Outer-Sphere Electron Transfer

Here we have an excellent model system, $(CuCl_5)_x(CuCl_4)_{(1-x)}(Co(NH_3)_6)$. We have studied the change in conduction of this system with x. Figure 5 shows the results, and in Fig. 6 we compare the intensity of the charge-transfer band (see Fig. 2) and the conductivity. The relationship is excellent, showing that conduction owes its origin to the Cu^{+}–Cu^{2+} exchange excitation. The activation energy ($\sim$15 Kcal) is independent of x for 0.1 to 0.9, which shows that the initial charge transfer is effectively localized between two copper ions of different charge. Thus a "hopping" conduction model is appropriate (1) The fact that the energy of the charge-transfer band (here 30 Kcal) is much greater than the activation energy for con-

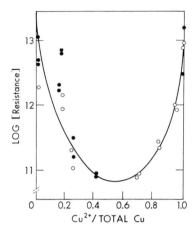

FIG. 5. The relationship between the resistance of $(CuCl_5)^{3-}_x(CuCl_4)^{3-}_{1-x}(Co(NH_3)_6)^{3+}$ and the composition. Open points are for measurements on single crystals while closed points are for measurements on powders.

duction (here 15 Kcal) is common to many systems in which hopping of electrons best describes mobility.

It should be clear that both here and in the inner-sphere systems the activation energies observed in single crystals are high. In order that rapid exchange of electrons (or rapid transport of atoms) should take place, as is observed in a biological system, the ease of electron transport must be increased. This will be achieved, we believe, by combining the metal atoms with polarizable ligands such that the complex has low-lying charge-transfer states; see Tables II and III.

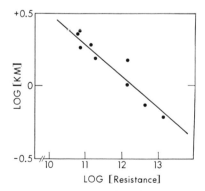

FIG. 6. The relationship between the absorbance at 590 mμ, expressed by the Kubelka–Munk function, and the resistance of the mixed (Cu$^+$–Cu^{2+}) compound.

C. Long-Range Electron Transfer

There are two possible mechanisms of long-range transfer. The most frequently postulated is transfer in a delocalized energy level as in metal conductors. I do not think this mechanism is probable in proteins, and we have no new evidence about it. The second mechanism involves hydrogen atom transfer, e.g.,

(a) $Cu^{2+}\ OH^-\cdots H_2O\cdots H_2O\ Cu^+$,
(b) $Cu^+\ OH^\bullet\cdots\cdots H_2O\cdots H_2O\ Cu^+$,
(c) $Cu^+\ OH_2\cdots OH^\bullet\cdots H_2O\ Cu^+$,
(d) $Cu^+\ OH_2\cdots OH_2\cdots HO^\bullet Cu^+$,
(e) $Cu^+\ OH_2\cdots OH_2\cdots HO^- Cu^{2+}$.

This mechanism has now been studied by several workers for Fe^{2+}–Fe^{3+} exchange in ice (5). It has been examined by us in iron silicates (6). It has not been deliberately studied yet in the case of copper complexes. Several facts make it worth detailed investigation. The only well-studied fast exchange between copper ions is that of the cuprous complex $(CuCl_4)^{3-}$ with Cu^{2+}–chloride complexes. It has a second-order rate constant of approximately 10^8 l mole^{-1} sec^{-1}. This is not a reasonable value if the activation energy is 15 Kcal or greater, as it appears to be for these complexes in the solid state (see above), for both cations are in anionic complexes. In such a case a high opposing entropy of activation is expected. It is worth asking if the electron exchange in solution goes via the solvent, as we have suggested for certain Fe^{2+} reactions. The postulate is open to simple experimental test in ice, and we are now investigating this possibility with a large number of complexes.

If this mechanism turns out to be correct, the functional significance of the multi-metal-atom enzymes becomes more pointed. For example, it appears that ceruloplasmin, laccase, and ascorbic acid oxidase contain copper in two oxidation states. The function of the two copper atoms is different, and some of the copper undergoes redox cycling. This is reasonable if part of the copper is involved as a binding center for a two-electron reagent, O_2, while the other undergoes one-electron cycles, e.g.,

(a) $O_2\ Cu^+\cdots(H_2O)\cdots Cu^{2+}$ substrate,
(b) $O_2\ Cu^+\cdots(H_2O)\cdots Cu^+$ substrate,$^\bullet$
(c) $O_2^-\ Cu^+\cdots(H_2O)\cdots Cu^{2+}$ + second substrate molecule,
(d) $O_2^-\ Cu^+\cdots(H_2O)\cdots Cu^+$ + substrate,$^\bullet$
(e) $O_2^{2-}\ Cu^+\cdots(H_2O)\cdots Cu^{2+}$,

and so on. A very similar mechanism is possible for Cu^{2+} in cytochrome c oxidase, indeed for all the iron atoms in the cytochrome chain, and for the different metal atoms in dehydrogenases such as xanthine oxidase. The intermediate hydrogen atom carrier need not be H_2O but can be any group, RH.

IV. Photoconduction

We have studied the photoconduction of two copper-containing systems (7). The first is copper phthalocyanin. The absorption spectrum and the response curve are shown in Fig. 7. The first point of interest is that the photoresponse follows the absorption very closely. The detail of the spectrum at long wavelength (i.e., beyond the first $\pi \rightarrow \pi^*$ singlet) is exactly parallelled in the photoresponse. We are not certain of the origin of the absorption at the long wavelengths. The work of Sharp and Schneider (8) on the photoconduction of triplet states in anthracene has shown that absorption in the triplet region can lead to photoconduction. In anthracene the efficiency of the photoresponse is 30 times as great in the triplet as in the singlet region. A similar ratio is found between the efficiency of absorption (in terms of photoresponse) in the singlet region as compared with the infrared region of copper phthalocyanin. The photoconduction is also extremely sensitive to added gases (e.g., O_2), as is the thermally activated electron transport. These gas effects are now being studied extensively. The simplest interpretation of the results is that the conductivity, which is a movement of electrons from one complex to a complex adjacent to it, is greatly enhanced by defects. Occluded gases such as O_2 can act as effective electron traps permitting positive hole migration. Be this as it may,

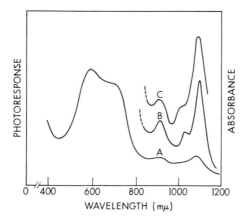

Fig. 7. Photoresponse (A), and, on a magnified scale, (C), of Cu^{2+} phthalocyanin and (B) the absorption spectrum of Cu^{2+} sulfonated phthalocyanin, in dimethylacetamide, at long wavelength.

the metal phthalocyanins are hardly suitable as models for chloroplasts and mitochondria, as, in particular, there is no evidence that the porphyrin units in the latter are in a crystalline alignment, which permits *direct* electron transfer from one unit to the next, in these biological systems.

V. Intermolecular Charge Transfer

Chloroplasts are complex units of (a) photoreceptors and (b) charge-transfer systems for directing the photon energy from electron or atom transport to chemical energy (9). The "chains" of units are roughly

(a)   Chlorophyll a_I (cytochrome f) $\rightarrow$ ferredoxin $\rightarrow$ NADP or NAD;
(b)   Chlorophyll a_{II} $\rightarrow$ plastoquinone (?) $\rightarrow$ cytochrome f.

In these chains there are (a) diamagnetic chelates such as magnesium chlorophyll (acting as photoreceptors), (b) species, such as quinones, that have good electron acceptor properties, and (c) paramagnetic metal chelates such as plastocyanin Cu^{2+}, ferredoxin Fe^{3+}, cytochrome f Fe^{3+}, and cytochrome $b_6 Fe^{3+}$. It is not unusual to suggest that the electrons generated by light absorption are trapped first on one or another of these paramagnetic centers. We have attempted to set up a model system for this type of reaction. The model contains molecules which are analogs of each of the three classes of biologically active molecules.

A. Spectra

The first step is to produce single crystals containing both a metal chelate and an acceptor molecule (10). This can be done by crystallizing a metal

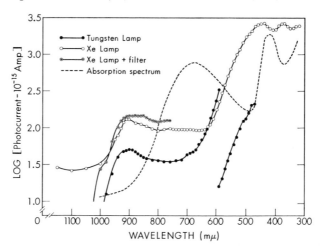

FIG. 8. Photoresponse of Pd^{2+}(bis-8-hydroxyquinolinate)–chloranil measured by different methods and the absorption spectrum of the compound.

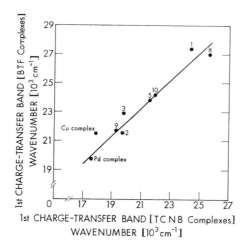

Fɪɢ. 9. The relationship between the first charge-transfer bands of tetracyanobenzene (TCNB) and benztrifuroxan (BTF) complexes with metal complex and other donors. The latter are numbered as follows: (1) naphthalene, (2) anthracene, (3) pyrene, (5) chrysene, (8) diphenyl, (9) azulene, (10) β-naphthol.

8-hydroxyquinolinate (also called oxinate) with, say, trinitrobenzene. The metals that can be so used are those giving square coplanar complexes, i.e., Cu^{2+}, Ni^{2+}, and Pd^{2+}. The spectrum of the complex of Pd^{2+}-oxinate–chloranil is shown in Fig. 8. There is a low-energy charge-transfer band. The energy of the charge-transfer band of the metal-chelate–acceptor complexes behaves exactly like that in simpler organic charge-transfer donor–acceptor systems. Thus Fig. 9 plots the energy of the charge-transfer bands of two acceptors for the same range of donors. The linear correlation implies that nothing very new has been introduced by the metal ion. It should be noted, however, that the use of a metal as a substituent in the *middle* of a donor or acceptor is a much more subtle change than the usual method of substituting organic groups in charge-transfer systems.

B. Crystal Structure

Systems of particular interest to us are those of Pd^{2+}-oxinate–chloranil and Cu^{2+}-oxinate–chloranil. The crystal structures, both determined by Kamenar *et al.*, are identical (11). Figure 10 shows the relative positions of the metal-chelate donor and the chloranil acceptor. The large donor molecules form an open network in which the smaller chloranil molecules sit. Both the palladium and copper are in a square coplanar environment with next nearest (octahedral) neighbors some 3.5 Å away. Each donor metal-oxinate molecule has 10 near neighbors of its own kind. Now we have found that the Cu^{2+} oxinate can be substituted for the Pd^{2+} oxinate in Pd^{2+}-oxin-

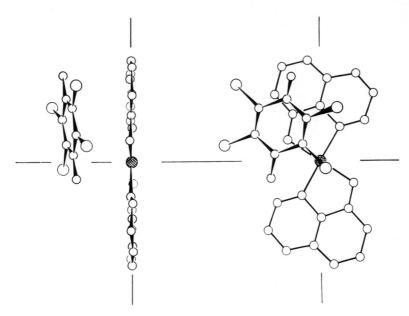

FiG. 10. The structure of the Pd^{2+}(bis-8-hydroxyquinolinate)–chloranil complex. The metal atom, shaded, can be replaced by Cu^{2+}.

ate–chloranil to any required degree. The amount of Cu^{2+} taken into the crystal is strictly proportional to and very nearly in the same ratio as the relative amounts of Cu and Pd in solution. This strongly suggests the Cu occupies the Pd sites randomly. This has been confirmed by EPR studies. Thus at 10% Cu in Pd each Pd^{2+} has one Cu^{2+} and nine Pd^{2+} near neighbors.

Before describing the photoconductivity of these systems, I should like

TABLE IV

PARALLELS BETWEEN CHLOROPLASTS, CYTOCHROME CHAINS, AND A MODEL COMPLEX

System	Donor: diamagnetic chelate	Trap: paramagnetic chelate	Acceptor: quinone
Chloroplasts	Mg chlorophyll	Cu^{2+}, Fe^{3+}	Various quinones
Model	Pd oxinate	Cu^{2+}	Chloranil
Cytochrome chain	Cytochrome in Fe^{2+} state	Cytochrome in Fe^{3+} state and Cu^{2+}	Various quinones

to call to your attention in Table IV to some parallels in structure between the cytochrome chains, chloroplasts, and the strictly ordered Cu-doped, Pd-oxinate–chloranil crystals.[2]

C. Photoconductivity

We now turn to the conductivity of the single crystals. Single crystals of Pd^{2+} oxinate itself have quite a good dark conductivity and show a photoresponse at wavelengths around 600 mμ where light absorption is feeble. The fact that the units of Pd oxinate can support electron transport is important in what follows. Cu^{2+} oxinate has a very low dark current and shows a poor photoresponse. Thus electrons do not become mobile on excitation in copper oxinate.

The Pd^{2+}-oxinate–chloranil crystal also has a considerable dark current. It shows two photoresponse regions which are only somewhat remotely related to the absorption spectrum of the charge-transfer complex (Fig. 8). The photoresponse is then totally unlike that in the metal-phthalocyanin systems in which photoresponse accurately follows the absorption spectrum. In this first case there is a linear relationship between photocurrent, i, and absorption; $i = k\epsilon_\lambda$, where ϵ_λ is the extinction coefficient at the wavelength λ. In the case of the charge-transfer systems the relationship is more like

$$i_\lambda = \frac{k_1 \epsilon_\lambda}{1 + k_2 \epsilon_\lambda}$$

This type of relationship has been observed in other systems and explained as follows. The rate of generation of current carriers, A*, depends on the concentration of excitons; e, i.e., $d[A^*]/dt = k_1[e]$. Removal of current carriers depends on transport to the electrodes, $k_2[A^*]$, and collision between the carrier and an exciton, $k_3 e[A^*]$. Now e is proportional to the extinction coefficient ϵ_λ and in the steady state

$$k_1[e] = k_2[A^*] + k_3[e][A^*] = k\epsilon_\lambda$$

The photocurrent is given by

$$i_\lambda = k_2[A^*] = \frac{k_2 k_1[e]}{k_2 + k_3[e]} = \frac{k_2 k \epsilon_\lambda}{k_2 + k_3 k \epsilon_\lambda / k_1}$$

If k_3 is very small, the copper phthalocyanin situation holds, $i_\lambda = k\epsilon_\lambda$, but if k_3 is much greater than k_1 and k_2 then, at high $[e]$, i falls to very low

[2] In what follows the imagination may be stretched a little, but it would be a pity not to put our observations against the background of an obvious biological system.

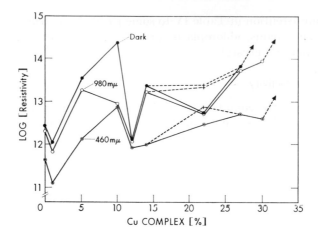

FIG. 11. The changes in the resistance of single crystals of Pd^{2+}(bis-8-hydroxy-quinolinate)–chloranil as Pd^{2+} is replaced by Cu^{2+}. Note the rapid changes around 10% Cu^{2+}.

values. In some cases large photocurrents are only seen in regions of light absorption on the *edges* of absorption bands. Apparently the charge-transfer crystals fall in this class.

Doping the Pd^{2+}-oxinate–chloranil system with increasing amounts of Cu^{2+} oxinate results in the patterns of change of dark current and photocurrent in the two sensitive regions that are shown in Fig. 11. The graph can be explained by assuming the pattern of energy states of Fig. 12. Charge-transfer excitation by light is easier energetically in the Pd compound. However, the Cu compound can relax to a Cu^{3+} oxinate, so stabilizing (trapping) the positive charge and leaving the negative charge on the chloranil. Let us suppose that both negative and positive charges are able to migrate through the Pd-oxinate–chloranil system. Doping of the Pd

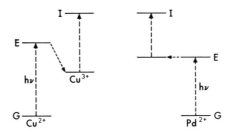

FIG. 12. A possible scheme of energy levels in Cu^{2+}-doped, Pd^{2+}(bis-8-hydroxy-quinolinate)–chloranil. G is the ground state, E the exciton state, and I the ionized state in the crystal.

system with small amounts of Cu^{2+} permits an easier charge separation, ionization of an exciton, so that there will be more negative mobile carriers in the Pd-oxinate–chloranil net although positive carriers are removed. Upon increase of the Cu concentration, the negatively charged species, $(Pd^+$-oxinate–chloranil$)^-$, will increasingly find itself with a neighboring Cu^{3+} species until, at 10% Cu, every Pd has one such Cu neighbor. At this point resistance is a maximum, for excitons will again be ionized only with difficulty.

D. Analogy with Biological Systems

Consider the light this system throws on a possible mechanism of action of chloroplasts. Light is initially absorbed by the magnesium chlorophyll. This light is transferred to a place in which the chlorophyll a_{II} is adjacent to an acceptor, such as plastoquinone, or chlorophyll a_I is adjacent to an alternative acceptor. This juxtaposition permits the conversion of the photon energy into an ion-pair "exciton" of the same kind as the exciton of $(Pd^+$-oxinate–chloranil$)^-$. The negative or positive charges will migrate to suitable trapping centers such as plastocyanin or ferredoxin (electron or H^- traps) and reduced cytochrome f (positive hold trap). The parallel is with electron migration to a Cu^{3+} oxinate. Unlike the present model, the biological system can now use these trapped oxidation states in chemical redox reactions. Thus reduced ferredoxin can be coupled to a hydrogenase for NAD or NADP reduction. Plastocyanin can be readily reoxidized by a great number of electron acceptors and is indeed entirely comparable with such enzymes as ascorbic acid oxidase.

In conclusion I believe that chemists and biologists should increase their interest in organized chemical reactions so as to unveil the importance of organization in biology. I have no doubt that copper ions play a major role in these reactions. However, it is not only the reactions at the organized centers which are so important, but also the processes of migration of atoms and energy which are so fundamentally linked to energy storage in biology. In this respect I should like to stress again the possibility that both in oxidative phosphorylation and in photophosphorylation it could well be that the hydrogen atom plays an essential role (12).

VI. Summary

Many of the biological systems in which copper occurs have more than one metal atom in them and these metal atoms are coupled together in oxidation-reduction reactions. We consider the nature of this coupling, taking, in the first instance, model copper-containing compounds in the solid state and considering how electrons migrate from one copper atom to another. Both thermally activated and photoactivated conduction are analyzed. Comparison of the systems with known organized biological systems makes it probable that the conduction of redox equivalents in a biological system occurs through an initial intermolecular charge-transfer mechanism. The importance of this mechanism in biological systems is briefly examined.

ACKNOWLEDGMENTS

I wish to thank my colleagues, Dr. P. Day, (especially) Mr. D. Culpin, Mr. P. Edwards, and Dr. J. Wright for their efforts, and the Medical Research Council for financial support.

REFERENCES

1. Williams, R. J. P., *in* A. San Pietro, (ed.), "Non-heme iron proteins: role in energy conversion," Antioch Press, Yellow Springs, Ohio, 1965, p. 7.
2. Brill, A. S., Martin, R. B., and Williams, R. J. P., *in* B. Pullman (ed.), "Electronic aspects of biochemistry," Academic Press Inc., New York, 1964, p. 519 and references.
3. Braterman, P. S., Phipps, P. B. P., and Williams, R. J. P., *J. Chem. Soc.*, p. 6164 (1965).
4. Terenin, A., *Proc. Chem. Soc.*, p. 321 (1961); Day, P., and Williams, R. J. P., *J. Chem. Phys.*, **37**, 567 (1962).
5. Horne, R. A., *J. Inorg. Nucl. Chem.*, **25**, 1139 (1963).
6. Littler, J. S., and Williams, R. J. P., *J. Chem. Soc.*, p. 6368 (1965).
7. Day, P., and Williams, R. J. P., *J. Chem. Phys.*, **42**, 4049 (1965).
8. Sharp, J. H., and Schneider, W. G., *J. Chem. Phys.*, **41**, 3657 (1964).
9. Calvin, M., *in* Bowen, E. J., (ed.), "Recent progress in photobiology," Blackwell, Oxford, 1965, p. 225.
10. Bailey, A. S., Williams, R. J. P., and Wright, J. D., *J. Chem. Soc.*, p. 2579 (1965).
11. Kamenar, B., Prout, C. K., and Wright, J. D., *J. Chem. Soc.* p. 4851 (1965).
12. Williams, R. J. P., *J. Theoret. Biol.*, **1**, 1 (1961); **3**, 209 (1962).

DISCUSSION

Dr. HEMMERICH: As I pointed out, we had instead of the chloride ions, mercaptide ions, and we got long —CuSCuS— chains in which the copper was in the reduced state. I would be interested in whether Dr. Williams could say anything about the possible conductivity mechanism with this type of ligand, and whether one has to assume that, under certain conditions and certain ligands, the activation energy might go down, so that we would have a delocalization of electrons. If you have a Cu^{2+} in a former Cu^+ center, might not the valence state be indeterminable?

Dr. WILLIAMS: Oh, yes. I think in a sense it's obviously the case. You use a very highly polarizable ligand, and you put it near the metal ion. If you take $(Co(CN)_6)^{3-}$ and crystallize it with any bivalent metal ion you like, from manganese through the periodic table to zinc, you will get compounds of the same crystal structure. If you now study the activation energy for conduction in the compounds, you find that the minimum energy comes with the most readily oxidizable of these ions, the Fe^{2+} ion. The activation energy, in fact, follows the pattern of the ionization potential, $M^{2+} \rightarrow M^{3+}$. So we want to do two things to make conduction occur easily over atoms AB. One wants to make sure that one partner, A, is a good donor and the other partner, B, is a good acceptor, and that any ligand in between them has a very strong overlap with both. Then, of course, one will get reasonably good conductivity. A second system that illustrates that is thallous ferricyanide. It might not look very like a biological molecule, but it is a fine conductor.

DR. MASON: But the Mössbauer experiments in ferrous ferricyanide show that one can still differentiate both valences.

DR. WILLIAMS: One can still differentiate the valence states in a case like this. It is really the mobility of the electron that is important. Hall effect measurements show that the electrons are hopping from site to site in $Tl_3Fe(CN)_6$. However, it won't be very long, I think, before we get systems of this charge-transfer kind where we can get a metal, i.e., a substance with high electron mobility. We do know already that the lithium-molybdenum blues are metallic. They show not an increase in conduction with an increase in temperature, but a decrease, and that could be explained by saying that the electron is more or less delocalized.

DR. CAUGHEY: In regard to your model of the chloroplast, I was interested in your assumption that the chlorophyll molecule must be diamagnetic. While that's a reasonable assumption, I wonder if this is necessarily true in the milieu of the chloroplast where there are quinones and other potential participants in donor-acceptor complex interactions around.

Also, you are dealing with a palladium complex in the model and a magnesium complex in the chloroplast—they are quite different.

DR. WILLIAMS: Yes, of course they are quite different. I wouldn't like to claim that this is the real mechanism. After all, all I can do is throw at you some ways of thinking about a chloroplast, but I don't want to give the impression that this is a chloroplast.

DR. MASON: I just wanted to ask whether a chloroplast is a semiconductor.

DR. WILLIAMS: If I may say so, that, I am afraid, is not relevant, because all the ideas I am suggesting are only relevant to a rather small region of the chloroplast. There are a lot of magnesium molecules and odd copper and some quinones. You can't really find out, by conductivity measurements, anything about chloroplasts.

DR. HAMILTON: If you generate the hydroxyl radical in aqueous solution, it does not exchange with water, so I would suggest that such a mechanism is not likely.

DR. WILLIAMS: Simple aqueous hydroxy radicals will not exchange?

DR. HAMILTON: Not with water, because if you generate an hydroxyl radical from ^{18}O-labeled hydrogen peroxide, it will not exchange with water. You get, for example, ^{18}O-labeled phenol from benzene in aqueous solution.

DR. WILLIAMS: What you are saying is that you need a more preferred route in order to make a long-range mechanism work.

DR. HAMILTON: Yes.

DR. WILLIAMS: You would have to have a preferred route through a set of substances like semiquinones. If you had semiquinones instead of water, you would probably get that as a preferred route.

DR. MASON: As a postscript, unquestionably the simple conductivity of chloroplasts might not be that irrelevant, because a chloroplast is pretty highly ordered, and, according to the quantasome idea, exists like a crystal.

DR. WILLIAMS: The trouble with making a measurement of this kind on the chloroplast is that you have so little idea of the meaning of the result in terms of the system you are trying to discuss. So what's the point of starting with the measurement?

DR. BLUMBERG: I might suggest a way to getting over Dr. Williams' objection to putting two electrodes inside a chloroplast: use microwave techniques which have been developed for measuring conductivity on an extremely local scale in the solid state [Snowden, D. P., and Portis, A. M., *Phys. Rev.*, **120**, 1983 (1960)]. Perhaps if it warrants the investment, such a technique could be developed for chloroplasts.

DR. MALMSTRÖM: We are moving a little away from copper. Don't you also want to say how copper proteins work?

DR. WILLIAMS: No. I don't want to say that, but I would like biologists to try to test a mechanism in some system. It's a very simple mechanism, and it has been proposed many times by others apart from myself. This is the long-range electron transfer illustrated in Section III, C of my paper. Consider a separated hydrated pair of one cupric and one cuprous ion and put a hydroxide ion on the cupric. Charge transfer can proceed from Cu^{2+} to hydroxide, giving an hydroxide radical, and then a water molecule lying in between Cu^{2+} and Cu^+ gives a hydrogen *atom* to that radical. And so on, until an hydroxide radical comes in contact with the cuprous ion. The last step is that the electron is transferred from the Cu^+ so that one gets Cu^{2+} and OH^-. Thus you see the whole system is completely symmetrical, and electron transfer over a distance takes place. How could you test this?

Catalysis of Carbon Dioxide Hydration by Cupric Chelates[*]

ESTHER BRESLOW

Department of Biochemistry,
Cornell University Medical College,
New York, New York

I. Carbonic Anhydrase Action

The uncatalyzed reaction between CO_2 and H_2O to give carbonic acid proceeds relatively slowly at neutral pH and is physiologically catalyzed by carbonic anhydrase. Mammalian carbonic anhydrase contains one mole of tightly bound zinc ion and studies of the effect of inhibitors suggest that zinc is at the active site (1). A number of oxy-anions have long been known to catalyze CO_2 hydration (2); by analogy with this and the known rapid reaction of hydroxide ion with CO_2 to give bicarbonate, a Zn-bound hydroxide ion has sometimes been invoked to explain the mechanism of the enzymatic reaction (3, 4).

We were interested in studying the mechanism of carbonic anhydrase action. The simplicity of the substrates, together with the availability of known inorganic catalysts, suggested that a fruitful approach would be to study the factors which determine the catalytic effectiveness of simple model systems. This approach was also given support by the demonstration that the tetrammine complexes of Zn^{2+} and Cu^{2+} were effective catalysts of CO_2 hydration, although not nearly as potent as the enzyme itself (5, 6). The system of greatest potential interest is an hydroxy-zinc chelate. Relatively few hydroxy-zinc chelates are known, however, and so we turned initially to the study of chelates of cupric ion. In particular, we were interested in the catalytic effectiveness of the 1:1 chelate of Cu^{2+} ion with glycylglycine. CuGG[1] dissociates a proton from a bound H_2O with a pK of 9.37 at 25° (7) and, like carbonic anhydrase,[2] the species CuGGOH⁻ has been shown to catalyze the hydrolysis of *p*-nitrophenylacetate (7). For comparison, homologous Cu^{2+} chelates in which the H_2O ionization was

* Supported by Grant No. HE–02739 from the National Institutes of Health.

[1] The following abbreviations are used: GG, glycylglycine; GGG, glycylglycylglycine; GGGG, glycylglycylglycylglycine; VG, L-valylglycine; GGEt, glycylglycine ethyl ester. CuGG, CuGGG, CuGGGG, CuVG, and CuGGEt represent the 1 : 1 cupric ion chelates of GG, GGG, GGGG, VG, and GGEt, respectively. CuGGOH⁻ represents that species of CuGG which contains a bound OH⁻ group; CuGG° is the conjugate acid of CuGGOH⁻.

[2] Pocker, Y. and Meany, J. E., presented at the Sixth International Congress of Biochemistry, New York, 1964.

absent were studied as well. These studies then represent an initial probe into the catalytic activity of a variety of Cu^{2+} chelates and ultimately of chelates of Zn^{2+} ion as well.

II. Experimental Procedure

A. Reagents

All reagents were analytical grade unless otherwise specified. Standard cupric ion solutions were prepared as previously described (8). Glycylglycine, glycylglycylglycine, glycylglycylglycylglycine, and glycylglycine ethyl ester were obtained from Nutritional Biochemicals Corp. The compounds appeared pure by H^+ ion titration and no effect of recrystallization upon activity was observed. Chromatographically pure L-valylglycine was obtained from Mann Laboratories.

B. Measurement of CO_2 Hydration

Because of the complexities of metallochelate-H^+ ion equilibria, it was necessary that the system used to measure rates of CO_2 hydration allow measurement at constant pH and in the absence of any buffer that might compete for the added metal ion. It was also important that the system allow a ready distinction between catalysis of CO_2 hydration and any noncatalytic interaction between the added metallochelate and CO_2 such as carbamate formation. It seemed less important that the system give highly accurate rate constants than that it give self-consistent data. A pH-stat system was chosen which allowed measurement of CO_2 hydration rates between pH 7 and 9; above pH 9, the rate of the uncatalyzed reaction became too fast for catalysis to be measured precisely. The procedure was as follows: 4 ml of the test solution was placed in an open vessel immersed in an ice bath; glass and calomel electrodes and an NaOH delivery tube connected to a Radiometer pH-stat were introduced along with a fritted disk gas inlet. When the temperature inside the vessel had fallen to 0°, continuous passage of CO_2 at constant pressure and flow rate was begun and the rate of NaOH addition necessary to maintain constant pH was recorded. Rapid equilibration of the gas and solution phases was insured by the fritted disk inlet tube and constant magnetic stirring. Studies at varying CO_2 flow rates and partial pressures showed that under the conditions used the rate of diffusion of CO_2 from the gas phase into solution was not limiting. At pH 8 and 9, in the absence of side reactions, a constant rate of NaOH delivery with time was observed. At these pH values, the back-reaction of HCO_3^- with H^+ ion to give CO_2 could be neglected during the early phases of the run and the observed rate per milliliter of solution could be written as:

$$\frac{d[HCO_3^-]}{dt} = k_{H_2O}[CO_2] + k_{OH^-}[OH^-][CO_2] + k_{cat}[Catalyst][CO_2] \quad (1)$$

The concentration of dissolved CO_2 at different CO_2 partial pressures was determined from the data of Harned and Davis (9). Values of k_{H_2O} and k_{OH^-} were determined from runs at each pH in the absence of catalyst. A slight rise in temperature was observed during each run; the average temperature at the time of reading was measured as $1.5 \pm 0.2°$. The value of k_{H_2O} determined was 0.0042 ± 0.0002 sec^{-1} and, considering the simplicity of the method, agrees reasonably with the values of 0.0033 sec^{-1} at this temperature interpolated from data in the literature (10). Values of k_{cat} were obtained by comparing rates at several different catalyst concentrations. Data at pH 7 were similarly interpreted except that at this pH correction was applied for the back-reaction from the known rate of H_2CO_3 dehydration (10).

III. Results and Discussion

A. The Catalytic Rate Constants

In Table I, values of k_{cat} in the pH region 7–9 are shown for two previously known catalysts, sulfite and borate, as well as for a series of cupric

TABLE I

CATALYTIC CONSTANTS OF CUPRIC ION CHELATES AND OTHER CO_2 HYDRATION CATALYSTS[a]

Catalyst	k_{cat}(l mole^{-1} sec^{-1})		
	pH 7	pH 8	pH 9
Na$_2$SO$_3$	0.90	1.3	1.3
H$_3$BO$_3$	—	0.02	0.18
CuGG	0.11	1.1	9.3 ± 1.0
CuGG (+ 1 mole imidazole)	—	—	0.60
CuGG (+ 2 moles imidazole)	—	—	0.30
CuGGEt	—	1.5 ± 0.4	6.7 ± 1.6
CuVG	—	—	7.9 ± 1.8
CuVG (+ 2 moles imidazole)	—	—	1.3
CuGGG	0.20	0.30	0.70
CuGGGG	0.05	0.27	1.31

[a] Values of k_{cat} showed an average deviation of less than $\pm 10\%$ unless otherwise noted. For CuGGEt and CuVG, a particularly wide scatter in k_{cat} was seen, which may be due to inhibition by HCO$_3^-$ as the reaction proceeds. To a certain extent, this effect is also present with CuGG at pH 9.

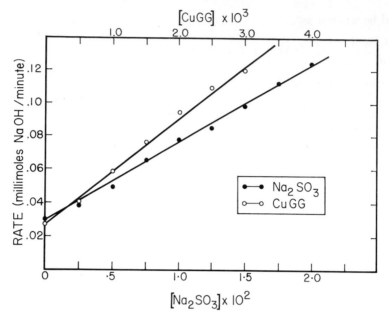

F<small>IG</small>. 1. Effect of catalyst concentration on the rate of CO_2 hydration at pH 9. The rate is given as millimoles NaOH added per minute; at pH 9, each millimole NaOH consumed represents 0.95 millimole CO_2 hydrated. Temperature, $1.5°$; ionic strength, 0.16; partial pressure CO_2, 0.2 atmospheres.

ion chelates. The self-consistency of k_{cat} at different concentrations of catalyst may be seen in Fig. 1, where the linearity between rate and concentration of sulfite and CuGG is evident. In Table I, the value of k_{cat} is formulated in terms of the total concentration of catalyst regardless of its state of ionization. The constancy of k_{cat} for sulfite between pH 8 and 9 and its decrease at pH 7 is compatible with a pK_a of 7 for sulfite at $0°$ and participation of only SO_3^{2-} as the catalytic species. These results are similar to those found by Roughton although sulfite appears somewhat less catalytic in this system than from his data (2). The value of k_{cat} for borate is seen to increase between pH 8 and 9 in good agreement with the pK_a value of approximately 9.5 for borate at this temperature. The results with sulfite support the general validity of the assay procedure.

It is apparent from Table I that all the Cu^{2+} chelates studied have at least a low level of catalytic activity between pH 8 and 9. The most significant catalysts, however, are the 1:1 chelates of Cu^{2+} with glycylglycine, glycylglycine ethyl ester, and L-valylglycine; at pH 9 these catalysts are about fivefold as active as sulfite, which was one of the most potent catalysts previously observed (2). With each of these ligands, at pH 7, Cu^{2+} is

possible stabilization of the developing HCO_3^- anion by the central Cu^{2+}. The second (II) involves simple general base catalysis by the OH^- of $CuGGOH^-$, and the last (III) invokes simultaneous general base catalysis by the OH^- of $CuGGOH^-$ with stabilization of the resultant HCO_3^- anion by Cu^{2+} in the transition state as shown.

The available data cannot unambiguously distinguish between the three mechanisms for catalysis by $CuGGOH^-$. For the other cupric ion complexes, mechanism (I) can be discarded on the grounds that no hydroxyl group is present in these catalysts. However, general base catalysis by one of the ligands on Cu^{2+}, as in (II) or (III), is compatible with the data.

It might be expected from mechanisms (I), (II), and (III) that some correlation between basicity and catalytic activity should be evident. While this is true to an extent, a detailed attempt to relate basicity and catalytic activity over the entire spectrum of catalysts reveals that factors other than basicity alone help determine catalytic activity. One such factor could be the extent to which the developing HCO_3^- anion is stabilized by the central Cu^{2+} ion. A possible stabilizing role of Cu^{2+} is perhaps most simply suggested by the aforementioned similarities in reactivity of $CuGGOH^-$ and free OH^- toward CO_2 in contrast to their vast differences in basicity. Similarly, CuGG is 50 times more active at pH 9 than is borate; yet the pK_a values of boric acid and CuGG are almost identical.

The relevance of these studies to carbonic anhydrase activity inevitably awaits the elucidation of the nature of the zinc-binding site in that enzyme. These studies do illustrate, however, that a ligand on a metal ion particularly an OH^-, might participate in the enzymatic reaction. Conceptually it is also attractive to suppose that the coordinated metal ion of carbonic anhydrase could have the dual role of supplying one of its ligands, either as a nucleophile or general base, and stabilizing the resultant HCO_3^- ion. With the cupric ion chelates studied here, some stabilization of HCO_3^- by the metal may be present, but it is not dramatic. Given the different stereochemistry of zinc chelates, however, such an effect might prove more important in carbonic anhydrase itself.

IV. Summary

The hydroxy forms of the 1:1 chelates of cupric ion with glycylglycine and related ligands are effective catalysts of CO_2 hydration. The results suggest that a ligand bound to metal might play a role in the action of mammalian carbonic anhydrase.

ACKNOWLEDGMENTS

The author is indebted to Miss Priscilla Anderson and to Mr. James Dauber for their excellent assistance.

REFERENCES

1. Lindskog, S., *J. Biol. Chem.*, **238**, 945 (1963).
2. Roughton, F. J. W., and Booth, V. H., *Biochem. J.*, **32**, 2049 (1938).
3. Davis, R. P., *J. Am. Chem. Soc.*, **81**, 5674 (1959).
4. Smith, E. L., *Proc. Natl. Acad. Sci.*, **35**, 80 (1949).
5. Gronvald, M., and Faurholt, C., *Acta Chem. Scand.*, **14**, 1374 (1960).
6. Johansen, E., and Faurholt, C., *Acta Chem. Scand.*, **14**, 2240 (1960).
7. Koltun, W. L., Fried, M., and Gurd, F. R. N., *J. Am. Chem. Soc.*, **82**, 233 (1960).
8. Breslow, E., and Gurd, F. R. N., *J. Biol. Chem.*, **238**, 1332 (1963).
9. Harned, H. S., and Davis, R., *J. Am. Chem. Soc.*, **65**, 2030 (1943).
10. Roughton, F. J. W., *J. Am. Chem. Soc.*, **63**, 2930 (1941).
11. Koltun, W. L., Roth, R. H., and Gurd, F. R. N., *J. Biol. Chem.*, **238**, 124 (1963).
12. Frost, A. A., and Pearson, R. G., "Kinetics and mechanism," John Wiley and Sons, New York, 1953, p. 72.
13. Williams, R. J. P., "Symposium IV, fifth international congress of biochemistry," MacMillan Company, New York, 1963, p. 133.
14. Sirs, J. A., *Trans. Faraday Soc.*, **54**, 201 (1958).

DISCUSSION

DR. PEISACH: I have a question about the role of imidazole in your mechanism. You showed that the K_{cat} is less for imidazole copper glycylglycine than for copper glycylglycine alone. How do you envision the mechanism of this? Is it a displacement of the copper from the glycylglycine complex or is it a binding of imidazole in the z-ligand position of the copper?

DR. BRESLOW: Copper glycylglycine and imidazole form a mixed complex as has been shown by Gurd [Koltun, W. L., Fried, M., and Gurd, F. R. N., *J. Am. Chem. Soc.*, **82**, 233 (1960)]. In the complex, copper is bound to the α-amino and peptide nitrogen of glycylglycine and an imidazole occupies another ligand position. When this occurs, the pK of the water molecules that are bound to copper is increased.

DR. BRINTZINGER: Is the copper complex a general base catalyst?

DR. BRESLOW: Well, it supplies a ligand as a general base.

DR. BRINTZINGER: Your idea, that the coordinated hydroxide does not react with

CO_2 directly, could perhaps be tested on the reverse reaction, because of the principle of microreversibility. In the catalysis of the dehydration of carbonate the copper should then act as a Brönsted acid, not as a Lewis acid. Perhaps this would give rise to some experiment concerning this problem.

DR. BRESLOW: Well, the most obvious experiments which have been suggested have to do with the role of the ligand as a general base, and the usual approach to this kind of problem, as I understand it, is to run reactions in D_2O and in H_2O and to look for isotope effects.

DR. JØRGENSEN: You made the very interesting remark that nothing was known about the possibility of neutral CO_2 acting as a ligand. It is interesting that Vogt, Katz, and Wiberly [*Inorg. Chem.*, **4,** 1157 (1965)] have described a Ru^{2+} compound containing SO_2 bound with sulfur to the ruthenium exactly the same way as sulfites are normally bound. I think it would be worth investigating whether CO_2 under any circumstances would form complexes comparable with the carbonate complexes. Have you made any sort of literature search as to whether such things are ever formed?

DR. BRESLOW: Well, there appears to be nothing in the literature. The kind of study, I suppose, that one could do would be to look for an increased solubility of CO_2 in the presence of some of these complexes, and I have not yet done this.

DR. JØRGENSEN: Well, I should think labeled CO_2 in acid solution is fairly stable with respect to its ^{18}O content, and one can imagine a certain acid solution where this exchange is speeded up very much.

DR. MASON: Certainly the experiments that you have described are among the very few lines of evidence bearing upon whether at pH 8 these copper chelates are hydrolated or neutral. It would be very desirable to have some kind of direct evidence. I'd like to suggest that one possibility would be to use ^{17}O, which has a nuclear spin, and therefore might show some hyperfine structure of its own in connection with cupric copper in the EPR.

DR. BRESLOW: Do you not know with certainty whether one has an hydroxide on the copper at these pH's?

DR. MASON: You don't know whether you are removing a positive charge to reach neutrality or adding a hydroxyl ion to make an negative charge. Isn't that true at this stage?

DR. BRESLOW: Whether one is adding an hydroxide or removing a proton from water—does it matter?

DR. HEMMERICH: I want to ask you if copper is unique in causing this catalytic effect. Carbonic anhydrase is a zinc enzyme. Did you try any other metals?

DR. BRESLOW: We, of course, are most interested in zinc chelates, which is why we started it. We ran into two difficulties with zinc chelates. First we did not at the time have any hydroxy-zinc chelates available to us. The second difficulty that we ran into with zinc chelates is that we were looking at zinc peptides. In our assay system we constantly bubble in CO_2, and we found that the CO_2 dissociated the zinc from glycylglycine, for example, because of the formation of the carbamate. This does not occur with copper derivatives, where the binding is stronger.

The Tissue Copper Proteins: Cerebrocuprein, Erythrocuprein, Hepatocuprein, and Neonatal Hepatic Mitochondrocuprein*

HUNTINGTON PORTER

Department of Neurology,
New England Medical Center Hospitals,
and Department of Medicine (Neurology),
Tufts University School of Medicine,
Boston, Massachusetts

I. Introduction

The copper proteins present in tissues may be divided into two groups: first, those such as cytochrome c oxidase (1) and tyrosinase (2) that have known enzymatic activities but account for a relatively small proportion of the total tissue copper, and, second, those copper proteins that account for a relatively large proportion of tissue copper but which have no enzymatic activity thus far determined. In the latter group are the subcellular soluble copper proteins cerebrocuprein I (3, 4), adult human hepatocuprein (5), and erythrocuprein (6), each of which may account for about 60% of the total tissue copper of, respectively, human brain, adult human liver, and human erythrocytes. Also accounting for a major amount of tissue copper is neonatal hepatic mitochondrocuprein from newborn liver (7, 8), which differs from these soluble copper proteins in that it is localized in the mitochondrial fraction, has a copper content about 10 times as great, is insoluble in aqueous media, and is normally specific to the neonatal period. The present paper will review the chief properties of cerebrocuprein I, adult human hepatocuprein, erythrocuprein, and neonatal hepatic mitochondrocuprein, and will also present some new data on the amino acid composition of the detergent insoluble subfraction containing neonatal hepatic mitochondrocuprein and on the separation from this material of a blue copper-rich tryptic peptide containing large amounts of lysine and arginine.

II. The Soluble Tissue Copper Proteins

In 1938, Mann and Keilin (9) first isolated soluble copper proteins from bovine erythrocytes and bovine liver. These copper proteins, designated

* The previously unpublished investigations described in this paper were supported by research grant NB–01733–06,07 from the National Institute of Neurological Diseases and Blindness, United States Public Health Service.

hemocuprein and hepatocuprein, both contained 0.34% copper and were estimated to have a molecular weight of about 35,000. The bovine hemocuprein was noted to have a distinct blue color in contrast to the bovine hepatocuprein, which was described as almost colorless. Mohamed and Greenberg (10) later isolated a copper protein from horse liver that was similar to bovine hepatocuprein in copper content and molecular weight but which differed from the bovine liver copper protein in having a definite bluish-green color.

A. Cerebrocuprein I

When we became interested in the copper in normal brain in relation to the pathologically high brain copper occurring in Wilson's disease, our first progress was to demonstrate that normal brain copper could be separated into three fractions (11). Fraction I, corresponding to the subcellular soluble fraction copper, accounted for about 60% of the total copper in human brain and could be extracted from the tissue with buffers at pH 4.5 or 8.2 or with water or with 0.25 M sucrose following centrifugation at 100,000 $\times$ g (12). Fraction II, also reproducible and exhaustible, which accounted for 23% of the copper in normal human cortex, was obtained by subsequent extraction of the tissue residue at pH 3.5 and vanishing ionic strength, leaving a residual insoluble Fraction III. The relation of Fractions II and III copper to histological subcellular components is not yet clear.

From bovine Fraction I prepared as the pH 4.5 acetate buffer extract, we isolated a green brain protein (3) which contained 0.3% copper and which appeared essentially homogeneous with a molecular weight of the

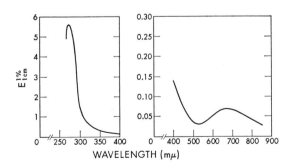

Fig. 1. Absorption spectrum of human hepatocuprein in barbital buffer pH 8.6; ionic strength 0.10 in visible range, 0.0244 in ultraviolet, read against buffer blank at the same concentrations. Protein concentrations at the time of measurement were approximately 5% for the visible range and 0.123% for the ultraviolet. After Porter, Sweeney, and Porter (5).

order of 30,000, indicating two atoms of copper per molecule. Its absorption spectrum showed a broad maximum of relatively low extinction at about 660 mμ and less extinction than most proteins in the ultraviolet with absorption at 270 mμ exceeding that at 280 mμ, indicating the presence of little or no tryptophan. This absorption spectrum was similar to that later found for adult human hepatocuprein, shown in Fig. 1. The protein retained all of its copper on dialysis at a pH as low as 4.5. Since this absorption spectrum and stability to acid pH had not been previously described in other copper proteins and since there appeared to be more than one type of copper protein in brain, we designated the isolated copper protein as cerebrocuprein I.

TABLE I

PURIFICATION OF HUMAN CEREBROCUPREIN I[a]

Step	Fraction	Concentration of copper in fraction (%)	Yield per gram fresh tissue	
			Copper (μg)	Solids[b] (mg)
	Total human brain	—	4.2	—
1	pH 4.5 buffer extract	0.008	2.38	30.00
2	75% acetone precipitate	0.030	1.85	6.11
3	45–75% chloroform–ethanol precipitate	0.095	1.24	1.31
4	Undialyzable material	0.17	1.31	0.78
5	50–75% acetone precipitate	0.15	0.78	0.53
6	Paper electrophoresis eluate	0.29	0.15	0.05

[a] After Porter and Ainsworth (4).
[b] Based on dry weight.

Cerebrocuprein I was also isolated from normal human brain (4) by utilizing the modified procedure shown in Table I. Human cerebrocuprein I was similar to bovine cerebrocuprein I in copper content, sedimentation coefficient, absorption spectrum, ability to retain all of its copper on dialysis at a pH as acid as 4.5, and in the failure of its copper to react directly with sodium diethyldithiocarbamate. The absorption spectrum of cerebrocuprein I showing a peak in the visible range with relatively low extinction at a relatively long wavelength and the stability of the copper-protein bond to acid pH suggested that the copper in cerebrocuprein I may be bound to carboxyl groups (3).

B. Human Hepatocuprein

A purified copper protein was also obtained from normal adult human liver (5) by essentially the same method as that employed with brain

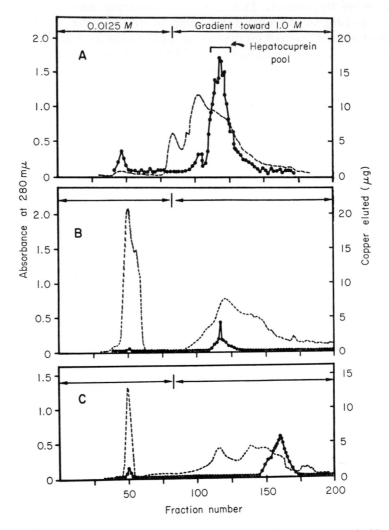

FIG. 2. Chromatographic separation of copper proteins of human liver and of human brain on DEAE cellulose eluted with ammonium bicarbonate in a linear gradient from 0.0125 toward 1.00 M. – – –, Absorbance at 280 mμ. –·–·–, Copper eluted (μg). A, chromatography of partially purified hepatocuprein. B, chromatography of whole sucrose extract of liver. C, chromatography of whole sucrose extract of brain. Protein applied to the column was about 850 mg in A and 900 mg in B and C. After Porter, Sweeney, and Porter (5).

except that it was necessary to start with the entire sucrose subcellular soluble fraction and to employ a chromatographic fractionation step. The chromatography of partially purified human hepatocuprein compared with that of whole sucrose extracts of normal human liver and normal human brain is illustrated in Fig. 2. The adult human hepatocuprein obtained appeared essentially homogeneous on ultracentrifugation and was similar to cerebrocuprein I in copper content, sedimentation coefficient, absorption spectrum, in failure of its copper to react directly with sodium diethyldithiocarbamate, and in electrophoretic mobility under the same conditions. It appeared to differ from the bovine hepatocuprein described by Mann and Keilin (9) in that the latter was described as almost colorless whereas human hepatocuprein has a distinct bluish-green color. This human hepatocuprein differs from the copper-binding protein obtained from human liver by Shapiro, Morell, and Scheinberg (13) in that the latter has a molecular weight of only about 10,000, is colorless with a different absorption spectrum, and has a different amino acid composition.

C. Erythrocuprein

Subsequent to our report on the isolation of bovine cerebrocuprein I, the isolation of a similar copper protein, erythrocuprein, from human erythrocytes was described by Markowitz, Cartwright, and Wintrobe (6). This copper protein appeared immunologically homogeneous and it was possible to remove a major portion of its copper with retention of immunological reactivity. Its amino acid composition and physical properties were studied in more detail (14) than those of cerebrocuprein I and human hepatocuprein. Erythrocuprein was found to contain no methionine and only a very small amount of tyrosine. The molecular weight calculated from its composition was 33,180.

Erythrocuprein has been further purified by use of chromatography (15, 16) to yield preparations of greater immunological homogeneity and copper content. Using this more purified antigen, erythrocuprein has been estimated to account for about 60% of the total erythrocyte copper (16), a proportion similar to the total subcellular soluble copper found in human brain and human liver (12). Erythrocuprein copper can exchange with ^{64}Cu. Most recently, Stansell and Deutsch (17) have prepared crystalline human erythrocuprein utilizing chromatographic and gel filtration methods without the denaturing procedures such as treatment with chloroform–ethanol that had usually been employed previously in the isolation of this group of soluble tissue copper proteins. Crystalline erythrocuprein prepared by this method contained 0.38% copper, all in the cupric form, and had a molecular weight calculated as 33,600 both by velocity sedimentation and by amino acid composition. It contained no tryptophan, no methionine, and less than 0.1% tyrosine.

An erythrocyte protein fraction capable of binding large amounts of radioactive copper has also been obtained from the initial nonadsorbed chromatography peak of erythrocyte hemolyzates (16) but the extent to which this protein normally contributes to physiological erythrocyte copper, as opposed to its capacity to bind extraneous copper, has not yet been determined.

D. Relationship among Cerebrocuprein I, Erythrocuprein, and Human Hepatocuprein

Cerebrocuprein I from human brain (3, 4), erythrocuprein from human erythrocytes (6, 16, 17), and human hepatocuprein from adult human liver (5) have many similarities. The three copper proteins are similar in copper content, in order of magnitude of sedimentation coefficient, and in ability to retain copper at a pH as acid as 4.5. They are of similar bluish-green color with an absorption spectrum showing a broad maximum in the visible range at 655–670 mμ and showing absorption at 270 mμ greater than at 280 mμ with less extinction than most proteins in the ultraviolet ($E_{1cm}^{1\%}$ at 265–270 mμ about 5.6). They are also similar in solubility properties during differential precipitations with organic solvents during isolation procedures. Human hepatocuprein is also similar to erythrocuprein in absence of methionine and low tyrosine content (5, 14), and similar to cerebrocuprein I in mobility on paper electrophoresis at pH 8.6.

The above similarities of cerebrocuprein I, erythrocuprein, and (or) human hepatocuprein are impressive and suggest that the soluble copper proteins of this type from human brain, erythrocytes, and liver may be identical. However, it should be noted that the bulk of the subcellular soluble fraction copper from human liver and from human brain on chromatography appeared reproducibly as single peaks which consistently differed from one another in point of elution under the same conditions (Fig. 2) (5). Also, it has been reported that, although human liver and brain contain material reacting with antierythrocuprein serum, copper in the erythrocuprein fraction of liver and brain accounted for less than 10% of the total copper in these organs (16). Since the soluble copper in human liver and brain accounts for more than 60% of the total organ copper (12), the concept that hepatocuprein, cerebrocuprein I, and erythrocuprein are identical, based on the immunological data, would imply that liver and brain contain large amounts of other soluble copper protein or proteins. The single copper peaks obtained on chromatography of whole sucrose extracts of human liver and human brain shown in Fig. 2 provide no evidence of the occurrence of major amounts of such other soluble copper proteins. These considerations suggest that, despite their similarities, there may possibly be some differences among the soluble copper proteins of human brain, liver, and erythrocytes (5).

III. Neonatal Hepatic Mitochondrocuprein

A. Previous Work

That immature liver, including that of the newborn human infant, contains a much larger concentration of copper than other tissues has long been known (18–22). In preliminary investigations, we found the largest proportion of the copper accumulating in immature liver to be localized in the mitochrondrial fraction (23), which, in the case of newborn human liver, contained more than 30 times as much copper as the mitochondrial fraction from adult human liver (8). The mitochondrial copper in newborn bovine (7) or human (8) liver could be further concentrated by successive differential centrifugations in different detergents to yield a brownish-green subfraction which consistently contained more than 3.0% copper

TABLE II

PREPARATION OF HUMAN CRUDE NEONATAL HEPATIC MITOCHONDROCUPREIN[a]

Step	Fraction	Concentration of copper in fraction (%)	Yield per gram fresh tissue	
			Copper (µg)	Solids[b] (mg)
	Total immature liver		63.8	
1	Mitochondria	0.12	27.4	22.8
	(Nuclei)[c]	(0.06)	(11.7)	(19.1)
	(Microsomes)[c]	(0.02)	(6.1)	(30.3)
	(Supernatant)[c]	(0.01)	(17.9)	(155)
2	Deoxycholate, 14000 × g sediment	1.5	21.8	1.5
	(Deoxycholate, 1800 × g sediment)[c]	(0.4)	(1.2)	(0.27)
	(Deoxycholate, 14000 × g supernatant)[c]	(0.02)	(4.9)	(21.4)
3	Tween, 1600 × g sediment	2.6	18.4	0.71
	(Tween, 1600 × g supernatant)[c]	(0.5)	(3.6)	(0.77)
4	Dodecyl sulfate, 1600 × g sediment	4.4	15.4	0.35
	(Dodecyl sulfate, 1600 × g supernatant)[c]	(1.0)	(3.1)	(0.32)

[a] After Porter, Sweeney, and Porter (5).

[b] Dry weight of acetone-insoluble material.

[c] Fractions in parentheses are those of lower copper concentration discarded during the isolation procedure.

(except in some cases of human material with markedly premature birth). The preparative procedure is illustrated in Table II. The name "neonatal hepatic mitochondrocuprein" was suggested for the copper protein of immature liver mitochondria represented by this subfraction. Since the material obtained was insoluble and could not be tested for homogeneity, it is possible that the true copper content of more completely purified neonatal hepatic mitochondrocuprein is even higher than the 3 to 5% copper content thus far found. The subfraction also consistently contained some iron but in variable amounts as low as one-seventeenth the amount of copper. The iron found in the subfraction may therefore not be actually bound to the copper protein.

In both bovine and human liver, significant concentrations of neonatal hepatic mitochondrocuprein were found only in the neonatal, as opposed to adult, subject (7, 8). Thus yield of copper and concentration of copper in the neonatal hepatic mitochondrocuprein subfraction from newborn human livers averaged, respectively, more than 100 times and more than 80 times the yield and concentration of copper in the corresponding material from adult human livers. These results are illustrated in Table III.

It was established that this mitochondrial copper of immature liver did not represent cytochrome c oxidase copper (1, 7) and that it did not resemble any of the copper proteins previously isolated from liver or other tissues. Neonatal hepatic mitochondrocuprein differs, for example, from the soluble tissue copper proteins described in the preceding section in its extraordinarily high copper content, which is at least 10-fold that of other

TABLE III

RELATION OF AGE OF SUBJECT TO YIELD
OF HUMAN CRUDE NEONATAL HEPATIC MITOCHONDROCUPREIN[a]

| Subject age (days) | Gestation | Yield per gram fresh tissue | | Concentration of copper in fraction (%) |
		Copper (μg)	Solids (mg)	
2	8 weeks premature	14.0	0.57	2.5
1	5 weeks premature	15.4	0.35	4.4
12	Full term	18.4	0.53	3.5
Adult		0.1	0.16	0.06
Adult		0.2	1.1	0.02

[a] After Porter, Sweeney, and Porter (5).

known normal copper proteins, in its failure to be extracted from the tissue in soluble form by either water or detergents, and in its normal specificity to the neonatal period. The copper in this subfraction and in the parent total mitochondrial fraction was insoluble in water over a wide pH range, in detergents, and in a variety of organic solvents, but could be quantitatively released into soluble form by treatment with trypsin (7, 8). The copper in the neonatal hepatic mitochondrocuprein-containing subfraction appeared stable to acid pH but reacted directly with sodium diethyldithiocarbamate, although at an extremely slow rate (7, 8). This direct reaction is not attributable solely to any denaturing effect of sodium dodecylsulfate on the protein, since similar rates of direct reaction were also observed in mitochondrial fractions treated only with the relatively mild detergents Tween 80 or sodium deoxycholate (7).

The extraordinarily high copper content of neonatal hepatic mitochondrocuprein compared with that of copper proteins known to have enzymatic activity and its other differences from such proteins suggest that neonatal hepatic mitochondrocuprein may have a storage function for copper in the immature animal analogous to that of ferritin for iron storage. In the single case of Wilson's disease thus far studied, a significant portion of the pathological hepatic copper was found in the mitochondrial fraction in a detergent-insoluble form possibly similar to neonatal hepatic mitochondrocuprein (12). This finding suggests that mitochondria of adult liver may possibly form a protein similar to neonatal hepatic mitochondrocuprein which is capable of binding large amounts of copper if abnormal amounts of copper enter the organism.

B. Amino Acid Composition of the Detergent-Insoluble Subfraction

In collaboration with the McLean Hospital Research Laboratory, a study has been made of the amino acid composition of the detergent-insoluble subfraction containing neonatal hepatic mitochondrocuprein. The amino acid composition of three preparations from newborn bovine liver, each containing more than 4.0% copper, compared with that of corresponding material from adult bovine liver, is shown in Table IV. The most striking feature of these results is the unusually high half-cystine content, which averaged 17.1% of the recovered amino acids in the detergent-insoluble subfraction from newborn livers. Consideration that the yield of solids in this subfraction from newborn bovine livers was more than twice that obtained from adult bovine livers shows an even greater contrast in yield of half-cystine between the newborn and the adult. Thus the yield of half-cystine as μmoles per 100 g fresh tissue in the subfraction from newborn livers was more than 5 times as great as that in the cor-

TABLE IV

Amino Acid Composition of Detergent-Insoluble Crude Neonatal Hepatic Mitochondrocuprein Subfractions From Mitochondria of Newborn and Adult Bovine Liver[a]

Constituent	Newborn[b]	Adult[b]
Lysine	9.23	7.13
Histidine	1.39	2.02
Arginine	4.13	5.56
Aspartic acid	5.28	6.63
Threonine	4.03	4.56
Serine	10.29	6.80
Glutamic acid	7.28	7.04
Proline	6.02	5.87
Glycine	11.75	12.13
Alanine	8.15	8.92
Half-cystine	17.06	9.51
Valine	4.63	5.56
Methionine	0.91	1.27
Isoleucine	2.34	3.68
Leucine	4.14	6.88
Tyrosine	1.06	1.99
Phenylalanine	1.93	3.17

[a] Amino acids expressed as moles per 100 moles total amino acids recovered.
[b] Average of three different preparations.

responding material from adult livers. The subfraction from newborn livers also contained relatively high proportions of lysine, serine, and glycine and contained less aspartic and glutamic acids, less tyrosine and phenylalanine, and less leucine than many proteins.

The extraordinarily high half-cystine content found in the subfractions from newborn livers suggested that the copper in this material might be bound to the protein through sulfhydryl groups. Therefore, a study was made of the free sulfhydryl groups in subfractions from newborn bovine liver, utilizing the method of Boyer (24), before removal of copper and after complete removal of copper by treatment with sodium diethyldithiocarbamate and extraction of the copper carbamate with cold acetone. No significant increase in free sulfhydryl groups could be demonstrated after removal of copper from the subfraction, providing no evidence that the copper in neonatal hepatic mitochondrocuprein is bound to the protein through this type of linkage.

C. Separation and Properties of Blue Tryptic Peptides of Neonatal Hepatic Mitochondrocuprein

All of the copper in the detergent-insoluble subfractions from mitochondria of newborn liver could be brought into soluble form by brief treatment with trypsin, although treatment with even very large proportions of trypsin left considerable copper-free solids from such subfractions in insoluble form (7). The material dissolved by the trypsin had a dark purplish-blue color in concentrated solution. This soluble material was subjected to preparative paper electrophoresis in 0.1 M ammonium carbonate adjusted to pH 8.8 by the technique previously described (4). On completion of the electrophoresis, in each of four preparations a zone of blue material which had migrated toward the cathode was visible on the unstained paper. Material between the zone of maximal blue color and the origin had a more purple hue, whereas that migrating toward the anode was yellow or brown. Staining for copper with sodium diethyldithiocarbamate and copper analyses of eluted fractions both showed the largest proportion of copper to be in the zone of maximal blue color, which accounted for about one third of the total copper eluted. Copper was, however, spread rather diffusely throughout the range of blue or purple material migrating toward the cathode, suggesting the formation of a considerable number of in-

TABLE V

AMINO ACID COMPOSITION OF BLUE COPPER-RICH
TRYPTIC PEPTIDES OF NEONATAL HEPATIC MITOCHONDROCUPREIN[a]

Constituent	μMoles per milligram	Percentage (by μmoles) o f total amino acid
Lysine	0.769	32.2
Arginine	0.596	25.0
Aspartic acid	0.046	1.9
Threonine	0.183	7.7
Serine	0.178	7.5
Glutamic acid	0.045	1.9
Glycine	0.035	1.5
Alanine	0.111	4.7
Valine	0.062	2.6
Isoleucine	0.172	7.2
Leucine	0.180	7.6
Phenylalanine	0.015	0.6

[a] Average of three different preparations.

completely separated copper-containing peptides which were positively charged at pH 8.8. Significant amounts of copper were not found in the material migrating toward the anode even though, on staining for peptides with ninhydrin or wool black, such material appeared to make up the larger proportion of the total peptides applied to the paper.

The amino acid composition of the peptides eluted from the zone of maximal blue color is shown in Table V. The most striking feature of these results is the very high proportion of the basic amino acids lysine and arginine which, together, on a molar basis, accounted for more than 50% of the total amino acids recovered from the blue peptides in each of the three preparations analyzed. The blue copper-rich peptides also contained significant amounts of threonine, serine, isoleucine, leucine, and alanine. Since it is probable that the material in the electrophoretic bands of maximal blue color was contaminated with small amounts of other peptides, the significance of the amino acids found in lesser proportions is uncertain. The blue copper-rich peptides contained no half-cystine, histidine, proline, methionine, or tyrosine and no tryptophan was detectable in the unhydrolyzed peptides by the fluorometric procedure of Teale (25). Direct reaction of copper in these peptides with sodium diethyldithiocarbamate was immediate rather than delayed.

The absorption spectrum of the blue copper-rich tryptic peptides of neonatal hepatic mitochondrocuprein is illustrated in Fig. 3. The peak in the visible range at about 605 mμ and absorption at 270 mμ greater than at 280 mμ were found in each of the four preparations thus far examined. The basis for the apparent high ultraviolet extinction in peptides containing no tryptophan, tyrosine, or cystine and only minimal amounts of phenylalanine has not yet been determined. The position of the peak in the visible range at 605 mμ is consistent with binding of copper to nitrogenous

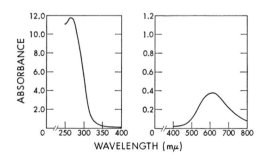

FIG. 3. Absorption spectrum of blue tryptic peptide of neonatal hepatic mitochondrocuprein in 0.1 M ammonium carbonate, pH 8.8, read against buffer blank at the same concentration. Protein concentrations at the time of measurement were estimated as approximately 0.32% for the visible range and 0.016% for the ultraviolet.

groups (26), and one may speculate that the lysine and arginine found in such large proportions in these peptides play some part in the binding of the copper in neonatal hepatic mitochondrocuprein.

IV. Summary

(a) The soluble tissue copper proteins cerebrocuprein I from brain, erythrocuprein from human erythrocytes, and human hepatocuprein from adult human liver are characterized by a copper content of about 0.3% (0.38%), a molecular weight of about 30,000 (33,600), bluish-green color with an absorption maximum in the visible range at 655–670 mμ, and ability to retain copper at a pH as acid as 4.5. Their numerous similarities suggest that these copper proteins may possibly be identical but there is evidence suggesting that there may be some differences between the soluble copper proteins from the three different tissues.

(b) Neonatal hepatic mitochondrocuprein, which represents a major proportion of the copper accumulating physiologically in newborn liver, can be concentrated in a subfraction containing more than 3.0% copper. It differs from the soluble copper proteins in that it is localized in the mitochondrial fraction, has a copper content about 10 times as great, is insoluble in water or detergents, and is normally specific to the neonatal period. Its extraordinarily high copper content suggests that it may have a storage function for copper in the immature animal analogous to that of ferritin for iron storage.

(c) New data are presented on the amino acid composition of the detergent-insoluble subfraction containing neonatal hepatic mitochondrocuprein and on the separation from this material of blue copper-rich tryptic peptides. The detergent-insoluble subfraction has an unusually high half-cystine content. The blue tryptic peptides show an absorption maximum in the visible range at 605 mμ and contain very large proportions of the basic amino acids lysine and arginine.

REFERENCES

1. Griffiths, D. E., and Wharton, D. C., *J. Biol. Chem.*, **236**, 1857 (1961).
2. Brown, F. C., and Ward, D. N., *Proc. Soc. Exp. Biol. Med.*, **100**, 701 (1959).
3. Porter, H., and Folch, J., *J. Neurochem.*, **1**, 260 (1957).
4. Porter, H., and Ainsworth, S., *J. Neurochem.*, **5**, 91 (1959).
5. Porter, H., Sweeney, M., and Porter, E., *Arch. Biochem. Biophys.*, **105**, 319 (1964).
6. Markowitz, H., Cartwright, G. E., and Wintrobe, M. M., *J. Biol. Chem.*, **234**, 40 (1959).
7. Porter, H., Johnston, J., and Porter, E., *Biochim. Biophys. Acta*, **65**, 66 (1962).
8. Porter, H., Sweeney, M., and Porter, E., *Arch. Biochem. Biophys.*, **104**, 97 (1964).

9. Mann, T., and Keilin, D., *Proc. Roy. Soc. (London)*, *Ser. B.*, **126**, 303 (1939).
10. Mohamed, M. S., and Greenberg, D. M., *J. Gen. Physiol.*, **37**, 433 (1954).
11. Porter, H., and Folch, J., *Arch. Neurol. and Psychiat.*, **77**, 8 (1957).
12. Porter, H., *Arch. Neurol.*, **11**, 341 (1964).
13. Shapiro, J., Morell, A. G., and Scheinberg, I. H., *J. Clin. Invest.*, **40**, 1081 (1961); Morell, A. G., Shapiro, J. R., and Scheinberg, I. H., *in* J. M. Walshe and J. N. Cumings, (eds.), "Wilson's disease: some current concepts," Blackwells Scientific Publications, Oxford, 1961, p. 36.
14. Kimmel, J. R., Markowitz, H., and Brown, D. M., *J. Biol. Chem.*, **234**, 46 (1959).
15. Nyman, P. O., *Biochim. Biophys. Acta*, **45**, 387 (1960).
16. Shields, G. S., Markowitz, H., Klassen, W. H., Cartwright, G. E., and Wintrobe, M. M., *J. Clin. Invest.*, **40**, 2007 (1961).
17. Stansell, M. J., and Deutsch, H. F., *Fed. Proc.*, **24**, 222 (1965).
18. McHargue, J. S., *Am. J. Physiol.*, **72**, 583 (1925).
19. Cunningham, I. J., *Biochem. J.*, **25**, 1267 (1931).
20. Lorenzene, E. J., and Smith, S. E., *J. Nutrition.*, **33**, 143 (1947).
21. Bruckmann, G., and Zondek, S. G., *Biochem. J.*, **33**, 1845 (1939).
22. Butt, E. M., Nusbaum, R. E., Gilmour, T. C., and DiDio, S. L., *Am. J. Clin. Path.*, **30**, 479 (1958).
23. Porter, H., Weiner, W., and Barker, M., *Biochim. Biophys. Acta*, **52**, 419 (1961).
24. Boyer, P. D., *J. Am. Chem. Soc.*, **76**, 4331 (1954).
25. Teale, F. W. J., *Biochem. J.*, **76**, 381 (1960).
26. Klotz, I. M., Faller, I. L., and Urquhart, J. M., *J. Phys. Colloid Chem.*, **54**, 18 (1950).

DISCUSSION

Dr. Cumings: Do you know at what age mitochondrocuprein disappears from the liver?

Dr. Porter: Within a month. It is obviously hard to obtain normal newborn human liver, so one has to start out with bovine material. I am somewhat dependent on the judgment of the slaughterhouse foreman as to how old these animals are, and, assuming that he is correct, by the end of the second to third week the yield of this material declines very markedly. By the end of one month it is not practical to attempt to isolate it.

Dr. Peisach: What is the relationship between the concentration of mitochondrocuprein and ceruloplasmin levels in newborns?

Dr. Porter: They are inverse. This has been pointed out several times, but we might say once again that the newborn infant is similar to the patient with Wilson's disease in two respects. First, he lacks a normal amount of ceruloplasmin; and second, he has a very high concentration of copper in his liver.

Dr. Peisach: What is the extinction coefficient of the copper in the tryptic digest?

Dr. Porter: We have not measured the absorption spectrum in the total tryptic digest, as opposed to material which is separated from that by preparative paper electrophoresis. In the material arbitrarily selected for its maximal blue color, the extinction coefficient for 1 gram atom of copper per liter at 605 mμ has been calculated as about 70. We don't know anything about the size of this peptide or, presumably, group of peptides.

DR. CURZON: If you denature a protein, you tend to increase its ability to bind metal. Could you be picking up here a difference in denaturability between the neonatal and mature protein rather than a specific *in vivo* copper protein?

DR. PORTER: There is a difference between the adult human hepatocuprein and the neonatal hepatic mitochondrocuprein. These are different from the starting point, in that one is obtained from the subcellular soluble fraction and the other only from the mitochondria, so I don't believe there is any possibility that they could be the same.

DR. CURZON: But the difference could be in the form of the denatured protein.

DR. PORTER: Yes, but I don't believe that they are the same in the tissues. One can follow them at every step along the way and find differences between them, starting with the part of the cell that they are in. The first step after treatment with sucrose, which is not, so far as I know, a denaturing procedure, is to treat them with deoxycholate in relatively low concentration. Many enzymes certainly survive this, and yet the neonatal copper is insoluble in both the sucrose and deoxycholate steps. The soluble copper protein from adult liver and the mitochondrial copper protein from newborn liver also differ markedly from each other in amino acid composition.

With regard to whether we are picking up extra copper, I shall say that we have been at some pains to keep this completely under metal-free conditions. No preparation is accepted in which the sum of the copper in all of the fractions, including those discarded, exceeds that of the copper in the starting material.

DR. DAWSON: I understand that all of the copper in the mitochondrocuprein is tightly bound.

DR. PORTER: The copper in the neonatal protein will react with sodium diethyl-dithiocarbamate, but at an extremely slow rate.

DR. DAWSON: Ordinary dialysis will not remove the copper?

DR. PORTER: No, it will not.

DR. DAWSON: Will ion exchange remove the copper?

DR. PORTER: No.

DR. DAWSON: Is all the copper alike, as near as you can tell?

DR. PORTER: We have no way of knowing.

DR. DAWSON: Did you use dodecyl sulfate to solubilize this material?

DR. PORTER: Unsuccessfully. We used it to get rid of the other stuff.

DR. DAWSON: In our experience with another copper protein, ascorbate oxidase, dodecyl sulfate is a very effective agent for removing the copper. As we unfold the protein with dodecyl sulfate the copper falls right out. Apparently this is not the case with your preparations.

DR. PORTER: When we found the copper in this material reacted directly with carbamate, we went back and tested at the total mitochondrial stage, the stage only after treatment with deoxycholate, and after treatment with only Tween 80, and we found that it still reacted directly. I don't think any of the properties that we found are directly related to the dodecyl sulfate specifically.

DR. SCHEINBERG: Dr. Blumberg has said (this symposium) that much of the discussion about why proteins were blue would be obviated if one could get at a blue protein or peptide of known structure with a group of 12 measurements made on it. Dr. Freeman said that we shall never know why a protein is blue until we get a peptide or a small fragment of it that has blue color. You now have a peptide which fulfills the requirements of both these people. It's very blue. It looks bluer than ink, as a matter of fact. I wondered whether or not this really isn't a handle to get at the crux of the problem.

DR. PORTER: Well, I think it is. However, since I'm a neurologist and not a bio-chemist, I would be grateful for any assistance that anybody wants to offer me in getting the measurements done, but I think it should help to get some of those answers.

DR. WALSHE: I should like to know whether these mitochondria with all the copper in them are able to oxidize pyruvate like normal mitochondria do. Both Sir Rudolph Peters and I feel that copper is very toxic to mitochondria.

DR. PORTER: It is possible that the toxic action of copper is on the mitochondria. Certainly, however, the bulk of the pathological brain copper in Wilson's disease is not in the mitochondria.

A Study of the Toxic Action of Copper on Brain Tissue in *Vivo* and *in Vitro**†

SIR RUDOLPH A. PETERS

Department of Biochemistry,
University of Cambridge,
Cambridge, England

For more than 30 years, I have been interested in the genesis of convulsions, since first coming into contact with the pigeon in opisthotonus due to deficiency of thiamine (1). In this case we proved that the biochemical lesion started with a fault in the pyruvate oxidase system. More recently my interest has been extended to the effects of monofluorocarbon compounds; the convulsions in this case were traced to a lethal synthesis of fluoroacetate to fluorocitrate, which in very small amounts induced convulsions when injected into the subarachnoid space in the pigeon. Recent work has proved that 0.57 μg fluorocitrate injected intracerebrally will produce lethal convulsions in rats (2). From this and other work, it appeared that the biochemical lesion began with interference with the smooth functioning of the citric acid cycle, and so with mitochondria.

In the course of experiments aimed at reversing the convulsion induced by fluorocitrate, I ran into the curious fact, about 12 years ago, that minute amounts of Cu^{2+} induced convulsions and death when injected into the subarachnoid space in the pigeon's brain. It gave cause for thought, because it was so clearly a misplacement of copper, since Cu^{2+} is a normal component of several tissue enzymes, especially cytochrome *c* oxidase. It has never been clear what was the connecting link between the biochemical lesion in the mitochondria and the change in the potential of the membrane concerned which initiates the excitation. The effect of the Cu^{2+} could have been due to a positive inhibition of reactions which would cut off the synthesis of ATP; but it might also have been altering the ionic charge on the essential membrane, so one had to look further than the mitochondrion. Dr. Bangham suggested that it might be induced by smaller amounts of some other metals, because he and Dawson (3) had found such effects when phospholipase B was acting upon lecithinase at a surface. I tried Th^{4+} and found this much less convulsive than Cu^{2+}.

* Review of work carried out in collaboration with Dr. J. M. Walshe, Department of Experimental Medicine, and Mrs. M. Shorthouse, Department of Biochemistry, Cambridge.

† The author is grateful to the Wellcome Trust for a grant which enabled this work to be carried out.

It was at this stage that I became aware of the remarkable effects produced in Wilson's disease by Walshe (4) with penicillamine, which reduces the accumulation of copper in the patients. We decided to join forces in the attempt to decide whether BAL or penicillamine was the better antidote, using the pigeon's brain as a test object.

In work with Mrs. Davies, we found that a Cu–BAL mixture was not toxic; if, however, the Cu^{2+} was injected first, BAL then had no curative effect (5). Although 10 μg Cu^{2+} when injected was usually fatal, we used 20 μg Cu^{2+} in these experiments to make certain of the toxicity. The case of penicillamine was curious, because injection of a mixture of Cu and penicillamine had a delayed toxicity up to 20 minutes (or more), and sometimes the birds recovered slowly after a convulsive stage. Lipoate (thioctate) had an action somewhat like that of BAL.

When we attempted to probe deeper, with lipoate in mind, we found, as would be expected, that approximately 0.1 mM Cu^{2+} was very toxic to mitochondria, and again, that although Cu–BAL was nontoxic, once the Cu^{2+} inhibition was established, we could not reverse the toxicity. There was one difficulty in taking the view that the Cu^{2+} was attacking mitochondria *in vivo*: there did not seem time for diffusion to take place, as the Cu^{2+} action was immediate, unless there were mitochondria in very close contact with the brain membranes.

After some discussion, we extended our observations to brain slices, when we found to our surprise that addition of Cu^{2+} was much less toxic than with the isolated mitochondria. This experiment appeared to us to rule out the simple mitochondrial hypothesis. Clearly, respiratory observa-

TABLE I

DISTRIBUTION OF INJECTED ^{64}CU IN PIGEON BRAIN[a]

	Convulsions[b]	Protected[c]
Right hemisphere	17.2	17.7
Left hemisphere	6.8	4.2
Optic lobes and pons	9.6	5.1
Cerebellum	3.1	1.9
Medulla	2.9	5.5
Vault of skull	13.6	9.9
Not accounted for	46.8	55.7

[a] 24.5 μg Cu^{2+} injected. Means expressed as percentage of total dose.
[b] Eight birds.
[c] Six birds.

tions in the Warburg apparatus were not picking up the point which mattered *in vivo*.

It was at this stage that we used ^{64}Cu to trace the path of the injected Cu^{2+}. Table I shows that after injection the ^{64}Cu was distributed in most of the brain fractions, with the emphasis on the site of injection in the right hemisphere. About 25% (5 μg) was left in the brain; if one considers that convulsions arise in the optic lobes, then about a maximum of 2 μg is inducing convulsions. If the bird lives on, as one did after it was given also cetyl trimethylammonium bromide, the Cu^{2+} becomes gradually transferred to the liver. When we fractionated the tissue containing ^{64}Cu by the usual techniques there was always Cu attached to the insoluble neurokeratin fraction (6). This was so even after a careful cold acetone fractionation, kindly carried out for us by R. A. Gregory. The ^{64}Cu was distributed in several of the protein fractions from the brain when examined by electrophoresis (Fig. 1) (7).

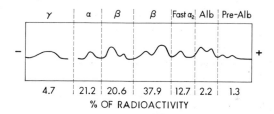

FIG. 1. Distribution of ^{64}Cu in protein fractions of brain by electrophoresis of Trissoluble fraction of acetone extract.

The failure to observe immediate effects of Cu on slices of brain tissue and their relative insensitivity to Cu led us to think of membranes more specifically, and thence to the membrane enzyme ATPase, which is the subject of so much brilliant work at the present time (8–12). Accordingly the microsomal fraction was prepared from the brains of pigeons by the method of McIlwain *et al.* (13); this involves homogenizing in 0.32 M sucrose solution, removing nuclei and cell debris by centrifuging at 500 $\times$ g, bringing down the mitochondria at 8000 $\times$ g, and spinning down the microsomes at 20,000 $\times$ g for 1 hour. In this work we had Mrs. M. Shorthouse as a colleague (14). The microsomes so obtained were carefully suspended in cold sucrose solution (0.32 M), and the equivalent of one quarter of one brain was used for each determination (volume, 0.5 ml). The reaction mixture contained in a total volume of 1.5 ml, 0.5 ml ATPase (microsomes), 100 mM NaCl, 30 mM KCl, 3 mM MgCl$_2$, 3mM Na-ATP + additions. Experiments were made in duplicate; there was usually good agreement except in the presence of ouabain.

TABLE II

MEMBRANE ATPASE AND Cu^{2+} [a,b]

Cu^{2+} in 1.5 ml	Percentage of controls
Expt. 1	
10 μg	78.6
5 μg	79.2
2 μg	78.6
Expt. 2	
2 μg	84.9
1 μg	90.7

[a] Pigeon brain prepared by method of Schwartz, Bachelard, and McIlwain. Data of Peters, Shorthouse, and Walshe.

[b] Phosphate liberated in 10 minutes at 37°. 0.5 ml enzyme (e.g., one-quarter pigeon brain) splits off an average 108 μg P_i from ATP in 10 minutes.

Table II shows the effect of Cu^{2+} in reducing the amount of phosphate split from ATP in 10 minutes at 37° by the membrane ATPase present. This became maximal at amounts of 5–10 μg of Cu^{2+} in 1.5 ml and could be even observed with 1.0 μg, i.e., 10.6 μM, an amount surprisingly close to that inducing convulsions in the pigeon *in vivo*.

In order to make sure that the Cu^{2+} was not involved merely in reversing the charge on some surface, we compared the effect of copper with that of thorium, cobalt, and cadmium. From Table III it will be seen that even

TABLE III

MEMBRANE ATPASE, EFFECT OF OTHER IONS[a,b]

	μM	Percentage of controls
Cu^{2+}	21	78.6
Cd^{2+}	106	91.1
Co^{2+}	354	97.0
Co^{2+}	708	91.1
Th^{4+}	58	100
Th^{4+}	115	105

[a] Data of Peters, Shorthouse, and Walshe.

[b] Details as in Table II.

40 μg Th^{4+} had no inhibitory action; some effect was induced by Cd^{2+}, and here again there was a parallel with injection experiments in the pigeon. It may be concluded, therefore, that there is a parallelism between the action on our membrane ATPase and the induction of the convulsive effect.

Our membrane preparation usually split off an average of 3.5 μmoles of phosphate in 10 minutes per 1 mg protein. The ATPase seems to have an —SH component; as has been previously described for rat brain and kidney membrane ATPase, it is sensitive to p-CMB (15, 16). We also find that addition of the thiols, penicillamine, BAL, thioctic acid, and diethyldithiocarbamate induces increases in activity of 25% and upward; see Table IV.

TABLE IV

MEMBRANE ATPASE,
INCREASES IN ACTIVITY INDUCED BY —SH COMPOUNDS[a]

No. of experiments	Compound	Concentration (mM)	Change (%)
5	Penicillamine	2.24	14 to 31
3	BAL	0.59	24 to 37
3	Thioctic acid	0.97	30 to 42
2	Diethyldithiocarbamate	1.12	27 to 33

[a] Data of Peters, Shorthouse, and Walshe.

On the basis of the evidence that I have presented so far, we advance the hypothesis that Cu^{2+} induces convulsions by interfering with an —SH-containing group in a membrane ATPase. The effect of the Cu never fails, even with diverse ATPase preparations, and has been observed with similar fractions from rat brain.

We next asked ourselves which ATPase was concerned in the effect. This we cannot answer dogmatically, mainly, although not entirely, because of the uncertain effect of ouabain in our hands. Some of our earlier preparations showed an inhibition with ouabain, not greater than 20%. Some of our later experiments showed none. Furthermore, with the pigeon microsomes, we found no effect when we omitted K$^+$; our medium then contained only about 0.4 meq K$^+$ per liter, as kindly determined for us by Dr. Lehmann. Hence we can conclude that Cu^{2+} is attacking part of the ATPase present, which need not be K$^+$ sensitive. Since the effect of the Cu is limited, there must be at least two forms of ATPase present.

TABLE V

MEMBRANE ATPASE,
EFFECTS OF PENICILLAMINE ± OUABAIN AND Cu^{2+} [a]

Addition	Percentage of control	Change (%)
Penicillamine [b]	131	+31
Ouabain [c]	94.8	−5
Cu^{2+} [d]	84.9	−15
Penicillamine + ouabain	105.2	−26
Penicillamine + Cu^{2+}	81.1	−50
Penicillamine + ouabain + Cu^{2+}	81.0	−50

[a] Data of Peters, Shorthouse, and Walshe.
[b] see Table IV.
[c] 100 μM.
[d] 21 μM.
[e] 53 μM.

There is an additional point that we should like to present. We have evidence that the extra activity induced by treatment with penicillamine is sensitive to both ouabain and Cu (Table V), ouabain producing decreases of up to 26% in a penicillamine-stimulated preparation. Hence, if we assume that our ouabain has normal activity, there appear to be three ATPase components in our microsomal preparation from the pigeon:

(a) Not inactivated by Cu or ouabain.
(b) Little affected by ouabain; sensitive to Cu.
(c) Stimulated by penicillamine; sensitive to ouabain and Cu.

In a very recent paper (17), it is stated that sometimes ouabain can increase activity in membrane ATPase preparations, a fact that we have occasionally observed. The authors suggest that some variations may be due to changes in orientation.

Turning to another point, we have made some observations on the antidotal effects of thiol compounds. It was found that none of the —SH substances could reverse the toxicity. This is in agreement with our findings *in vivo*, and it suggests that the compound which Cu^{2+} forms with the tissue constituent is irreversible.

In conclusion, we incline to the hypothesis that the effect of Cu^{2+} is on membrane transport, which would explain the convulsions; we realize that much more work is needed to prove this. It is indeed remarkable that Cu is normally so well regulated that it does not become physiologically displaced, although the "oligodynamic" effect of copper has been known since the past century (18).

Summary

(a) The aim of the research has been to define in biochemical terms the reason for the rather specific convulsive and lethal action of Cu^{2+} (10 μg) when injected into the subarachnoid space in the pigeon, in the hope of finding antidotes for the toxicity in the brain in Wilson's disease. Even dithiols will not act as antidotes. The amount of Cu^{2+} able to cause convulsions was determined by ^{64}Cu to be less than 5 μg. Though much of the copper is attached to soluble proteins, some remains combined after extraction with the insoluble neurokeratin fraction.

(b) Though the respiration of mitochondrial homogenates is also sensitive to copper, that of brain tissue slices is not. Owing to this and to the immediate action *in vivo*, the toxicity of Cu^{2+} to microsomal membrane ATPase has been examined. There was good correspondence between specific effects on this ATPase *in vitro* and *in vivo*, and similarly, failure of reactivation by dithiols. The action of Cu^{2+} appears to be on some —SH component; there is an increase of ATPase action by exposure to various thiols. As determined by copper and ouabain, there was more than one ATPase present in our preparation. The hypothesis is advanced that the convulsions induced by copper are due to an inhibition of the membrane transport of ions.

REFERENCES

1. Peters, R. A., "Biochemical lesions and lethal synthesis," Pergamon Press Ltd. Oxford, 1963.
2. Garattini, S., Morselli, P. L., Peters, R. A., and Valzelli, L., unpublished observations.
3. Bangham, A. D., and Dawson, R. M. C., *Biochem. J.*, **72**, 486 (1959).
4. Walshe, J. M., and Cumings, J. N., (eds.), "Wilson's disease," Blackwell Scientific Publications, Oxford, 1961.
5. Davies, A., Peters, R. A., and Walshe, J. M., *J. Physiol.*, **159**, 32P (1961).
6. Folch, J., and Lees, M., *J. Biol. Chem.*, **191**, 807 (1951).
7. Porter, H., *Arch. Neurol.*, 544 (1959).
8. Dunham, E. T., and Glynn, I. M., *J. Physiol.*, **156**, 274 (1961).
9. Whittam, R., and Blond, D. H., *Biochem. J.*, **92**, 147 (1964).
10. Albers, R. W., Arnaiz, G., and Robertis, E. De., *Proc. Natl. Acad. Sci.*, **53**, 557 (1965).
11. Post, R. L., Sen, A. K., and Rosenthal, A. S., *J. Biol. Chem.*, **240**, 1437 (1965).
12. Aldridge, W. N., *Biochem. J.*, **83**, 527 (1962).
13. Schwartz, A., Bachelard, H. S., and McIlwain, H., *Biochem. J.*, **84**, 626 (1962).
14. Peters, R. A., Shorthouse, M., and Walshe, J. M., *J. Physiol.*, **181**, 27 (1965)
15. Skou, J. C., *Biochem. Biophys. Res. Communs.*, **10**, 79 (1963).

16. Wheeler, K. P., and Whittam, R. *Biochem. J.*, **93,** 349 (1964).
17. Brown, H. D., Neucere, N. J., Altschul, A. M., and Evans, W. J., *Life Sciences*, **4,** 1439 (1965).
18. Bayliss, W. M., "Textbook of general physiology," Longmans, Green and Co. Ltd., New York, 1915, p. 222.

DISCUSSION

Dr. Porter: I would just like to reconsider my previous comment about mitochondria. May I suggest the possible protective effect of neonatal-type mitochondrocuprein against the copper accumulating in the liver. We know that the copper accumulates for many years in the brain in Wilson's disease. We have people who have had brains perfectly normal by histological examination, as well as perfectly normal in neurological function, who nonetheless had brain copper concentrations many times the normal. It may be that the pathological copper becomes bound to a number of different proteins where it has no toxic effect, and finally it spills over to one which is the significant toxic one.

Dr. Schubert: There exist metabolic differences between D- and L-penicillamine [Aposhian, H. V., *in* M. J. Seven (ed.), "Metal binding in medicine," J. B. Lippincott Co., Philadelphia, 1960, p. 290]. I wonder if you tried D- and L-penicillamine in your pigeon brain to see whether there was a difference.

Dr. Peters: I don't think we ever used the L- isomer so I'm afraid we can't answer that one.

Quite recently we thought the Cu^{2+}-binding site might be an imidazole, so we tried imidazole. It didn't do anything at all to the effect of the copper on the membrane ATPase.

Copper—Amino Acid Complexes in Human Serum[*]

BIBUDHENDRA SARKAR[†] AND THEO P. A. KRUCK

Department of Pediatrics, Faculty of Medicine,
University of Toronto and The Research Institute,
The Hospital for Sick Children,
Toronto, Canada

Human serum contains approximately 1 μg of copper per milliliter. Most of this is bound to the copper protein ceruloplasmin. A small fraction (approximately 5%), however, is loosely bound to albumin. The copper bound to ceruloplasmin is not exchangeable *in vivo* (1). It is the albumin-bound fraction of serum copper that is in rapid equilibrium with copper in tissues (2), and which is considered to be the transport form of copper in blood. Recently it has been found that there is a third form of serum copper, bound to amino acids. This fraction is in equilibrium with the fraction bound to albumin. It was suggested that copper transport between blood and the tissues may be mediated by amino acids (3, 4).

An investigation was started to isolate and characterize the copper-amino acid complexes from human serum and to study some of their properties. A preliminary account of the results will be presented here and their significance will be discussed in relation to biological systems.

I. Experimental Procedure

A. Materials

Whole blood obtained by venipuncture from normal and healthy individuals was allowed to clot and the serum was obtained by centrifugation. A preparation of ^{64}Cu with a high specific activity (20 mC $^{64}Cu/\mu g$ Cu) was supplied by McMaster University. ^{14}C-histidine, ^{14}C-threonine, and ^{14}C-glutamine were obtained from Schwartz Bioresearch, Inc. All the glassware, reagents, and distilled water were copper free.

B. Preparation of Synthetic Copper—Amino Acid Complexes

Freshly prepared copper hydroxide gel was added in excess to 20 ml of 0.2 M solutions of amino acids in water. Immediately upon the addition of the gel, an intense blue color developed. The preparations were stirred for

[*] Supported by funds from the John A. Hartford Foundation of New York.
[†] Medical Research Scholar, Medical Research Council of Canada.

5 minutes during which time the pH was maintained at 7.5. Excess copper hydroxide was separated by centrifugation. Crystals of copper–amino acid complexes were obtained by slow evaporation of the solutions at 40°. Synthetic complexes were also prepared by adding a solution of cupric acetate or cupric nitrate to a solution of amino acid in a molar ratio of 1:2 and adjusting the pH to 7.5 with sodium hydroxide. The complex synthesized by the former method had the advantage of not containing any salt associated with the complex formed in the solution.

The histidine-Cu-threonine complex was prepared by adding 20 ml of 0.2 M cupric nitrate solution to a mixture of 10 ml of 0.4 M histidine and 10 ml of 0.4 M threonine. The solution was stirred for 5 minutes and the pH was adjusted to 7.5. The histidine-Cu-threonine complex was prepared also by mixing an equimolar concentration of Cu-histidine and Cu-threonine.

C. Separation of the Nonprotein-Bound Fraction of Serum Copper

a. Ultracentrifugation. Cupric nitrate containing ^{64}Cu was mixed with serum to achieve a copper-to-albumin molar ratio of 2:1. The pH was then adjusted to 7.4 and the serum sample was centrifuged in a Spinco Model L preparative ultracentrifuge at 114,000 × g for 24 hours. The supernatant was separated by inserting a Pasteur pipette halfway down the centrifuge tube and carefully withdrawing the supernatant without disturbing the residual protein. The activity in the original serum and the supernatant was measured in a well-type scintillation counter.

b. Ultrafiltration. A sample of serum with a copper-to-albumin molar ratio of 2:1, at pH 7.4, prepared as stated above, was ultrafiltered by Toribara's method (5) with slight modification. This consisted of substituting air for the 5% CO_2 atmosphere. The activity in the serum and the ultrafiltrate was measured as above.

For the identification of copper–amino acid complexes in serum trace amounts of [64]Cu (<0.002 μg Cu/ml) were added to the serum before ultrafiltration. In some instances the serum was ultrafiltered first and the ^{64}Cu was added to the ultrafiltrate. These mixtures showed similar copper-binding patterns on thin-layer chromatograms no matter at what stage the ^{64}Cu was added.

D. Desalting

The serum ultrafiltrate was desalted by adsorption of the amino acids onto Dowex 50 resin and subsequent elution of the amino acids from the resin. An 8 mm wide and 5 cm long column was prepared by filling a suitable tube with a slurry of Dowex 50 in water. The column was first washed with 2 M NH_3 followed by water. It was then washed with 2 M HCl followed again by water. The ultrafiltrate (1–4 ml) was diluted to 10 ml total volume with water, adjusted to pH 4.5 with dilute acetic acid, and poured onto the column. The amino acids were eluted with 2 M NH$_3$ and assayed by two-dimensional chromatography using pyridine–3 M NH$_3$–acetone (5:2:3) and isopropanol–formic acid–water (8:1:1) as the solvents. The eluate was taken to dryness in a flash evaporator at room temperature and dissolved in a volume of water corresponding to the original sample in order to obtain the amino acids in the concentration at which they were present in the serum.

E. Separation and Identification of Copper–Amino Acid Complexes

Thin-layer chromatography on silica gel, using 60%(v/v) acetone in water as solvent, was found to be the most suitable method for the isolation of the Cu–amino acid complexes from serum. The duration of chromatography was 20 minutes unless stated otherwise, at room temperature, and the pH was maintained at 7.5–8.0. Amino acids were located by spraying the plates first with 2 M HCl and then with ninhydrin. Copper was located by spraying with 0.015% zinc dibenzyldithiocarbamate in carbon tetrachloride.

Autoradiography was used to locate ^{64}Cu- and ^{14}C-labeled amino acids on the plates. When both copper and amino acids were used as radioactive components the thin-layer plates were first exposed for ^{64}Cu. After the ^{64}Cu (half-life 12.8 hours) had decayed completely, the same plates were reexposed for ^{14}C. The synthetic copper–amino acid complexes prepared by the methods outlined above were used to identify the spots obtained from the serum ultrafiltrates.

The radioactive spots on the thin-layer plates were scraped off in some instances and the scrapings were directly counted for ^{64}Cu in a scintillation well counter. Carbon-14 radioactivity was measured in a liquid scintillation counter.

F. Absorption Spectra

Visible and near-ultraviolet absorption spectra were taken with a Beckman DK-2 spectrophotometer using a 1.0 cm light path. An attempt to study the kinetics of the formation of the histidine-Cu-threonine complex was carried out at 620 mμ by using equimolar concentrations of copper and amino acids in both cuvettes. One cuvette contained the histidine-Cu-threonine complex; the other contained Cu-threonine. An equimolar concentration of Cu-histidine was added to the second cuvette and the change in optical density was measured as quickly as possible.

II. Results

A. Separation of the Amino Acid–Bound Form of Copper from Human Serum

The two different methods for the separation of the nonprotein-bound fraction of copper in serum were compared. Part of a sample of normal human serum was extensively dialyzed at 4° against 0.85% NaCl solution, the pH of which was adjusted to 7.4 with dilute HCl. To this "predialyzed" sample of serum, and also to an undialyzed sample of the same serum, radioactive-labeled copper was added to achieve a copper-to-albumin molar ratio of 2:1. The nonprotein-bound fraction of serum copper was then separated in parallel samples of these mixtures by both ultracentrifugation and ultrafiltration. The percentage of the ^{64}Cu activity remaining in the supernatant and in the ultrafiltrate are shown in Table I. The dif-

TABLE I

Separation of the Amino Acid–Bound Form of Copper from Human Serum by Ultracentrifugation and Ultrafiltration

| | Percentage of initial activity | |
	Ultrafiltrate	Supernatant following ultracentrifugation
Native serum	4.25	5.40
Dialyzed serum	0.42	0.54

ference between the results obtained by the two methods is small. The percentage of the activity in the ultrafiltrate was somewhat lower. This could be due to a slight dilution of the sample caused by wetting the dialysis bags before ultrafiltration.

The ultrafiltration method had the advantage of yielding larger amounts of ultrafiltrate in a shorter period of time and therefore this method was used subsequently to obtain the protein-free fraction of serum copper.

B. Identification of Copper–Amino Acid Complexes Present in Human Serum

When trace amounts of ^{64}Cu were added to native serum and the ultrafiltrate chromatographed on a thin-layer plate, separation of copper–amino acid complexes into rather diffuse bands was obtained (Fig. 1, strip A). When the ^{64}Cu was added to the ultrafiltrate of serum the separation was better but still not satisfactory (strip B). It was thought that this

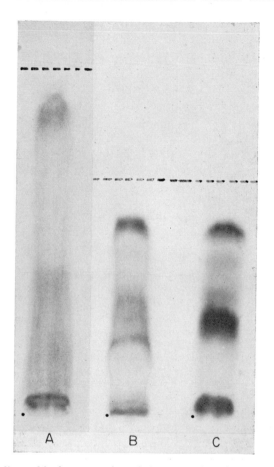

FIG. 1. Autoradiographic demonstration of the separation of copper–amino acid complexes from serum ultrafiltrates by thin-layer chromatography. The black dots mark the line of origin. The solvent front is marked by the dotted line. A, Ultrafiltrate from a mixture of serum and ^{64}Cu; B, ^{64}Cu added to the serum ultrafiltrate; C, ^{64}Cu added to the desalted serum ultrafiltrate.

was mainly due to the presence of salts in the ultrafiltrate. Since we were mainly interested in the copper binding of the amino acids in serum, the serum ultrafiltrate was first desalted and the ^{64}Cu was added thereafter in order to avoid interference by salts. When this mixture was chromatographed, separation into much sharper bands was achieved, as illustrated in Fig. 1, strip C.

Strip E in Fig. 2 is an autoradiogram of a thin-layer chromatogram obtained from a mixture of ^{64}Cu with desalted serum ultrafiltrate. Four distinct bands were found to move. Two of these, the fastest and the

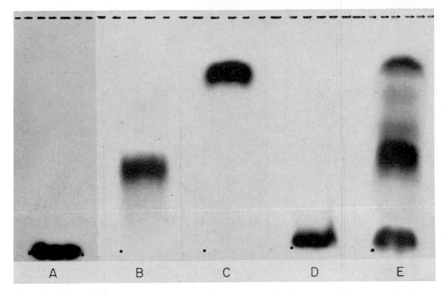

Fig. 2. Identification of the copper–amino acid complexes in serum ultrafiltrate by thin-layer chromatography. Autoradiographic picture of thin-layer chromatograms. A, $^{64}Cu(OH)_2$; B, ^{64}Cu-histidine; C, ^{64}Cu-threonine; D, ^{64}Cu + ultrafiltrate from dialyzed serum; E, ^{64}Cu + desalted serum ultrafiltrate.

slowest moving bands, coincided with the bands of Cu-histidine and Cu-threonine complexes, respectively (strips B and C). When the solution of ^{64}Cu was placed on the plate alone it remained at the origin (strip A). When ^{64}Cu was added to the desalted ultrafiltrate of predialyzed serum, it remained at the origin also (strip D). A certain amount of ^{64}Cu was found at the origin in the samples in strip E as well.

The amino acid concentration was shown to influence the ^{64}Cu binding in certain cases. This effect is shown in Fig. 3, where an excess amount (10–20 times the physiological concentration) of one amino acid was added to a solution containing physiological concentrations of all the other amino acids. The amino acid added in excess was labeled with ^{14}C and parallel chromatograms were exposed for ^{64}Cu and ^{14}C. When glutamine was added in excess (Fig. 3, strip E), ^{64}Cu was located mostly in the region of Cu-glutamine and Cu-histidine. Practically no ^{64}Cu was in the position of Cu-threonine. When threonine was in excess (strip C) ^{64}Cu binding was shown largely with threonine and histidine and there was no binding to glutamine. When histidine was added in excess (strip A), ^{64}Cu bound mostly with histidine, very little with threonine, and not at all with glutamine. Strips B, D, and F, which were exposed for ^{14}C contained in the amino acids added

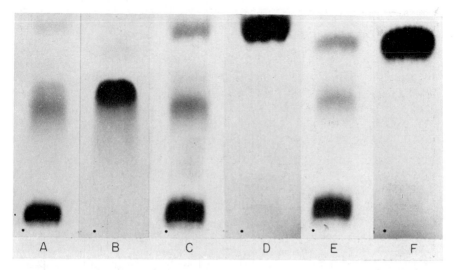

Fig. 3. Influence of the variation of the concentration of a single amino acid on the formation of copper–amino acid complexes in a solution containing physiological concentrations of all the other amino acids. A and B, ^{64}Cu + physiological concentrations of amino acids + excess ^{14}C-histidine. C, and D, ^{64}Cu + physiological concentrations of amino acids + excess ^{14}C-threonine. E and F, ^{64}Cu + physiological concentrations of amino acids + excess ^{14}C-glutamine. A, C, and E, exposed only for ^{64}Cu; B, D, and F, exposed only for ^{14}C.

in excess, helped to identify the copper–amino acid complexes in strips A, C, and E. From the distribution of the ^{64}Cu and ^{14}C amino acid spots in Fig. 3, one is tempted to suggest that the faster of the two intermediate bands in Fig. 2, strip E, is Cu-glutamine.

In further experiments solutions containing physiological concentrations of both histidine and threonine were prepared with added trace amounts of ^{64}Cu. Autoradiograms of thin-layer chromatograms of these mixtures exposed for ^{64}Cu revealed activity in three distinct bands (Fig. 4, strip C). The fastest-moving one of these coincided with a spot obtained by chromatographing synthetic Cu-threonine complex (strip B). The slowest band corresponded to a spot of Cu-histidine complex (strip A). It was suggestive that the intermediate band in strip C was a complex of histidine-Cu-threonine. Strip D in Fig. 4 is an autoradiogram of a thin-layer chromatogram of a mixture of ^{14}C-histidine, copper, and threonine exposed for ^{14}C. Activity is located in the slow band of Cu-histidine, but also in the intermediate band. Strip E is an autoradiogram of a chromatogram of histidine, copper, and ^{14}C-threonine. Carbon-14 activity is again present in the intermediate band as well as in the location typical for Cu-threonine. The logical conclusion from these findings is that the ^{64}Cu in the inter-

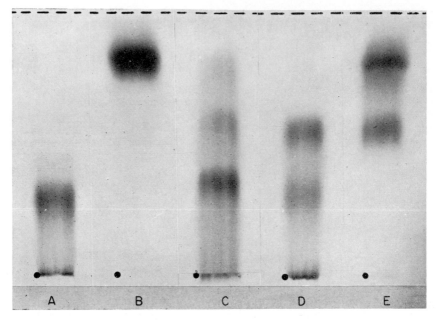

Fig. 4. Autoradiograph of a thin-layer chromatogram showing the formation of the mixed complex of histidine-Cu-threonine. A, ^{64}Cu + histidine; B, ^{64}Cu + threonine; C, ^{64}Cu + histidine + threonine; D, Cu + ^{14}C-histidine + threonine; E, Cu + histidine + ^{14}C-threonine.

mediate band of strip C is in the form of an histidine-Cu-threonine complex. It may also be safe to assume that the fourth hitherto unidentified band in thin-layer chromatograms of ^{64}Cu added to desalted serum ultrafiltrate (strip C, Fig. 1 and strip E, Fig. 2) is the same complex.

C. Molar Ratio of Amino Acid to Copper in the Complexes Separated by Thin-Layer Chromatography

Trace amounts of ^{64}Cu were added to a solution containing physiological concentrations of both ^{14}C-histidine and ^{14}C-threonine. This mixture was subjected to thin-layer chromatography and the resulting bands of Cu-histidine, Cu-threonine, and histidine-Cu-threonine were scraped off and assayed quantitively for ^{64}Cu and ^{14}C activity. From these measurements the amounts and molar ratios of the amino acids and copper in the individual bands were calculated. These data are shown in Table II. It appears that the molar ratio of amino acids to copper in each case is very close to 2, indicating that these are complexes between one atom of copper and two molecules of the single or the two different amino acids.

TABLE II

MOLAR RATIO OF AMINO ACID AND COPPER IN THE COPPER–AMINO ACID COMPLEXES

Copper–amino acid complex	Copper (μmoles)	Amino acid (μmoles)	Molar ratio, amino acid to Cu
Cu-histidine	3.99	8.93	2.23
Cu-threonine	4.94	11.45	2.32
Histidine-Cu-threonine	1.14	2.16	1.89

At pH 7.5 the complexes formed in the presence of widely different molar ratios of copper and amino acids were found, by thin-layer chromatography, to be similar to the complexes obtained by the addition of trace amounts of copper to physiological concentrations of amino acids.

D. Physicochemical Properties of the Histidine-Cu-Threonine Complex

Repeated attempts to purify and isolate the histidine-Cu-threonine complex were unsuccessful. Repeated chromatography of this complex always resulted in the finding of three components: Cu-histidine, Cu-threonine, and histidine-Cu-threonine. From the preliminary studies it looked as though the amount of the histidine-Cu-threonine complex remained constant as long as it was in an equilibrium mixture with Cu-histidine and Cu-threonine and that the histidine Cu-threonine complex started to break down as soon as Cu-histidine and Cu-threonine were not present.

The following experiment illustrates these points. Histidine, threonine, and copper labeled with ^{64}Cu were disolved in water in equimolar concentration, and the pH adjusted to 7.5. On a series of thin-layer chromatographic plates this mixture was allowed to run for various lengths of time and distance. The plates were then dried, the spots were located by autoradiography, and their distance from the origin measured. The spots were then scraped off and assayed for ^{64}Cu activity. The activity in the individual spots was expressed as a percentage of the total activity applied to the origin. These data are plotted in Fig. 5 against the distance of the spot from the origin, measured in inches.

The percentage of total ^{64}Cu activity bound to histidine and threonine remained relatively constant except for a slight decline, which is probably due to minor degree of dissociation with increasing length of migration. The ^{64}Cu activity associated with the intermediate band, formerly identified as the histidine-Cu-threonine complex, showed a marked decline. This phenonmenon is best explained by the suggestion that rapid dissociation

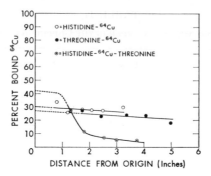

FIG. 5. Stability of the copper–amino acid complexes in the course of thin-layer chromatography. Percentage of original ^{64}Cu activity plotted against distance of migration.

of the histidine-Cu-threonine complex into Cu-histidine and Cu-threonine complexes occurs as soon as the former is separated in the course of the chromatography.

Extrapolation of the lines connecting the percentage of ^{64}Cu activity in the bands of Cu-histidine complex and the bands of Cu-threonine complex to zero time and distance allows the conclusion that in the original mixture 31% of the copper was in association with histidine and 27% in association with threonine. Disregarding the probably insignificant amount of copper which may not be complexed by amino acids, this leaves 42% of the copper in the form of the histidine-Cu-threonine complex. Accordingly and somewhat arbitrarily we have extrapolated the line connecting the percentage ^{64}Cu activity contained in the bands of the histidine-Cu-threonine complex to this point.

Visible and near-ultraviolet absorption spectra of these complexes at pH 7.5 are shown in Fig. 6. A solution of Cu-histidine, Cu-threonine, and a solution of both the former complexes and histidine-Cu-threonine together

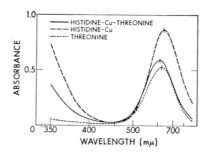

FIG. 6. Absorption spectra of Cu-histidine, histidine-Cu-threonine, and Cu-threonine at pH 7.5.

had absorption peaks very close to each other in the visible range around 600 mμ, probably due to copper complexes with electron-donating nitrogens. Around this wavelength the solution of Cu-histidine has a higher absorption than the other solutions. In the near-ultraviolet range there was no significant peak of absorption in the case of any one of these solutions. The difference spectra of histidine-Cu-threonine which were taken at 620 mμ after addition of Cu-threonine to Cu-histidine showed that the formation of the histidine-Cu-threonine complex proceeded faster than could be measured by this technique.

III. Discussion

A. Quantitative Importance of Copper–Amino Acid Complexes

Evidence that strongly suggested the presence of a low molecular weight, amino acid–bound form of copper in human serum was presented earlier from our laboratories. These studies and subsequent experiments suggested also that amino acids are the only low molecular constituents of serum which bind copper. These observations were confirmed and extended by the results of the studies reported here. Separation of amino acid–copper complexes from the ultrafiltrates of normal human sera was achieved. Copper-histidine, Cu-threonine, and Cu-glutamine complexes were isolated and identified. The results of the previous studies suggested that in human serum there may be a complex between copper and two different amino acids. In the present study a complex form of copper consisting of units of histidine, threonine, and copper in a 1 : 1 : 1 molar ratio was isolated chromatographically and identified in human serum ultrafiltrates.

The order of quantitative importance of these copper–amino acid complexes in normal serum has also been established by the results of this study. Considering the complexes of copper with single amino acids the decreasing order of quantitative importance was Cu-histidine, Cu-threonine, Cu-glutamine. The same order of quantitative importance was suggested by the results of previous studies on the basis of completely different experimental evidence. Complexes of copper with single amino acids other than the above three have not been detected in chromatograms of the ultrafiltrates of normal human serum. This suggests that from a quantitative point of view they are of minor importance, if any.

It was more difficult to establish the quantitative importance of the histidine-Cu-threonine complex in relation to the complexes of copper with the single amino acids because of the instability of the former in the course of chromatographic separation. However, the results of experiments with a purified system, with simple mixtures of histidine, threonine, and copper in the presence of an excess of the amino acids, suggested that as much as 40% of the copper may be present in the form of histidine-Cu-threonine complex. This means that the latter complex form of copper may well be more important from a quantitative point of view than would appear from the relative intensity of the copper-complex bands in the chromatograms of normal serum ultrafiltrates.

From the experiments in which the concentration of a single amino acid was varied in the presence of physiological concentrations of the others it would appear that the relative amounts of copper bound by the different amino acids depends very largely on the concentration of the amino acids relative to each other. The concentrations of individual amino acids and the stability constants of the various copper–amino acid complexes will ultimately determine the distribution of nonprotein-bound copper in the various complexes. This suggests that in patients with abnormal plasma free amino acid levels there may be abnormal patterns of copper–amino acid complexes that could have pathological consequences. Further exploration of this problem is warranted.

Concerning the physicochemical characteristics of these copper–amino acid complexes only a few conclusions can be deduced from the presently available experimental results. In the case of the complexes of copper with both single amino acids and with histidine and threonine a 2:1 molar ratio between amino acids and copper was found. This molar ratio was independent of the relative concentration of amino acids and copper in the solutions, within a wide range of relative concentrations. Whether these complexes between two molecules of amino acids and one atom of copper are in monomeric, dimeric, or even in a low polymeric form, cannot be decided on the basis of available data.

B. Equilibrium in the Copper–Histidine–Threonine System

The existence of a complex between copper and two different amino acids has not been reported as yet to our knowledge. The findings point to the fact that the histidine-Cu-threonine complex is in dissociation equilibrium with Cu-histidine and Cu-threonine, and these in turn are in equilibrium with histidine, threonine, and cupric ions according to the following equations:

$$2\ Cu^{2+} + 2\ His + 2\ Thr \rightleftharpoons Cu^{2+}\text{-}(His)_2 + Cu^{2+}\text{-}(Thr)_2 \qquad (1)$$

$$Cu^{2+}\text{-}(His)_2 + Cu^{2+}\text{-}(Thr)_2 \rightleftharpoons 2\ His\text{-}Cu^{2+}\text{-}Thr \qquad (2)$$

Preliminary evidence points to the fact that a very significant proportion of copper is in fact in the form of histidine-Cu-threonine complex and that this may be a rather preferred molecular configuration.

To complete the picture it should be mentioned here that, according to earlier work (3, 4) in human serum there is an equilibrium between copper bound to albumin and copper bound to amino acids. This can be described by the following equations:

$$Cu^{2+} + \text{Amino acids} \rightleftharpoons Cu^{2+}\text{-Amino acid complexes} \qquad (3)$$

$$Cu^{2+} + \text{Albumin} \rightleftharpoons Cu^{2+}\text{-Albumin complex} \qquad (4)$$

$$Cu^{2+}\text{-Amino acid complexes} + \text{Albumin} \rightleftharpoons Cu^{2+}\text{-Albumin complex}$$
$$+ \text{Amino acids} \qquad (5)$$

The biological role of this system is probably in the transport of copper through biological membranes. The amino acid complexes of copper, which are of a much lower order of molecular size than the albumin-copper complexes may mediate transport through biological membranes by virtue of the equilibrium between these two molecular species of copper. Some evidence pointing in this direction has already been obtained in our laboratories (6). However, much further work will be necessary to characterize more specifically both the nature and the role of this system.

IV. Summary

(a) The amino acid–bound form of copper has been isolated from normal human serum by ultrafiltration and ultracentrifugation.

(b) Four major amino acid–bound forms of copper were separated and identified by thin-layer chromatography. Three individual copper–amino acid complexes, Cu-histidine, Cu-threonine, and Cu-glutamine, and one complex of histidine-Cu-threonine were shown to be present in normal serum.

(c) The complexes made by using different molar ratios of copper and amino acids at pH 7.5 were found to be similar to those complexes obtained by addition of ^{64}Cu to a physiological concentration of all the amino acids including ^{14}C-labeled histidine, threonine, and glutamine. The molar distribution of copper and amino acids in Cu-histidine, Cu-threonine, Cu-glutamine, and histidine-Cu-threonine complexes was found to be 1:2.

(d) Considering the complexes of copper with single amino acids in serum the order of quantitative importance was Cu-histidine, Cu-threonine, Cu-glutamine, in decreasing order. Experiments with a purified system, consisting of simple mixtures of histidine, threonine, and copper, suggested that as much as 40% of the copper may be present in the form of an histidine-Cu-threonine complex.

(e) Preliminary studies showed that the histidine-Cu-threonine complex was formed very rapidly and that it was stable in an equilibrium mixture of Cu-histidine and Cu-threonine complex.

ACKNOWLEDGMENT

Grateful thanks are due to Dr. Andrew Sass-Kortsak for his criticism and assistance in reviewing this manuscript.

REFERENCES

1. Sternlieb, I., Morell, A. G., Tucker, W. D., Green, M. W., and Scheinberg, I. H., *J. Clin. Invest.*, **40**, 1834 (1961).
2. Bearn, A. G., and Kunkel, H. G., *Proc. Soc. Exp. Biol. Med.*, **88**, 44 (1954).
3. Neumann, P. Z., and Sass-Kortsak, A., *Vox Sanguinis*, **8**, 111 (1963).
4. Neumann, P. Z., and Sass-Kortask, A., personal communication.
5. Toribara, T. Y., Raymond Terepha, A., Deway, P. A., *J. Clin. Invest.*, **36**, 738 (1957).
6. Harris, D. I. M., and Sass-Kortsak, A., *Proc. Can. Fed. Biol. Soc.*, **7**, 8 (1964).

DISCUSSION

DR. FRIEDEN: Is the concentration of cysteine, glutathione, and related compounds, which I think would strongly interact with Cu^{2+} so low as to exclude these from being the ultrafilterable copper ion carrier?

DR. SARKAR: If one dialyzes out all the ultrafilterable compounds from human serum and reconstitutes the dialyzed serum with the physiological concentrations of all the amino acids, one can find the same amount of copper in the nonprotein fraction of serum after the addition of copper as was in the native serum. We have not been able to locate the copper complexes of glutathione and cysteine in the normal serum by our method.

DR. SASS-KORTSAK: May I add to the answer to the previous question? Glutathione is not present in human serum. When we dialyzed human serum, we found almost no nonprotein-bound copper. Then we added back the amino acids in the concentrations originally present and measured the nonprotein-bound copper. We found that by just adding the amino acids we could account for all the nonprotein-bound copper.

DR. AISEN: Do you have any idea of the magnitude of the binding constants for the copper–amino acid complexes that you have studied?

DR. SARKAR: No, we do not have any idea at present. The literature shows values for the binding constants of some, but not all, of the complexes we have studied. This work is now under way.

The Essential Role of Cupric Ion in the Biological Activity of 3-Ethoxy-2-oxobutyraldehydebisthiosemicarbazone, A New Antitumor Agent

H. G. PETERING AND G. J. VanGIESSEN*

Biochemical Research Division,
The Upjohn Company,
Kalamazoo, Michigan

The chelation of transition metal ions has long been studied in the hope of finding a mechanism that might explain the carcinogenic action of certain metals and some organic chemicals and has recently been invoked as a basis for the design of carcinostatic drugs (1). French and Freedlander in 1958 (2) reported that several dithiosemicarbazones similar to KTS[1] had antitumor activity under special circumstances and suggested that this activity was in some way due to the metal-sequestering action of the drugs. However, until the work on KTS, which forms the basis of this report, had been carried out there was no evidence available to identify or specify the nature of the antitumor activity of any member of this class of agents.

I. Antitumor Activity

In 1962, Petering and Buskirk (3) showed that KTS had pronounced antitumor activity, and in 1964 Petering, Buskirk, and Underwood (4) described in detail their studies with KTS and a series of related bisthiosemicarbazones, indicating the greater therapeutic activity of KTS against several transplanted rat tumors. It was also stated that the action of KTS was in some way dependent on the presence of cupric ion in the diet or environment of the tumor-bearing animals. The experiments carried out by us and others, which clearly indicate that the biological action of KTS requires the interaction of this drug and cupric ion, are summarized here.

Although all of the compounds listed in Fig. 1 are strong chelators of cupric ion, there is a marked difference in their *in vivo* antitumor activity. KTS was the most active of the series studied (4). This high level of activity has been confirmed by Mihich and Nichol (5), Martin (6), and French (7).

KTS has been found to active *in vivo* against a large spectrum of tumors in rodents, among them the following: in the mouse against C_3H (trans-

---

* Not at meeting.
[1] The abbreviations used are: KTS, 3-ethoxy-2-oxobutyraldehydebisthiosemicarbazone; Cu-KTS, the cupric chelate of KTS.

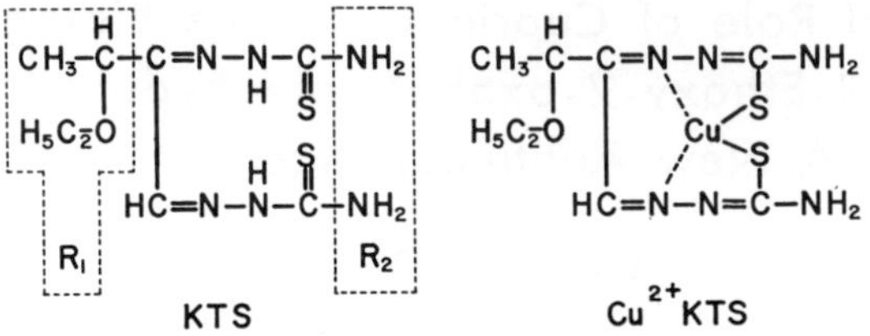

SUBSTITUTIONS

ABBREV.	KTS	KTSM	KMTS	KATS	PTS	PTSM	EPTSM
R_1	$CH_3-CH(OC_2H_5)-$	$CH_3-CH(OC_2H_5)-$	$CH_3-CH(OCH_3)-$	$CH_3-CH(OCOCH_3)-$	H_3C-	H_3C-	$H_2C(OC_2H_5)-$
R_2	$-NH_2$	$-NHCH_3$	$-NH_2$	$-NH_2$	$-NH_2$	$-NHCH_3$	$-NHCH_3$

FIG. 1. Structure of 3-ethoxy-2-oxobutyraldehydebisthiosemicarbazone or KTS, its cupric chelate, and several closely related compounds. All of these compounds have been shown to have antitumor activity or cytotoxicity, and all chelate copper readily (21). K, kethoxal, another name for 3-ethoxy-2-oxobutyraldehyde; P, pyruvaldehyde.

planted) mammary carcinoma, Ca 755, Sarcoma 180, Ehrlich's carcinoma, Lewis lung carcinoma, and Ridgeway osteogenic sarcoma; and in the rat against Walker 256 carcinosarcoma (nitrogen mustard-resistant and sensitive variants), Jensen sarcoma, Murphy-Sturm lymphoma, and Guerin carcinoma.

TABLE I

EFFECT OF CUPRIC ION INTAKE OF TUMOR-BEARING RATS[a] FED COPPER-DEFICIENT DIET[b] ON ANTITUMOR ACTIVITY OF KTS DAY 4–DAY 17

Cu supplement (μg/rat/day)	Δ Average Body wt. (g)	Δ Average tumor diameter (mm)	Survival	Regression
None	57.7	27.5	3/5	0
None[c]	45.6	34.0	5/5	0
40	51.8	27.8	5/5	0
40[c]	59.6	18.8	5/5	0
160	87.0	37.2	5/5	0
160[c]	37.8	−2.0	5/5	2

[a] Walker 256 carcinosarcoma was used.

[b] Diet No. 44 was composed of 30% casein, 57% sucrose, 5% soybean substitute oil (with fat-soluble vitamins), 4% salts W (modified-free of Cu^{2+}), and 4% starch (with water-soluble vitamins).

[c] KTS was given orally daily at 25 mg/Kg.

TABLE II
ANTITUMOR ACTIVITY OF Cu-KTS (ORAL) IN RATS BEARING WALKER 256 CARCINOSARCOMA[a]

Drug and dose (orally)	Δ Average body wt. (g ± S.D.)	Δ Average tumor diameter (mm ± S.D.)	Survival
None	70.0 ± 9.3	33.9 ± 2.6	9/10
KTS–25 mg/Kg	61.4 ± 5.1	−1.8 ± 2.6	5/5
Cu-KTS, 2 mg/Kg	79.3 ± 19.2	37.5 ± 3.9	4/5
Cu-KTS, 4 mg/Kg	67.6 ± 4.0	27.7 ± 1.1	5/5
Cu-KTS, 8 mg/Kg	40.0 ± 8.1	9.0 ± 2.6	5/5
Cu-KTS, 16 mg/Kg	−5.3 ± 13.1	−4.8 ± 1.6	4/5

[a] Stock Diet BA was used.

Dietary regimens have been found to affect the activity of KTS (8); the activity of the drug was always greater when the animals were fed a purified diet of known composition than when they were given a diet of natural feedstuffs. When we investigated the cause of these dietary effects, we found that some of the side effects of KTS could be minimized by feeding the experimental animals diets high in good quality protein, thiamine, pantothenic acid, and ascorbic acid. An excess of the water-soluble vitamins also appeared to potentiate the antitumor activity of KTS. The most important dietary component insofar as drug action was concerned, however, was the mineral supplement. Diets low in cupric ion or devoid of it, when fed to tumor-bearing rats, caused a marked reduction in both the toxicity of the drug and in its antitumor activity. A representative experiment taken from our report (9) is summarized in Table I. In the presence of 25 mg per kilogram of KTS per day there is a linear response in antitumor action when the daily intake of cupric ion is increased logarithmically.

These and other data suggested to us that there was an interaction of cupric ion and KTS with the possible formation of the cupric chelate of KTS. The experiment shown in Table II shows Cu-KTS indeed does have marked antitumor activity when given orally in doses of 8–16 mg/Kg to rats bearing the Walker 256 carcinosarcoma.

II. *In Vitro* Cytotoxicity

With the antitumor activity of KTS definitely related to the dietary intake of copper, we found it necessary to turn to *in vitro* mammalian cell culture systems in order to study the nature of this relationship in more detail than could be done in the animal experiments. Using the KB-cell dilution method of Smith *et al.* (10), we could show that KTS and Cu-KTS were highly cytotoxic, but the presence of 10% calf serum in the culture medium prevented any measure of control of the level of trace metal concentration. We therefore modified the method of Arai and Suzuki (11) for our purposes, with a medium kept as simple as possible so that all metal ion concentrations could be defined.

We incubated standardized suspensions of freshly isolated viable tumor cells in buffered balanced salt medium with doubling concentrations of drug and cupric acetate for 1 hour and then mixed these preparations with buffered agar containing methylene blue. After this the gelled mixture was incubated at 37° until the end point was reached. The end point in this system is the inhibition of respiration of the cells at a time when the control suspension shows complete decolorization of the dye. The inhibitory concentration is then taken as that level which inhibits respiration to an extent equal to that caused by a reduction in cell concentration of 20% of the control suspension. Consistent quantitative results are readily achieved if suitable controls are included in each experiment. The cytotoxic level of cupric ion was first determined and then a level substantially below this was used with the drug to determine the interaction.

Representative data from the report of Petering, Buskirk, and Kupiecki (12) are shown in Table III. These indicate that KTS is highly cytotoxic for Walker 256 tumor cells in our system when noncytotoxic levels of cupric ion are present. In addition, these data show that the cytotoxicity

TABLE III

Effect of Cu^{2+} on Cytotoxicity[a] (*in Vitro*) of KTS

Drug	Cu^{2+} conc.[b] (μg/ml)	Cytotoxic level of KTS (μg/ml)
KTS	None	>800
KTS	0.4	0.8
KTS	0.8	0.2
KTS	1.6	0.1
Cu–KTS	None	0.8–1.6
Cu–KTS	0.4	0.1–0.2

[a] Modification of Arai and Suzuki method (11). Walker 256 carcinosarcoma cells were used.

[b] 3.2 μg of Cu^{2+}/ml was found to be cytotoxic in this test. Cu^{2+} supplied as cupric acetate.

of the cupric chelate Cu-KTS is increased when 0.4 μg Cu²⁺/ml is present in the medium.

It would appear that the cytotoxicity of the combination of cupric ion and KTS, or the copper chelate itself, is of a highly specific nature since noncytotoxic levels of other essential trace metal ions have little effect on the activity of KTS in our system. The effect of cupric ion on the cytotoxicity of KTS has been found to occur with the cells of many spontaneous and transplanted tumors.

Sartorelli, Welch, and Booth (13) have reported that Cu-KTS markedly reduces DNA synthesis in Sarcoma 180 cells *in vivo*, and Bhuyan (14) has found similar evidence for the inhibition of DNA synthesis in KB cells in tissue culture systems. In neither investigation did KTS itself have any appreciable effect.

III. Chemistry of KTS and Cu-KTS

The chelation of bisthiosemicarbazones with transition metal ions has been known for some time and the reaction of 1,2-disubstituted-glyoxal bisthiosemicarbazones with Cu²⁺, Ni²⁺, and Pd²⁺ was studied by Bahr (15, 16). French and Freedlander (2) appear to have been the first to suggest that the antitumor activity of some α-ketoaldehydebisthiosemicarbazones was in some way related to their chelation properties. These authors and Furst (1) assumed that the probable role of these agents was to remove certain undefined essential transition metal ions from the tumor cell or its environment in a somewhat specific manner. This depletion of essential metal ions would then lead to cell death.

Our data and those of Sartorelli *et al.* (13) on the other hand point to the probable therapeutic action of the copper chelate itself in the case of KTS. For this reason we have undertaken a study of the chemistry of Cu-KTS as a basis for a better understanding of the biological action of KTS.

KTS reacts with cupric ion under a variety of solvent and pH conditions, and crystallization and recrystallization is conveniently carried out in aqueous alcoholic solutions, the crystal form being orthorhombic. The over-all reaction is given in Eq. (1), where KTS is written as KTS(H₂) to indicate the pseudoacidic nature of the ligand and the displacement of two hydrogen ions by cupric ion.

$$\text{KTS(H}_2) + \text{Cu}^{2+} \rightleftarrows \text{Cu-KTS} + 2\text{H}^+ \tag{1}$$

A. Crystallography

Taylor (17) has carried out an X-ray crystallographic analysis of the triclinic crystal modification of Cu-KTS. His results suggest that the

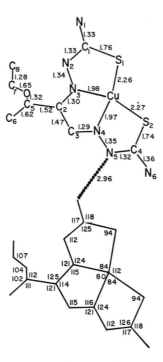

Fig. 2. Interatomic distances and bond angles in the triclinic crystal modification of Cu-KTS as deduced from X-ray crystallographic studies by Taylor (17). The dotted line represents a hydrogen bond. (Used by permission of M. R. Taylor.) These distances and angles correspond to an R value of 5.9%, but should be regarded as preliminary since the refinement is not complete. The ethoxy and methyl groups are disordered. The interatomic distances within these groups result from fitting an ordered model to this disorder.

chelate exists in a distorted planar structure, with cupric ion bound to two sulfur atoms and two nitrogen atoms of the tetradentate KTS ligand as is shown in Fig. 2. Taylor has found that there is a high degree of resonance in the chelate, which agrees with our spectroscopic data, and that the amido groups could hydrogen-bond with either sulfur or ring nitrogen atoms although there seems to be much less hydrogen bonding than might be expected. Interestingly, Taylor found that copper seems to have axial bonds perpendicular to the ligand plane with bond orders of about 0.2, which coordinate with sulfur in adjacent molecules. This finding may have important implications in understanding the biological activity of the chelate.

B. pH Titration Studies

Since the over-all reaction of KTS and cupric ion to form an uncharged ligand involves the liberation of two hydrogen ions as indicated in Eq.

(1), conventional titration studies were carried out. The method of Calvin and Melchior (18) was followed in which KTS and cupric chloride were mixed in 30% dioxane and the hydrogen ion titrated with standard alkali.

Since two unsymmetrical reactive thiosemicarbazone groups are present in KTS there seemed to us to be a possibility that an intermediate charged complex might be formed in which only one ligand group was involved. This would imply a two-step process as outlined in Eq. (2), which could be investigated.

$$\tag{2}$$

The data given in Fig. 3 show that a very stable chelate is formed during the reaction of KTS and CuCl₂ and that more than 95% of the total hydrogen ion liberated has been titrated at pH 4.0. In attempting to calculate stability constants from these data by the method of Pratt and Martin (19), we became aware of the fact that Cu-KTS was basic enough to form acid salts with strong acids. Therefore, Eq. (3) must describe an additional equilibrium which exists in aqueous solutions of KTS and cupric chloride and our titration with alkali probably measured this reaction rather than that described by Eq. (1) or (2).

$$(\text{Cu-KTS} \cdot 2\text{H})^{2+} \rightleftarrows \text{H}^+ + (\text{Cu-KTS} \cdot \text{H})^+ \rightleftarrows \text{Cu-KTS} + \text{H}^+ \tag{3}$$

Since Cu-KTS is a very stable complex which is undissociated in 2 M

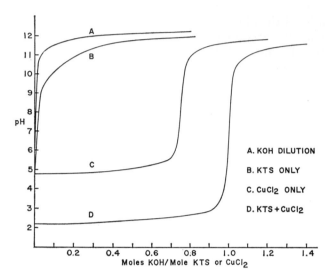

FIG. 3. Titration with 0.1 M KOH: A, dilution curve of 0.1 M KOH; B, 0.25 mM KTS; C, 0.25 mM CuCl$_2$; D, 0.25 mM KTS + 0.25 mM CuCl$_2$. All titrations were performed at 25°C, under N$_2$ atmosphere, in 30% dioxane in water.

HCl, a mixture of KTS (0.01 M) and CuCl$_2$ (0.01 M) should liberate enough hydrogen ion to produce a solution 0.02 M in acidity or having a pH of 1.7. Instead the pH is 2.2, which indicates that two-thirds of the hydrogen ion is bound to the chelate in an acid salt. This seems a more adequate explanation of our data than the alternative conclusion that the formation of Cu-KTS as described in Eq. (1) is only one third complete.

Similar titrations carried out with an excess of cupric chloride being present or in a solution of 0.01 M HCl yielded data that were identical with that found in curve D of Fig. 3.

Our experiments did not indicate that an ionic intermediate was formed under our conditions, but they also did not rule out this possibility. In order to obtain additional information which might bear on this point, several experiments using an absorption spectrophotometric method were carried out.

C. Absorption Spectra

KTS reacts with cupric salts in aqueous solutions to form a brownish chelate which changes to a green color in 1.0 M HCl. This chelate is readily extractable from aqueous solutions above pH 1.0 with immiscible polar organic solvents, in which it is colored a deep red. This deep red color is also found when the chelate is dissolved in alcohols, pyridine, chloroform,

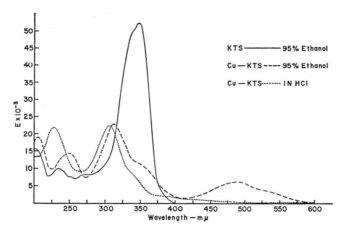

FIG. 4. The absorption spectra of KTS (———) and Cu-KTS (– – – –) in 95% ethanol and Cu-KTS in 1.0 M HCl (····). The absorption spectrum of Cu-KTS in H_2O is similar to that in 95% ethanol except that the maxima are shifted to 250, 306, and 467 mμ.

ether, or ethyl acetate. The absorption spectra of KTS and Cu-KTS in 95% ethanol are given in Fig. 4, as well as the change in absorbance of Cu-KTS in strongly acidic solution.

Using the difference in the spectra of KTS and Cu-KTS at 348 mμ as an indication of the ratio of these two species in a given solution, we have studied the reaction of KTS and cupric chloride at a number of molar ratios

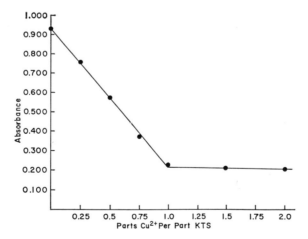

FIG. 5. The effect of Cu^{2+} on the absorbance of KTS at 348 mμ. The reaction was carried out in 10 ml of 95% ethanol containing 2 μmoles of KTS, and $CuCl_2$ varying from 0 to 4 μmoles. The absorption spectra were determined on 1 : 10 dilutions of the reaction mixtures in which the concentration of KTS + Cu-KTS was $2 \times 10^{-5} M$.

of these two reactants. The results are shown in Fig. 5. They show that at molar ratios of $KTS:Cu^{2+}=0.25–2.0$, only KTS and Cu-KTS can be detected and that the formation of the chelate is quantitative with respect to the limiting reactant. Thus there is no evidence from these data that a stable ionic intermediate complex is formed with only one of the thiosemicarbazone groupings.

IV. Conclusions

KTS has been shown to have marked *in vivo* antitumor activity and *in vitro* cytotoxicity against a spectrum of tumor cells by virtue of the activity of the cupric chelate Cu-KTS which is formed *in situ* in the experimental systems. Our data and those of others indicate that these activities probably depend on some specific and unique properties of the cupric chelate itself rather than on the sequestering action of the ligand KTS as was assumed by French and Freedlander (2) and Furst (1) to be the case with respect to a series of related bisthiosemicarbazones.

Although many bisthiosemicarbazones chelate copper readily, KTS has a much higher therapeutic activity as an antitumor agent than any of those reported by French and Freedlander (2, 20) or by us (4, 21), which emphasizes the importance of other chemical properties of KTS. Nevertheless, we must recognize the uniqueness of the copper chelating property since the presence of other essential transition metal ions in our system does not potentiate the cytotoxic activity of KTS even though chelation occurs with some of them. Therefore, we conclude that much of the biological activity of KTS is dependent on the physical and chemical properties of Cu-KTS itself. Among those that need to be considered in this regard

TABLE IV

TOXICITY SYMPTOMS IN RATS RECEIVING KTS FOR PROLONGED PERIODS AND AT HIGH LEVELS

Symptom	Essential metal ions possibly depleted
Growth restriction–weight loss	Zn
Ataxia	Cu
Alopecia	Zn
Anemia	Cu,Fe
Mild hypoglycemia	Zn
Cataract	Zn
Heart lesions	Cu

are the basicity of the chelate, its great stability, and the presence of axial copper bonds.

Many of the toxic symptoms or side effects of KTS, which are shown in Table IV, may be due to the sequestering activity of KTS; all of which have nothing to do with its antitumor activity. Reducing the importance of this activity while still maintaining the formation of the cupric chelate provides a way to minimize the toxicity of this compound. The greater toxicity of Cu-KTS over KTS agrees well with the greater cytotoxicity of the chelate. However, the fact that KTS may have better therapeutic activity than Cu-KTS in relation to toxicity when the agents are given orally may be due to the pharmacodynamics involved—i.e., the chelate is very stable and immediately available for cytotoxic action wherever it may localize, while the ligand must first react with cupric ion before similar toxicity manifests itself.

V. Summary

KTS, 3-ethoxy-2-oxobutyraldehydebisthiosemicarbazone, has antitumor and cytotoxic activity by virtue of the formation of a cupric chelate *in situ* in the experimental systems studied. This activity appears to be due to specific properties of the cupric chelate, Cu-KTS, and not due to the copper-sequestering action of the ligand itself. Among the physical and chemical properties of the cupric chelate that may be of importance biologically are its great stability, its basicity, and the probable presence of weak axial copper coordination bonds.

REFERENCES

1. Furst, A., "The chemistry of chelation in cancer," Charles C. Thomas, Publisher, Springfield, Illinois, 1963.
2. French, F. A., and Freedlander, B. L., *Cancer Res.*, **18,** 1290 (1958).
3. Petering, H. G., and Buskirk, H. H., *Fed. Proc.*, **21,** 163 (1962).
4. Petering, H. G., Buskirk, H. H. and Underwood, G. E., *Cancer Res.*, **24,** 367 (1964).
5. Mihich, E., and Nichol, C. A., *Proc. Am. Assoc. Cancer Res.*, **4,** 44 (1963).
6. Martin, D. S., *Proc. Am. Assoc. Cancer Res.*, **4,** 42 (1963).
7. French, F. A., personal communication.
8. Petering, H. G., Buskirk, H. H., and Vrim, J. A., *Proc. Am. Assoc. Cancer Res.*, **4,** 52 (1963).
9. Petering, H. G., Buskirk, H. H. Crim, J. A., and VanGiessen, G. J., *The Pharmacologist,* **5,** 27 (1963).
10. Smith, C. G., Lummis, W. L., and Grady, J. E., *Cancer Res.*, **19,** 843 (1959).
11. Arai, T., and Suzuki, M., *J. Antibiotics, Ser. A.*, **9,** 169 (1956).
12. Petering, H. G., Buskirk, H. H., and Kupiecki, F. P., *Fed. Proc.*, **24,** 454 (1965).
13. Sartorelli, A. C., Welch, A. D., and Booth, B. A., *Fed. Proc.*, **24,** 454 (1965).
14. Bhuyan, B. K., personal communication.

15. Bahr, G., *Z. anorg. W Allgem. Chem.*, **268,** 351 (1952).
16. Bahr, G., *Z. anorg. Allgem. Chem.*, **273,** 325 (1953).
17. Taylor, M. R., *Abstracts of the American Crystollographic Association*, Gatlinburg, Tennessee, 1965, Abstract D–4.
18. Calvin, M., and Melchior, N. C., *J. Am. Chem. Soc.*, **70,** 3270 (1948).
19. Platt, H. A., and Martin, A. N., *J. Am. Pharm. Assoc.*, **49,** 518 (1960).
20. French, F. A., and Freedlander, B. L., *Cancer Res.*, *Suppl. VII*, **20,** 505 (1960).
21. VanGiessen, G. J., and Petering, H. G., *Abstracts of the 149th Meeting of the American Chemical Society*, Detroit, 1965, Abstract p–13N.

DISCUSSION

DR. PETERS: Do you think that if you put a dithiol, such as BAL or lipoic acid, in contact with Cu-KTS, it would take the copper out, or would this copper be stable?

DR. PETERING: This agent will take copper from penicillamine; I think it may very well take copper from thiols, too. One of the interesting properties of Cu-KTS is that it will preferentially go into the organic phase when it is introduced into a biphasic system composed of an aqueous layer (water or buffer) and a polar organic liquid layer such as ether, ethyl acetate, etc. In this regard it appears to be lipophilic.

DR. GOLDSTEIN: I would like to ask you in what concentrations Cu-KTS inhibits tumor growth, and in what system you got this inhibition?

DR. PETERING: In the KB cell culture system, Cu-KTS inhibits tumor cell growth at concentrations of 0.005–0.01 $\mu g/ml$. *In vivo*, the chelate inhibits the growth of transplanted rodent carcinomas and sarcomas at levels of 5–10 mg/Kg. Bhuyan of the Upjohn Laboratories has shown that the chelate inhibits the incorporation of thymidine into DNA of KB cells at 10 $\mu g/ml$; and Sartorelli of Yale has found that 2.5 mg/Kg given to mice with Sarcoma 180 ascites tumors will inhibit DNA synthesis in the tumor cells.

DR. BRINTZINGER: I want to ask you if your complex is stable against the action of oxygen, because in the hydrazine antitumor agent, an indication has been made that oxidation could produce radical species which would be the real agents.

DR. PETERING: I haven't measured any rates on this, but our impression is that it is extremely stable.

DR. MASON: But the question is what the redox potential would be. If it were very readily reduced, it might autoxidize readily and produce these free radicals.

DR. CUMINGS: It doesn't give rise to demyelinization in the nervous system, does it?

DR. PETERING: I really don't know.

DR. SCHEINBERG: Does Cu-KTS promote the excretion of copper from rats? Is Cu-KTS toxic in doses that increase excretion, if it does?

DR. PETERING: I don't think we have any evidence to know what it does with respect to increasing excretion. This hasn't been our problem.

DR. SCHEINBERG: It is a problem for some of us.

DR. PETERING: There are problems in determining the exact mechanism of excretion of Cu-KTS. It is not excreted in any amount in the urine of rats or human subjects, and we believe that the primary route of excretion of the chelate is through the bile.

Dr. Cumings: If Cu-KTS is more soluble in lipid than in water, this is one of the reasons why it is going out in the bile—because of its cholesterol content. That's why it might not come out in the urine.

Dr. Petering: That's right.

Dr. Taylor: I would like to say that in view of the lack of hydrogen bonding found in the solid state the binding normal to the plane of the copper becomes rather important if one is to consider a binding mechanism for the action of Cu-KTS. This binding is rather surprisingly strong for a square planar copper complex that has 2 sulfurs and 2 nitrogens in the plane of the coordination sphere. If you work it out using some sort of adjusted bond numbers as Dr. Freeman has done [Freeman, H. C., Schoone, J. C., and Simp, J. G., *Acta Cryst.*, **18,** 381 (1965)], the bond order is something around one quarter both above and below the plane. It is strong enough to distort the square plane. The sulfurs in one complex are displaced toward the coppers in neighboring ones.

We have just worked out the crystal structure of the free KTS. There are two molecules in the asymmetric unit; one of each hand. The bisthiosemicarbazone chain is in extended form in this crystal so that the packing of the molecules is quite different from that found in Cu-KTS. In particular, the molecules in KTS engage in a maximal amount of hydrogen bonding between nitrogen and sulfur atoms, whereas in Cu-KTS only one of the four hydrogen atoms that could participate in hydrogen bonding seems to do so.

Cytochrome c Oxidase: Introductory Remarks

Dr. Peisach: I was accused yesterday of starting this meeting somewhat irreverently, and for greater reverence, I suppose I could read the Bible, but instead I would like to quote the following discussion from a symposium on copper metabolism held in 1950 [W. D. McElroy and B. Glass (eds.), "Copper metabolism," The Johns Hopkins Press, Baltimore, Maryland]:

"Dr. Chance: Would Dr. Nelson care to comment upon the possibility that cytochrome oxidase is a copper enzyme?

"Dr. Nelson: No, we have had no particular experience with this problem.

"Dr. Chance: But don't you think this is a related question?

"Dr. Nelson: That may be, but I have no information on the point.

"Dr. Granick: I would like to ask Dr. Britton Chance what he thinks about copper and cytochrome oxidase, since he seems to have a strong feeling about this.

"Dr. Chance: I think it is a relevant question and warrants discussion."

Cytochrome c Oxidase: Present Knowledge of the State and Function of Its Copper Components

HELMUT BEINERT*

Institute for Enzyme Research,
University of Wisconsin,
Madison, Wisconsin

I. Introduction

The history of developments that have laid the basis for our present knowledge about the enzyme cytochrome c oxidase was thoroughly covered only a year ago at the Symposium on Oxidases at Amherst (1), particularly in the contribution of Slater and his colleagues (2). It would be hard even to equal in authority the presentation of an author who can draw on his personal experience in the late Dr. Keilin's laboratory and has been close to this field ever since. Any effort to this end would appear redundant at this time.

It may, however, be timely to review our present knowledge and position concerning the copper component or components of cytochrome c oxidase, as developments concerning this aspect have been rather rapid, and those not immediately active in this area of research may have difficulties in assembling all the detailed and scattered information into a picture that readily permits distinguishing the areas of certainty from those of uncertainty. An attempt will be made, therefore, to expose how far contro-

* The experimental work of the author was supported by research grants from the National Institutes of Health, USPHS (GM–05073, GM–06762, GM–12394). The author is the recipient of a research career program award (GM–K6–18,442) from the same agency.

versies have been settled and where disagreement persists or where essential experimental information is still lacking.

II. Early Results on Copper in Preparations with Cytochrome c Oxidase Activity

A. Detection and Questions of Significance

Copper was detected in cytochrome c oxidase preparations almost 30 years ago by Keilin and Hartree (3, 4). Although they considered and discussed the possibility that the oxidase may be a copper protein, they were careful to point out that only indirect evidence was available for such a suggestion, whereas direct evidence pointed to the hemoprotein nature of the enzyme. The early evidence suggesting that copper may be a constituent of cytochrome oxidase was not only provided by the analytical results of Keilin and Hartree but also by independent nutritional studies (5–7) that were confirmed in more recent work (8, 9).[1] In addition, attention was drawn to a possible relationship between the plant polyphenol oxidases, which were known to be copper proteins, and cytochrome oxidase (3, 10).

After the advances in the chemistry and spectrophotometry of heme compounds made the heme constituent of cytochrome c oxidase a much more attractive target of research efforts, the problem of the copper constituent remained dormant until, in 1950, Wainio and his colleagues (11) presented analyses on their deoxycholate-solubilized purified oxidase preparation. Their data indicated a relationship between the absorption band at 601 mμ (reduced) and the copper content of the preparation, whereas no such relationship was apparent for the iron content. Acceptance of these findings implied that cytochrome oxidase might be a copper-porphyrin compound. Subsequent work by the same authors (12), however, as well as by Dannenberg and Kiese (13) left no doubt that the porphyrin moiety of the enzyme, considered as the "prosthetic group,"[2] did not contain copper but an iron nucleus, as had been strongly suggested by the earlier work in Warburg's and Keilin's laboratories. It was, however, left open (12) whether copper was a constituent of the enzyme or merely a contaminant.

Not long after this repeated failure to establish copper as a meaningful constituent of cytochrome c oxidase, Green, Basford, and Mackler (14)

---

[1] A concise and recent review of the nutritional experiments is found in Ref. (9).

[2] The metal–porphyrin group was considered the "prosthetic group" and this designation was obviously not considered appropriate for copper bound directly to the usual constitutents of proteins.

and Mackler and Penn (15), in the same laboratory, found that copper was concentrated with preparations of NADH oxidase, a submitochondrial fraction containing the cytochrome oxidase component. On further purification of cytochrome oxidase and after elimination of assay difficulties (16, 17), Wainio et al. (16) and Okunuki et al. (18), as well as Griffiths and Wharton (19), confirmed the finding that copper was concentrated together with oxidase activity and a hemes.

B. Stoichiometry and Valence State

With the more purified material, the question of the stoichiometry and the valence state of the copper was now raised. Ratios of copper to heme or copper to iron very close to 1 or at least sufficiently below 2 were found with several preparations (19, 20, 21) so that an ideal 1:1 ratio between heme and copper became very probable. Initially chemical determinations indicated that copper was present in the cuprous state in the resting enzyme (22). When, however, copper was determined in the presence of sulfhydryl-binding agents, only cupric copper was found (20, 23). It was, therefore, concluded that secondary reduction of the initially cupric copper by sulfhydryl groups that arose on denaturation was responsible for originally finding cuprous copper. As recently pointed out by Hemmerich (24, 25) and discussed below, this conclusion is not necessarily valid, but at the time it was thought that the difficulties and ambiguities inherent in chemical determinations of valency had been overcome by eliminating SH groups arising on denaturation. The idea that copper in the enzyme is present in the cupric state received support when Sands and Beinert (26, 27) found, by the nondestructive EPR technique, that Cu^{2+} was present in the enzyme. This was presumably reduced to Cu^+ by substrate, as the EPR signal typical of Cu^{2+} disappeared. In a subsequent, more thorough, EPR analysis Beinert et al. (28) showed, however, that only a fraction ($\sim 40\%$) of the total copper was detectable by EPR in the cupric form. An explanation was suggested at that time—viz., an exchange interaction between a $Cu^{2+}–Cu^{2+}$ or a $Cu^+–Cu^{2+}$ pair. An exchange interaction implies that two copper atoms or possibly one copper atom and another paramagnetic species are in very close proximity. This interaction could lead to a diminution in intensity even if all copper in the enzyme were cupric and in the same binding state.[3] However, no conclusive evidence could be produced (29) that an exchange interaction is involved although the possibility was also not ruled out. Almost simultaneous with this work was the demonstration by Ehrenberg and Yonetani (32) that Cu^{2+} was present in cytochrome c oxidase but that no significant reduction by an

[3] For more detailed discussions of this aspect, see Refs. (28–31).

excess of reduced cytochrome c could be achieved, although heme was readily reduced. These authors concluded that all the copper in the resting enzyme was cupric. In line with the observation that copper was not reducible by substrate was Yonetani's finding (33) that a considerable fraction (60–70%) of the copper present in his cytochrome oxidase preparation (copper-to-iron ratio of 1.7) could be bound by BCS when reduced to Cu^+, without any effect on enzymatic activity or optical absorption, other than the appearance of the absorption due to the Cu^+–BCS complex.

C. Functional Significance; Active and Inactive Species

These reports (32, 33), which clearly spoke against any role of the copper associated with cytochrome c oxidase as an oxidation-reduction catalyst, appeared to open up a controversy, which in the minds of many outsiders to the field does still exist. Beinert et al. (28) and Beinert and Palmer (34) have, however, provided an explanation for the apparent discrepancy, an explanation that has been generally accepted by workers in the field; at least no controversy was apparent at the Symposium on Oxidases in 1964 (1), when all investigators involved were present. The experimental findings of both groups are correct, but differences in the type of preparation used and in the conditions of observation explain, without difficulty, the seemingly contradictory observations. Beinert et al. (28) had pointed out that the EPR signals of enzyme preparations that had high activity and had undergone a minimum of treatment showed little Hfs[4] of the copper EPR spectrum, whereas a variety of treatments that damage the enzyme produced Hfs, which was very similar, irrespective of the type of treatment (Fig. 1). Ehrenberg and Yonetani (32), however, had considered this Hfs as a feature of the active, "native"[5] enzyme. The question as to the assignment of the Hfs could be decided by Beinert and Palmer (34) by studies on the saturation of the EPR signals by microwave power. It could be clearly shown that the signal responsible for the Hfs was readily power saturated (at $-170°$) whereas the principal signal in Beinert and Palmer's (34) preparation, viz., that attributed by them to the native enzyme, was not saturable at this temperature. The saturable signal, that responsible for Hfs, was not abolished on addition of substrate, that is, the corresponding copper was not reduced, whereas the nonsaturable signal was

[4] Abbreviations: Hfs, hyperfine structure or hyperfine splitting; p-CMS, p-chloromercuribenzenesulfonate; PMS, phenazine methosulfate; a, a_3, cytochromes a and a_3, respectively.

[5] I realize that the expressions "active" and "native" sound too apodictic, and that I cannot be the judge of what "native" really is. What is meant is rather "closer to the native state." I feel compelled to use some such terms merely for the sake of simplicity and, hopefully, clarity.

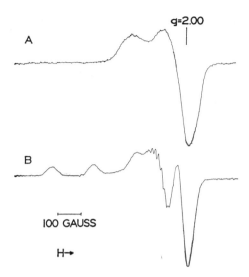

FIG. 1. EPR spectra of cytochrome *c* oxidase. (A). Beef heart cytochrome *c* oxidase (71), 70 mg protein dissolved in 1 ml of 0.5 M sucrose–0.1 M Tris, pH 7.4. (B). Cytochrome *c* oxidase (final concentration approximately 25 mg/ml) after exposure to 6.5 M urea and 25 mM p-CMS for 2.5 hours. The EPR spectra shown represent the first derivatives of the absorption spectra. They were obtained at X-band frequency with a microwave power of 0.9 mW incident on the cavity, a modulation amplitude of 12 Gauss, a scanning rate of 110 Gauss/min, and a temperature of $-165°$. Note the difference in protein concentration, indicating the increase in signal size on denaturation.

readily and almost completely reduced (Fig. 2). Beinert *et al.* (28) and Beinert and Palmer (34) suggested that the saturable signal that is uninfluenced by substrate is due to adventitious copper that becomes bound to the protein. It could also be due to copper that was originally part of the enzyme but became liberated on partial denaturation and was then rebound at different, inactive sites, as does extraneous copper. The content of saturable copper, the species that shows the Hfs, was relatively high in the preparation investigated by Ehrenberg and Yonetani (32) (copper-to-iron ratio of 2). These investigators used low microwave power during their observation (which shows adventitious copper at full strength while the copper of the native enzyme is only represented by 40% at any power.[6]) On the other hand, Beinert *et al.* (28) and Beinert and Palmer (34) used a microwave power 100 × higher and their preparation showed very little Hfs (indicating that any adventitious copper was almost completely saturated). Thus the results of both groups of investigators can be reconciled.

[6] For details, see footnote 7 of Ref. (34).

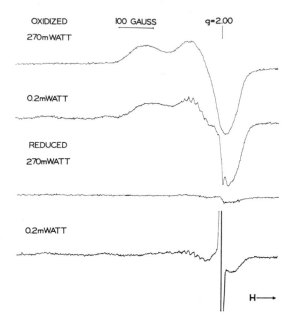

FIG. 2. Difference in power saturation of two different species of copper present in cytochrome c oxidase preparations. Cytochrome c oxidase, 0.8 mM, was dissolved in 0.1 M Tris-chloride, pH 8.3, and placed in EPR tubes equipped with two valves for anaerobic work. The spectra of the oxidized sample were obtained at different microwave powers. The sample was then reduced with 0.05 mM cytochrome c and 0.02 M ascorbate, and EPR spectra were again recorded. The conditions of EPR spectroscopy were: power, 0.2 or 270 mW as indicated; modulation amplitude, 6 Gauss; scanning rate, 60 Gauss/min; temperature, $-173°$. To obtain spectra of sufficient size, the amplification at the lower power was adjusted to 25 times the value used at high power. After addition of ascorbate, a strong, easily saturating (cf. line 4 and line 3) free-radical signal appeared. This signal is sufficiently narrow so that it does not interfere with an evaluation of the Cu^{2+} spectra.

III. Present Problems Concerning the Copper Component(s) of Cytochrome c Oxidase

A. Information from "Static" Experiments

1. The State of Copper in Cytochrome c Oxidase; Quantitative Chemical and EPR Analysis, Titration, Denaturation

The apparent discrepancy concerning the ability of the copper to accept or donate electrons is thus resolved and today's problems concerning the state of the copper of cytochrome oxidase lie elsewhere. First, the number of copper species and their state in the reduced and oxidized forms of the oxidase is not clear, and second, the kinetics of electron transfer involving the copper of the enzyme, and hence its role in catalysis, is not understood.

We shall first discuss the "static" experiments, considering the state of copper at equilibrium (with the other electron carriers) and then "kinetic" experiments that bear on the role of copper in cytochrome oxidase.

It was mentioned above that the EPR signal in cytochrome oxidase that is attributable to Cu^{2+} accounts for only a fraction ($\sim 40\%$) of the copper found in the enzyme by chemical determinations. This was confirmed by Morrison, Horie, and Mason (35). Beinert and Palmer (29), however, showed that all the copper of the enzyme is readily accounted for in the signal after denaturation in the presence of p-CMS,[4] even under anaerobic conditions. These experiments, although not unambiguous (cf. 24, 25), could be taken as lending support to the idea that the copper of the enzyme is all present in the cupric form, although not all detectable by EPR (cf. Section II, B above).[7] This idea was strongly supported by the titration experiments of van Gelder and Slater (36) (cf. 2) and van Gelder and Muijsers (37), who showed that two electron equivalents per heme were taken up by the enzyme on anaerobic titration with NADH using PMS[4] as mediator. By chemical analysis and particularly by observing absorbance changes at 830 mμ, a wavelength probably characteristic for optical absorption of copper in cytochrome c oxidase (38), van Gelder and his colleagues (36, 37, 39) concluded that it was very likely that the extra electron acceptors of the enzyme were two copper atoms in the cupric state. It should be noted here that extraneously added copper is not reduced under the conditions of these experiments. When similar titrations were carried out by van Gelder and Beinert[8] observing both heme (605 mμ) and copper (EPR), the previous results (36, 37) were confirmed in principle. However, in these experiments, sigmoid titration curves were obtained for the copper, i.e., the EPR-detectable Cu^{2+} was not significantly reduced until approximately one half of a reducing equivalent per heme had been added. After addition of one equivalent the copper signal rapidly disappeared. A schematic drawing of such a titration curve is shown in Fig. 3. In these experiments, the titrated samples were frozen at $-170°$ and observed at this temperature. In their earlier experiments, when the optical spectra were observed at room temperature, van Gelder and his colleagues (36, 37, 39) had found linear titration curves, indicating that all optically detectable electron carriers in the enzyme behaved as a unit with a single redox

---

[7] The possibility of an exchange interaction was mentioned above. This is an electrostatic interaction which may lead to a decrease of the total paramagnetism of the system; cf. Ref. (30). Another possibility is that magnetic dipolar interactions produce not a true decrease in intensity but merely a broadening of the EPR spectrum which makes it practically impossible to perform a sufficiently accurate quantitative determination. However, since the copper spectrum of cytochrome c oxidase is relatively sharp and well defined, the latter explanation is not satisfactory.

[8] van Gelder, B. F., and Beinert, H., unpublished experiments.

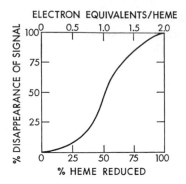

Fig. 3. Schematic drawing of type of titration curve obtained in experiments by van Gelder and Beinert.[8] Cytochrome oxidase was titrated with NADH and PMS as described in Refs. (36) and (37). A quartz tube of 3 mm inner diameter was attached to the anaerobic cell instead of a spectrophotometer cuvette as in Refs. (36) and (37). After reagents were mixed anaerobically the optical absorption at 605 mμ was determined in a special adapter to a Beckman spectrophotometer. The solution was then frozen in liquid nitrogen and the EPR spectrum was measured. The curve shows disappearance of EPR signal of Cu^{2+} plotted versus increase of absorption at 605 mμ (lower abscissa) or electron equivalents of titrant added (upper abscissa).

potential. Since quantitative measurement of both absorptions, optical and EPR, on the same sample, has not yet been possible at either low or high temperature, it is not possible at this time to explain the sigmoid titration curves of Fig. 3 unambiguously. It is obvious that some electron acceptor is titrated before the EPR-detectable copper accepts electrons (cf. Fig. 3), and it also appears that this acceptor equilibrates rapidly with the EPR-detectable copper when one electron equivalent per heme has been taken up. This follows from the sudden steep rise of the titration curve of the EPR-detectable Cu^{2+} at approximately one reducing equivalent per heme. The electron acceptor, which is titrated before the EPR-detectable Cu^{2+}, may be heme, although this is obviously not observed at room temperature (36, 37). The redox potentials of the components of the oxidase may, however, be shifted on freezing. Since we know from van Gelder and his colleagues' titrations (36, 37) that four electron equivalents are taken up per cytochrome c oxidase unit (i.e., per two hemes, $a + a_3$), it appears more likely that the additional acceptor that is titrated initially (cf. Fig. 3) is not heme but yet another component of the enzyme. Since the enzyme is found to contain approximately 60% of the copper in an EPR-undetectable form, it is probable that the extra electron acceptor involves also copper. Although none of the following arguments is by itself conclusive, a relationship of copper to the extra acceptor is further suggested by van Gelder and Muijsers' chemical analyses (37), their titrations in the presence of inhibitors, and the finding that, in the presence of cyanide, a straight and not a sigmoid titration curve is found even at low temperature.[8] It may be recalled from experiments of van Gelder and his colleagues (2, 36, 37) that only one equivalent per heme is consumed in the presence of cyanide, with heme *a* and EPR-detectable copper being reduced in linear fashion. However, the suggestion that the EPR-undetectable electron acceptor in the enzyme (other than heme), if it contains copper, can necessarily be equated with Cu^{2+}, although plausible, has to be considered with caution. We have witnessed in the past year the characterization of a natural iron complex which can function as an electron acceptor but in which the resting "oxidized" form of the iron atom is Fe^{2+} (40, 41). Nevertheless, this structure can take up an electron, which is shared between a redox-active ligand, probably sulfur, and the iron. A similar situation may exist for the EPR-undetectable copper in cytochrome oxidase; we may be dealing with a Cu^+–disulfide system in which an electron can be taken up (25).[9] The experiments involving denaturation in the presence of *p*-CMS (19, 20, 29) have uniformly yielded all copper in the enzyme in the cupric form. This finding may also be taken as lending support to the concept of a Cu^+–disulfide

$$Cu^+ + \tfrac{1}{2} (RS)_2 \rightleftharpoons Cu^{2+} + RS^-$$

system, which, in the presence of mercurial, would be converted to a Cu^{2+}–mercaptide system. If the EPR-undetectable electron acceptor were made up of such a system, it should, according to the experiments of Fig. 3, acquire the ability, after consumption of one electron equivalent, to interact with the EPR-detectable copper and suddenly equilibrate, so that the "reduced" Cu^+–sulfur system can now donate electrons to the EPR-detectable Cu^{2+}, leading to rapid disappearance of the signal.

Van Gelder and his colleagues (2, 39) have shown that apparently both copper systems, the EPR-detectable and the undetectable one, are represented by absorption at 830 mμ. This may be hard to reconcile with the idea that both copper systems are of very different structure. What is at the moment needed is a titration with observation of heme and EPR-detectable copper at one and the same temperature, preferably room temperature, to rule out that the sigmoid titration curves are due to heme, so that heme would have been the only acceptor initially. If heme could be eliminated as the initial acceptor, the properties of the EPR-undetectable copper could be better defined. It would then be certain that the observed EPR

[9] One has to consider that in such a system assignment of the valency $1+$ to copper is only formal and that, in fact, through back donation to the ligand(s), the $3d$ shell of copper is not completely filled. Uptake of one electron would then indeed lead to further "reduction" of the copper, in the sense that the electron density at the copper increases.

signal of Cu^{2+} does not represent all copper in the enzyme merely at a weakened intensity (cf. Section II, B above and footnote 7) but that there must definitely be two distinct copper species in the native enzyme. Another approach which appears promising at this stage is that of designing model systems. A sufficient number of observations may be at hand for the design of a model system which would exhibit the specific properties discussed in this section. An effort in this direction is the subject of another presentation in this symposium (25).

2. Relationship to Heme, Stoichiometry of Cytochrome a to a_3

The discussion up to this point has tacitly assumed an approximate $1:1$ ratio of cytochrome a to a_3. This is implicit in the results of van Gelder and his colleagues' (36, 37, 39) experiments. While the ratio of EPR-undetectable to EPR-detectable copper has been rather uniformly found to lie close to 1.5 (28, 29), the ratio of a to a_3 has been a matter of controversy in the past year. Since it has a sufficient bearing on the problem of the state of the copper, particularly of copper species associated specifically with a or a_3, it cannot be ignored in this context.

The pertinent literature concerning this point is very recent and partly in the stage of being published at the time of this symposium. It is, therefore, possible that the discussion following this paper will bring out some new and decisive aspects. At this time, it appears that the experimental difficulties in the determination of this ratio and the assumptions that have to be made in the interpretation of the results still leave considerable room for uncertainties. The most direct method of determination of a_3 utilizes its capacity to bind CO in the reduced state. The determination of the small quantities of protein-bound CO demands utmost experimental skill. It has been attempted by gasometry (42), by chemical determination of CO with $PdCl_2$ (43), and by the use of ^{14}CO (44, 45). Cytochrome a cannot be directly determined in a similar fashion and a value for $a + a_3$ must therefore be obtained by an independent procedure. Iron determination, when applied to this problem, may be fallacious, if contaminating nonheme iron is present. Spectrophotometry is the method of choice here, but the needed extinction coefficients are not accurately known or agreed upon. In addition to these two sources of error, viz., the difficulties in CO determination and the uncertainty of the total a heme present, a serious complication has been pointed out by Gibson et al. (44): Since a_3 binds CO only in the reduced state, an accurate determination of a_3 demands quantitative reduction. This has been generally attempted with dithionite. Reduction of a_3 in cytochrome c oxidase by dithionite is, however, not a rapid reaction (44, 46) and, as Gibson et $al.$ (44) point out, will never go to completion with a number of preparations. Hence, what is measured by CO binding is the dithionite-reducible a_3 which may possibly be equated with enzymatically active a_3. It would then appear that the ratios of a to a_3 ranging from 1 up to 5 reported from different laboratories do not constitute a discrepancy but mean ratios of a to reducible (or active?) a_3. The lowest ratios would indicate the most intact preparations. This viewpoint is now shared by several investigators (44, 45, 47) and is supported by analyses on the CO binding capacity of more complex particulate preparations that contain cytochrome oxidase, such as electron transport particles or a Keilin–Hartree preparation. In the latter experiments a to a_3 ratios of 1.1 to 1.2 (electron transport particles) (44) and 1 (Keilin–Hartree preparation) (45) were found. In view of all these results and the data obtained by van Gelder and colleagues (36, 37), it seems the most reasonable assumption at this time that in native cytochrome oxidase the ratio of a to a_3 is close to 1 but that modifications may occur in the isolated enzyme—as is also found for the copper component (28)—which complicate the experimental determination of this ratio.

Gibson and his colleagues (44) attribute these modifications mainly to the lability of a_3. This apparent lability and the presence of inactive, i.e., nonreducible and non-CO-binding forms of a_3, have obvious implications in the evaluation and correlation of static and kinetic experiments on cytochrome oxidase, as Gibson and his colleagues have pointed out repeatedly (44, 48). Additional complications in the definition of extinction coefficients arise. In the difference spectra obtained in the presence of CO and in kinetic experiments, when the reduced oxidase–CO complex is dissociated in a light flash (44, 48) and the enzyme exposed to reoxidation by O_2, obviously only a_3 that binds CO will be observed. Moreover, the enzyme active in the rapid kinetic experiments may show a different distribution of absorbance changes between a_3 and a than that deduced from static experiments. On the other hand, in van Gelder and his colleagues' (36, 37, 39) titration experiments, in which NADH with PMS is used as reductant, the complications revealed by the use of CO are not at all apparent and the cytochrome c oxidase components seem quite stable. This means only, of course, that this method is not suited to expose the complications. Nevertheless, one has to keep in mind that extinction coefficients determined in one type of experiment—one which may not show certain complexities—cannot indiscriminately be applied in any other approach.

Gibson et $al.$ (44) considered the possibility that not only a_3 but a may also undergo modifications of the type that seem to occur to some extent in most cytochrome c oxidase preparations. Since they observed a correlation between the ratio of ΔA_{444} to ΔA_{605} and the CO-binding capacity of preparations, they favored the view that a is relatively stable. Van Gelder[10], on the other hand, found a quite constant ($\pm 4\%$) ratio of ΔA_{445} to ΔA_{605}, while the ratio of A_{444}(red) to A_{424}(red) (cf. 44) varied considerably ($\pm 15\%$). If the latter ratio of absorbances really depends on nonreducible components of cytochrome oxidase, as suggested by Gibson *et al.* (44), van Gelder's findings would indicate that both a and a_3 are modified.

It appears then that the complications concerning the heme components are not less than those experienced with the copper components, discussed above (Sections II, B, C; III, A, 1), only that EPR spectroscopy offers different means to resolve some of them. It may be of interest to mention here that we have searched for a correlation between decrease of CO-binding capacity and EPR-detectable copper. It was possible that preparations that showed an unusually high a-to-a_3 ratio in CO-binding experiments might also have a high amount of copper that shows the typical Hfs of denatured enzyme. Such a correlation was, however, not found. It may be anticipated from the subsequent discussion that the EPR-detectable copper appears to be more related to a than to a_3, so that such a correlation may not be expected.

It is at this stage difficult to reconcile the picture presented above concerning the probable a-to-a_3 ratio in native cytochrome oxidase with Horie and Morrison's results on the chemical and physical separation of a and a_3 (49). Horie and Morrison have been able to effect a change in cytochrome oxidase when the reduced enzyme is treated with borohydride in the presence of cyanide, which they interpret as the selective destruction of a_3. In this work the authors find that most of the heme (80%) persists in the preparation as a. It is also interesting that the copper-to-heme ratio remains close to 1 (49) and that the shape of the copper signal as well as the ratio of EPR-detectable to undetectable copper remains constant.[11] This would mean that, considering the total composition and all the electron carriers involved, relatively little change has taken place in the preparation except that 20% of the heme has been destroyed, supposedly in a_3. However, no complete quantitative account of this type of separation has yet been presented and may, in fact, be very difficult to obtain experimentally. Particularly, one would like to see a and a_3 both obtained separately from the same starting material, so that the possibility is ruled out that part of what was originally a_3 does not appear as a after the "destruction." Difficulties and ambiguities in the procedure of Horie and Morrison and in the interpretation of their results are fore-

---

[10] van Gelder, B. F., personal communication.
[11] Morrison, M., and Mason, H. S., personal communication.

shadowed by more recent reports from King's (50), Person's (51), and Horie's (52) laboratories.

3. Contribution of Copper to the Optical Absorption; the Band at 830 mμ

As was pointed out above, the exploration of the functional role of the copper component(s) of cytochrome *c* oxidase lagged so much behind that of the heme constituents because no distinguishing characteristic of the copper was known other than those revealed by chemical analysis. When evidence accumulated, however, that copper is a real constituent of cytochrome oxidase and that at least part of it must be in the cupric state, attention was drawn (26, 53) to the obvious possibility that the cupric copper is also represented in the optical spectrum of the enzyme,[12] in analogy to observations on other copper proteins (cf. 54). Although unequivocal proof is not available, it is very likely that a broad absorption band of cytochrome oxidase centered at 820–830 mμ is a manifestation of cupric copper in the enzyme (38, 48, 55). An absorption band in this spectral region is found in plastocyanin (56), the blue proteins from *Rhus vernicifera* (57) and mung bean seedlings (58), and in ascorbic acid oxidase (59) and can also be recognized by more careful analysis of the spectra in ceruloplasmin (60), laccase of *Rhus succedanea* (61), and *Pseudomonas* blue protein (62). Properties of this absorption band are discussed in another contribution to this symposium (63). It disappears on reduction of the enzyme or on removal of copper from the enzyme by strong cyanide (38). However, since reduction affects all electron carriers and the enzyme is profoundly affected by cyanide treatment, these arguments are not convincing. As Wharton and Tzagoloff (38) point out, only reincorporation of the copper with recovery of the 830 mμ absorption would furnish proof. It may, however, never be possible to restore the very specific bonding of copper in this enzyme after it has been removed, as the EPR spectra indicate an unusual binding site (cf. 30). Morrison (64), Wharton (55), and Tzagoloff and Wharton (65) have reported experiments to show that the 830 mμ band, typical of the oxidized enzyme, and the EPR signal of cupric copper (55, 65) can be observed while a_3 is present as the CO complex

---

[12] In the review by Slater and his colleagues (2) it is erroneously stated that Yonetani's data (33) "appear to provide unequivocal evidence that the copper makes no contribution to the visible spectrum. He quantitatively trapped the copper in the cytochrome oxidase by adding bathocuproine in the presence of $Na_2S_2O_4$, without affecting the absorption spectra, or the effect of cyanide or CO in the spectra in the visible region" (see Section II, C), indicating that copper is not represented in the optical spectrum. It is, however, known now (19, 28, 34) that the "active" copper of the native enzyme is not bound by BCS and hence the argument only applies to "inactive" copper.

in the reduced state. This leads to the conclusion that the 830 mμ band cannot belong to a_3. Van Gelder and his colleagues' (39) experiments also indicate that the 830 mμ band is not due to a_3, as it is abolished on titration in the presence of fluoride, which prevents the reduction of a_3. On the other hand, on titration in the presence of EDTA only part of the 830 mμ band does not respond, whereas the reduction of a_3 is unaffected. There is thus agreement that a_3 is not represented in this band. The "static" experiments do not permit a clear decision whether a may contribute to the 830 mμ band as the oxidation state of a parallels that of the EPR-detectable copper. Kinetic results (48), to be discussed below, show quite clearly a biphasic response of the 830 mμ band,[13] indicating that it represents two different species. The contribution of a component that is neither a nor a_3 (48) accounts for two thirds of the absorption, but it appears possible that the remaining one third represents a. Gibson and Greenwood's (48) experiments are compatible with the interpretation that a single copper species accounts for two thirds of the extinction at 830 mμ. According to van Gelder and his colleagues' (39) results, all the copper of the native enzyme is represented in the band at 830 mμ, the copper which, according to these authors, is associated with a[14] and that associated with a_3, with approximately equal extinction coefficients. Again, there might be a discrepancy between kinetically and statically determined extinction coefficients. These uncertainties in addition to the low intensity of the 830 mμ absorption ($\Delta A_{830} \cong 0.1\ \Delta A_{605}$) make it at this time difficult to use this absorption in any decisive quantitative approach.

4. Heme-free Copper Protein Isolated from Cytochrome c Oxidase

In this context, the separation of a copper protein from cytochrome c oxidase deserves consideration (66). This protein, obtained by succinylation of an acetone extracted cytochrome oxidase preparation had copper enriched 1.2-fold over the original preparation, with a copper-to-heme ratio of 11, indicating, essentially, elimination of heme in the separated protein. After Sephadex chromatography of this material, however, a fraction could be obtained in which copper was enriched about ninefold over the starting material with a copper-to-iron ratio of 426. Unfortunately, the band at 830 mμ has been lost in this material and the EPR spectrum is that of denatured enzyme (cf. 28, 29) (cf. Fig. 2). The copper is therefore

---

[13] Gibson and Greenwood measured at 820 mμ.

[14] According to van Gelder and Slater (39), the contributions to the 830 mμ band of a and the copper associated with it cannot at present be separated. Although it is probable that some or all the contribution is from the copper, the possibility remains that it could be due only to a.

obviously no longer in the native state. Since it has been shown that H. arises in the EPR spectra of cytochrome oxidase after addition of extraneous copper (28), one could not have expected that the copper of the native enzyme, after release by, for instance, acetone treatment, would appear as ionic copper in the medium. The copper is rebound at sites producing the Hfs (probably stemming from nitrogenous ligands such as histidine) (28), but these sites are not identical with the original, very specific, binding sites in the native enzyme. No information is available as to what relationship, if any, these secondary sites have to the original binding sites. This work, therefore, shows that copper is not randomly distributed throughout the protein after a particular way of (partial) denaturation, but conclusions as to the constitution of the native enzyme cannot be drawn on the basis of the isolation of the copper-enriched protein.

B. Information from "Kinetic" Experiments

When it became probable that copper in cytochrome *c* oxidase could participate in oxidation-reduction, the question of a sequence of the various carriers in electron transport was, of course, raised. Earlier suggestions and discussions not supported by kinetic data had to remain speculative. Nevertheless, the well-studied reaction of CO with a_3 in cytochrome oxidase was a strong argument in favor of placing a_3 at the oxygen end of any linear arrangement of carriers. First, there was the evidence for the direct reaction of a_3 with CO from absorption spectra and second, a similar reaction of copper compounds with CO was not known. Although these considerations would not exclude that copper in the enzyme may be a secondary site of CO attack, the stoichiometry established in the recent titration experiments with CO (44, 45, 47) argues against any strong binding at such sites. Cyanide, on the other hand, appears to affect both copper[15] and a_3 so that results obtained in the presence of this inhibitor cannot be interpreted unambiguously in terms of a sequence.

We owe almost all recent progress on this most interesting issue to the brilliant kinetic studies of Gibson and his colleagues. Despite the uncertainties concerning the extinction coefficients of the α and γ bands of

[15] Cyanide produces a change in the shape of the copper EPR spectrum of cytochrome oxidase. This was interpreted (28) as an indication of a direct interaction of cyanide and the EPR-detectable copper. This copper is, however, reducible in the presence of cyanide. On the other hand, van Gelder and his colleagues' titrations (36,37,39) have clearly shown that the EPR-undetectable extra electron acceptor, the copper species which is thought to be associated with a_3, is not reduced by NADH with PMS, when cyanide is present. This copper species is, therefore, probably directly affected by cyanide and it appears now possible that the cyanide effect on the EPR-detectable copper is only secondary.

and a_3 and those of the origin of the absorption band at $830 \, m\mu$, Gibson and Greenwood (48) have pushed the application of rapid reaction techniques and spectrophotometry as far ahead as appears feasible at this time. In view of this work, which will be discussed in another contribution to this symposium (67) and will also be summarized below, all earlier kinetic analyses aimed at a detailed reaction mechanism of the oxidase components require only brief mention. Gibson and Greenwood, in their earlier work (42), had clearly demonstrated that the reaction of cytochrome oxidase with oxygen was complex, but they tended to the view that it could be described in terms of two constituent reactions, namely the oxidation of a^{2+} by a_3^{3+} and the oxidation of a_3^{2+} by oxygen. Although their kinetic scheme did not require the participation of additional components at that time, results reported in the same paper forecast further complexity. Gibson and Greenwood (42) found that (a) on reoxidation of reduced oxidase by oxygen two electron equivalents per heme were consumed and (b) the typical copper EPR signal of cytochrome oxidase is restored to full intensity within milliseconds when a reduced preparation is mixed with oxygen (68). The same authors, in collaboration with Wharton and Palmer, also showed that the reduction of cytochrome oxidase by cytochrome c was a complex reaction (69). Again, the copper component(s) of the enzyme were not invoked in this analysis. On the other hand, Beinert et al. (28) showed by kinetic studies by means of the EPR technique in the conventional seconds range that the rates of reduction of copper and heme were indistinguishable. Beinert and Palmer (34) extended this work to the millisecond range by the aid of a rapid freezing technique and included studies on the reoxidation of reduced oxidase and on the redox behavior of copper in submitochondrial particles (29). Again, in these experiments, as in those of Atherton, Gibson, and Greenwood (68), the EPR-detectable copper was found to react at a rate not significantly different from that of the heme. It should be pointed out, however, that under most conditions (particularly at high concentrations as required for EPR) reduction as well as reoxidation of all carriers in cytochrome oxidase is sufficiently rapid so that rates could not be followed and discrepancies in the rates of individual components would have gone unnoticed. The critical time range for the reactions of cytochrome oxidase, namely $\sim$50–1000 microseconds, was covered by Gibson and Greenwood in the work mentioned above (48). The authors observed the α and Soret bands as previously (42, 70), and in addition, the 830 mμ band,[13] mainly in the reaction of the reduced enzyme with oxygen. The results obtained in this more comprehensive work could only be rationalized by assuming three instead of two (as previously) reacting species; and the demonstration that the third, the new species, has a measurable contribution in the spectral region of 600 mµ ($\lambda_{max} \sim 610$ mµ) is of particular interest. Gibson and Greenwood suggested as the most plausible explanation that the known copper component of cytochrome oxidase is the third reacting species and stated (48): "Although there is as yet insufficient evidence to establish the sequence of the reactions with certainty, the simplest linear scheme with copper as an obligatory intermediate between *a* and a_3 is consistent both with the experiments on the oxidation of the reduced enzyme by oxygen and those on its reduction by dithionite."

Van Gelder and Muijsers (37) had shown that copper chelating agents such as EDTA or salicylaldoxime prevented the reduction of approximately one half of the extra electron acceptor, assumed to be cupric copper. Gibson and Greenwood (48), however, found no effect of these agents on the kinetics of reduction or reoxidation as observed optically. Gibson and Greenwood, therefore, attributed the 830 mµ band to the cupric copper species only, which is supposedly associated with *a*. A copper species more closely related to *a* was suggested by van Gelder and Muijsers' (37) experiments and this species is, according to van Gelder and Beinert's titrations,[8] identical with the EPR-detectable copper. On the other hand, van Gelder and Muijsers' (37) titrations indicated that the 830 mµ band represented all of the extra electron acceptor, presumed to be Cu^{2+}, including the copper associated with *a*.[14] It appears, however, that no real discrepancy exists between these observations, except that in the kinetic experiments the contribution from one copper species appears to amount to two thirds (48), whereas the static experiments rather indicate an equal contribution from both the copper species (37, 39)[10]—a discrepancy similarly observed in the two types of approaches with the 445 mµ band (48). If the reduction by dithionite of the copper complex associated with a_3 were slow—in analogy to what is observed with a_3—kinetic measurements would largely measure reduction of the EPR-detectable copper, the species associated with *a*, and one would not expect any effect of the chelators on the kinetics of the 830 mµ band. In fact, the EPR-undetectable copper complex can be reduced by NADH and PMS in the presence of EDTA if the titration is carried to the end point; only the slope of the titration curve is affected.[10] The titration curves obtained by EPR spectroscopic observation,[8] analogous to the experiments of Fig. 3, have the same sigmoid shape, whether EDTA is present or not. Also, no effect of 1 m*M* EDTA on the over-all activity of the enzyme has been found (71) in routine assays, although approximately 50% inhibition by chelators such as salicylaldoxime and ethylxanthate (both 10 m*M*) was reported by Takemori *et al.* (23). It seems, therefore, that the effect of chelators, such as EDTA, is a subtle one that only becomes apparent under certain experimental conditions, and certainly more work is needed to define such effects more clearly and correlate them with other observations.

IV. Synopsis of Information on the Copper Components of Cytochrome c Oxidase

In an attempt to summarize the information gathered in this review and to present what appears to me the most plausible interpretation of presently available data concerning the copper components of cytochrome oxidase, I have to abandon objective neutrality to some extent and make some more or less subjective choices of the various possibilities discussed above.

Since by now the presence of different copper species in cytochrome oxidase has been discussed for several years (28) it is well to point out at the outset that there is always a certain small but measurable amount of extraneous[16] cupric copper present in all enzyme preparations that have not been specifically purified for this purpose. This copper is measured by the Hfs produced in the EPR spectra (28), by its saturability with microwave power (29, 34), its reducibility with borohydride (34, 35), and its availability to chelators such as BCS (28, 33, 35) (after reduction) and partly also to EDTA. Most of this copper can be removed as the Cu^+–BCS complex by gel filtration (35) or more completely by dialysis against relatively strong cyanide (20, 23, 28). It constitutes a variable percentage of the total copper depending on the history of the preparation. This copper is not reduced by cytochrome c (32, 34) or NADH and PMS (37) and only slowly by ascorbate.

I do not consider this copper species of any significance for our further considerations on the nature of the copper in native cytochrome oxidase[17] and will therefore no longer refer to it. We are then considering only the different native copper species in the following. Forty per cent of the copper is detectable as cupric copper by EPR spectroscopy. It is represented in a relatively sharp and well-defined spectrum, which argues against the possibility that broadening, due to dipolar interaction with other paramagnetic species, is responsible for our failure to account for all the copper as Cu^{2+}. An exchange interaction between closely spaced paramagnetic

[16] This "extraneous" or "inactive" copper may include copper that was originally "active" and bound to "native" enzyme but was released on damaging treatment.

[17] The "inactive" or adventitious copper species has, however, to be considered in all calculations that are based on chemical analyses for total copper or on EPR signal intensity, as it is fully represented in the EPR signal, except at high microwave power. There may also be several different "inactive" species of similar properties.

species, which would diminish the total paramagnetism, is not excluded. Although we believe that our quantitative estimates of copper compounds are not subject to a 20% error, we still consider it reasonable at this time to equate 40% with one half of the copper unless possibilities of error are rigorously excluded or a specific meaning of the 2:3 stoichiometry becomes apparent. Otherwise, the complications introduced by the odd stoichiometry appear unnecessary and rather formidable. This EPR-detectable copper is represented in the absorption band at 830 mμ (39), although not as the only species (39, 48), is rapidly reduced by cytochrome c (34) and reoxidized by oxygen (34, 68), and is related to the a cytochrome in the enzyme (37).[8] The EPR spectrum of this copper indicates, however, that it is not bonded in the same fashion as in the more well-known ionic Cu^{2+} complexes (72) but in a rather specific way. The suggestion has been made (30) on the basis of the unusually low g values and the lack of nuclear Hfs that in this case the copper–ligand interactions have considerable covalent character. A sulfur ligand or ligands may be responsible for this feature.

In addition to this copper species, which we can now study and measure quantitatively and which we may call Cu(a), there must be an additional species of rather unique properties, which, unfortunately, we can only determine "by difference," so to speak. This is the species that makes up the balance between EPR-detectable and total copper, chemically determined. This copper may or may not be cupric, but it must be present in a complex that is able to take up or release one electron equivalent per copper atom since it (or better, the complex as a whole) is titratable with reducing and oxidizing agents. This copper is readily accounted for as cupric copper on anaerobic denaturation of cytochrome oxidase in the presence of mercurial, and *only* in the presence of mercurial (29). This may mean that the copper is not originally present as Cu^{2+} but rather in a Cu^{+}–disulfide system, which, on addition of mercurial, is converted into a Cu^{2+}–sulfhydryl system, the sulfhydryls being bound by the mercurial (24, 25). This second, EPR-undetectable copper species is represented in the 830 mμ band according to titrations (39), and is chelated with EDTA (37, 39) to the extent that the shape of the titration curves is altered, although no effects of EDTA on enzymatic activities have been observed (28, 71). This second copper species appears to be more closely related to a_3 (37)[8] and may be called here Cu(a_3). Its redox potential is higher than that of the EPR-detectable species Cu(a), as it is titrated before Cu(a) by NADH plus PMS.[8] There is evidence from these titrations that uptake of more than two electrons per $a + a_3 \cdots$ Cu(a) + Cu(a_3) assembly induces a rapid equilibration between Cu(a) and the Cu(a_3) system such that Cu(a) receives electrons accumulated in the Cu(a_3) system.

The copper species represented in the 830 mμ band (48) and almost certainly also the species detectable by EPR (34, 68) (the former may include the latter) are participating as electron carriers in the reactions of cytochrome c oxidase. This copper may occupy a position as intermediate electron carrier between a and a_3 (48).

This is probably as far as presently available information allows us to visualize the state and function of the copper in cytochrome c oxidase. In order to sharpen up this picture, we need a direct method to study the EPR-undetectable copper, $Cu(a_3)$, but we require also more definitive information on the properties of the heme components. As for the copper, chemical analysis is too unspecific and ambiguous in its interpretation, because of its destructive character; optical spectrophotometry is not specific with respect to this component; EPR has thus far failed; and measurements of magnetic susceptibility as well as proton relaxation techniques are suffering too much from interference by the iron component to be of much value.

V. Summary

According to the weight of the evidence at present available the "unit" of cytochrome oxidase is tentatively pictured as consisting of one cytochrome a and one cytochrome a_3. Each cytochrome is associated with one copper atom. The copper atom associated with a is cupric; the state of that associated with a_3 is unknown. The unit as a whole is able to take up four electrons on reductive titration.

Kinetic studies indicate that the cytochromes as well as one of the copper species—presumably that associated with a—participate in the enzymatic reaction as electron carriers. Although such a function is also likely for the copper complex associated with a_3, no direct evidence for this is available.

ACKNOWLEDGMENTS

I am indebted to my colleagues Quentin H. Gibson, David E. Griffiths, Peter Hemmerich, Graham Palmer, Richard H. Sands, Alexander Tzagoloff, B. F. van Gelder, and David C. Wharton, for clarifying discussions, criticism, and practical support at various stages of my own work and development of concepts.

REFERENCES

1. King, T. E., Mason, H. S., and Morrison, M., (eds.), "Oxidases and related redox systems." John Wiley and Sons, Inc., New York, 1965.
2. Slater, E. C., van Gelder, B. F., and Minnaert, K., *in* T. E. King, H. S. Mason, and M. Morrison, (eds.), "Oxidases and related redox systems," John Wiley and Sons., Inc., New York, 1965, p. 667.

3. Keilin, D., and Hartree, E. F., *Nature*, **141**, 870 (1938).
4. Keilin, D., and Hartree, E. F., *Proc. Roy. Soc. (London) Ser. B.*, **127**, 167 (1939).
5. Cohen, E., and Elvehjem, C. A., *J. Biol. Chem.*, **107**, 97 (1934).
6. Schultze, M. O., *J. Biol. Chem.*, **129**, 729 (1939).
7. Schultze, M. O., *J. Biol. Chem.*, **138**, 219 (1941).
8. Gubler, C. J., Cartwright, G. E., and Wintrobe, M. M., *J. Biol. Chem.*, **224**, 533 (1957).
9. Lemberg, R., Newton, N., and Clarke, L., *Australian J. Exptl. Biol. Med. Sci.*, **40**, 367 (1962).
10. Graubard, M., *Am. J. Physiol.*, **131**, 584 (1941).
11. Eichel, B., Wainio, W. W., Person, P., and Cooperstein, S. J., *J. Biol. Chem.*, **183**, 89 (1950).
12. Person, P., Wainio, W. W., and Eichel, B., *J. Biol. Chem.*, **202**, 369 (1953).
13. Dannenberg, H., and Kiese, M., *Biochem. Z.*, **322**, 395 (1952).
14. Green, D. E., Basford, R. E., and Mackler, B., *in* W. D. McElroy and B. Glass (eds.), "A symposium on inorganic nitrogen metabolism," Johns Hopkins Press, Baltimore Maryland, 1956, p. 628.
15. Mackler, B., and Penn, N., *Biochim. Biophys. Acta*, **24**, 294 (1957).
16. Wainio, W. W., Van der Wende, C., and Shimp, N. F., *J. Biol. Chem.*, **234**, 2433 (1959).
17. Wharton, D. C., and Griffiths, D. E., *Arch. Biochem. Biophys.*, **96**, 103 (1962).
18. Okunuki, K., Sekuzu, I., Yonetani, T., and Takemori, S., *J. Biochem. (Tokyo).*, **45**, 847 (1958).
19. Griffiths, D. E., and Wharton, D. C., *J. Biol. Chem.*, **236**, 1857 (1961).
20. Takemori, S., *J. Biochem. (Tokyo).*, **47**, 382 (1960).
21. Yonetani, T., *J. Biol. Chem.*, **236**, 1680 (1961).
22. Wainio, W. W., *in* J. E. Falk, R. Lemberg, and R. K. Morton (eds.), "A symposium on haematin enzymes," Macmillan Company (Pergamon), New York, 1961, p. 281.
23. Takemori, S., Sekuzu, I., and Okunuki, K., *Biochim. Biophys. Acta*, **38**, 158 (1960).
24. Hemmerich, P., *in* T. E. King, H. S. Mason, and M. Morrison, (eds.), "Oxidases and related redox systems," John Wiley and Sons, Inc., New York, 1965, p. 216.
25. Hemmerich, P., this symposium.
26. Sands, R. H., and Beinert, H., *Biochem. Biophys. Res. Communs.*, **1**, 175 (1959).
27. Sands, R. H., and Beinert, H., *Biochem. Biophys. Res. Communs.*, **3**, 47 (1960).
28. Beinert, H., Griffiths, D. E., Wharton, D. C., and Sands, R. H., *J. Biol. Chem.*, **237**, 2337 (1962).
29. Beinert, H., and Palmer, G., *in* T. E. King, H. S. Mason, and M. Morrison (eds.), "Oxidases and related redox systems," John Wiley and Sons, Inc., New York, 1965, p. 567.
30. Beinert, H., and Palmer, G., *Advan. Enzymol.*, **27**, 105 (1965).
31. Kato, M., Jonassen, H. B., and Fanning, J. C., *Chem. Rev.*, **64**, 99 (1964).
32. Ehrenberg, A., and Yonetani, T., *Acta Chem. Scand.*, **15**, 1071 (1961).
33. Yonetani, T., *Biochem. Biophys. Res. Communs.*, **3**, 549 (1960).
34. Beinert, H., and Palmer, G., *J. Biol. Chem.*, **239**, 1221 (1964).
35. Morrison, M., Horie, S., and Mason, H. S., *J. Biol. Chem.*, **238**, 2220 (1963).
36. van Gelder, B. F., and Slater, E. C., *Biochim. Biophys. Acta*, **73**, 663 (1963).
37. van Gelder, B. F., and Muijsers, A. O., *Biochim. Biophys. Acta*, **81**, 405 (1964).
38. Wharton, D. C., and Tzagoloff, A., *J. Biol. Chem.*, **239**, 2036 (1964).
39. van Gelder, B. F., and Slater, E. C., this symposium.
40. Beinert, H., DerVartanian, D. V., Hemmerich, P., Veeger, C., and van Voorst, J. D. W., *Biochim. Biophys. Acta*, **96**, 530 (1965).

41. Blumberg, W. E., and Peisach, J., *in* A. San Pietro (ed.), "Non-heme iron proteins: role in energy conversion," Antioch Press, Yellow Springs, Ohio, 1965, p. 101.
42. Gibson, Q. H., and Greenwood, C., *Biochem. J.*, **86**, 541 (1963).
43. Morrison, M., and Horie, S., *J. Biol. Chem.*, **240**, 1359 (1965).
44. Gibson, Q. H., Palmer, G., and Wharton, D. C., *J. Biol. Chem.*, **240**, 915 (1965).
45. Vanneste, W. H., *Biochem. Biophys. Res. Communs.*, **18**, 563 (1965).
46. Lemberg, R., Pilger, T. B. G., Newton, N., and Clarke, L., *Proc. Roy. Soc. (London)*, Ser. B., **159**, 205 (1964).
47. Mansley, G. T., Stanbury, J. T., and Lemberg, R., *Biochim. Biophys. Acta*, in press.
48. Gibson, Q. H., and Greenwood, C., *J. Biol. Chem.*, **240**, 2694 (1965).
49. Horie, S., and Morrison, M., *J. Biol. Chem.*, **239**, 1438 (1964).
50. Kuboyama, M., and King, T. E., *Fed. Proc.*, **24**, 545 (1965).
51. Person, P., and Zipper, H., *Biochim. Biophys. Acta*, **92**, 605 (1964).
52. Horie, S., *J. Biochem.*, **56**, 57 (1964).
53. Griffiths, D. E., and Wharton, D. C., *Biochem. Biophys. Res. Communs.*, **4**, 199 (1961).
54. Blumberg, W. E., Levine, W. G., Margolis, S., and Peisach, J., *Biochem. Biophys. Res. Communs.*, **15**, 277 (1964).
55. Wharton, D. C., *Biochim. Biophys. Acta*, **92**, 607 (1964).
56. Katoh, S., Shiratori, I., and Takamiya, A., *J. Biochem.*, *(Tokyo)*, **51**, 32 (1962).
57. Omura, T., *J. Biochem. (Tokyo)*, **50**, 394 (1961).
58. Shichi, H., and Hackett, D. P., *Arch. Biochem. Biophys.*, **100**, 185 (1963).
59. Tokuyama, K., Clark, E. E., and Dawson, C. R., *Biochemistry*, **4**, 1302 (1965).
60. Blumberg, W. E., Eisinger, J., Aisen, P., Morell, A. G., and Scheinberg, I. H., *J. Biol. Chem.*, **238**, 1675 (1963).
61. Omura, T., *J. Biochem. (Tokyo).*, **50**, 264 (1961).
62. Horio, T., *J. Biochem. (Tokyo).*, **45**, 267 (1958).
63. Tzagoloff, A., this symposium.
64. Morrison, M., *in* T. E. King, H. S. Mason, and M. Morrison (eds.), "Oxidases and related redox systems," John Wiley and Sons, Inc., New York, 1965. p. 639.
65. Tzagoloff, A., and Wharton, D. C., *J. Biol. Chem.*, **240**, 2628 (1965).
66. MacLennan, D. H., and Tzagoloff, A., *Biochim. Biophys. Acta*, **96**, 166 (1965).
67. Wharton, D. C., and Gibson, Q. H., this symposium.
68. Atherton, N. M., Gibson, Q. H., and Greenwood, C., *Biochem. J.*, **86**, 554 (1963).
69. Gibson, Q. H., Greenwood, C., Wharton, D. C., and Palmer, G., *J. Biol. Chem.*, **240**, 888 (1965).
70. Gibson, Q. H., and Greenwood, C., *J. Biol. Chem.*, **239**, 586 (1964).
71. Griffiths, D. E., and Wharton, D. C., *J. Biol. Chem.*, **236**, 1850 (1961).
72. Malmström, B. G., and Vänngård, T., *J. Mol. Biol.*, **2**, 118 (1960).

Spectrophotometric Characterization and Function of Copper in Cytochrome c Oxidase[*]

DAVID C. WHARTON†

Institute for Enzyme Research,
University of Wisconsin,
Madison, Wisconsin

QUENTIN H. GIBSON‡

Johnson Research Foundation,
University of Pennsylvania,
Philadelphia, Pennsylvania

The thesis that copper is an integral constituent of cytochrome c oxidase with a role in the transfer of electrons has been a subject of controversy for quite some time. Many of the arguments pertaining to a functional role have been reviewed recently elsewhere (1–3). Those arguments that favor a functional role include the observations that animals fed a diet deficient in copper exhibit a subnormal level of cytochrome oxidase (4–10); that all purified preparations of cytochrome oxidase from mammalian sources contain copper (11–19); that when properly characterized these preparations possess an equimolar ratio of copper and heme components (20–23); that during purification there is a parallel increase of copper and enzymatic activity (22, 23); that copper undergoes oxidation and reduction (22, 25); and that inhibitors which block the reoxidation of the heme components also prevent the reoxidation of the copper (22, 25).

I. Oxidation and Reduction of Copper

Although it constitutes a necessary preliminary, the demonstration that copper in cytochrome c oxidase can undergo oxidation and reduction is not sufficient to show that the metal has a role in the function of the enzyme. It is necessary, in addition, to show that the rates of the oxidation and reduction reactions are as rapid as those of the cytochrome components. This is especially difficult in the case of cytochrome c oxidase because the

* Supported, in part, by the United States Public Health Service through Research Grants (HE 09741 and GM 11231) and by the United States Atomic Energy Commission through Contract AT (11-1)-1151.

† Present address: Department of Biochemistry, University of Virginia, Charlottesville, Virginia.

‡ Not at meeting. Present address: Department of Biochemistry, Cornell University, Ithaca, New York.

rates of reaction, both of the reduced enzyme with oxygen and of the oxidized enzyme with cytochrome c, are extremely fast. Thus, Gibson and Greenwood (26) have shown that the rate of reaction of cytochrome a_3 with oxygen is 5×10^7 M^{-1} sec^{-1} and that this rate constant may be used up to oxygen levels where the actual measured rate reaches 10,000 per second. They further showed that the oxidation of cytochrome a is independent of oxygen concentration, provided this exceeds the limiting value (about 2×10^{-5} M) and has a rate of about 700 per second. Consequently, copper should be shown to react at rates of the same general order if it is to qualify as an integral constituent of the enzyme.

The first general steps in this direction were taken by Sands and Beinert (24), who showed by EPR spectroscopy that there were changes in the oxidation state of copper in the oxidase during turnover. Griffiths and Wharton (22) obtained similar results by means of a chemical technique. These were steady state experiments which are open to the objection that the copper need not participate directly in the reaction but constitutes a redox couple which equilibrates itself relatively slowly with the steady state redox condition existing in the enzyme during turnover.

A second approach has been to use the rapid-flow and quick-freezing technique of Bray (27) coupled with EPR spectroscopy to follow changes in the redox state of copper on mixing the reduced enzyme with oxygen or the oxidized enzyme with ferrocytochrome c. Thus, Atherton et al. (28) and Beinert and Palmer (29) have shown that in both cases there is a rapid change in the oxidation state of the copper within the limits of the time resolution of the quick-freezing technique. However, since this resolution time is approximately 10 msec, even these experiments do not show satisfactorily that copper undergoes valence changes at a rate compatible with those of the cytochrome components.

II. A Possible Chromophore of Copper

A solution to this problem might be found if the copper in cytochrome c oxidase were to exhibit an absorption band which during oxidation and reduction underwent changes in absorbance of sufficient amplitude to be measured spectrophotometrically. A candidate for this role is the absorption band found by Griffiths and Wharton (16) near 815 mμ (cf. Fig. 1). This band, which has an extinction coefficient of 1.4 mM^{-1} cm^{-1}, was found to lose absorbance when the enzyme was reduced by the substrate ferrocytochrome c or by such chemical reducing agents as sodium dithionite and to regain absorbance when the enzyme was reoxidized. Because of the presence of somewhat similar absorption bands in some copper proteins and the

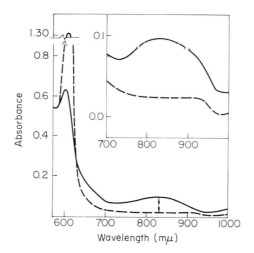

FIG. 1. Absorption spectrum of oxidized (———) and reduced (– – – –) cytochrome *c* oxidase.

demonstration that their purified preparations of cytochrome oxidase contain copper, Griffiths and Wharton suggested that the near infrared band might be due to a chromophore of copper.

In order to test this hypothesis Wharton and Tzagoloff proposed to remove copper gradually from the enzyme and to determine whether this resulted in a concomitant loss of absorbance at 815 mμ. Furthermore, if copper is an integral constituent of the oxidase then its removal should also be accompanied by a parallel loss of enzymatic activity. Conversely, the replacement of copper into the copper-depleted hemoprotein could be analyzed for its effect on activity and the near infrared band.

Wharton and Tzagoloff (30) found that the removal of copper from their preparations of cytochrome *c* oxidase was accompanied by a concomitant loss of near infrared absorption and of enzymatic activity. An example of this correlation is illustrated in Fig. 2, which shows the loss of copper, of near infrared absorbance, and of enzymatic activity after the enzyme had been dialyzed against 1 *M* cyanide. An identical correlation was observed at lower concentrations of cyanide although a longer dialysis time was required to achieve the same results. However, cyanide concentrations of 0.01 *M* or less had no effect on the content of enzymatic copper or on the near infrared band.

Wharton and Tzagoloff also found that copper could be removed with a loss of absorbance in the near infrared region by dialyzing the enzyme against phosphate, borate, or glycine buffers at concentrations in excess of 0.1 *M* and at a pH greater than 9. This effect was not due simply to pH

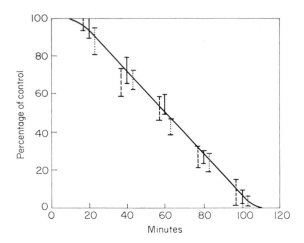

FIG. 2. Decrease of the near infrared band, specific activity, and copper content of cytochrome c oxidase after dialysis against 1 M potassium cyanide for the times indicated and after dialysis for 48 hours against 0.05 M Tris-Cl buffer, pH 8 (four changes). ——, The range of values of absorbance at 830 mμ; – – – – , the range of values of specific activity; · · · · ·, the range of values of copper content.

since KOH even at pH 12 produced no similar effect. In other experiments copper was removed from the oxidase with a parallel loss of the near infrared band and of enzymatic activity by treating the enzyme with the copper-complexing agent BCS in the presence of acetate buffer at a pH below 6. In all these experiments the percentage losses of copper as determined by chemical techniques and by EPR spectroscopy were in agreement.

The conditions that Wharton and Tzagoloff used to remove the copper from the oxidase also resulted in a change of the absorption spectrum in the visible region. Thus, the position of the α peak of the reduced enzyme was shifted from 605 to 600 mμ and the position of the Soret peak from 444 to 437–439 mμ. In addition, there appeared to be an over-all decrease in absorbance in the visible region. No change was observed, however, in the absorption spectrum of the pyridine hemochromogen.

Although this close correlation has been observed between the presence of copper and the near infrared band, an element of doubt still remains as to its identity because of the failure to replace copper into a copper-depleted enzyme or to restore the lost absorbance of the near infrared band.

III. Kinetics of the Near Infrared Band

Quite recently, following improvements in the photochemical method for following the rates of the cytochrome reactions, a series of experiments was undertaken in which absorbance changes at 820 mμ were measured (31). These experiments were stimulated by the increasing assurance that, despite the remaining uncertainties, the near infrared band may be related to the presence of copper in the enzyme. The principle of the method is that the carbon monoxide compound of the cytochrome oxidase is mixed with oxygen and the mixture flowed into a flash photolysis apparatus. There the firing of the photolysis flash releases reduced cytochrome *c* oxidase in the presence of oxygen, with which it is then able to react; the corresponding reaction is then followed spectrophotometrically using appropriate rapid recording techniques. The time resolution of this method in its modified form is quite good.

A. The Fast Reaction

Carbon monoxide can be removed by flash photolysis with a half-time of the order of 3.5 μsec and reactions with rates of up to 70,000 per second have been followed. When this method was applied to the cytochrome oxidase, observations were made on the same solutions at 820 and 605 mμ, and the results of the two wavelengths correlated. At low concentrations of oxygen, it was found that there is a good correlation between the absorbance changes at the two wavelengths, but that at higher oxygen concentrations there was a breakdown in correlation. An example of the kinetic results is shown in Fig. 3. At 605 mμ there is a well-marked rapid phase which, by comparison with results at other wavelengths from previous

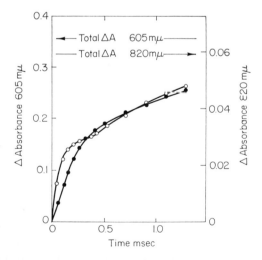

Fig. 3. Oxidation of reduced cytochrome *c* oxidase by molecular oxygen followed at 820 mμ (●) and at 605 mμ (○) in the flow-flash apparatus. The absorbance change measured was a decrease at 605 mμ and an increase at 820 mμ.

work (26, 32, 33), may be correlated with the reaction of cytochrome a_3 with oxygen. Thereafter, there appears to be a short plateau during which little absorbance change takes place and, then, a further decline in absorbance follows corresponding to the oxidation of cytochrome a, which is the major contributor to the absorbance change at this wavelength. At 820 mμ the appearances are somewhat different. The very rapid phase corresponding to the oxidation of cytochrome a_3 is unrepresented, and there is an intermediate rate of reaction instead with a rate of about 5,000 per second, which is less than the rate corresponding to the oxidation of cytochrome a_3. The reaction of this intermediate accounts for about two thirds of the absorbance change at 820 mμ. The remaining one third takes place at a rate equivalent to that for the oxidation of cytochrome a. The first conclusion then that can be drawn is that the component responsible for the greater part of the absorbance at 820 mμ is kinetically independent of cytochromes a and a_3. Next, not only is this rate different, it is quite enough to permit copper, if indeed the identification is correct, to participate in the enzyme reaction.

B. The Plateau Region

A further and equally significant finding is pointed to by the plateau seen about 150 μsec after initiation of the reaction in the observations at 605 mμ. One explanation of such a plateau is that the 820 mμ species contributes also to the absorbance changes at 605 mμ and does so in the direction opposite to that corresponding to the oxidations of cytochromes a_3 and a. This possibility was explored by carrying out a series of experiments using a high oxygen concentration and following the absorbance changes at a number of wavelengths covering the α-band region of the oxidase. It was found that the prominence of the plateau region in the records varied with the wavelength and at some wavelengths there was an actual reversal in the absorbance change with time (cf. Fig. 4). This result appears to show conclusively that there must be a change taking place other than the conversion of the reduced forms of cytochromes a_3 and a to the oxidized forms, and this change is satisfactorily correlated in time with the changes in the 820 mμ region. A reasonable interpretation of the results is that copper in cytochrome oxidase, like copper in other copper proteins (34–39), contributes not only to the near infrared absorbance but also to the absorbance in the visible region of the spectrum, particularly around 600 mμ. Unfortunately, with three colored substances changing rapidly in the solution, it is difficult to assign accurate extinction coefficients for any one of them, but it would seem that a plausible value for the

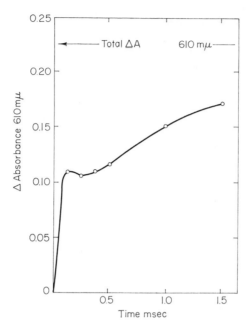

FIG. 4. The reaction of reduced cytochrome *c* oxidase with oxygen followed at 610 mμ by the flow-flash method.

α-region contribution of the copper components would be about 1 to 2 per millimolar for the change oxidized to reduced, a value which is not far out of line with the other copper compounds.

IV. Other Experiments

The titrimetric experiments of van Gelder and Slater (40) and of Chance and Yonetani (41, 42) deserve comment because of their bearing on the question of the function of copper in cytochrome oxidase. Van Gelder and Slater have shown that the two reducing equivalents of NADH, oxidized by 1 mole of cytochrome oxidase via phenazine methosulfate, reduced only one hematin iron in the enzyme, and van Gelder and Muijsers (43) have demonstrated that the other reducing equivalent is used to reduce copper. Although Chance and Yonetani (41, 42) originally concluded that only one oxygen-reducing equivalent was contained in 1 mole of reduced cytochrome oxidase and used this to question the participation of copper in the reaction, their data could be recalculated with different extinction coefficients to give a value closer to 2 (42).

V. Conclusion and Comment

It seems to these writers that the evidence in favor of a functional role for copper in cytochrome c oxidase is fairly strong, particularly if the identification of the near infrared band as a chromophore of copper is correct. The argument, of course, would be made stronger if copper could be reintroduced into the copper-deficient hemoprotein with a corresponding restoration of enzymatic activity and the near infrared band.

Should copper prove to be a prosthetic group of the enzyme many questions remain to be answered. One of the outstanding involves the relation of copper to cytochromes a and a_3. In this connection the work of van Gelder and Muijsers (43) is of interest. They have reported the results of experiments using metal-complexing agents, such as cyanide, azide, EDTA, and salicylaldoxime, from which they suggest that a portion of the copper is linked with cytochrome a and another portion is associated with cytochrome a_3. The relationship of these results, should they prove to be correct, to those of Beinert and his associates (25, 29), which indicate that only about one third of the copper can be accounted for in the EPR spectrum of the oxidase, should be considered carefully. Thus, a typical preparation of mammalian cytochrome oxidase, as normally prepared, might contain three types of copper: (a) a contaminating species of variable amount that can be removed without any significant loss of enzymatic activity (22, 23, 25, 29); (b) a species having an EPR spectrum; (c) a species without an EPR spectrum.

A question posed by the recent report of MacLennan and Tzagoloff (44) is that of the separate identity of a copper protein, containing some or all of the enzymatic copper, as part of a large cytochrome c oxidase complex.

No doubt the problems of copper in cytochrome c oxidase will keep researchers busy for some time to come.

VI. Summary

A correlation has been found between the presence in cytochrome c oxidase of copper and an absorption band near 815 mμ. By means of a flow-flash technique it has been shown that the changes in the absorbance of the near infrared band are kinetically independent of cytochromes a and a_3, and are of a rate that is sufficient to qualify the chromophore as a participant in the enzyme reaction. A change of absorbance in the region of the α band has been correlated with the change in the absorbance of the near infrared band, suggesting that copper has an absorption band in the visible region, also. If the identification of the chromophore is correct, the evidence favoring copper as an integral component of cytochrome *c* oxidase is considerably stronger.

ACKNOWLEDGMENT

The authors wish to acknowledge the significant contributions of Dr. Colin Greenwood and Dr. Alexander Tzagoloff to the development of this work.

REFERENCES

1. Yonetani, T., *in* P. D. Boyer, H. A. Lardy, and K. Myrbäck (eds.), "The enzymes" Vol. VIII, Academic Press Inc., New York, 1963, p. 41.
2. Malmström, B. G., and Neilands, J. B., *Ann. Rev. Biochem.*, **33**, 331 (1964).
3. Massey, V., and Veeger, C., *Ann. Rev. Biochem.*, **32**, 579 (1963).
4. Cohen, E., and Elvehjem, C. A., *J. Biol. Chem.*, **107**, 97 (1934).
5. Schultz, M. O., *J. Biol. Chem.*, **129**, 729 (1939).
6. Schultz, M. O., *J. Biol. Chem.*, **138**, 219 (1941).
7. Gallagher, C. H., Judah, J. D., and Rees, K. R., *Proc. Roy. Soc. (London), Ser. B*, **145**, 134 (1956).
8. Gubler, C. J., Cartwright, G. E., and Wintrobe, M. M., *J. Biol. Chem.*, **224**, 533 (1957).
9. Howell, J. M., and Davison, A. N., *Biochem. J.*, **72**, 365 (1959).
10. Mills, C. F., and Williams, R. B., *Biochem. J.*, **85**, 629 (1962).
11. Eichel, B., Wainio, W. W., Person, P., and Cooperstein, S. J., *J. Biol. Chem.*, **183**, 89 (1950).
12. Mackler, B., and Penn, N., *Biochim. Biophys. Acta*, **24**, 294 (1957).
13. Okunuki, K., Sekuzu, I., Yonetani, T., and Takemori, S., *J. Biochem. (Tokyo)*, **45**, 847 (1958).
14. Wainio, W. W., VanderWende, C., and Shimp, N. F., *J. Biol. Chem.*, **234**, 2433 (1959).
15. Yonetani, T., *J. Biol. Chem.*, **236**, 1680 (1961).
16. Griffiths, D. E., and Wharton, D. C., *J. Biol. Chem.*, **236**, 1850 (1961).
17. Fowler, L. R., Richardson, S. H., and Hatefi, Y., *Biochim. Biophys. Acta*, **64**, 170 (1962).
18. Greenwood, C., *Biochem. J.*, **86**, 535 (1963).
19. Horie, S., and Morrison, M., *J. Biol. Chem.*, **238**, 1855 (1963).
20. Takemori, S., *J. Biochem. (Tokyo)*, **47**, 382 (1960).
21. Takemori, S., Sekuzu, I., and Okunuki, K., *Biochim. Biophys. Acta*, **38**, 158 (1960).
22. Griffiths, D. E., and Wharton, D. C., *J. Biol. Chem.*, **236**, 1857 (1961).
23. Morrison, M., Horie, S., and Mason, H. S., *J. Biol. Chem.*, **238**, 2220 (1963).
24. Sands, R. H., and Beinert, H., *Biochem. Biophys. Res. Communs.*, **1**, 175 (1959).
25. Beinert, H., Griffiths, D. E., Wharton, D. C., and Sands, R. H., *J. Biol. Chem.*, **237**, 2337 (1962).
26. Gibson, Q. H., and Greenwood, C., *Biochem. J.*, **86**, 541 (1963).
27. Bray, R. C., *Biochem. J.*, **81**, 189 (1961).
28. Atherton, N. M., Gibson, Q. H., and Greenwood, C., *Biochem. J.*, **86**, 554 (1963).
29. Beinert, H., and Palmer, G., *J. Biol. Chem.*, **239**, 1221 (1964).
30. Wharton, D. C., and Tzagoloff, A., *J. Biol. Chem.*, **239**, 2036 (1964).
31. Gibson, Q. H., and Greenwood, C., *J. Biol. Chem.*, **240**, 2694 (1965).

32. Gibson, Q. H., Greenwood, C., Wharton, D. C., and Palmer, G., *J. Biol. Chem.*, **240,** 888 (1965).
33. Gibson, Q. H., and Greenwood, C., *J. Biol. Chem.*, **239,** 586 (1964).
34. Omura, T., *J. Biochem. (Tokyo)*, **50,** 394 (1961).
35. Katoh, S., Shiratori, I., and Takamiya, A., *J. Biochem. (Tokyo)*, **51,** 32 (1962).
36. Suzuki, H., and Iwasaki, H., *J. Biochem. (Tokyo)*, **52,** 193 (1962).
37. Blumberg, W. E., Eisinger, J., Aisen, P., Morell, A. G., and Scheinberg, I. H., *J. Biol. Chem.*, **238,** 1675 (1963).
38. Mosbach, R., *Biochim. Biophys. Acta*, **73,** 204 (1963).
39. Shichi, H., and Hackett, D. P., *Arch. Biochem. Biophys.*, **100,** 185 (1963).
40. van Gelder, B. F., and Slater, E. C., *Biochim. Biophys. Acta*, **73,** 663 (1963).
41. Chance, B., and Yonetani, T., *Fed. Proc.*, **18,** 202 (1959).
42. Chance, B., *in* J. E. Falk, R. Lemberg, and R. K. Morton (eds.), "Haematin enzymes," Macmillan Company (Pergamon), New York, 1961, p. 316.
43. van Gelder, B. F., and Muijsers, A. O., *Biochim. Biophys. Acta*, **81,** 405 (1964).
44. MacLennan, D. H., and Tzagoloff, A., *Biochim. Biophys. Acta*, **96,** 166 (1965).

The Effect of Chelating Agents on the Reducibility of Copper in Cytochrome c Oxidase

B. F. van GELDER AND E. C. SLATER

Laboratory of Biochemistry,*
University of Amsterdam,
Amsterdam, The Netherlands

I. Different Species of Copper in Cytochrome c Oxidase

Beinert and co-workers (1, 2) have distinguished by EPR spectroscopy between functionally active copper in cytochrome c oxidase and functionally inactive copper, either initially present in the preparation or induced by treatment with alkali or urea. Beinert et al. (1) and Morrison et al. (3) showed further that the EPR signal of the functionally active copper accounts for only 30 to 40% of the copper found in the enzyme by chemical analysis. As Beinert recently wrote (4): "The simplest explanation for this finding would be the presence of a corresponding amount of cuprous copper. As an alternative explanation one may again suggest an exchange interaction between a cupric-cupric pair or concievably copper and heme iron."

We have examined the valence of the copper by titrating cytochrome c oxidase with NADH in the presence of phenazine methosulfate (5-8).

Figure 1 shows a titration at 605 mμ. Reduction of the enzyme in the absence of NADH is due to the fact that phenazine methosulfate catalyzes the reduction by endogenous donors. By extrapolating the straight line to the abscissa, the number of equivalents of NADH needed for the total reduction of cytochrome c oxidase could be calculated. It was found that 46.0 μmoles NADH reduced 46.6 μmoles of heme a. Since 1 molecule of NADH provides two reducing equivalents, and one is required to reduce a molecule of ferriheme a to ferroheme a, it may be concluded that a second reducing equivalent is used for another oxido-reduction reaction. Using the procedure of Griffiths and Wharton (9), it was found that the second acceptor of electrons from phenazine methosulfate in cytochrome c oxidase is Cu^{2+}. When an excess of NADH in the presence of phenazine methosulfate was used, 0.90–1.15 atoms of Cu^+ per heme a molecule were formed. With limiting amounts of NADH 0.98 atom of Cu^+ was formed per molecule of heme a reduced. These results indicate that the copper in oxidized cytochrome c oxidase is cupric.

* Formerly Laboratory of Physiological Chemistry.

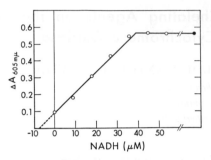

FIG. 1. Titration of cytochrome c oxidase with NADH under anaerobic conditions at 605 mμ. A 1 cm Thunberg cuvette contained 0.1 M phosphate buffer, 1% cholate, and 51.8 μmoles cytochrome c oxidase in a volume of 2.25 ml. The final pH was 7.3. A reference cuvette contained the same solution in air. One part of the double hollow stopper of the Thunberg cuvette contained various amounts of NADH in a volume of 0.2 ml and the other 0.05 ml 0.01% phenazine methosulfate. The contents of the reference cell were diluted with 0.25 ml water. The Thunberg cuvette was flushed six times with purified nitrogen, which had been washed through a 10% pyrogallol–10% KOH solution and evacuated. Before starting the reaction with phenazine methosulfate, the NADH was tipped in. The increment of absorbance was followed on a Cary model 14 spectrophotometer until the slope of the absorbance against time was constant. By extrapolating to zero time the immediate increment in absorbance was found. The NADH concentration was determined from the total absorbance at 340 mμ, using an E_{mM} of 6.22 when reduced with an excess of $Na_2S_2O_4$.

The straight line of Fig. 1 suggests that under the conditions of the titration the heme a and the copper are reduced at about the same speed, indicating that the acceptors are not acting independently of one another.

It is interesting to note that although the preparation contained copper in excess of heme a only one atom of copper was reduced per heme a molecule reduced. When Cu^{2+} was added to the enzyme no change in the slope of the straight line was found, suggesting that only the functionally active copper could be reduced.

This has also been demonstrated by EPR measurements by Beinert and van Gelder (10). When cytochrome c oxidase was completely reduced by NADH in the presence of phenazine methosulfate, the signal of the functionally active copper disappeared, whereas the signal of the functionally inactive copper was still present even 15 minutes after the reduction was completed.

It was clearly of interest to determine the effects of chelating agents which prevent the reduction of part of the cytochrome c oxidase. Three different kinds of effects were found (see Fig. 2), namely:

(a) Cyanide, azide, EDTA + fluoride, or salicylaldoxime + fluoride caused a large increase in the slope at 605 mμ and a slight decrease at 445 mμ.

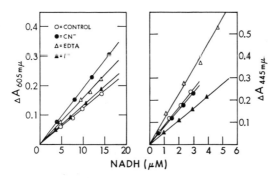

FIG. 2. Titration of cytochrome c oxidase with NADH and phenazine methosulfate under anaerobic conditions. The final concentrations were 0.09 M phosphate buffer (pH 7.4), 0.9% cholate, and 50–60 μM cytochrome c oxidase at 605 mμ and 15–20 μM cytochrome c oxidase at 445 mμ. The titration was carried out as described in the legend to Fig. 1. The increment in absorbance was corrected for the absorbance increment obtained in a similar experiment without NADH added. O—O, control, without a chelating agent; ●—●, with 7 mM cyanide; △—△, with 10 mM EDTA; ▲—▲, with 10 mM fluoride.

(b) EDTA or salicylaldoxime caused an increase in the slope at both 605 mμ and 445 mμ.

(c) Fluoride caused a slight increase in the slope at 605 mμ and a decrease at 445 mμ.

From these effects it could be calculated that the reagents in group (a) prevent the reduction of half the heme a and half the copper, those in group (b) the reduction of half the copper, and those in group (c) the reduction of half the heme a (6–8). Thus, the composition of the elementary unit and the site of action of the metal-binding agents must be as given in Fig. 3.

These results show not only that cytochrome a and cytrochrome a_3 are present in equal amounts in cytochrome c oxidase, as has been confirmed by other laboratories (11 13), but that there are also two species of functionally active copper, one of which is unreactive toward cyanide, azide, EDTA, and salicylaldoxime, and the other of which is reactive. These two kinds of copper atoms occur in equal amounts in the enzyme.

Thus, three kinds of copper have been found in cytochrome c oxidase preparations: (a) functionally inactive copper, which may be removed by dialysis against cyanide; (b) functionally active copper that does not react with cyanide; (c) functionally active copper that is not removed by dialysis against cyanide but which reacts with cyanide and other copper-chelating agents in such a way that, under the conditions of the titration, its reduction by reduced phenazine methosulfate is inhibited.

Some support for our conclusion that cytochrome c oxidase contains two different kinds of functionally active copper comes from MacLennan and

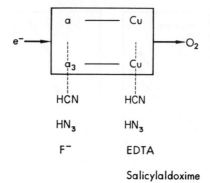

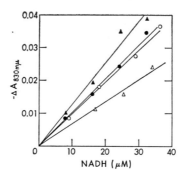

Fig. 3. Diagrammatic representation of cytochrome c oxidase, and the site of action of the metal-binding agents discussed in this paper.

Tzagoloff's observations (14) that, after treatment of the enzyme with 90% acetone and succinylation of the insoluble precipitate, part of the copper is found bound to a soluble protein, whereas most of the heme a and the remaining copper are still present in the insoluble precipitate.

II. The 830 mμ Absorption Band

Although the α and γ bands of cytochrome c oxidase have been known for many years, the band in the near infrared has only been recently discovered. Griffiths and Wharton (15) and Wharton and Tzagoloff (16) found that the absorption spectrum of the oxidized enzyme contains a

Fig. 4. Titration of cytochrome c oxidase with NADH under anaerobic conditions at 830 mμ. The final concentrations were phosphate buffer (pH 7.3), 0.06 M; cholate, 0.9%; and cytochrome c oxidase, 100 μM. The absorbance was measured on a Cary model 14 spectrophotometer with a slidewire of 0–0.1. The titration was carried out as described in the legend of Fig. 1. $\bigcirc$—$\bigcirc$, without any addition; $\bullet$—$\bullet$, with 10 mM cyanide; $\triangle$—$\triangle$, with 5 mM EDTA; $\blacktriangle$—$\blacktriangle$, with 10 mM fluoride.

TABLE I

CALCULATIONS OF THE CONTRIBUTIONS OF THE HEME a AND COPPER OF CYTOCHROME a AND CYTOCHROME a_3 TO THE DIFFERENCE SPECTRUM (OXIDIZED MINUS REDUCED) AT 830 Mμ

Addition	$-\Delta A$:[NADH][a]	Calculation
None	0.98	$\dfrac{[\%\Delta A \text{ cyt. } a \text{ (Fe + Cu)} + \%\Delta A \text{ cyt. } a_3 \text{ (Fe + Cu)}]0.01 \times 0.98}{0.98} = 1$
		$\%\Delta A \text{ cyt. } a \text{ (Fe + Cu)} + \%\Delta A \text{ cyt. } a_3 \text{ (Fe + Cu)} = 100$
Cyanide	1.02	$\dfrac{[\%\Delta A \text{ cyt. } a \text{ (Fe + Cu)} + 0]0.01 \times 0.98}{1.02} = 0.50$
		$\%\Delta A \text{ cyt. } a \text{ (Fe + Cu)} = 52$
EDTA	0.68	$\dfrac{[52 + \%\Delta A \text{ cyt. } a_3 \text{ (Fe)}]0.01 \times 0.98}{0.68} = 0.75$
		$\%\Delta A \text{ cyt. } a_3 \text{ (Fe)} = 0$
Fluoride	1.29	$\dfrac{[52 + \%\Delta A \text{ cyt. } a_3 \text{ (Cu)}]0.01 \times 0.98}{1.29} = 0.75$
		$\%\Delta A \text{ cyt. } a_3 \text{ (Cu)} = 47$

[a] Millimolar concentration.

broad band, with a peak at 830 mμ, which disappears after reduction. They suggested that this band is due to copper.

Our titrations at 830 mμ (Fig. 4) confirm these conclusions. It is striking that the copper-chelating agent EDTA causes a decline in the slope at 830 mμ, whereas it increases the slope at 445 mμ (Fig. 2), and that the heme-combining agent fluoride has precisely the opposite effect. Thus, if the effect on the 445 mμ absorption is an effect on the iron, then the effect on the 830 mμ absorption must be due to an effect on copper.

The contributions to the absorption in the difference spectrum due to heme a and copper of cytochrome a and cytochrome a_3 have been calculated in Table I. The calculations were made as follows: The absorption expressed as percentage of that found in the absence of chelating agents is multiplied by 0.01 to convert percentage to fraction and by $\Delta A/[\text{NADH}]$ found in the absence of chelating compounds. This is divided by $\Delta A/[\text{NADH}]$ found in the presence of a chelating compound to give the ratio of operating reducible groups in the presence of a metal-binding agent to reducible groups in the absence of any addition. In the presence of cyanide the heme a and copper of cytochrome a_3 are not reduced; thus the contribution of cytochrome a_3 to the decrease in absorption is zero. According to the calculation, the contribution of the heme a and copper of cytochrome a is 52%. Thus, the contribution of heme a and copper of cytochrome a_3 should be 48%. In the presence of EDTA, the cyanide-sensitive copper will not be reduced. According to the third calculation in Table I, the iron of cytochrome a_3 makes no contribution in the difference spectrum at 830 mμ. The fourth calculation based on the data with fluoride shows that the iron and copper of cytochrome a_3 contribute 47% of the absorption, in good agreement with the conclusion drawn from the cyanide data.

Unfortunately it is not possible to distinguish between the heme a and copper of cytochrome a by this method. We may conclude that approximately one half of the 830 mμ band in the difference spectrum is due to copper of cytochrome a_3 and one half is due to copper or heme a (very likely also to copper) of cytochrome a.

Our results support the conclusion of Morrison (17) and Wharton (18) that the heme a of cytochrome a_3 does not contribute to the difference spectrum at 830 mμ.

III. Summary

(a) Cytochrome c oxidase has been titrated with NADH and phenazine methosulfate. It was found that equimolar amounts of heme a and copper are simultaneously reduced.

(b) Functionally inactive copper, present in the enzyme preparation or added as Cu^{2+} salts, was not reduced.

(c) Two kinds of functionally active copper have been found in equal proportions. One is unreactive toward chelating agents such as cyanide, azide, EDTA, and salicylaldoxime, whereas, under the conditions of the titration, the reduction of the other can be prevented.

(d) The cyanide-sensitive copper contributes about one half of the difference spectrum (oxidized minus reduced) at 830 mμ, whereas the contribution of the other half is due to either heme a of cytochrome a or the cyanide-insensitive copper, or to both. The heme a of cytochrome a_3 does not contribute to the difference spectrum at 830 mμ.

ACKNOWLEDGMENTS

The authors wish to thank Mr. A. O. Muijsers for his cooperation in some experiments and for valuable discussions, and Mr. R. Le Clerq for his technical assistance.

The Cary spectrophotometer was purchased from funds made available by the Rockefeller Foundation.

REFERENCES

1. Beinert, H., Griffiths, D. E., Wharton, D. C., and Sands, R. H., *J. Biol. Chem.*, **237,** 2337 (1962).
2. Beinert, H., and Palmer, G., *J. Biol. Chem.*, **239,** 1221 (1964).
3. Morrison, M., Horric, S., and Mason, H. S., *J. Biol. Chem.*, **238,** 2220 (1963).
4. Beinert, H., and Palmer, G., *in* T. S. King, H. S. Mason and M. Morrison (eds.), "Oxidases and related redox systems," John Wiley, and Sons, Inc., New York 1965, p. 567.
5. van Gelder, B. F., and Slater, E. C., *Biochim. Biophys. Acta,* **73,** 663 (1963).
6. van Gelder, B. F., and Muijsers, A. O., *Biochim. Biophys. Acta,* **81,** 405 (1964).
7. Slater, E. C., van Gelder, B. F., and Minnaert, K., *in* T. S. King, H. S. Mason, and M. Morrison (eds.), "Oxidases and related redox systems," John Wiley and Sons, Inc., New York, 1965, p. 667.
8. van Gelder, B. F., *6th Intern. Congr. Biochem., New York, 1964,* Abstr. X, p. 79 (1964).
9. Griffiths, D. E., and Wharton, D. C., *J. Biol. Chem.*, **236,** 1857 (1961).
10. Beinert, H., and van Gelder, B. F., unpublished experiments.
11. Gibson, Q. H., Palmer, G., and Wharton, D. C., *J. Biol. Chem.*, **240,** 915 (1965).
12. Vanneste, W. A., *Biochem. Biophys. Res. Communs.*, **18,** 563 (1965).
13. Mansley, G. E., Stanbury, J. T., and Lemberg, R., *Biochim. Biophys. Acta,* in press.
14. MacLennan, D. H., and Tzagoloff, A., *Biochim. Biophys. Acta,* **96,** 166 (1965).
15. Griffiths, D. E., and Wharton, D. C., *J. Biol. Chem.*, **236,** 1850 (1961).
16. Wharton, D. C., and Tzagoloff, A., *J. Biol. Chem.*, **239,** 2036 (1964).
17. Morrison, M., *in* T. S. King, H. S. Mason, and M. Morrison (eds.), "Oxidases and related redox systems," John Wiley and Sons, Inc., New York, 1965, p. 639.
18. Wharton, D. C., *Biochim. Biophys. Acta,* **92,** 607 (1964).

The Copper Protein Component of Cytochrome c Oxidase*

ALEXANDER TZAGOLOFF AND DAVID H. MacLENNAN†

Institute for Enzyme Research,
University of Wisconsin,
Madison, Wisconsin

I. The Identification of the 830 mμ Band with Copper

The presence of a broad absorption band in the near infrared region of the oxidized spectrum of cytochrome c oxidase was first noted by Griffiths and Wharton (1). This band (Fig. 1) has an absorption maximum at 830 mμ and is usually measured in concentrated solutions of the enzyme because of its low extinction coefficient. The 830 mμ band undergoes oxidation-reduction changes which are similar in relative magnitude to the changes observed in the visible spectrum (1). Several different lines of evidence can now be presented to support the view of Griffiths and Wharton (1) that this band is part of the absorption spectrum of copper.

A. Absorbance and Copper Content

Dialysis of cytochrome c oxidase against 1.0 M cyanide or exposure to acid or alkaline pH results in a parallel loss of copper and absorbance at 830 mμ. These conditions also lead to some modification in the visible spectrum (shift of α and Soret bands toward lower wavelengths), and therefore it is possible that the 830 mμ absorption is due to some specific binding of the heme. This alternative explanation, however, is made less likely by the finding that similar shifts of the visible spectrum can be induced without any decrease in the 830 mμ absorption or denaturation of the EPR signal. Thus, succinylation of cytochrome oxidase with succinic anhydride causes a 3–4 mμ shift of the α and Soret bands toward lower wavelengths while the EPR signal and the extinction coefficient of the near infrared band remain unchanged. These results are summarized in Table I.

More direct evidence indicates that the 830 mμ absorption is not part of the cytochrome a_3 spectrum. In previous studies, Tzagoloff and Wharton (2) have shown that under anaerobic conditions, carbon monoxide causes

* This research was supported in part by U.S. Public Health Service research grants HE–00458 from the National Heart Institute and GM–12,847 from the National Institute of General Medical Sciences.

† Not at meeting.

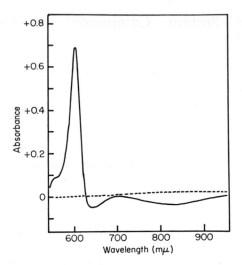

FIG. 1. Reduced minus oxidized difference spectrum of cytochrome c oxidase. The protein concentration was 6.5 mg/ml.

a slow reduction of cytochrome a_3, but not of cytochrome a, to form an a^{3+} a_3^{2+}–CO complex. Such preparations showed no reduction of the 830 mμ band or of the copper detectable by EPR. Wharton (3) and Morrison (4) have reached similar conclusions by forming the carbon monoxide complex with a completely reduced cytochrome oxidase and by selectively reoxidizing the cytochrome a with ferricyanide.

B. Changes in Absorbance under Oxidation-Reduction

The usual spectrophotometric methods show that the 830 mμ and 605 mμ bands undergo similar oxidation-reduction changes. Gibson and Greenwood (5), however, have been able to detect differences in the kinetic behavior of the two bands by the use of stop-flow techniques. These authors have

TABLE I

PROPERTIES OF NATIVE AND SUCCINYLATED CYTOCHROME c OXIDASE

	Native	Succinylated
α Band (reduced)	605 mμ	602 mμ
Soret band (reduced)	442 mμ	438 mμ
ΔA per milligram of protein (oxidized–reduced)	0.0074	0.0075
EPR signal	"Native"	"Native"

concluded that the 830 mμ band does not constitute part of the heme spectrum of cytochrome oxidase. A further conclusion from these studies was that the chromophore which absorbs at 830 mμ has a second absorption band which centers at about 600 mμ but which is obscured by the more pronounced cytochrome spectrum. In this connection it is of interest that the spectrum of oxidized cytochrome oxidase has a broad absorption that ranges from 600 to 550 mμ and is bleached when the enzyme is reduced. This absorption is not present in cytochrome oxidase preparations that have been denatured and in which the 830 mμ band is no longer present.

The oxidation-reduction potential of the chromophore absorbing at 830 mμ has been measured by titrating a solution containing cytochrome *c* oxidase and cytochrome *c* with potassium ascorbate. In view of the autoxidizability of cytochrome oxidase (6) it was technically feasible to carry out these measurements only in the presence of cyanide. The oxidation-reduction potential was determined from the equilibrium values of the relative states of reduction of the α band of cytochrome *c* and the 830 mμ band as shown in Fig. 2. The difference in potential between cytochrome *c*

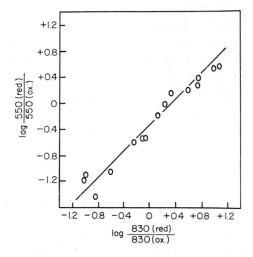

Fig. 2. Oxidation-reduction potential of the near infrared band at 830 mμ. A mixture containing 37 mμmoles cytochrome *a*, 31 mμmoles cytochrome *c*, 100 mμmoles KCN, 50 μmoles Tris-HCl, pH 8.0, and 10 mg potassium deoxycholate per milliliter was made anaerobic by a series of evacuations and flushings with N_2. A sample was removed to serve as the oxidized reference. The mixture under nitrogen was then titrated by additions of 2 μl of a 5 mM solution of potassium ascorbate. The oxidation-reduction state of cytochrome *c* and the near infrared band were determined spectrophotometrically at 550 mμ and 830 mμ after 2–5 minutes equilibration following each addition of the reducing agent. The completely reduced state was obtained after adding a few grains of sodium dithionite.

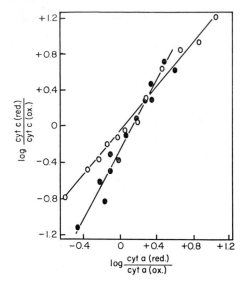

FIG. 3. Oxidation-reduction potentials of cytochrome a in different preparations of cytochrome oxidase. ● A mixture containing 40 mμmoles cytochrome a, 32 mμmoles cytochrome c, 50 μmoles Tris-HCl, pH 8.0, and 10 mg potassium deoxycholate per milliliter was made anaerobic by a series of evacuations and flushings with N$_2$. The equilibrium states of reduction of the two cytochromes was determined spectrophotometrically after stepwise additions of 2 μl of a 5 mM solution of potassium ascorbate. Reduced cytochrome c was measured at 550 mμ and reduced cytochrome a at 605 mμ. The completely reduced enzyme was obtained by the addition of solid sodium dithionite. ○ A solution containing Cu-free cytochrome oxidase was titrated under the conditions described above. To remove Cu, cytochrome oxidase was dialyzed against 1 M borate buffer, pH 11.3 containing 0.01 M KCN for 3 hours. Borate and cyanide were removed from the enzyme by a subsequent dialysis for 16 hours against 0.05 M Tris–HCl, pH 8.0.

and the 830 mμ band, calculated from three separate experiments, was 24 mVolts, thus placing the potential of the chromophore at 284 mVolts. This value is very close to the estimated potential of cytochrome a (7–11) and is in keeping with the observation that in the carbon monoxide complex the oxidation-reduction properties of the 830 mμ band resemble more closely those of cytochrome a than a_3. An n value of 1 was obtained from the slope of the line, indicating that the 830 mμ band undergoes a one-electron reduction. Previous studies on the potential of cytochrome a (8–11) have shown that the n value for cytochrome a as measured at 605 mμ is 0.5. This result has been interpreted by Slater, van Gelder, and Minnaert (11) to mean that the reduction of cytochrome a by ferricytochrome c involves the participation of a second electron donor, present in cytochrome c oxidase. These authors have considered the possibility that the internal donor is Cu$^+$. This suggestion has been examined by us by

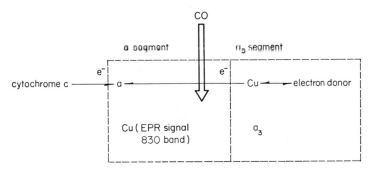

F IG . 4. Diagrammatic illustration of the relationship between the hypothetical electron donor, copper, and cytochromes a and a_3.

comparing the titration curves of normal cytochrome oxidase and cyto-chrome oxidase from which copper had previously been removed. The results illustrated in Fig. 3 show that unlike the native enzyme, cytochrome a in the copper-free preparation has an n value of 1. The potential is de-creased by about 20 mVolts and is almost equal to that of cytochrome c. This interesting result must be interpreted with caution since the observed differences in the potential could be due to some secondary changes in the heme binding. Nevertheless it is of interest that the oxidation-reduction potential of cytochrome a in the copper-free oxidase is very similar to that of cytochrome c oxidase in which cytochrome a_3 has reacted with carbon monoxide (2). If the interpretation of Slater and colleagues is correct, we would expect the internal donor to be the copper associated with cyto-chrome a_3.

The data on the oxidation-reduction potentials of cytochrome a in the different preparations of cytochrome c oxidase, as well as data on the two forms of copper described by van Gelder (12), permit us to make certain interpretations on the relationship between the various components. These interpretations are illustrated diagrammatically in Fig. 4. The copper associated with cytochrome a is responsible for the 830 mμ band and the EPR signal while the copper associated with cytochrome a_3 has no EPR signal or absorption at 830 mμ. Since no Cu^+ can be detected by chemical assay, the reducing equivalents are postulated to come from some other group which is in equilibrium with the copper of a_3.

II. Subunit Proteins of Cytochrome c Oxidase

A role for copper in cytochrome c oxidase has been established by studies on the intact enzyme. We have attempted to extend these studies by

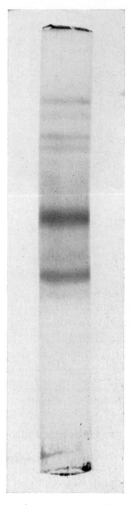

Fig. 5. Photograph of the protein components of cytochrome *c* oxidase separated by electrophoresis on polyacrylamide gel. Cytrochrome oxidase was extracted with 90% acetone and dissolved in a solution consisting of phenol–acetic acid–water (2:1:1, w/v/v). The protein concentration was adjusted to 10 mg/ml and solid urea was added to achieve a final concentration of 2 M. Polyacrylamide gel was prepared by the method of Reisfeld *et al.* (15), except that acetic acid and urea were additional components. The system consisted of 7.5% aceylamide, 35% acetic acid, and 5 M urea. A disc electrophoresis apparatus ismilar to that described by Davis (16) was used. The height of the polyacrylamide column was 45 mm.

resolution of the enzyme complex into its component parts. Cytochrome c oxidase is a large molecular weight enzyme. Light-scattering measurements have shown the average molecular weight to be about 230,000 (13) and indicate that each unit contains at least two molecules of heme a and two atoms of copper. The enzyme can be partially depolymerized by the use of such reagents as sodium dodecyl sulfate (14) and urea (13) and can be highly depolymerized by 66% acetic acid, by 66% acetic acid plus 6 M urea, or by phenol–acetic acid–water (2:1:1, w/v/v). We have subjected the dissolved proteins to electrophoresis on starch gel containing 6 M urea and on polyacrylamide gel and have been able to detect several protein bands after staining the gel with amido black (15, 16). A photograph of these separated bands is presented in Fig. 5.

The finding of some eight protein subunits in cytochrome c oxidase raises a fundamental question about the functional subunits of the oxidase. Are the identifiable prosthetic groups, cytochrome a, cytochrome a_3, and the two forms of copper, attached to one or to separate proteins? This question has been answered for other components of the electron-transfer chain. Thus several laboratories including those of Okunuki (17, 18), Wainio (19), and Green (20, 21) have established that cytochrome b and cytochrome c_1 can be isolated as single proteins and Rieske, MacLennan, and Coleman (22) have conclusively demonstrated that the nonheme iron of complex III is bound to a protein separate from the cytochromes.

III. Isolation of a Copper Protein from Cytochrome c Oxidase

Cytochrome c oxidase has been found to be resistant to the combination of reagents (bile acid, salt, and heat) that achieves a separation of the component proteins of complex III (23). Removal of phospholipid does not appear to have any effect on the organization of the component proteins. Exposure of cytochrome oxidase to the strong solubilizing agents containing acetic acid denatures the enzyme and removes the prosthetic groups. A milder solubilizing method has been developed which has proven to be successful for the isolation of a copper protein (24, 25). The first step in this procedure is the extraction of the enzyme with 90% acetone as described by Brierley and Merola (26). This step removes phospholipid and bile acid, leaving the cytochrome oxidase in a polymerized and water-insoluble form. The acetone extraction also leads to some denaturation of the enzyme. This denaturation is evidenced by the appearance of hyperfine structure in the EPR signal of copper (Fig. 6) and in a shift of the visible absorption bands to lower wavelengths. The extent of the denaturation does not

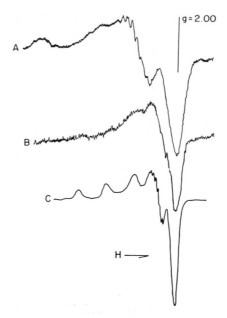

F<small>IG</small>. 6. EPR spectra of acetone-extracted and succinylated cytochrome c oxidase and of the purified copper protein. Each spectrum is aligned at $g = 2.00$ (A) Acetone-extracted cytochrome oxidase; power was 10 mWatt and the temperature $-156°$. (B) Succinylated cytochrome oxidase; power was 10 mWatt and the temperature $-156°$. (C) Cu protein oxidized with ferricyanide; the power was 25 mWatt and temperature $-170°$.

exceed 50%, however, since reactivation of 50% of the original activity of such preparations has been reported by Brierley and Merola (26).

The second step involves a selective solubilization of part of the polymerized material by the introduction of succinyl groups into the proteins. Succinylation at a level of 0.5 mg of succinic anhydride per milligram of protein results in a solubilization of 21% of the total protein containing 25% of the copper (25). This material is essentially free of heme but contains copper at levels of about 11 mμmoles per milligram of protein. Purification of a copper protein from the crude soluble fraction has been possible only through the use of molecular sieve filtration. We have been able to obtain four major protein fractions by a single passage of the soluble material through a 5 × 100 cm column of Sephadex G-100. (Fig. 7). Copper is greatly enriched in the second fraction which appears as a shoulder on fraction I. The concentration of copper in this fraction is generally in the range of 40–50 mμmoles per milligram of protein. Fraction I appears to be a polymerized fraction containing some copper and most of the degraded heme protein, which is solubilized by succinylation. Fractions III and IV have no detectable prosthetic groups. A further purifica-

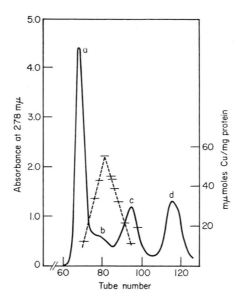

Fɪɢ. 7. Elution pattern of the crude copper protein fraction on a 5 × 60 cm column of Sephadex G–100 gel expanded in 0.05 *M* phosphate, pH 7.5. ——, Absorbance at 278 m*μ*; • • •, specific copper contents of fractions spanned by the horizontal lines.

tion of the copper protein can be achieved by a second passage through Sephadex G-100.

A. Characteristics of the Copper Protein

The copper protein obtained after a second Sephadex separation has the characteristics described in Table II. It contains a very small amount of heme or degraded heme products as seen by the iron content. The visible spectrum shows some absorption through the range of 600–400 m*μ*. Reduction with dithionite causes a bleaching in the 450 m*μ* region, which may be due to "mitochrome" (27).

TABLE II

Cᴏᴍᴘᴏsɪᴛɪᴏɴ ᴏғ Sᴜᴄᴄɪɴʏʟᴀᴛᴇᴅ Cᴏᴘᴘᴇʀ Pʀᴏᴛᴇɪɴ ᴀғᴛᴇʀ Sᴇᴄᴏɴᴅ Pᴀssᴀɢᴇ ᴛʜʀᴏᴜɢʜ Sᴇᴘʜᴀᴅᴇx G–100

Copper content	81 m*μ*moles/mg protein
Iron content	0.19 m*μ*moles/mg protein
Heme content	<0.19 m*μ*moles/mg protein
Labile sulfide	0

TABLE III

CHELATION OF COPPER FROM COPPER PROTEIN

Dialysis conditions	Cu content (mμmoles/mg protein)[a]
None	13.0
10 mM phosphate, 22 hours	14.0
1 mM EDTA, 10 hours; 10 mM phosphate, 12 hours	0
10 mM diethyldithiocarbamate, 10 hours; 10 mM phosphate, 12 hours	13.5
10 mM cyanide, 10 hours; 10 mM phosphate, 12 hours	0

[a] The crude succinylated fraction before Sephadex separation was used.

A minimum molecular weight of 12,300 can be estimated on the basis of 1 copper per molecule from the specific copper content of 81 mμmoles per milligram of protein. Although we have not obtained an accurate molecular weight of the protein, the S value has been found to be 1.6–1.8. This value corresponds to a molecular weight of about 25,000. We would

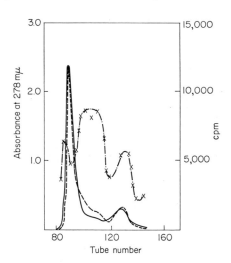

FIG. 8. Distribution of ^{64}Cu in the proteins of the crude copper protein fraction. ^{64}Cu was added to cytochrome c oxidase after acetone extraction in an amount equivalent to that present in the enzyme. The succinylated crude copper protein fraction was chromatographed on Sephadex G–100 under conditions described for Fig. 7. The fractions were analyzed for protein, ——, and ^{64}Cu, ------. The specific ^{64}Cu content, –·–·–, is also indicated.

predict therefore that the copper content would be at least two atoms per molecule.

The EPR spectrum of the copper protein indicates that the copper is no longer in the "native" state. The secondary binding of copper is also seen in its lability to dialysis against cyanide or EDTA as indicated in the results of Table III. Copper is not removed from the protein when it is dialyzed against phosphate buffer or diethyldithiocarbamate, however.

The copper in the purified protein was found to be freely exchangeable with ^{64}Cu. When ^{64}Cu was added to cytochrome *c* oxidase prior to succinylation, radioactive copper was present in all the protein fractions separated on the Sephadex column (Fig. 8). The specific copper content per unit protein, however, was much higher in the region of the copper protein, indicating a greater capacity of this protein to interact with copper. While it may be argued from this experiment that the copper protein is artifactual because it can bind free copper in solution during isolation, an equally valid argument for its reality can be presented from the fact that even though all the succinylated proteins can complex copper under the usual purification procedure, the copper in a normal preparation is concentrated in fraction II.

B. Residue after Succinylation

The residue after succinylation of the acetone-extracted cytochrome *c* oxidase is slightly enriched in heme *a*. This material can be solubilized by further succinylation with 4 mg succinic anhydride and 0.8 mg deoxycholate per milligram of protein. Fractions with heme contents averaging 15 mμmoles of heme *a* per mg protein can be obtained by fractionation with ammonium sulfate in the presence of 3% cholate. This protein fraction separates as a single peak on Sephadex G-100 and appears relatively homogeneous in the ultracentrifuge. Heme-to-copper ratios in this fraction as low as 0.3 can be obtained. We have not, however, succeeded in isolating a heme protein free of copper.

The experiments on the isolation of a copper protein do not allow any conclusive statements concerning copper in cytochrome *c* oxidase. They do, however, indicate that the enzyme is made up of subunit proteins, one of which contains copper and no heme, and another of which is a specific heme protein. The degradation of the EPR signal during isolation holds little hope for the possibility of establishing the nature of the copper linkage by tactics of isolation. In fact, it has been our experience that the fractionation of cytochrome *c* oxidase into fractions which are enriched in copper or in heme is possible only under conditions which lead to a loss of the properties of the "native" copper. Thus the very environment responsible for the specific properties of copper and heme may also be responsible for linking the subunits.

IV. Summary

(a) The relationship between the near infrared band and copper in cytochrome c oxidase is discussed. Conditions leading to a loss of copper result in a parallel decrease in absorbance at 830 mμ. Succinylation of cytochrome oxidase modifies the visible spectrum without denaturation of the copper or decrease in absorbance at 830 mμ.

(b) The oxidation-reduction potential of the chromophore absorbing in the near infrared region has been estimated at 284 mVolts. This value corresponds closely with previously reported values for the potential of cytochrome a. The distinct nature of the two, however, is made evident by differences in the n values.

(c) The oxidation-reduction potential of cytochrome a in a copper-free preparation of cytochrome c oxidase is about 20 mVolts lower than in a native preparation which contains copper. A model of the enzyme in which a hypothetical electron donor participates in the reduction of cytochrome a is presented.

(d) Evidence is presented which indicates that cytochrome c oxidase is a high molecular weight enzyme which consists of multiple protein subunits. The partial separation of the component proteins points to the existence of a separate heme protein and a separate copper protein.

(e) The isolation and properties of a copper protein from cytochrome c oxidase are described. The protein contains two copper atoms per molecule. The EPR signal of the copper in the isolated protein has hyperfine structure indicating that the metal binding has been modified.

ACKNOWLEDGMENTS

We wish to thank Dr. David E. Green for his encouragement and advice during the course of this study. The EPR analyses were performed through the courtesy of Dr. Helmut Beinert.

REFERENCES

1. Griffiths, D. E., and Wharton, D. C., *J. Biol. Chem.*, **236**, 1850 (1961).
2. Tzagoloff, A., and Wharton, D. C., *J. Biol. Chem.*, **240**, 2628 (1965).
3. Wharton, D. C., *Biochim. Biophys. Acta*, **92**, 607 (1964).
4. Morrison, M., *in* T. E. King, H. S. Mason, and M. Morrison (eds.), "Oxidases and related redox systems," John Wiley and Sons, Inc., New York, 1965, p. 639.
5. Gibson, Q., and Greenwood, C., *J. Biol. Chem.*, **240**, 2694 (1965).

6. Wainio, W. W., *in* J. E. Falk, R. Lemberg, and R. K. Morton (eds.), "Haematin enzymes," Macmillan Company (Pergamon), New York, 1961, p. 281.
7. Tzagoloff, A., and MacLennan, D. H., *Biochim. Biophys. Acta*, **99,** 476 (1965).
8. Ball, E. G., *Biochem. Z.*, **295,** 262 (1938).
9. Wainio, W. W., *J. Biol. Chem.*, **216,** 593 (1955).
10. Minnaert, K., *Fed. Proc.*, **20,** 42 (1961).
11. Slater, E. C., van Gelder, B. F., and Minnaert, K., *in* T. E. King, H. S. Mason, and M. Morrison (eds.), "Oxidases and related redox systems," John Wiley and Sons, Inc., New York, 1965, p. 667.
12. van Gelder, B. F., and Slater, E. C., *Biochim. Biophys. Acta*, **73,** 405 (1964).
13. Tzagoloff, A., Yang, C. P., Wharton, D. C., and Rieske, J. S., *Biochim. Biophys. Acta*, **96,** 1 (1965).
14. Criddle, R. S., and Bock, R. M., *Biochem. Biophys. Res. Communs.*, **1,** 138 (1959).
15. Reisfeld, R. A., Lewis, J. U., and Williams, D. E., *Nature*, **195,** 281 (1962).
16. Davis, B. J., *Ann. N. Y. Acad. Sci.*, **121,** 404 (1964).
17. Okunuki, K., Sekuzu, I., Orii, Y., Higuchi, M., Takemori, S., and Yonetani, T., *Proc. Japan. Acad.*, **34,** 379 (1958).
18. Sekuzu, I., and Okunuki, K., *J. Biochem. (Tokyo)*, **43,** 107 (1956).
19. Feldman, D., and Wainio, W. W., *J. Biol. Chem.*, **235,** 3635 (1960).
20. Goldberger, R., Smith, A. L., Tisdale, H. D., and Bomstein, R., *J. Biol. Chem.*, **236,** 2788 (1961).
21. Green, D. E., Jahrnefelt, J., and Tisdale, H. D., *Biochim. Biophys. Acta*, **31,** 34 (1959).
22. Rieske, J. S., MacLennan, D. H., and Coleman, R., *Biochem. Biophys. Res. Communs.*, **15,** 338 (1964).
23. Rieske, J. S., Zaugg, W. S., and Hanson, R. E., *J. Biol. Chem.*, **239,** 3023 (1964).
24. MacLennan, D. H., Tzagoloff, A., and Rieske, J. S., *Arch. Biochem. Biophys.*, **109,** 383 (1965).
25. MacLennan, D. H., and Tzagoloff, A., *Biochim. Biophys. Acta*, **96,** 166 (1965).
26. Brierley, G. P., and Merola. A. J., *Biochim. Biophys. Acta*, **64,** 205 (1962).
27. Elliott, W. B., Hulsmann, W. C., and Slater, E. C., *Biochim. Biophys. Acta*, **33,** 509 (1959).

Cytochrome c Oxidase Discussion

Dr. Mason: I would like to comment on the relationship of copper to heme in cytochrome oxidase. I have been helping Dr. Morrison study an a_3-free cytochrome oxidase using EPR. I might take the liberty in his absence of telling you that if one compares his starting cytochrome oxidase with his cytochrome a preparation one finds that the shape of the signal, the g value of the signal, the amount of EPR-detectable and EPR-nondetectable copper, and the behavior of copper with respect to saturation are identical in the two preparations. It seems to me that this must mean that the relationship between cytochome a_3 and the two types of presumably functional copper in the cytochrome oxidase is a loose one if Morrison's preparation is truly free of cytochrome a_3.

I would like to make one other point with respect to the titrations. We have been making similar titrations with microsomal material, and a student, Mr. Waterman, has found peroxidation repeatedly with membranous material. It's well known that the lipids of these particles peroxidize very readily. Ernster has been reporting on the formation of malondialdehyde from microsomes for some time, so I feel that in various preparations there can be a certain amount of hydrogen peroxide.

Looking at Fig. 1 of Dr. van Gelder's paper and projecting his curves to zero change, one finds that in that particular preparation a certain amount of NADH was consumed without causing any optical change. If cytochrome oxidase preparations do peroxidize, this may explain some of the anomalous details of the titration.

Dr. van Gelder: When I put in only phenazine methosulfate and no NADH, there was a small reduction of cytochrome oxidase. This is due to endogenous reducing groups. Calculating the amount of reducing equivalents needed can be done in two ways: first, from the slope and, second, by extrapolating to the abscissa. The intercept thus found represents an amount of NADH which was not needed for the titration.

Dr. Mason: How about the EPR titration with respect to copper? It seems to me that some of the vagaries of that titration curve might be explained by having some other electron acceptor. It could conceivably be lipid peroxide. That's not saying it is, but I just wondered whether that might not be a factor.

Dr. Slater: The titration at room temperature is exactly the reverse of what you said. There is endogenous reducing agent, not endogenous acceptor. To our knowledge there is no need to invoke any peroxides for the titrations at room temperature.

Dr. Mason: It seemed to me it was the other way around. If the curve was extended to zero optical change, a certain amount of NADH had been consumed.

DR. SLATER: A negative amount.

DR. YONETANI: I have a question for Dr. van Gelder. You assume that EDTA is bound to a_3 copper. Since EDTA does not inhibit cytochrome oxidase activity, can we conclude a_3 copper is not needed for enzymatic activity?

DR. VAN GELDER: We did find an effect of EDTA on the activity. EDTA is a competitive inhibitor, but the K_i value is very high, around 10 mM. I should like to mention that the conditions for determining the activity and doing the titration are completely different. In the titration, oxygen and cytochrome *c* are absent, whereas in the activity determination, cytochrome *c* and oxygen are present.

DR. CHANCE: Was the inhibition competitive or noncompetitive with oxygen?

DR. VAN GELDER: It was competitive with cytochrome *c*.

DR. CHANCE: But I wished to know about the competition of EDTA and oxygen. To justify your point you should have demonstrated that more EDTA was required as you used more oxygen. Yonetani also asked about the interaction of EDTA with cytochrome a_3. Maybe you haven't done it, but I do think it's a relevant question.

DR. VAN GELDER: No, I haven't done it.

DR. SLATER: The data are clear that EDTA is having the effect on the titration that Dr. van Gelder described, and it is also correct that EDTA in this range of concentrations does not inhibit under the conditions of determining manometrically cytochrome oxidase activity. I agree with Dr. Yonetani that this is very puzzling.

DR. BRESLOW: Dr. Wharton, I was wondering under what conditions you tried adding back copper to apoprotein. Did you try it in both the cupric and cuprous states?

DR. WHARTON: Yes, we tried both under various conditions of pH, and in the presence and absence of oxygen. We have tried just about everything we can think of, but we haven't been successful.

DR. AISEN: Does the absorption spectrum change qualitatively in the presence of substrate?

DR. WHARTON: The absorption spectrum of the treated cytochrome oxidase—that is, the oxidase from which the copper has been removed— does change. There is a shift in the alpha peak to about 600 mμ in the reduced enzyme. Furthermore, the Soret peak also shifts toward the violet region. However, the change is identical no matter how the copper is removed, whether by cyanide, by the alkaline buffers, or by BCS.

DR. TZAGOLOFF: As Dr. Wharton has pointed out, we were worried at the time we did the experiments on the removal of copper that the 830 mμ band might be some expression of heme bound to specific ligands. This possibility could not be excluded since the visible spectrum of the cytochrome was affected by the treatments used to remove copper. Recently, we have found that if we succinylate cytochrome oxidase directly, we can observe the same type of shift in the visible spectrum as we do after the removal of copper by the methods used by Dr. Wharton. Nevertheless, in this preparation we still observe the 830 mμ band, the copper is still resistant to dialysis in dilute cyanide, and the EPR signal does not exhibit hyperfine structure.

Dr. WILLIAMS: It seems to me that people have established a fairly strong case that this is a copper band. I myself believed until this meeting that it was an iron band because I had not read the recent literature on cytochrome oxidase.

Dr. AISEN: It's interesting that the meeting has produced at least one convert.

Dr. JØRGENSEN: I agree with Dr. Williams that it is a copper band in cytochrome oxidase.

Dr. HEMMERICH: I should like to emphasize once more the probable role of a RSSR–2 RS⁻ system as a copper-complexing site in cytochrome oxidase. There are certainly two possibilities, neither of which can be ruled out at present.

(a) Mercaptide and Cu at different sites (Fig. 1): Conformational change taking place upon blocking of S⁻ sites by mercurial reduces the Cu^{2+}–Cu^{2+} interaction and gives rise to increased EPR signal.

(b) Mercaptide and Cu at the same site (Fig. 2): This possibility is in good agreement with the results of Dr. Tzagoloff and Dr. van Gelder and is supported by our model studies. The question is, how many bonding electrons are contained in molecular orbitals extending over the four centers. In the zero state (see Fig. 3), there is no bonding between Cu and SS; the

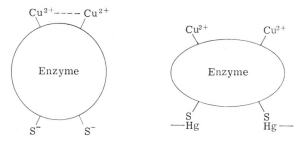

FIG. 1. RSSR system in cytochrome oxidase with mercaptide and Cu at different sites. See text for explanation.

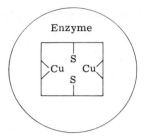

Fɪɢ. 2. RSSR system in cytochrome oxidase with mercaptide and Cu at the same site.

system, were it not for the protein, would fall apart to give 2 Cu^{2+} and disulfide. In state 4, there is only slight bonding along the broken lines; the system would presumably fall apart, to give a linear $(CuSR)_2$ unit. States 1 and 3 are paramagnetic and state 2 may be or not, whereas state 4 is diamagnetic. Further, state 1 should be EPR-active, states 2 and 3 may be or not, and state 4 should be EPR-inactive. Does the enzyme shuttle between 1 and 3 or between 2 and 4? Magnetic susceptibility measurements, difficult as they might be, seem necessary to resolve this question.

DR. WILLIAMS: You can tackle this problem experimentally, I think, because if the copper and sulfur are together, you will see not only the bands in the visible but also some charge-transfer bands. You should pick those up by doing exactly the same experiments as Dr. Wharton did, plotting the rate curve and watching the bands at lower wavelengths. There should be a band with an extinction coefficient of the order of 5000 in the region of about 350 to 450 mμ which you should be able to follow.

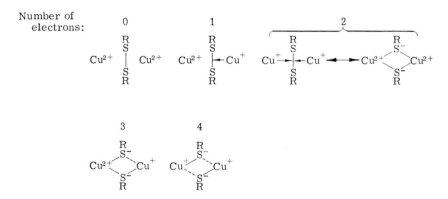

Fɪɢ. 3. Possible electronic states of the system of Fig. 2. See text for explanation.

TABLE I

NEAR INFRARED SPECTRA OF FERRIC COMPLEXES OF DEUTEROPORPHYRIN IX
DIMETHYL ESTER IN CHLOROFORM

Ligand	λ_{max} (mμ)	E_M
Chloride	909	540
Fluoride	799	500
Acetate	761	390
Azide	870	560
Methoxide	760	310

DR. CAUGHEY: Dr. McCoy and I have recently obtained data on the near infrared spectra of hemins. These data do not pertain to copper per se but, in view of the rather considerable discussion of the 830 mμ band of cytochrome oxidase, perhaps I should mention some of our results.

The absorption maxima of heme a and hemin a preparations in the near infrared region exhibit intensities in the same range as those found for cytochrome oxidase. Both wavelengths and intensities vary considerably with changes in solvent and (or) ligands. We have found that other hemins behave similarly; at present our widest range of data is for the derivatives of the Fe^{3+} deuteroporphyrin IX dimethyl ester. Data for chloroform solutions of complexes with several different ligands are in Table I. Neither the wavelengths nor the intensities of the near infrared band maxima were found to vary greatly as a function of substituents at the periphery of the ring. However, both the wavelength and intensities of these bands are quite sensitive to the nature of the ligands bound to iron. The heme components can be expected to contribute significantly to the 830 mμ absorption in cytochrome oxidase. Indeed changes in heme environment could result in differences in heme absorption great enough to account for *all* the changes observed in 830 mμ band. The fact that any change in the copper components of the oxidase could at the same time affect, either directly or indirectly, heme absorption must be considered in any attempt to ascribe changes in absorption at 830 mμ solely to changes of the copper components.

DR. WHARTON: I think that Dr. Caughey's comment is well taken, and that caution has to be applied here. We are well aware of the work of George and Hanania [*Disc. Faraday Soc.*, **20**, 293 (1955)], who showed that the high-spin forms of the hydroxides of ferrimyoglobin and ferrihemoglobin possess bands in the near infrared region with extinction coefficients comparable to those found in cytochrome oxidase. However, these were high-spin forms.

Ehrenberg and Yonetani [*Acta Chem. Scand.*, **15,** 1071 (1961)] have done some work on relating high-spin and low-spin states to the various cytochromes, *a* and a_3, in cytochrome oxidase. They have attributed a low-spin form to cytochrome *a*, and an intermediate-spin form to cytochrome a_3. If we can relate the near infrared bands more closely to cytochrome *a* than we can to cytochrome a_3 and if cytochrome *a* is indeed low spin, then it would seem to me that this would be one bit of evidence against the 830 mμ band being due to a high-spin iron.

DR. CAUGHEY: One comment that I should make on this is that the fluoride is high spin. The methoxide is mostly high spin in chloroform. On the other hand, the methoxide when placed in pyridine produces a low-spin complex; nevertheless, it still has a band at about the same region with an extinction coefficient only slightly lower. Thus, I would like to point out that there is no necessary correlation between spin state and either the position or the intensity of these bands.

DR. CHANCE: One does not have to go far to document Dr. Caughey's remark: one only has to open the back cover of Lemberg and Legge ["Haematin compounds and bile pigments," John Wiley & Sons, Inc. (Interscience), New York, 1949] to observe the infrared absorption bands of hemoblogin, which do not correlate very well with the spin states.

DR. CAUGHEY: I think this should be emphasized. Several generalizations along these lines have appeared in the literature, and now with more data available, they do not always seem to hold. Anything that could be happening to cytochrome oxidase to bring about a configurational change or a change of ligands could affect this band in the heme components. I'm not sure how you could distinguish between this and a direct involvement of copper.

DR. PALMER: I would like to ask if the bands you measured disappear on reduction to the Fe^{2+} state.

DR. CAUGHEY: In heme *a* they may be reduced somewhat in intensity but there is a residual, broad absorption.

DR. WILLIAMS: I have discussed this band, and I am guilty of the original association of this band with the high-spin form. As far as I know, there is no band in any cyanide complex at the long wavelengths. As far as I know, this band is also extremely sensitive, in its position, to its ligands. The 830 mμ band that we are talking about hardly moves at all when the carbon monoxide or fluoride complex of a_3 is formed. Thus it looks like a Cu^{2+} band.

Now, as far as the association of spin states and spectra is concerned, one must be very careful to discuss exactly how the measurements referred to were made, over what temperature ranges, and so on. One has to realize that the extinction coefficient as measured may only represent a fairly small proportion of a magnetically active form. For instance, the extinction coefficient in the 700–1200 mμ region for all the different derivatives of hemoglobin in a completely high-spin form could vary between 100 and 1,000, very easily. So we need to know the temperature dependence of these bands and of the magnetism before we can start arguing about whether to associate them with low- or high-spin forms.

DR. JØRGENSEN: Recently there have been some studies on pentacyano–iron–monoligands. If the ligand is sufficiently reducing, the iron remains low spin but the band goes into that region. The specific case I would like to mention is that Professor Nast (private communication) has allowed triphenylphosphine, triphenylarsine, and triphenylstibine to react with pentacyano-Fe^{3+}, and these complexes are all dark green. In the case of the stibine, the most reducing of these ligands, the electron-transfer band has moved as far as 840 mμ, whereas in the other two cases it is around 740 mμ. These are all extremely reducing when added to Fe^{3+}. The low-spin Fe^{3+} species probably cannot be prevented from having bands in that region if you take sufficiently reducing ligands, but these have not been studied very much until recently.

Pseudomonas Cytochrome Oxidase*

T. YAMANAKA

Department of Biology, Faculty of Science,
University of Osaka, Osaka, Japan,†
and Department of Chemistry,
University of California, San Diego,
La Jolla, California‡

I. Introduction

It is well known that in living cells cytochrome c oxidase catalyzes the reaction of molecular oxygen with electrons liberated from various substances. In most animal tissues, in many plants, and in some bacteria, a cytochrome which has heme a (Fig. 1) (1, 2) as its prosthetic group is known to function as the cytochrome oxidase (3–5). This cytochrome c oxidase is sometimes called cytochrome a, or cytochrome $a + a_3$ (4, 5). On the other hand, it is generally assumed that a cytochrome which has heme a_2 (Fig. 2) (2, 6) as its prosthetic group functions as a cytochrome oxidase in many bacteria which do not possess cytochrome c oxidase (7). However, the cytochrome a_2 which has heme a_2 as the only prosthetic group has never been isolated. From a few kinds of bacteria, *Pseudomonas aeruginosa* (8–13), *Azotobacter vinelandii* (14), and *Micrococcus sp.* (15), heme a_2-bearing cytochromes have been isolated, and it seems that they all contain not only heme a_2 but also other heme or hemes.

Pseudomonas cytochrome oxidase (8–13) isolated and highly purified from *Pseudomonas aeruginosa* has heme a_2 as its prosthetic group and is very different in its molecular features from cytochrome c oxidase. It contains heme c beside heme a_2 (16) and, unlike cytochrome c oxidase (4, 5), does not contain copper (10). Heme a_2 is different from the other hemes (e.g., protoheme, hematoheme, and heme a) in that it is a chlorin, i.e., it has two extra hydrogen atoms on one of its pyrrole rings (6). Nevertheless, *Pseudomonas* cytochrome oxidase has the general properties of a cytochrome oxidase, although its biological significance seems to be to function as a nitrite reductase (13, 17, 18). Further, by comparison of

* This research was begun in Professor K. Okunuki's laboratory, University of Osaka, and was extended in Professor M. D. Kamen's laboratory, University of California by grants-in-aid from the National Institutes of Health (HD–01262) and from the National Science Foundation (GB 2892).

† Permanent address.

‡ Present address.

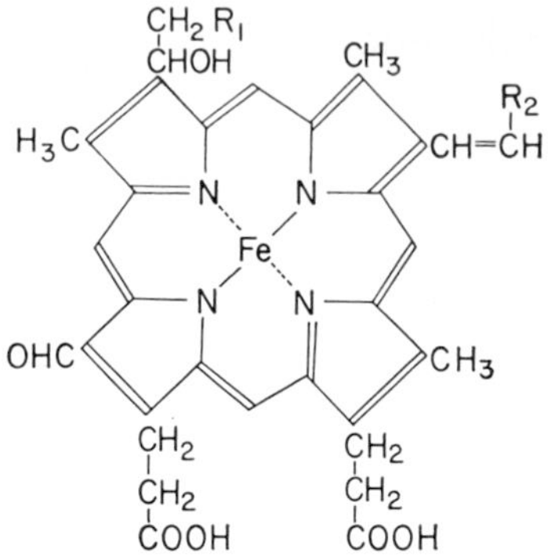

FIG. 1. Structural formula for heme a (1,2). R_1 and R_2 are alkyl groups.

Pseudomonas cytochrome oxidase with cytochrome c oxidase, some clues to significant structural factors for the cytochrome oxidase activity may be found.

II. Molecular Features

Pseudomonas cytochrome oxidase shows a very complicated absorption spectrum (Fig. 3), with peaks at 280, 412, 525, and 635 mμ in the oxidized form, and at 418, 523, 549, 554, 629, and 652 mμ with a shoulder at 460 mμ, when reduced with $Na_2S_2O_4$ at pH 7.0. At lower concentrations of the enzyme, the peaks at 629 and 652 mμ appear as a plateau from 620 to 650 mμ. The absorption spectrum of $Na_2S_2O_4$-reduced enzyme in the red region varies considerably with pH, and is affected greatly by CN^-, CO, and NO

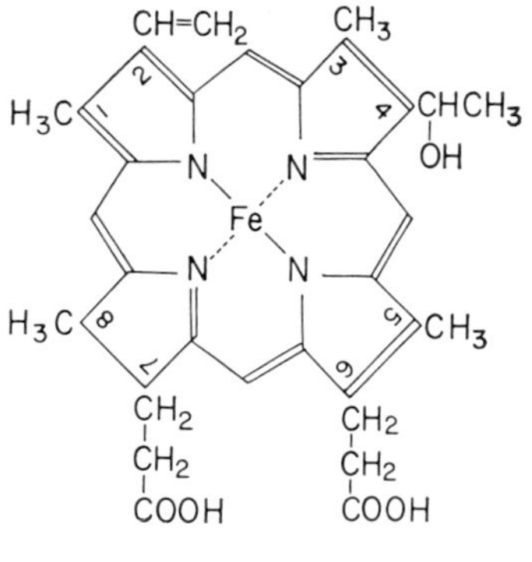

FIG. 2. A possible structural formula for heme a_2 (6).

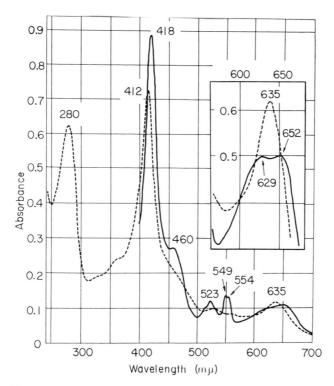

Fɪɢ. 3. Absorption spectrum of *Pseudomonas* cytochrome oxidase at pH 7.0. ------, Oxidized; ——, reduced with $Na_2S_2O_4$.

(Table I). The ratio A_γ/A_α (due to heme a_2) is small, as compared with that of cytochrome *c* oxidase (Table I).

The complicated absorption spectrum of the enzyme arises from the two kinds of hemes present. *Pseudomonas* cytochrome oxidase contains one heme a_2 and one heme *c* per molecule (10, 16). When the enzyme is extracted with acid acetone, the heme a_2 is extracted into the acetone and the protein moiety which precipitates shows an absorption spectrum very similar to that of a *c*-type cytochrome except for the splitting of the α band into peaks at 549 and 554 mμ (Fig. 4). From the protein moiety, heme *c* is split off as hematoheme by the silver sulfate method (21). The original *Pseudomonas* cytochrome oxidase is very soluble in aqueous solution, whereas the protein moiety is insoluble in aqueous solution at neutral pH, but soluble in an alkaline solution.

Heme a_2 which is extracted into the acetone can be separated as an aqueous solution from the acetone by adding NaOH (16). As seen in Fig. 4 and Table II, heme a_2 and its derivatives show very complicated γ-peaks,

TABLE I

Summary of the Positions of the Absorption Peaks of
Pseudomonas Cytochrome Oxidase[a]

Reagent added	State	pH	λ_{max} (mμ)		A_γ/A_α
			γ Peak	α Peak	
None	Oxidized	7.0	—	630	—
None	Reduced	7.6	460	(620)[b] 655	2.7
None	Reduced	7.0	460	629 652	2.5[c]
None	Reduced	5.6	460	625	1.9
CN⁻	Reduced	7.0	443 (472)	627	2.3
CO	Reduced	7.0	—	622 658	—
NO	Reduced	7.0	—	617 665	—
Cytochrome *c* oxidase[d]	Oxidized	7.4	424	600	—
(bovine)	Reduced	7.4	444	605	4.1

[a] Absorption peaks due to heme a_2. For experimental conditions, see Ref. (19).
[b] Values in the parentheses show shoulders.
[c] Higher peaks were selected where two peaks were present.
[d] See Ref. (20).

and the ratio A_γ/A_α of the pyridine hemochrome is small as compared with those of heme *a* and chlorocruroheme pyridine hemochromes. The latter two hemes have formyl groups on one of the pyrrole rings (23).

From the sedimentation and diffusion coefficients and partial specific volume, the molecular weight of *Pseudomonas* cytochrome oxidase is calculated to be about 90,000, whereas two gram atoms of iron are found in 94,000 g of the enzyme. Copper has not been detected (10). The isoelectric point of the enzyme is about pH 5.8. The addition of $CuSO_4$ to the culture medium enhances considerably the production of the enzyme, so it is likely that copper is necessary for its biosynthesis (17).

III. Enzymatic Properties

Pseudomonas cytochrome oxidase shows the general properties of a cytochrome oxidase (9, 10, 12); that is, it oxidizes ascorbate, hydroquinone, and the reduced form of cytochrome *c* (551, *Pseudomonas aeruginosa*) (24). The latter protein is known to function in the organism just as cytochrome *c* does in animal tissues (25). The enzyme also catalyzes the oxidation of

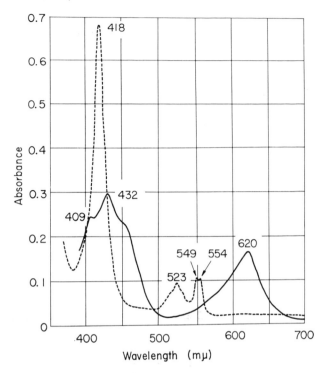

FIG. 4. Absorption spectra of pyridine hemochrome of heme a_2 (———), and of $Na_2S_2O_4$-reduced protein moiety of *Pseudomonas* cytochrome oxidase (------). The concentration of each material is not the same.

Pseudomonas blue protein, a copper-protein (see below) (8, 26, 27). These reactions are strongly inhibited by cyanide or carbon monoxide, which combine with the cytochrome oxidase. The enzyme is extremely labile in the presence of a trace of hydrogen peroxide (28). Thus, the oxidation rates of hydroquinone or ascorbate in the presence of cytochrome oxidase decrease rapidly after initiation of reaction while the presence of catalase in the reaction mixture largely prevents the decrease in reaction rates. However, when the reduced form of *Pseudomonas* cytochrome *c* is used as the electron donor, the decrease in reaction rate is not observed (28). Heme a_2 is very labile in air, possibly because of the formation of hydrogen peroxide from autoxidation.

One mole of *Pseudomonas* cytochrome oxidase catalyzes the oxidation of 154 and 600 moles of reduced *Pseudomonas* cytochrome *c* per minute in air at 16° and 27°, respectively (pH 6.5), for an activation energy of 18.3 Kcal. This figure is only a rough value, as the temperatures of the reaction mixtures have not been precisely controlled. From these data, the turnover

TABLE II

SUMMARY OF THE POSITIONS OF THE ABSORPTION PEAKS OF HEME a_2 AND ITS DERIVATIVES[a]

Compound	Solvent	λ_{max} (mμ)			A_γ/A_α[b]
		γ Peak	β Peak	α Peak	
Hemin a_2	Acetone	405 432	—	(529) (569) (606)[c]	—
Hematin a_2	Aqueous	(409) (480)	—	684	3.5
Heme a_2	Aqueous	409 453	—	626	3.0
Pyridine-heme a_2	Aqueous	(414) 432 (454)	—	620	1.8
CN⁻-heme a_2	Aqueous	407 449 480	—	(587) 632	1.7
NO-hematin a_2	Aqueous	408 (442)	—	645	2.8
NO-heme a_2	Aqueous	413 436 (462)	—	625	2.0
CO-heme a_2	Aqueous	(402) 440	—	(594) 644	2.0
Pyridine-heme a_2	Acetone	414 421 (453)	—	615	1.9
CN⁻-heme a_2	Acetone	450 (481)	—	(587) 635	1.9
Pyridine-heme a^d	Aqueous (pH 13)	430	—	587	4.6
Pyridine-heme a^d	Aqueous	429	530	587	3.7
Pyridine-chlorocruoroheme[e]	Aqueous	432	537	583	4.9

[a] For experimental conditions, see Ref. (16).
[b] The highest peak was selected where two or more peaks were present.
[c] Values in parentheses show shoulders or bumps.
[d] See Ref (22).
[e] Yamanaka, T., Mizushima, H., Miki, K., and Okunuki, K., unpublished observations.

number at 37° is calculated to be 2,400 per minute (12). The Michaelis constant (K_m) for oxygen is 28 μM at pH 6.0 and 30°.

Pseudomonas cytochrome oxidase acts also as a nitrite reductase (12, 29, 30), anaerobically reducing nitrite to nitric oxide with reduced *Pseudomonas* cytochrome c as the electron donor. One mole of the enzyme reduces 250 moles of nitrite to nitric oxide per minute at pH 6.5 and 19°. If the temperature dependence of the reaction velocity is the same as that in the aerobic oxidation of the reduced *Pseudomonas* cytochrome c, about 4,000 moles of nitrite are reduced per mole of *Pseudomonas* cytochrome oxidase per minute at 37° (12). The K_m for nitrite is 53 μM at pH 6.0 and 27°. The reaction is strongly inhibited by cyanide but not by carbon monoxide (12). From spectral studies carbon monoxide seems to have less affinity than nitrite ions for the enzyme (19). The behavior of the enzyme with these inhibitors is the same as that of whole cells of *Pseudomonas aeruginosa* (Table III), and the enzyme is isolated only from the cells that are cultivated in the presence of nitrate (17). Also, the nitrite reductase preparation partially purified by Walker and Nicholas (31) from *Pseudomonas aeruginosa* shows an absorption spectrum very similar to that of *Pseudomonas* cytochrome oxidase, and their enzyme also reduces nitrite to nitric oxide. Thus, *Pseudomonas* cytochrome oxidase seems to be the same entity as the nitrite reductase functioning in this organism. *Pseudomonas* cytochrome oxidase is named as cytochrome c (551, *Pseudomonas aeruginosa*): nitrite, O_2 oxidoreductase [EC 1.9 group] (32).

TABLE III

EFFECT OF KCN AND CO ON NITRITE REDUCTION BY *Pseudomonas* CYTOCHROME
OXIDASE AND WHOLE CELLS OF *Pseudomonas aeruginosa*

Inhibitor	NaNO₂ consumed		
	Pseudomonas cytochrome oxidase (12) (μmole/mg protein/hr)	Cells grown anaerobically in the presence of KNO₃ (17) (mμmole/mg cells/hr)	Cells grown aerobically in the absence of KNO₃ (17) (mμmole/mg cells/hr)
Control	167	48.8	0.3
KCN (1 mM)	10	0.3	0.0
CO (1 atm)	160	57.6	0.2

TABLE IV

RELATIVE ACTIVITIES OF THE RECONSTITUTED ENZYME AND VARIOUS ENZYME MODELS

Heme	Side chain			Ref.	Activity (33)	
	Position 2	Position 4	Position 8		Cytochrome oxidase (%)	Nitrite reductase (%)
Heme a_2	$CH_2=CH-$	CH_3CHOH-	CH_3, H—	(2,6)	100	100
Heme a_2 derivative	$CH_2=CH-$	CH_3CHOH-	CH_3-	(33)	21	24
Fe-Chlorophyllin	$CH_2=CH-$	CH_3CH_2-	CH_3-, H—	(23,33)	22	46
Protoheme	$CH_2=CH-$	$CH_2=CH-$	CH_3-	(23)	22	50
Hematoheme	CH_3CHOH-	CH_3CHOH-	CH_3-	(23)	13	24
Heme a	R_1CH_2CHOH-	$R_2CH=CH-$	CHO—	(1,2)	4.9	7.4

IV. Reconstitution

The protein moiety obtained by treating *Pseudomonas* cytochrome oxidase with acid acetone as described above combines with heme a_2 under appropriate conditions. The reconstituted enzyme shows an absorption spectrum similar to that of the original enzyme, is soluble at neutral pH, and shows about 50% of the enzymatic activity of the original enzyme on the basis of heme a_2 content (33). In the reconstitution, a heme derived from heme a_2 by removing hydrogen atoms at positions 7 and 8 is much less effective in the activation of the protein moiety, whereas iron chlorophyllin a (23), which is saturated at positions 7 and 8, is fairly effective as a substitute for heme a_2. It has also been demonstrated that protoheme is more effective than hematoheme in the reconstitution of the cytochrome oxidase (Table IV). Thus, it is concluded that saturated linkage at positions 7 and 8 and a vinyl group at position 2 of heme a_2 (6) are essential for the enzymatic activity of *Pseudomonas* cytochrome oxidase.

V. Reaction with *Pseudomonas* Blue Protein

As mentioned above, *Pseudomonas* cytochrome oxidase reacts with *Pseudomonas* blue protein, a copper-protein (8, 26, 27). *Pseudomonas* blue protein is isolated from *Pseudomonas aeruginosa* as a pure, crystalline

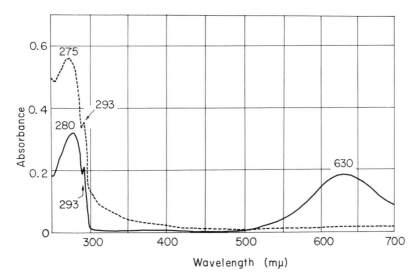

Fig. 5. Absorption spectrum of *Pseudomonas* blue protein. ———, Oxidized form; -----, reduced with $NaBH_4$.

TABLE V

EXTINCTION COEFFICIENTS FOR COPPER OF SEVERAL COPPER PROTEINS

Copper protein	Origin	λ_{max} (mμ)	E_{max} (M^{-1}cm^{-1}/Cu)	Ref.
(CuSO$_4$, aqueous)	—	740	9.0	—
Oxyhemocyanin	Octopus	575	0.73×10^3	(34)
Laccase	Rhus vernicifera	617	1.24×10^3	(35)
Laccase	Rhus succedanea	609	1.15×10^3	(35)
Plastocyanin	Spinach	597	4.9×10^3	(36)
Blue protein	Rhus vernicifera	608	4.03×10^3	(37)
Blue protein	Pseudomonas aeruginosa	630	6.95×10^3	(27)
Azurin	Bordetella pertussis	625	3.5×10^3	(38)

preparation (8, 26). The molecular weight of the protein is 16,600, and it contains one atom of copper per mole (26, 27). Its oxidized form is blue, and has an absorption peak at 630 mμ (Fig. 5). When it is reduced with Na$_2$S$_2$O$_4$ or NaBH$_4$, it becomes colorless, and the reduced form is not autoxidizable. The molar extinction coefficient at 630 mμ is 6,950. As shown in Table V, the extinction coefficient around 600 mμ per copper of this blue protein is very high as compared with other copper proteins. The copper atom in the blue protein is easily removed by dialysis against

TABLE VI

COMPARISON OF *Pseudomonas* CYTOCHROME *c* WITH *Pseudomonas* BLUE PROTEIN

Property	Pseudomonas cytochrome c (10, 24)	Pseudomonas blue protein (10, 26, 27)
Molecular weight	8,100	16,600
Isoelectric point (pH)	4.7	5.4
E_0' (pH 6.4)	+0.286	+0.328
Metal	Fe	Cu
Color	Red	Blue
λ_{max} (visible)	521, 551 mμ	630 mμ
Activity[a]	100[b]	98[b]
K_m[a]	19 μM	39 μM
pH optimum[a]	5.1	5.1

[a] In the reaction with *Pseudomonas* cytochrome oxidase. For experimental conditions, see Ref. (10).

[b] Relative values.

cyanide or EDTA. The colorless apoprotein formed combines with Cu^{2+} stoichiometrically, but not with other metal ions tested (Co^{2+}, Co^{3+}, Mn^{2+}, Cr^{3+}, Fe^{2+}, Fe^{3+}, Cd^{2+}) (27) The reconstituted protein shows the same absorption spectrum as that of the original blue protein and the same enzymatic activity in the reaction with *Pseudomonas* cytochrome oxidase (27).

The reduced form of *Pseudomonas* blue protein is easily oxidized by *Pseudomonas* cytochrome oxidase in air, and the turnover number is very similar to that in reoxidation of reduced *Pseudomonas* cytochrome *c* by the cytochrome oxidase (Table VI). *Pseudomonas* blue protein is a copper protein, whereas *Pseudomonas* cytochrome *c* is a cytochrome. They are very different from each other, but nevertheless react with *Pseudomonas* cytochrome oxidase at a comparable velocity. Perhaps they have a conformation which is common to the both proteins and is essential for their reaction with *Pseudomonas* cytochrome oxidase. Although there are some similarities between the amino acid compositions of *Pseudomonas* cytochrome *c* and *Pseudomonas* blue protein (39), sequence analysis shows them to be completely different.[1]

VI. The Uniqueness of *Pseudomonas* Cytochrome Oxidase

A. Comparison with Bovine Cytochrome c Oxidase

There is a strict biological specificity in the reaction of *c* cytochromes with cytochrome oxidases (12, 40, 41). For example, *Pseudomonas* cytochrome oxidase reacts with *Pseudomonas* cytochrome *c* very rapidly but reacts scarcely with cytochrome *c* (550, cow), whereas bovine cytochrome oxidase reacts with bovine cytochrome *c* very rapidly but does not react with *Pseudomonas* cytochrome *c*. Therefore, the cytochrome oxidases are very different from each other, probably in their protein moieties. However, we know little about the conformations of the protein moieties of the cytochrome oxidases.

Apart from the properties of the protein moieties, we would like to consider the structural factors which are necessary for cytochrome oxidase activity. *Pseudomonas* cytochrome oxidase contains two kinds of hemes in the molecule, heme a_2 and heme *c* (16), whereas bovine cytochrome oxidase has only one kind of heme, heme *a* (4, 5). This appears to be the major difference. However, *Pseudomonas* cytochrome oxidase is very autoxidizable, whereas bovine cytochrome oxidase is scarcely autoxidizable. When supplemented with mammalian or yeast cytochrome *c*, bovine

---

[1] R. P. Ambler, private communication to M. D. Kamen.

TABLE VII

COMPARISON OF VARIOUS PROPERTIES OF *Pseudomonas* CYTOCHROME OXIDASE WITH
THOSE OF BOVINE CYTOCHROME OXIDASE

Property	*Pseudomonas* cytochrome oxidase (9, 10, 12, 33)	Bovine cytochrome oxidase (4)
Color	Green	Reddish green
λ_{max} (mμ)	α[a] 629, 652 (pH 7.0) 625 (pH 5.6) γ[a] 460	α 605 γ 444
Heme	Heme a_2; Heme c	Heme a
Special functional group in heme	(heme structure diagram)	CHO
Molecular weight	90,000	100,000[b]
Isoelectric point (pH)	5.8	4–5
Iron per molecule	2	1[b]
Copper per molecule	0	1[b]
Autoxidizability	Very strong	Very weak, but much accelerated by mammalian or yeast cytochrome c
Inhibitor	CN$^-$, CO	CN$^-$, CO

[a] Absorption peaks due to heme a_2.
[b] Values for monomer.

cytochrome oxidase becomes very autoxidizable (20). Therefore, it appears that cooperation of two kinds of hemes, c-type heme and a-type heme, is necessary for the autoxidation of both enzymes.

A great difference in the structural factors between both enzymes is that bovine cytochrome oxidase contains copper (4, 5), whereas *Pseudomonas* cytochrome oxidase does not (10). It is known that oxidation and reduction of bovine cytochrome oxidase is accompanied by the oxidation and reduction of copper in the enzyme molecule (42–44). The fact that, although *Pseudomonas* cytochrome oxidase does not contain copper in the molecule, it still has the general properties of a cytochrome oxidase may favor the idea that the copper is not essential for the function of bovine cytochrome a (5). However, when heme a_2 in *Pseudomonas* cytochrome oxidase is replaced by heme a, the enzyme model obtained shows little cytochrome oxidase activity (33). Therefore, it may be that heme a_2 is functionally comparable with heme a plus copper, although the inactivity of the enzyme model obtained may be mainly due to the possibility that heme a is not well accommodated by the protein portion of *Pseudomonas* cytochrome oxidase. Heme c present in the protein moiety of *Pseudomonas* cytochrome oxidase may also affect the activity of the enzyme model. In any case, it seems to be certain that copper is necessary for biosynthesis of both cytochrome oxidases (17, 45–47).

B. Comment on the Mechanism of *Pseudomonas* Cytochrome Oxidase Reactions

As described above, *Pseudomonas* cytochrome oxidase has two kinds of activities, cytochrome oxidase activity and nitrite reductase activity. If

TABLE VIII

REACTIONS OF *Micrococcus* CYTOCHROME c AND *Navicula* CYTOCHROME c WITH OXYGEN AND NITRITE IN THE PRESENCE OF *Pseudomonas* CYTOCHROME OXIDASE[a]

| | Turnover number/min | | |
Electron donor	(A) Cytochrome oxidase activity	(B) Nitrite reductase activity	B/A
Cytochrome c (548,554, *Micrococcus* sp.)	705[b] (pH 5.7)	1362[b] (pH 6.3)	1.9
Cytochrome c (554, *Navicula pelliculosa*)	43.2 (pH 5.7)	19.6 (pH 6.3)	0.45

[a] Reaction mixtures were as follows: (a) *Micrococcus* cytochrome $c \rightarrow NO_2^-$: 1.8 ml of citrate phosphate buffer (48), 0.4 ml 149 μM cytochrome c, 0.02 ml 0.1 M NaNO$_2$, and 0.02 ml 1.62 μM *Pseudomonas* cytochrome oxidase. The total volume was made up to 2.4 ml with distilled water. (b) *Micrococcus* cytochrome $c \rightarrow O_2$: 0.9 ml citrate phosphate buffer, 0.2 ml 149 μM cytochrome c, and 0.01 ml 1.62 μM *Pseudomonas* cytochrome oxidase. (c) *Navicula* cytochrome $c \rightarrow NO_2^-$: 1.5 ml citrate phosphate buffer, 0.1 ml 83 μM cytochrome c (E_{554} was assumed to be $27 \times 10^3 \, M^{-1} cm^{-1}$), 0.02 ml 0.1 M NaNO$_2$, and 0.1 ml 3.66 μM *Pseudomonas* cytochrome oxidase. The total volume was made up to 2.3 ml by distilled water. (d) *Navicula* cytochrome $c \rightarrow O_2$: 0.75 ml citrate phosphate buffer, 0.25 ml 83 μM cytochrome c, and 0.05 ml 3.66 μM *Pseudomonas* cytochrome oxidase.

Reactions were carried out in air for cytochrome oxidase reaction, and under anaerobic conditions for nitrite reductase reaction, at 24° and at pH optima. pH's were measured after the reactions had been carried out.

[b] *Micrococcus* cytochrome c contains two hemes per molecule (15). These are turnover numbers based on one heme.

the cytochrome oxidase reacts with O_2 or NO_2^- after it has received electrons from the reduced form of c cytochrome used as an electron donor (Fig. 6–1), the ratio of cytochrome oxidase activity to nitrite reductase activity should be constant regardless of the kind of c cytochrome used as the electron donor. However, as shown in Table VIII, the ratio varies with c cytochromes used as the electron donors. With cytochrome c (548, 554, *Micrococcus sp.*) (15) as the electron donor, nitrite reductase activity is always larger than cytochrome oxidase activity through the pH range from 4.5 to 7.0 where pH optima of the both reactions are included. On the other hand, when cytochrome c (554, *Navicula pelliculosa*) (49) is used as the electron donor, cytochrome oxidase activity is larger than nitrite reductase activity. This means that the c-type cytochromes which were used as the electron donors affect to a great extent the final reaction step in the cytochrome oxidase (or nitrite reductase) reaction, i.e., the reaction of cytochrome oxidase with the final electron acceptor, O_2 or NO_2^-.

We can consider three schemes, as shown in Fig. 6, for the cytochrome oxidase reaction mechanisms. From the present studies, the scheme shown in Fig. 6–1 seems improbable. The cytochrome oxidase reaction probably proceeds as shown in Fig. 6–2 or 6–3. The phenomena presented in the present studies are very easily explained by Fig. 6–2, where c-type cytochrome couples directly with the electron acceptor. In the scheme shown in Fig. 6–3, the energy level in the ternary complex, i.e., the resonance energy of the whole reaction system, may depend upon both electron donor and acceptor.

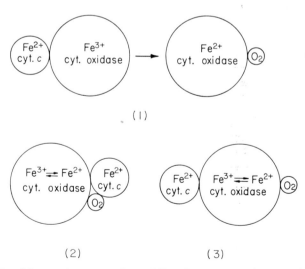

FIG. 6. Possible reaction mechanisms of *Pseudomonas* cytochrome oxidase.

VII. Concluding Remarks

It seems likely that, for cytochrome oxidase activity heme a or heme a_2 is necessary (3).[2] The former has an aldehyde group (1, 2) at position 8, whereas the latter has carbon saturation at positions 7 and 8 (2, 6). Thus, saturation at positions 7 and 8 in the porphyrin may be functionally equivalent to an aldehyde group at position 8 (51).

In denitrifying bacteria it is known that nitrate can act as the ultimate electron acceptor instead of molecular oxygen under anaerobic conditions (52–59). In this phenomenon, called nitrate respiration (54, 55), the available free energy is smaller than that in oxygen respiration (60). Thus, nitrate respiration seems to be a more primitive respiration mechanism than oxygen respiration (61, 62). Since nitrite produced by reduction of nitrate is poisonous it must be eliminated. Therefore, nitrite-reducing systems may have appeared in evolution with nitrate-reducing systems. The nitrite-reducing system in *Pseudomonas aeruginosa* is composed of a highly developed cytochrome system (25). Nitrite reductase is the heme a_2-containing enzyme, *Pseudomonas* cytochrome oxidase. After molecular oxygen appeared on the earth, the nitrite reductase system may have also functioned as a cytochrome oxidase system, because *Pseudomonas* cytochrome oxidase has the two kinds of enzymatic activities. However, heme a_2-containing cytochrome oxidase is extremely labile in the presence of hydrogen peroxide. Therefore, on an evolutionary basis, the appearance of molecular oxygen on the earth is thought to have been unfavorable to the heme a_2-containing cytochrome oxidase. Thus, heme a-bearing cytochrome oxidase has been more favorable to most organisms dependent on oxygen respiration. It may be said that heme a_2-bearing cytochrome oxidase does not contain copper in the molecule, whereas the heme a-containing enzyme requires copper. However, copper is necessary for the biosynthesis of both types of cytochrome oxidases. In any case, heme a-bearing cytochrome oxidase appears to be more efficient as a cytochrome oxidase than the heme a_2-bearing enzyme.

VIII. Summary

Pseudomonas cytochrome oxidase contains one heme a_2 and one heme c in one molecule, but no copper. The heme a_2 can be split off by acid acetone from the protein moiety. The enzyme can be reconstituted from the heme

---

[2] In some bacteria, it is assumed that a "CO-binding pigment" or "cytochrome o" is functioning as the cytochrome oxidase (50). However, little is known about this type of cytochrome oxidase.

a_2 and the protein moiety. It is made clear that two extra hydrogen atoms at positions 7 and 8 and a vinyl group at position 2 of heme a_2 are essential for the enzymatic activity of *Pseudomonas* cytochrome oxidase. The enzyme not only shows the general properties of a cytochrome oxidase but also acts as a nitrite reductase and is apparently the same entity as *Pseudomonas* nitrite reductase. Reduced *Pseudomonas* blue protein (a copper protein) as well as reduced cytochrome c (551, *Pseudomonas aeruginosa*) are good electron donors for *Pseudomonas* cytochrome oxidase. The mechanisms of cytochrome oxidase reactions, and the structural factors which are necessary for cytochrome oxidase activity are discussed.

ACKNOWLEDGMENTS

The author wishes to thank Professors K. Okunuki and M. D. Kamen for their interest and encouragement during this work, and Dr. S. Taniguchi (Department of Biochemistry, The Nobel Medical Institute, Stockholm, Sweden) for his generosity in supplying *Micrococcus* cytochrome c. He also wishes to thank Dr. A. Ota (Department of Biochemistry, Osaka University School of Medicine, Osaka, Japan) and Miss S. Kijimoto (University of Osaka, Osaka, Japan) for their cooperation.

REFERENCES

1. Clezy, P. S., and Barrett, J., *Biochem. J.*, **78**, 798 (1961).
2. Lemberg, R., Clezy, P., and Barrett, J., *in* J. E. Falk, R. Lemberg, and R. K. Morton (eds.), "Haematin enzymes," Macmillan Company (Pergamon), New York, 1961, p. 344.
3. Morton, R. K., *Rev. Pure Appl. Chem.*, **8**, 161 (1958).
4. Okunuki, K., *in* O. Hayaishi (ed.), "Oxygenases," Academic Press Inc., New York, 1962, p. 409.
5. Yonetani, T., *in* P. D. Boyer, H. Lardy and K. Myrbäck (eds.), "The enzymes," Vol. VIII, Academic Press Inc., New York, 1963, p. 41.
6. Barrett, J., *Biochem. J.*, **64**, 626 (1956).
7. Smith, L., *in* I. C. Gunsalus and R. Y. Stanier (eds.), "The bacteria," Vol. 2, Academic Press Inc., New York, 1961, p. 365.
8. Horio, T., *J. Biochem. (Tokyo)*, **45**, 195, 268 (1958).
9. Horio, T., Higashi, T., Matsubara, H., Kusai, K., Nakai, M., and Okunuki, K., *Biochim. Biophys. Acta*, **29**, 297 (1958).
10. Horio, T., Higashi, T., Yamanaka, T., Matsubara, H., and Okunuki, K., *J. Biol. Chem.*, **236**, 944 (1961).
11. Yamanaka, T., Kijimoto, S., Okunuki, K., and Kusai, K., *Nature*, **194**, 759 (1962).
12. Yamanaka, T., and Okunuki, K., *Biochim. Biophys. Acta*, **67**, 379 (1963).
13. Yamanaka, T., *Ann. Rep. Sci. Works, Osaka Univ.*, **11**, 77 (1963).
14. Layne, E. C., and Nason, A., *J. Biol. Chem.*, **231**, 889 (1958).
15. Hori, K., and Taniguchi, S., *Symp. Enzyme Chem. (Tokyo)*, **15**, 330 (1961); Hori, K., *J. Biochem. (Tokyo)*, **50**, 440 (1961).
16. Yamanaka, T., and Okunuki, K., *Biochim. Biophys. Acta*, **67**, 407 (1963).
17. Yamanaka, T., Kijimoto, S., and Okunuki, K., *J. Biochem. (Tokyo)*, **53**, 416 (1963).
18. Yamanaka, T., *Nature*, **204**, 253 (1964).

19. Yamanaka, T., and Okunuki, K., *Biochim. Biophys. Acta*, **67**, 394 (1963).
20. Okunuki, K., Sekuzu, I., Yonetani, T., and Takemori, S., *J. Biochem. (Tokyo)*, **45**, 847 (1958).
21. Paul, K. G., *Acta Chem. Scand.*, **4**, 239 (1950).
22. Morell, D. B., Barrett, J., Clezy, P. S., and Lemberg, R., *in* J. E. Falk, R. Lemberg, and R. K. Morton (eds.), "Haematin enzymes," Macmillan Company (Pergamon), New York, 1961, p. 320.
23. Falk, J. E., "Porphyrins and metalloporphyrins," Elsevier Publishing Co., Amsterdam, 1964.
24. Horio, T., Higashi, T., Sasagawa, M., Kusai, K., Nakai, M., and Okunuki, K., *Biochem. J.*, **77**, 194 (1960).
25. Yamanaka, T., *J. Biochem. (Tokyo)*, **46**, 1289 (1959).
26. Horio, T., Sekuzu, I., Higashi, T., and Okunuki, K., *in* J. E. Falk, R. Lemberg, and R. K. Morton (eds.), "Haematin enzymes," Macmillan Company (Pergamon), New York, 1961, p. 302.
27. Yamanaka, T., Kijimoto, S., and Okunuki, K., *J. Biochem. (Tokyo)*, **53**, 256 (1963).
28. Yamanaka, T., Ota, A., and Okunuki, K., *J. Biochem. (Tokyo)*, **49**, 350 (1961).
29. Yamanaka, T., Ota, A., and Okunuki, K., *Biochim. Biophys. Acta*, **44**, 397 (1960).
30. Yamanaka, T., Ota, A., and Okunuki, K., *Biochim. Biophys. Acta*, **53**, 294 (1961).
31. Walker, G. C., and Nicholas, D.J.D., *Biochim. Biophys. Acta*, **49**, 350 (1961).
32. "Report of the Commission on Enzymes of the International Union of Biochemistry." Macmillan Company (Pergamon), New York, 1961.
33. Yamanaka, T., and Okunuki, K., *Biochem. Z.*, **338**, 62 (1963).
34. Kubowitz, F., *Biochem. Z.*, **299**, 32 (1938).
35. Omura, T., *J. Biochem. (Tokyo)*, **50**, 264 (1961).
36. Katoh, S., Shiratori, I., and Takamiya, A., *J. Biochem. (Tokyo)*, **51**, 32 (1962).
37. Omura, T., *J. Biochem. (Tokyo)*, **50**, 394 (1961).
38. Sutherland, I. W., and Wilkinson, J. F., *J. Gen. Microbiol.*, **30**, 105 (1963).
39. Coval, M. L., Horio, T., and Kamen, M. D., *Biochim. Biophys. Acta*, **51**, 246 (1961).
40. Yamanaka, T., and Okunuki, K., *J. Biol. Chem.*, **239**, 1813 (1964).
41. Yamanaka, T., and Kamen, M. D., *Biochim. Biophys. Acta*, **96**, 328 (1965).
42. Takemori, S., *J. Biochem. (Tokyo)*, **47**, 382 (1960).
43. Beinert, H., and Palmer, G., *J. Biol. Chem.*, **239**, 1221 (1964).
44. Wharton, D. C., and Tzagoloff, A., *J. Biol. Chem.*, **239**, 2036 (1964).
45. Cohen, E., and Elvehjem, C. A., *J. Biol. Chem.*, **107**, 97 (1934).
46. Yoshikawa, H., *J. Biochem. (Tokyo)*, **25**, 625 (1937).
47. Gallagher, C. H., Judah, J. H., and Rees, K. R., *Proc. Roy. Soc. (London)*, *Ser. B*, **145**, 134 (1956).
48. McIlvaine, T. C., *J. Biol. Chem.*, **49**, 183 (1921).
49. Yamanaka, T., and Kamen, M. D., *Biochem. Biophys. Res. Communs.*, **19**, 751 (1965).
50. Castor, L. N., and Chance, B., *J. Biol. Chem.*, **234**, 1587 (1959).
51. Barrett, J., and Williams, R. J. P., *in* J. E. Falk, R. Lemberg, and R. K. Morton (eds.), "Haematin enzymes," Macmillan Company (Pergamon), New York, 1961, p. 360.
52. Quastel, J. H., Stephenson, M., and Whetham, M. P., *Biochem. J.*, **19**, 304 (1925).
53. Verhoeven, W., *in* W. D. McElroy and B. H. Glass (eds.), "Symposium on inorganic nitrogen metabolism," Johns Hopkins Press, Baltimore, Maryland, 1956, p. 61.
54. Sato, R., *in* W. D. McElroy and B. H. Glass (eds.), "Symposium on inorganic nitrogen metabolism," Johns Hopkins Press, Baltimore, Maryland, 1956, p.

55. Takahashi, H., Taniguchi, S., and Egami, F., *in* M. Florkin and H. S. Mason (eds.), "Comparative biochemistry," Vol. 5, Academic Press Inc., New York, 1963, p. 91.
56. Yamanaka, T., Ota, A., and Okunuki, K., *J. Biochem. (Tokyo)*, **51**, 253 (1962).
57. Ohnishi, T., *J. Biochem. (Tokyo)*, **53**, 71 (1962).
58. Ota, A., Yamanaka, T., and Okunuki, K., *J. Biochem. (Tokyo)*, **55**, 131 (1964).
59. Yamanaka, T., Ota, A., and Okunuki, K., *Abstr.* **6th** *intern. Congr. biochem.*, New York, 1964, p. 750.
60. Dolin, M. I., *in* I. C. Gunsalus and R. Y. Stanier (eds.), "The bacteria," Vol. 2, Academic Press Inc., New York, 1961, p. 319.
61. Ishimoto, M., and Egami, F., *in* A. I. Oparin, A. G. Pasynskii, A. E. Braunstein, and T. E. Pavlovskaya (eds.), "The origin of life on the earth," Macmillan Company (Pergamon), New York, 1959, p. 555.
62. Nason, A., *Bacteriol. Rev.*, **26**, 16 (1962).

DISCUSSION

DR. CHANCE: In your Scheme II, which is the Okunuki scheme for the mechanism of cytochrome oxidase, one would expect cytochrome c to be oxidized very nearly as fast as cytochrome oxidase. This, however, is not true. The kinetic measurements simply show that this cytochrome c in the respiratory chain requires at least 1.5 msec to be oxidized, and Dr. Wharton mentioned that cytochrome oxidase or a_3 can be oxidized in microseconds. It is difficult to ignore the disparity in times of oxidation of cytochromes c and a_3.

DR. YAMANAKA: You are talking about mammalian cytochrome oxidase. My scheme is for *Pseudomonas* cytochrome oxidase, which includes a c cytochrome in the molecule. Thus, unlike mammalian cytochrome oxidase, it needs no c cytochrome added from outside to show activity. So, cytochrome c in the scheme is just the electron donor to the cytochrome oxidase.

DR. PEISACH: Am I correct in what you say, that mammalian cytochrome c is not oxidized by the *Pseudomonas* cytochrome oxidase, and mammalian cytochrome oxidase will not oxidize *Pseudomonas* cytochrome c?

DR. YAMANAKA: Right.

DR. WHARTON: I'd like to ask if you have observed a near infrared band in either the *Pseudomonas* cytochrome oxidase or the blue protein.

DR YAMANAKA: I checked the spectrum between 700 and 1000 mμ, but I was not able to detect any appreciable peak there, in either protein. However, I did not use very concentrated enzyme solutions. If we were to use very, very concentrated solutions, above 1mM, we might be able to find it.

Spectrophotometic Observations of Absorbance Changes in the Infrared Region in Suspensions of Mitochondria and in Submitochondrial Particles*

BRITTON CHANCE

*Johnson Research Foundation,
University of Pennsylvania,
Philadelphia, Pennsylvania*

I. Introduction

Infrared recording of the oxidized and reduced spectra of purified cytochrome c oxidase (1, 2) showed the disappearance of a broad absorption band at 830 mμ on reduction of the enzyme. The origin of this band has been further discussed (3, 4) and it has been identified with copper of cytochrome oxidase in a number of laboratories (5). More recently, Gibson and Greenwood have observed the kinetics of the absorbance change at 830 mμ relying upon the photodissociability of cytochrome a_3-CO (6) as the basis for flash photolysis (7) with the stopped flow apparatus (8, 9).

While components of the respiratory chain, such as cytochromes, flavins, and pyridine nucleotides, were first observed in cells, mitochondria, and submitochondrial particles, this component has only been observed in purified cytochrome oxidases. In view of the discrepancies between the properties of isolated cytochrome oxidase and those observed in intact mitochondria, particularly the ratio of cytochrome a_3 to a being approximately 1:1 in mitochondria and submitochondrial particles (10) and a variable quantity in cytochrome oxidase preparations (11), we were led to consider the development of an adequate technique for measuring the kinetics of the 830 mμ band in the highly scattering mitochondrial suspensions. The experimental difficulties are formidable and the paper describes the experimental methods and gives some preliminary results.

II. Experimental Methods

The technique employed here follows that developed for the study of chlorophyll changes in suspensions of *Chromatium* and *Rhodospirillum rubrum* in the infrared region (12). The low quantum efficiency of the CsO–Ag cathode ($<0.1\%$) makes sensitive detection of small absorbance

* Supported by a grant from the National Institutes of Health.

changes in the infrared region difficult. However, the use of grating mono-chromators of high resolution in which the overlapping second-order spectrum is cut out by a guard filter has proved a useful asset in this work. While the signal-to-noise ratio obtainable in the measurement of the absorbance changes in the infrared region is satisfactory for measurements of steady state changes, it is inadequate for rapid flow measurements where millisecond rise times are required. It has therefore been necessary to develop another type of dual wavelength spectrophotometer for this pur-pose, in which the light intensities available are increased. This has been accomplished by using broad band interference filters in a suitable double-beam spectrophotometric apparatus. The optics are approximately $f/2$. Also the amplitude of the vibration of the mirror has been increased to accom-modate a large light beam of a 45 Watt $W-I_2$ lamp. Interference filters manu-factured by Baird Atomic having a spectral interval of 1 to 2% of the nominal wavelength were used. It was found useful to employ the reference wavelength in the region of 1000 mμ in order to obtain optimal absorbance changes. This was accomplished by blocking off the higher frequencies of a filter designed for nominal operation at 714 or 707 mμ. As a consequence two pass bands were available as reference wavelengths, one at 1070 mμ trans-mitting 35% of the light and the other at 930 mμ transmitting 54%. However, the longer wavelength had a considerably wider spectral interval, extending from 1120 to 1000 mμ as compared with the pass band at the shorter wavelength, 920 to 940 mμ (half-power points). Thus, the majority of the energy for the reference wavelength came from the pass band at the longer wavelength. The sensitivity of the combination of the CsO–Ag surface and the tungsten lamp is maximal at 1060 mμ. This combination gave an approximately twofold increase of absorbance change over that obtained when 750 mμ is used as the reference wavelength. With this apparatus, a signal-to-noise ratio of better than 5:1 is obtained with the necessary response speed for the flow apparatus.

The 1 cm optical path, the high time resolution (1.5 msec), and the long duration of flow are features of the pulsed flow apparatus (13) that uniquely suit it to the problem of measurement of kinetics of oxidation in the infrared region. In order to obtain accurate recording with a narrow amplifier band-width suitable for filtering out objectionable noise, the duration of flow in the pulsed flow apparatus has been prolonged to approximately 0.5 to 2 sec, and times after mixing as long as 20 msec have been employed.

III. Experimental Preparations

Pigeon heart mitochondria prepared according to the method of Chance and Hagihara (14) were uniformly employed. These preparations are active and have a high concentration of cytochromes a and a_3. In addition, they retain full capacities for oxidative phosphorylation and for ion uptake (15). Rat liver mitochondria have also been prepared (15). Submitochondrial particles prepared from beef heart according to the method of Lang were also employed in kinetic studies. These particles were supplemented with 10 mM succinate and suspended in 0.1 M Tris phosphate buffer, pH 7.2 (16).

IV. Experimental Results

A. Steady State Responses

Figure 1A illustrates the steady state and aerobic-anaerobic transition for the pigeon heart mitochondria when measured at wavelengths appropriate to the infrared absorption band. Upon addition of 4 mM succinate and 4 mM glutamate, there is an abrupt downward deflection indicating a diminished absorption at 830 mμ with respect to 715 mμ. This initial deflection decreases so that the steady state level corresponds closely to that prior to the addition of the substrate. After slightly over 140 sec, an abrupt aerobic-anaerobic transition is observed. It is useful to compare this with the response of cytochrome $a + a_3$ recorded previously (10) and shown in Fig. 1B.

By repeating this experiment at appropriate wavelengths, the difference spectrum for the steady state and the oxidized minus reduced absorbance

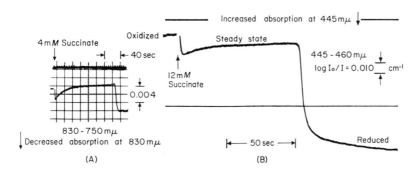

FIG. 1. (A) Steady state and aerobic-anaerobic transition for pigeon heart mitochondria; dual wavelength spectrophotometer, 830–750 mμ; approximately 7 mg/ml protein; mannitol–sucrose–Tris chloride medium; pH 7.4; temperature 24°. Other parameters indicated on the diagram. When the trace deflects downward abruptly, an absorbance change of 0.006 cm^{-1} is indicated.   (B) Steady state and aerobic-anaerobic transition for Keilin–Hartree heart muscle preparation recorded at wavelengths appropriate to cytochrome $a + a_3$ (445–460 mμ). Included as well is a recording of oxygen concentration by the platinum microelectrode. Other parameters are included in the figure.

changes can be obtained. As indicated in Fig. 1, the steady state to reduced change is seen to be approximately equal to the oxidized to reduced change.

B. Difference Spectra

An alternate method of obtaining the oxidized–reduced spectrum, and one that has been found to be particularly convenient under these circumstances where high concentrations of mitochondria were expended in a single experiment, was to reoxygenate the suspension by supplements of catalase and H_2O_2. Pigeon heart mitochondria themselves contain negligible catalase, and additions of 100 μg catalase per 7 mg protein were sufficient to decompose rapidly hydrogen peroxide concentrations of 150 μM. The resulting oxygen (75 μM) was adequate to give a characteristic "cycle" of oxidation and reduction. Repetitive additions of H_2O_2 allowed the construction of an accurate difference spectrum. It was found that the pigeon heart preparation responded reproducibly to this peroxide addition an adequate number of times for a precise determination of the difference spectra.

The oxidized-reduced difference spectrum obtained by successive additions of the H_2O_2 to the anaerobic system is plotted in Fig. 2. The resemblance to the difference spectrum of the purified oxidase is relatively good, not only with respect to the shape of the absorption band, but also with respect to its amplitude in relation to that of cytochrome a. The oxidized-reduced difference given by Griffiths and Wharton suggests the amplitude of the difference spectrum to be about 5% that of the difference spectrum at 605 mμ, in good agreement with these data. The spectrum of Fig. 2 which gives a value of 3.5%, is useful in determining optimal pairs of

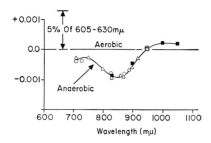

Fig. 2. Infrared absorption changes in pigeon heart mitochondria caused by aerobic-anaerobic transition. Seven milligrams protein per milliliter; substrate, succinate and glutamate (4 mM); reoxidation of anaerobic system caused by additions of between 75 and 150 μM H_2O_2 in the presence of 100 μg of horse liver catalase. Reference wavelength for plotting these data is 950 mμ. (The horizontal line does not indicate an isosbestic point between the oxidized and reduced states, but merely refers the data to 950 mμ as a reference point.)

wavelengths for use with the double-beam spectrophotometer. The difference spectrum is asymmetrical, and a reference wavelength on the long-wave side gives a larger absorbance change, for example, 950 to 1050 mμ with a measurement wavelength anywhere in the region 830–870 mμ. It is desirable to move the measuring wavelength as close to the reference wavelength as possible, and in some of the kinetic measurements recorded here, 860 or 870 mμ has been used. Similar absorbance changes have been observed in suspensions of rat liver mitochondria.

C. Kinetic Responses

A brief survey of the kinetic response at various wavelengths is indicated by a selection of charts measured at several pairs of wavelengths which illustrate possible complexities of the response at these wavelengths.

Generally the kinetics of oxidation-reduction recorded here are measured by H_2O_2 addition as indicated above, and a typical record for the oxidation and reduction of cytochrome a is indicated by Fig. 3A. Here the abrupt downward deflections indicate the oxidation of reduced cytochrome a on adding 150 μM H_2O_2; the oxidation lasts approximately 35 sec and is followed thereafter by an abrupt reduction to the anaerobic steady state. The absorbance change is approximately 0.03 per centimeter.

The kinetics of the absorbance change at 830–950 mμ is indicated in Fig. 3B. The sensitivity is 5 times that employed for cytochrome a. Also the direction of the deflection is opposite to that in the previous figure because the absorption band increases in intensity on addition of the oxidant, H_2O_2. A further difference is that approximately one-half the concentration of H_2O_2 is added (75 μM). Otherwise the kinetics are superficially the same. It is noteworthy, however, that the absorbance change at

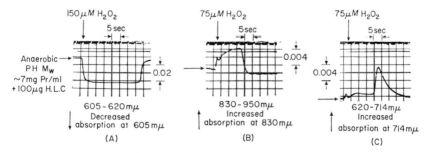

FIG. 3. Kinetics of oxidation and reduction of cytochrome a (A) as compared with the infrared absorption change (B) and at an intermediate wavelength (C). The pigeon heart mitochondrial suspension (7 mg/ml) initially anaerobic with 4 mM succinate and glutamate; additions of 150 and 75 μM H_2O_2 are indicated as are the wavelength and sensitivity and time scales.

830 mμ does not rise immediately to a plateau value; it is seen that at least 50% of the reaction occurs at a measurable rate, even on this slow time scale (5 sec/cm).

It is of interest to determine whether there are wavelengths near the absorption band of cytochrome a at which kinetic responses similar to those observed at 830 mμ can be recorded. We have chosen the pair 620–714 mμ and recorded the kinetics of oxidation and reduction in Fig. 3C. Upon adding H_2O_2 the initial reaction has kinetics similar to those of Fig. 3B and gives no evidence of the fast reaction of cytochrome a. As the oxygen is exhausted, however, a surprising kinetic event is observed. There is a rapid reduction followed by an exponential return to the baseline. It is apparent that these kinetics are due to the reduction of two components at different rates in which the absorbance changes are in the opposite direction. The fast component can be identified with cytochrome a. The slowly reduced component is not yet identified. It is noteworthy that this slowly reduced component is not seen at the wavelength pair 830–950 mμ.

In order to ensure that the absorbance changes recorded in Fig. 3B are due to a component on the oxygen side of the antimycin A sensitive point, we have observed whether or not antimycin A inhibition of electron transport would cause diminished oxidation-reduction changes on sequential additions of H_2O_2. Under conditions where the time required to expend the added H_2O_2 had been considerably increased, the absorbance changes on adding peroxide were constant. This seems an adequate test of the fact that we are dealing with components related to cytochrome oxidase in the infrared region since a large change in the steady state value would have been expected if material absorbing on the antimycin A side of the respiratory chain were involved (17, 18).

D. Kinetics of Absorbance Changes

Figure 3B shows that addition of H_2O_2 to the anaerobic material in the presence of catalase requires approximately 10 sec to reach a plateau value, while under identical conditions the trace for cytochrome a reaches a plateau value in less than 2 sec (limited in the latter case by the time to mix the H_2O_2 with the mitochondrial suspension).

Since mixing could possibly have been less efficient in Fig. 3B than in Fig. 3A, we have employed in Fig. 4 the regenerative flow apparatus to record the reaction kinetics after the flow has stopped. The second trace from the top indicates by a downward "pip" the discharge of reactants into the mixing chamber. Wavelengths appropriate to cytochrome a (608–707 mμ) and to the infrared absorbance change (860–940, 1070 mμ) are used. These wavelengths were obtained with interference filters. The bottom

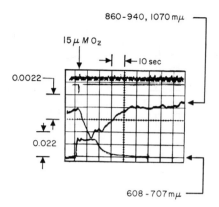

Fig. 4. Comparison of the kinetics of the absorption change corresponding to cyto-chrome *a* and the infrared change recorded in the regenerative flow apparatus and the filter double beam spectrophotometer. Top trace represents time, second trace represents flow velocity, third trace represents the kinetics of the infrared region, and the bottom trace represents kinetics of cytochrome *a*. The appropriate absorbance calibrations are indicated in the margins, as is the time of addition of oxygen to the anaerobic mito-chondria.

trace represents the oxidation or reduction of cytochrome *a* on mixing the anaerobic mitochondria with 15 μM oxygen. In this case, an upward de-flection represents an oxidation of cytochrome *a*, and it is seen that an absorbance change of approximately 0.02 is observed, and the steady state is maintained for 15 sec. The cytochrome is then reduced. When the re-action is repeated in the infrared region with a 10-fold increase of sensi-tivity, an injection of oxygen into the mixing chamber causes a downward deflection of the trace indicating an increase of absorption at 860 mμ with respect to the reference wavelength. The absorbance increase proceeds linearly with time for approximately 10 sec; thereafter, the oxygen is ex-hausted and the trace slowly returns to the baseline. The kinetic dis-crepancy of the two traces is obvious and is supported in detail by record-ings made on a faster time scale.

Since it was a matter of some surprise that the absorbance change was slow in intact mitochondria, we have obtained submitochondrial particles prepared from beef heart, through the kindness of Dr. Sanadi. Their re-action with oxygen is indicated in Fig. 5. Under these conditions the re-action is found to be much faster and thus the oxygen concentration was dropped to 2 μM. Also, measurements by the continuous flow method were employed. Lastly, the data are plotted on a more rapid time scale. The second trace from the top representing flow velocity is now clearly resolved (cf. Fig. 4), and this time scale indicates almost continuous flow at a time after mixing of 7 msec; thereafter, an abrupt stop is recorded. The scale

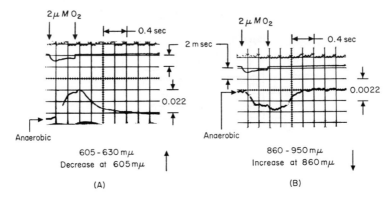

Fig. 5. A comparison of the kinetics of absorption changes in a suspension of sub-mitochondrial particles prepared from beef heart at wavelengths appropriate to the measurement of cytochrome *a* (A) and two wavelengths appropriate to measuring the infrared absorption change. The protein concentration is 3 mg/ml. The added oxygen concentration is 12 μM and the temperature is 24°; 0.1 M Tris phosphate buffer; pH 7.2.

indicates that a deflection of this trace of one large division corresponds to 2 msec and smaller deflections correspond in inverse proportion to longer times after mixing. The absorbance trace starts with the anaerobic mito-chondria and indicates a rise of the trace to a peak value during the flow; the amplifier response is 200 msec. The trace rises abruptly to a plateau when the flow stops. The absorbance change is approximately 0.02 per centimeter. The pseudo-first-order velocity computed from these data is 290 per second. In trace B the experiment is repeated with wavelengths appropriate to the infrared absorbance change and shows increased ab-sorption when oxygen is added. The trace in this case rises, then falls to a plateau similar to that of Fig. 5A, with a somewhat more distinct jump as the flow stops. A pseudo-first-order velocity constant is 230 per second.

V. Summary

An infrared absorbance change is observed in the oxidized-to-reduced transition in suspensions of intact pigeon heart mitochondria that agrees qualitatively and quantitatively with that observed in purified cytochrome *c* oxidase. The kinetics of the absorbance change either following H_2O_2 addition to the mitochondria suspended in a cuvette or following oxygen addition in regenerative flow apparatus appear slow in comparison with the kinetics of oxidation of cytochrome *a*. The reaction of submitochondrial particles showed a rapid infrared absorbance change. The possibility that a structural reorientation of copper occurs during the preparation of sub-mitochondrial particles and the purification of the oxidase is employed as a working hypothesis for the interpretation of these data. However, a detailed comparison of the kinetics of the infrared absorbance change in a variety of intact mitochondria and submitochondrial particles derived therefrom is required to further support and extend this hypothesis.

ACKNOWLEDGMENTS

I am particularly grateful to my technicians Tami Yoshioka and Leena Mela for excellent preparations of pigeon heart and rat liver mitochondria.

ADDENDUM

Since the presentation of this paper further experiments have been carried out to find an efficient method of converting the slow kinetics of the intact pigeon heart mitochondria to more rapid kinetics. A suspension of the pigeon heart mitochondria in a saline medium (0.15 M KCl) brings some preliminary success. Under conditions where H_2O_2 is added to oxidized respiratory components in the presence of an excess of catalase (as in Fig. 3), the half-time for the infrared absorbance change can be reduced to the mixing time for the H_2O_2 (0.5 sec).

REFERENCES

1. Smith, L., and Stotz, E., *J. Biol. Chem.*, **209,** 819 (1954).
2. Griffiths, D. E., and Wharton, D. C., *J. Biol. Chem.*, **236,** 1950 (1961).
3. Griffith, J. S., *in* F. Dickens and E. Neil (eds.), "Oxygen in the animal organism," Macmillan Company (Pergamon), New York, 1964, p. 141.
4. Griffiths, D. E., *J. Biol. Chem.*, **236,** 1857 (1961).
5. Slater, E. C., van Gelder, B. F., and K. Minnaert, *in* T. S. King, H. E. Mason, and M. Morrison (eds.), "Oxidases and related redox systems," John Wiley and Sons, New York, 1965, p. 667.
6. Chance, B., *J. Biol. Chem.*, **202,** 397 (1953).
7. Gibson, Q. H., and Greenwood, C., personal communication.
8. Chance, B., *J. Franklin Inst.*, **229,** Nos. 4,5,6 (1940).
9. Gibson, Q. H., *Biochem. J.*, **71,** 293 (1959).
10. Chance, B., *Nature*, **169,** 215 (1952).
11. Chance, B., Schoener, B., and DeVault, D., *in* T. S. King, H. E. Mason, and M. Morrison (eds.), "Oxidases and related redox systems," John Wiley and Sons, New York, 1965, p. 907.
12. Chance, B., and DeVault, D., Abstract WH5, Biophys. Soc., 9th Ann. Meeting, San Francisco, February, 1965.
13. Chance, B., *in* B. Chance, R. Eisenhardt, Q. H. Gibson, and K. K. Lonberg-Holm (eds.), "Rapid mixing and sampling techniques in biochemistry," Academic Press Inc., New York, 1964, p. 125.
14. Chance, B., and Hagihara, B., *Proc. 5th Intern. Cong. Biochem.*, **5,** Macmillan Company (Pergamon), New York, 1963, p. 3.
15. Chance, B., *J. Biol. Chem.*, **240,** 2729 (1965).
16. Sanadi, R., and Fluharty, A. L., *Biochemistry*, **2,** 523 (1963).
17. Chance, B., *Fed. Proc.*, **16,** 671 (1957).
18. Chance, B., *in* F. Dickens and E. Neil (eds.), "Oxygen in the animal organism," Macmillan Company (Pergamon), New York, 1964, p. 367.

DISCUSSION

Dr. WHARTON: In view of the rather small optical density changes that you observed at 830 mμ and the fact that a rather large difference is used between the 830 mμ band and the wavelength that you use as a reference, 750 or 960 mμ, all with quite turbid solutions, I wonder how much confidence you have in the significance of your figures.

Dr. CHANCE: Well, this is a fair question. It is apparent that I have enough confidence in my data to present them here. As for accuracy, the fact that I present original records for many of the figures in my presentation speaks directly to the point of accuracy, as judged by the noise level in the recordings. Generally, the accuracy is considerably better than 10% and quite adequate to record the kinetic changes reported. Also, the submitochondrial particles which react rapidly afford an excellent control. There, the pseudo-first-order velocity constants are high (190 sec^{-1} in the infrared region as compared with 200 sec^{-1} for cytochrome a). These results, currently ignored, can serve as an adequate control on the accuracy of the experimental method.

Dr. BEINERT: Do you have absolute spectra, not difference spectra, in the oxidized and reduced form?

Dr. CHANCE: No! The absolute spectra would be hard to get, even at high temperatures.

Dr. SCHEINBERG: Have I gotten the gist of what you have said? The kinetic data you obtained using intact of fractionated mitochondria or particles, are not consistent with data which Dr. Wharton obtained, using purified cytochrome oxidase. He concluded that copper *is* functional in the enzyme; and you–although you don't go out on a limb and say "No"–say that your data indicate that it is not functional in the intact and fractionated particles.

Dr CHANCE: The 830 mμ band doesn't satisfy kinetic criteria for a component near cytochromes $a + a_3$. That's the usual "gobbledygook."

Dr. SCHEINBERG: I tried to get away from the "gobbledygook": is there any evidence that copper does anything in the mitochondria *yet*?

Dr. CHANCE: It doesn't do anything fast.

Dr. SLATER: In that first experiment with the mitochondria did I see two coppers reacting?

Dr. CHANCE: You mean, was it biphasic?

Dr. SLATER: Yes.

Dr. CHANCE: I would say that might be pushing the data to the limit of their accuracy.

Dr. VAN GELDER: I should like to ask Dr. Chance if he has measured at 445 mμ. At 830 mμ both coppers have an absorbance. If you could compare the kinetics at these two wavelengths, perhaps you could say a little bit more about which ones you have studied.

Dr. CHANCE: I have often measured at 445 mμ. But here you have the sum of most of the protoheme bands, and it's difficult to disentangle them.

Dr. SCHUBERT: If we assume copper is involved in cytochrome oxidase, perhaps in view of the relatively large difference in stereochemistry of cupric and cuprous copper there may be a shuttling effect. That is, during the oxidation-reduction the copper acts as a hinge to line up the heme groups so as to facilitate electron conduction or transfer.

DR. CHANCE: Well, if we knew how the electron transfer occurs, I could give an intelligent answer, but we don't.

DR. WILLIAMS: There is another band associated with copper which occurs at about 600 mμ. This is supposed to have the same extinction coefficient as the one at about 850. (Professor Chance has the only machine that can measure this.) I wonder if he would mind going back and looking at that band, because then he ought to be able to see his changes at 830 mμ superimposed on the band changes at 600 mμ, and therefore you would have a check.

DR. CHANCE: This is an important point and it bears to some extent on Dr. Wharton's comment. As far as I can determine, however, the contribution of the 830 mμ band at 605 mμ is very small. In the mitochondrial preparations where we obtained a nice time separation of cytochromes a in the 830 mμ pigment, any contribution at 605 mμ due to the 830 mμ pigment would be kinetically distinct. It was not, however, observed.

Ascorbate Oxidase, A Review

CHARLES R. DAWSON*

Department of Chemistry,
Columbia Univeristy,
New York, New York

I. Introduction

Ascorbate oxidase, more commonly called ascorbic acid oxidase, is a copper-containing protein that catalyzes the aerobic oxidation of vitamin C. Concentrated aqueous solutions of the purified enzyme are intensely blue, and the color is very rapidly bleached when the substrate, L-ascorbate, is added under conditions of physiological pH. Such systems rapidly absorb

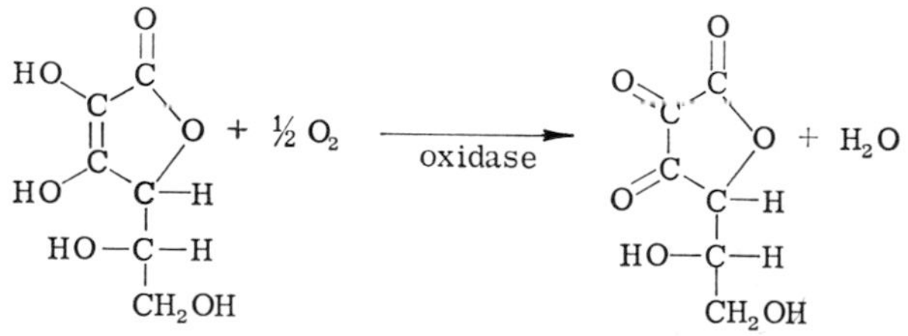

$$\text{L-Ascorbic acid (AH}_2\text{)} \qquad \text{Dehydroascorbic acid (A)}$$

oxygen in accordance with Eq. (1) and the original blue color of the enzyme is restored when the ascorbic acid has been completely oxidized. Under

*The Columbia University investigations described in this review were supported by grants from the U. S. Public Health Service (A–3200).

proper conditions the rate of the oxidation reaction is directly proportional to the amount of enzyme in the system, and it has been customary to assay the activity of the enzyme in terms of the rate of oxygen absorption as measured manometrically, i.e., one unit of oxidase activity has been defined as that amount of enzyme that causes an initial rate of oxygen absorption equal to 10 μl per minute under specified conditions of substrate concentration, pH, and temperature (1). In many cases it is convenient to determine the rate of the oxidation reaction spectrophotometrically based on the rate of loss of the characteristic ultraviolet absorption of the ascorbate (2, 3).

The enzyme was first detected in 1928 (4) and for an extended period thereafter there was controversy concerning the possible role of copper in the "oxidase-like" activity of a variety of plant extracts. It was not until 1940 (5) that the enzyme was sufficiently purified to justify the view that the oxidase was a new copper protein. During the next two decades a great deal of evidence was brought forward to substantiate this view; methods were developed to obtain the enzyme in highly purified form, and much effort was directed toward elucidating the joint role of the copper and the protein in the catalytic activity. These and other aspects of the history of ascorbate oxidase have been covered in earlier reviews (5–10). This paper will be concerned therefore primarily with the developments of recent years.

II. Occurrence and Function

During the past 6 years over 100 articles have been published dealing with some aspect of ascorbate oxidase enzymology. Most of the investigations have involved studies designed to evaluate the role of the enzyme in the respiratory and metabolic processes of a large number of plants, plant products, and microorganisms. No animal source of the enzyme has been described, but it has been reported that the blood copper protein, ceruloplasmin, possesses ascorbate oxidase activity (11–13) in contradiction to the finding of Scheinberg and collaborators (14).

In addition to the studies indicated in Table I, investigations dealing with the ascorbate oxidase activity of *Avena coleoptiles* (63), Azerbaidzhan fruit (64), barberry (65), beans (26, 66), buckwheat (67), Canada thistle (65), carrots (68), cherry leaves (16), grapefruit (46), hops (69), iris leaves (70), leguminous plants (71), lemons (46), lettuce (72), limes (46), nutgrass (73), paprika (74), peanuts (26), *Phaseolus mungo* (75), rape (19), *Rudbeckia bicolor* (76), Sphagnum moss (77), *Sorgham vulgare* (75), strawberries (60), tobacco pith (78), and winter rye (65) have been reported. The enzyme

TABLE I

RECENT INVESTIGATIONS INDICATING THE PARTICIPATION OF ASCORBATE OXIDASE IN
THE METABOLIC AND RESPIRATORY PROCESSES OF CERTAIN PLANTS

Plant	Refs.
Apple	15–18
Barley	19, 20
Corn	21–29
Cotton plant	26, 30
Cucumber	31, 32
Grape	33–43
Oats	26, 44
Orange	45, 46
Pea	19, 27, 44
Potato	25, 47–50
Rice	19, 51–54
Soybean	26, 53, 55
Spinach	31, 53
Squash	56, 57
Tomato	58–60
Wheat	19, 61, 62

has been reported to be involved in the respiration of the microorganism *Chlorella pyrenoidosa* (79), and an interesting atypical ascorbate oxidase from *Myrothecium verrucaria* has been described (80–82). An ascorbate oxidase, somewhat similar to that of plants, has been identified in a strain of *Aerobacter aerogenes* (83), and the rough forms of several species of bacteria have been found to possess a more active ascorbate oxidase than the smooth variants (84).

III. Purification and Characterization

As pointed out in an earlier review (10), the ascorbate oxidase of several plants has been purified, but the most highly purified enzyme has been obtained from the yellow crook-neck squash (*Cucurbita pepo condensa*). Recently the green zucchini squash (*C. pepo medullosa*) has also been used as a source of the purified enzyme involving a new procedure based on DEAE-cellulose column chromatography and starch column zone electrophoresis (85). Improved yields of an intensely blue colored enzyme of highest purity yet reported (specific activity of 3600 units per milligram of protein) have been obtained from either the yellow or the green summer squash by the new procedure.

TABLE II
Characteristics of Purified Ascorbate Oxidase

Source	Yellow crook-neck squash (*C. pepo condensa*) or green zucchini squash (*C. pepo medullosa*)
Preparation	DEAE-cellulose column chromatography and starch column zone electrophoresis
Homogeneity	100% (ultracentrifuge and electrophoresis)
Molecular weight	140,000 (ultracentrifuge)
Copper content	0.34%, corresponding to 8 copper atoms per molecule
Specific activity	3600 units per mg protein; 1100 units per μg copper
Color	Intense blue in aqueous solution; absorption max. at 608 mμ (dependent on O_2 and substrate)
State of copper in resting enzyme	75% Cu^{2+} = 6 atoms = active; 25% Cu^+ = 2 atoms = inactive
Apoenzyme	Copper-free and colorless; inactive
Nitrogen	16.8%; 18 different amino acids plus hexosamine; no free terminal amino group
Sulfur	Native enzyme; no free —SH groups. Denatured enzyme (urea or detergent); 10–12 —SH groups and 3 to 4 disulfide groups per molecule. Apoenzyme; about 10 free —SH groups
Phosphorus and calcium	None

The enzyme thus purified was found to be homogeneous in electrophoresis and in ultracentrifugation and to have a higher copper content (0.34%) than the 0.26% previously reported for the homogeneous enzyme (86). Based on the sedimentation data, and information concerning the amino acid content of the enzyme, as reported by Stark and Dawson (87), a molecular weight range of 134,000–140,000 was indicated for the enzyme. The 140,000 value is in good agreement for an enzyme molecule containing eight copper atoms. The characteristics of the purified enzyme are summarized in Table II.

It may be recalled that earlier preparations of the enzyme having a copper content of about 0.26% and specific activities of about 2000 units per milligram of protein or 750 units per microgram of copper showed no measurable inhomogeneity either in the Tiselius apparatus or in the ultracentrifuge (86). Such homogeneous preparations, having a copper content and molecular weight corresponding to 6 copper atoms per enzyme molecule, have been duplicated many times and used for exchange experiments with radioactive ^{64}Cu (87), investigations of the amino acid composition (88, 89), the finding that the enzyme has no N-terminal amino acid residue (90), the finding that the native enzyme has no free —SH group but when denatured either by urea or detergent exposes 10–12 sulfhydryl groups and 3–4 disulfide groups (88), and experimental investigations concerning the specificity and mechanism of action (91) and deactivation of the enzyme (92).

It is particularly worth noting, therefore, that in the new procedure for preparing the enzyme (85), samples obtained from the third DEAE-cellulose chromatographic column had a specific activity of about 2000 units per milligram of protein and showed only a trace of detectable protein contaminant by ultracentrifugal analysis. In other words, the significant increase in specific activity and copper content was achieved in the last operation of the purification, i.e., the starch column zone electrophoresis steps, without apparent change in homogeneity. Such results are explainable in terms of the removal of a protein contaminant, or contaminants (lower in copper content than the enzyme), that is not distinguishable from the enzyme in the ultracentrifuge (and presumably also the Tiselius apparatus) under the conditions investigated. In this connection it is of interest that the apoenzyme (copper-free) is not distinguishable from the native enzyme in the ultracentrifuge (93). These observations therefore suggest that the earlier "homogeneous" preparations (six copper atoms per enzyme molecule) may have been contaminated with a modified form, or forms, of the enzyme having a lower activity and copper content. The fact that such preparations have not been observed to be activated by the addition of cupric ion does not invalidate the above suggestion because it is now recognized (94) that the restoration of activity to the apoenzyme requires cuprous ion, and is dependent on the age (presumably the extent of modification) of the apoenzyme.

IV. Specificity and Reaction Intermediates

A number of interesting reports concerning investigations of the specificity of ascorbate oxidase, and the mechanism of its catalytic reaction, have appeared in recent years. As pointed out elsewhere (10), prior to about 1960 numerous investigators had demonstrated that the oxidase exhibits a high degree of specificity toward L-ascorbate and certain related compounds whose structures include a dienol grouping adjacent to a carbonyl and a closed ring. Although it has often been reported (10) that the enzyme does not catalyze the aerobic oxidation of mono-, di-, and triphenolic substrates, particularly catechol and hydroquinone, it has more recently been observed that a number of substituted polyhydric- and aminophenols are oxidized by the enzyme and the rate increases with increase in pH (91).

Of particular interest is the observation that the leuco-form of 2,6-dichloroindophenol is rather rapidly converted into the blue quinoid dye by the enzyme under aerobic conditions; see Eq. (2). The experimental findings

$$(2)$$

Colorless   Blue

2,6-Dichloroindophenol

on the nature of the reaction may be summarized as follows: (a) Oxygen is absorbed, and the reaction is not catalyzed by free Cu^{2+} or by Cu^{2+} in the presence of inert protein; (b) the reaction is first order in respect to both enzyme and substrate concentration; (c) the rate of the reaction increases with increase in pH, thus implicating the monoanion of the leuco dye as the active form of the substrate; (d) inhibition studies indicate that the Copper of the enzyme plays a role in the oxidation.

Additional studies with chlorophenols and aminophenols structurally related to the dye have revealed that 2,6- and 2,5-dichlorohydroquinone and hydroxy hydroquinone are oxidized by the enzyme at pH 5.7 at a rate one-twelfth as fast as ascorbic acid. A similar situation has been observed in an aminophenol and catechol series of compounds. At pH 5.7 hydroquinone and catechol are not oxidized, but at pH 7.2 they are. It is suggested that ascorbate oxidase will catalyze the aerobic oxidation of any compound that fulfills the structural requirements summarized in Table III.

By means of an EPR spectrometer, adapted with a flow apparatus, Yamazaki and Piette (95) have concluded that a free radical derived from ascorbate is involved in the main pathway of the ascorbate oxidase–catalyzed oxidation of ascorbic acid. The free radical completely dis-

TABLE III
Structural Requirements for an Ascorbate Oxidase Substrate[a]

(a) An anionic form

(b) A conjugated system

(c) Oxidizable to a quinoid product via a semiquinoid intermediate.

(d) Contain an atom with a pair of unbonded electrons diagonally opposite the anion atom at an approximate distance of 5.8–6.2 Å that can interact with some group in close proximity on the enzyme surface

[a] After Dayan and Dawson (91).

appeared after the reaction was over even in the presence of ascorbate under the oxygen-limiting conditions of the ascorbate oxidase reaction. They concluded that the enzyme catalyzes a one-electron transfer and depicted the role of the enzyme's cupric copper with ascorbate (AH_2) as shown in Eq. (3).

$$Cu^{2+} + AH_2 \xrightarrow{k_1} Cu^+ + AH\cdot + H^+ \tag{3}$$

Although no detailed mechanism was reported, they suggested that the mechanism involves a temporary intermediate between the cuprous enzyme and molecular oxygen. They pointed out similarities of the ascorbate oxidase kinetics to those of the peroxidase oxidation of ascorbic acid, and to the laccase reaction as reported by Nakamura (96).

Yamazaki has also observed (97) that ascorbate oxidase catalyzes the reduction of cytochrome c in the presence of ascorbic acid and oxygen. The free radical derived from ascorbic acid during the ascorbate oxidase reaction appears to be the active species for the cytochrome c reduction.

The kinetics of the ascorbate oxidase reaction has also been studied using a polarographic method for following the oxygen consumption (98).

V. Inactivation, Deactivation, and Inhibition

A. Production of Peroxide

It has long been recognized that during the catalysis of the aerobic oxidation of ascorbic acid, by purified samples of the oxidase, extensive inactivation of the enzyme occurs. Because the free cupric ion catalysis of ascorbate oxidation (and cupric ion catalysis in the presence of inert proteins) produces essentially stoichiometric amounts of H_2O_2, an agent known to be deleterious to many enzymes, much attention has been given to establishing a relationship between the enzyme inactivation and the formation of H_2O_2 (7–10). However, the oxygen consumption in the purified oxidase reaction is in agreement with the reduction of the oxygen to water rather than to H_2O_2 (see Eq. (1)), and until recently numerous attempts to detect H_2O_2 production in the enzymatic reaction system have failed.

By means of a technique involving increment additions of the substrate to the enzyme, and also increments of the enzyme to the substrate, it has been demonstrated that the inactivation of the enzyme is not due to any product of the enzymatic activity but is dependent rather on the ratio of enzyme to substrate and the time of the reaction (99). These results indicated that the inactivation was due to the accumulation of a byproduct of the reaction (presumably H_2O_2), and it was demonstrated that only extremely small amounts of H_2O_2 were required to account for the experimentally observed enzyme inactivation. It was suggested that a minor fraction of the enzyme's prosthetic copper, a fraction not involved in the enzyme's activity, might be responsible for the production of H_2O_2 as a byproduct via a relatively slow copper-catalyzed (nonenzymatic) oxidation of substrate.

TABLE IV

A COMPARISON OF THE INACTIVATING EFFECT OF H_2O_2 ON FUNCTIONING
VERSUS RESTING ENZYME[a]

System[b]	Initial enzyme state	Incubation conditions	Before dialysis		After dialysis[c]	
			A_{605}	% Activity recovered	A_{605}[d]	% Activity recovered
1	Resting	With H_2O_2	0.066	97	0.057	82
2	Functioning	With H_2O_2	0.015[e]	21	0.023[e]	0
3	Functioning	No H_2O_2	0.062[e]	98	0.063[e]	86

[a] After Poillon and Dawson (100).

[b] All systems contained a 0.5 ml aliquot of purified enzyme. Systems 2 and 3 were made 2.0×10^{-2} M in ascorbic acid and systems 1 and 2 were made 1.0×10^{-2} M in H_2O_2, using suitable stock solutions, before all systems were made up to 2.5 ml with phosphate-citrate buffer, pH 5.6. The final prosthetic copper concentration corresponded to 4.6×10^{-5} M.

[c] All systems were exhaustively dialyzed with stirring at refrigeration temperature against four 1 liter changes of phosphate-citrate buffer, pH 5.8, over a 4-day period.

[d] Theoretical A_{605} for full blue color = 0.060.

[e] Pure O_2 was bubbled into both systems for 5 min followed by centrifugation to remove haze and debris.

A highly pertinent feature of the problem, which has become apparent more recently, is the fact that the functioning enzyme is much more sensitive to the inactivating action of H_2O_2 than is the resting (nonfunctioning) enzyme (100). As can be seen from the data in Table IV, H_2O_2 has no significant effect on the activity or color of the resting enzyme (system 1) during a 20 hour incubation period under the conditions described in the legend. On the other hand, when the enzyme was allowed to function by catalyzing the oxidation of ascorbate in the presence of the same amount of H_2O_2 during the 20-hour incubation period (system 2), there was a 79% loss in activity and a very appreciable loss in blue color. Furthermore, this

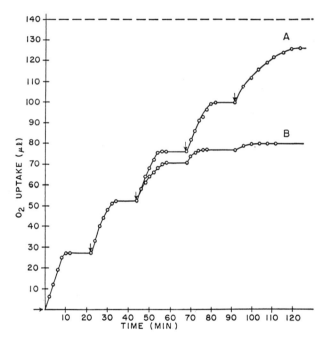

FIG. 1. The activity of the BCS-modified (curve A) and the native enzyme (curve B) resulting from the stepwise addition of substrate. Oxygen uptake was measured manometrically at 25° in $4 \times 10^{-2}M$ phosphate-citrate buffer, pH 5.8. Both reaction vessels contained initially the same amount of enzyme: that equivalent to 7.3×10^{-4} μg of enzyme copper. However, in the case corresponding to curve A, approximately 25% of the enzyme's prosthetic copper had been complexed by BCS. Each system also contained initially an 0.02 ml increment of ascorbic acid (0.44 mg = 1.0×10^{-3} M) equivalent to an O_2 uptake of 28 μl for complete oxidation. The systems were made up to a final volume of 2.40 ml with copper-free water. Successive increments of ascorbic acid, each equivalent to the original, were added as indicated. The dashed line corresponds to the theoretical O_2 uptake for the addition of five increments of ascorbic acid. After Poillon and Dawson (100).

H₂O₂-induced inactivation did not effect the Cu-protein bond because after dialysis essentially all of the prosthetic copper was found inside the dialysis bag. The results for system 2 should also be compared with those of the control, in which no H_2O_2 was present (system 3).

As pointed out earlier, the H_2O_2-inactivation studies led to the suggestion that all of the enzyme's prosthetic copper is not functionally equivalent, and that the H_2O_2 generation involved a minor fraction of the enzyme-copper in a nonenzymatic catalysis. The experimental observations given in Fig. 1 (100) support this view and show that the enzyme inactivation was prevented when the Cu^+ fraction (25%) of the enzyme's prosthetic copper was complexed with the valence specific chelating agent BCS.

B. The Deactivating Effect of Urea

The deactivating effect of increasing concentrations of urea, and of hydrogen ion, on purified ascorbate oxidase has been correlated with the

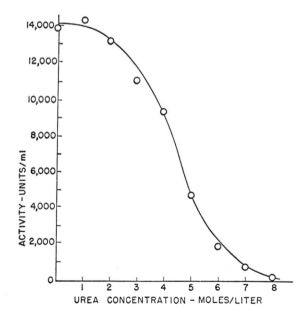

FIG. 2. The effect of urea on the activity of ascorbate oxidase. The experiments were carried out in duplicate using an enzyme sample that originally had a specific activity of 1660 units per milligram and a copper content of 0.28%. A 0.2 ml sample of the enzyme was added to 4.0 ml of a urea solution made up in 0.1 M McIlvaine's buffer (final pH 5.8). After the addition of 0.8 g of washed ion exchange resin (Amberlite IR–100), the system stood for 1½ hours at 4° with periodic agitation. Aliquots were then removed and assayed for copper and activity. After Greenwald (92).

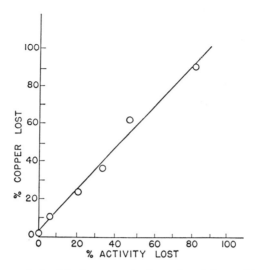

FIG. 3. The linear relationship between the loss of activity and loss of copper in ascorbate oxidase after incubation with urea (see legend of Fig. 2). After Greenwald (92).

copper content of the enzyme (92). The urea experiments were performed by incubating samples of the purified enzyme, at 4° for $1\frac{1}{2}$ hours with periodic agitation, in a system containing buffer (pH 5.8), urea, and ion exchange resin (Amberlite IR-100). Resin-free aliquots were then removed and assayed for both activity and copper content. Preliminary experiments had established that the resin would bind all free cupric ion liberated from the enzyme under the conditions employed. The activity results are shown in Fig. 2, and a very similarly shaped curve was obtained when the amount of protein-bound copper remaining in the enzyme was plotted against the urea concentration in the system. A linear relationship was observed between the activity loss and the copper loss (see Fig. 3), thus confirming that the activity of the enzyme is critically dependent on its copper content. At no time was there any detectable protein precipitation during the urea incubation. The loss in activity was not reversed by diluting the system, nor by removing the urea by dialysis, nor by adding cupric ion after the dialysis.

A great deal has been written on the phenomenon of protein denaturation. The term is difficult to define because it has been applied in so many different ways to changes in the properties of proteins. Thus it is commonly accepted that denaturation will often lead to loss in activity of a catalytically active protein (enzyme). However, loss in activity can occur without denaturation, and denaturation can occur (to some degree at least) without loss in activity. Consequently, the term deactivation seems appropriate to describe a loss in enzyme activity, when the extent or nature of the denaturation process is not known. There is much experimental support, notably the work of Sternman and Foster (101), for the view that the essential feature of the effect of urea on the structure of proteins is to cause an unfolding of coiled peptide chains. Thus it may be argued, on the basis of the urea deactivation experiments described above, that a unique folding of the polypeptide chain of ascorbate oxidase brings two or more functional groups into a proximity suitable for the binding of the copper in the enzyme. It is therefore not surprising that the stability of the copper-protein complex and its catalytic activity are both sensitive to conformational and/or structural changes in the polypeptide chain.

C. The Deactivating Effect of Hydrogen Ion

The deactivation of purified ascorbate oxidase by exposure to increasing hydrogen ion concentration has also been systematically investigated within the past few years (92). The experiments were performed by incubating samples of the purified enzyme, at 4° for $4\frac{1}{2}$ hours, in systems containing 0.05 M McIlvaine's buffer adjusted stepwise between pH 1.00 and 5.70. An appropriate amount of ion exchange resin (Amberlite IR-100) was then introduced into the system and equilibrated for an hour to bind all copper liberated from the enzyme. Resin-free aliquots were then removed and assayed for both activity and copper content. The results shown in Fig. 4 were obtained with three different enzyme samples having specific activities within the range 1660–2380 units/mg and copper contents of 0.28–0.29%.

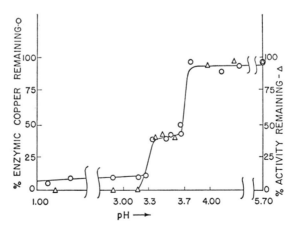

Fig. 4. The effect on the activity and copper content of ascorbate oxidase produced by equilibrating the enzyme in buffer at the pH indicated. The incubations were carried out for 4 hours at 4° after which the copper liberated from the enzyme was removed by means of an ion exchange resin (see text for additional details). After Greenwald (92).

From the curve in Fig. 4 it is apparent again that there is a direct relationship between the losses in activity and copper. It is particularly noteworthy that as the pH was lowered from the region of optimal activity (pH 5.7) there was no significant loss in either activity or copper above pH 3.8. Then a striking loss in both copper (61% loss) and activity (65% loss) occurred as the pH of the incubation system was lowered by another 0.02 units to 3.78. As shown in the figure, no additional change was observed between pH 3.78 and 3.45, but a further lowering of the pH led to a second sharp decrease in activity and copper. At a pH lower than 3.45 essentially 100% of the activity and 90% of the copper was lost.

The exposure of the enzyme to increasing increments of hydrogen ion, for a finite period of time suitable to establish equilibrium after each increment, may be considered as a titration of the copper in the enzyme and represented as follows (Eq. 4):

$$Cu^{2+}\text{---}Protein + H^+ \rightleftharpoons Protein\text{---}H^+ + Cu^{2+} \qquad (4)$$

In other words, the titration can be viewed as the displacement of a weak acid (the Cu^{2+} ion) from the salt of a weak base (the protein moiety) and a weak acid, by a stronger acid (the hydrogen ion).

In the case of the titration curve, the pH of the inflection point corresponds to the apparent pK of the copper-protein complex, or more strictly speaking, the pH at the inflection point corresponds to the apparent pK of the group or groups involved in binding the copper to the protein. It appears that the curve shown in Fig. 4 is actually the superposition of two titration curves, having inflection points at pH 3.7 and 3.3, respectively. Therefore the apparent pK values for the group or groups binding the copper to the protein in ascorbate oxidase are 3.7 and 3.3. It is noteworthy that these values correspond very closely to the pK values which can be calculated from the data obtained (102, 103) on investigating the stability of copper complexes of a variety of α-amino acids, in which it was known that both the carboxyl and α-amino groups were participating in the formation of the complex (104). The apparent pK of the metal chelate (approximately 3.6) was significantly lower than that of either carboxyl (pK of 4) or α-amino groups (pK of 7). Since it is known that the imidazole group is similar to the α-amino groups in pK value, pK of 7, it seems likely that the apparent pK of a copper-protein complex involving carboxyl and imidazole ligands would not be very different from that of a complex involving carboxyl and α-amino group ligands. Thus it has been suggested (92) that the copper in ascorbate oxidase is bonded in two ways, one involving carboxyl and α-amino groups, and the other involving carboxyl and imidazole groups.

The fact that the titration curve in Fig. 4 indicates two types of copper bonding in ascorbate oxidase is of particular interest in relation to the finding (105) that the copper in the resting native enzyme exists in a mixed valence state, in a ratio of Cu^{2+} to Cu^+ of approximately 3:1. This feature of the copper in the enzyme is discussed below, but it is of interest here to point out that cupric ion chelation complexes tend to be square coplanar, and cuprous complexes tetrahedral (106, 107). Thus the mixed valence state of copper in the enzyme is in agreement with the suggestion that the binding of copper in ascorbate oxidase involves two different chelate systems.

The fact that the inflection points in the curve of Fig. 4 occur at pH values significantly lower than the pK values of carboxyl, α-amino, or imidazole groups can be accounted for in terms of the observations of other workers. It has been found that pK values can be significantly depressed by factors such as the charge of the protein (108), masking due to steric effects (109, 110), buffer effects (111), presence of neighboring charged groups (112), and ionization of substrate (112).

D. Reactivation

It has been found (92) that the 60% deactivated enzyme, existing in the pH range 3.45 to 3.78 (see Fig. 4), does not regain activity simply by raising the pH to 4.2. However, when the pH elevation was carried out in the presence of a large excess of cupric ion (10- to 1000-fold molar excess

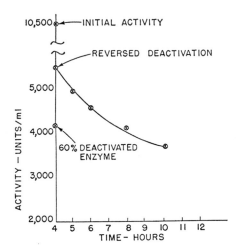

FIG. 5. The reversal of the H^+ ion deactivation of ascorbate oxidase, by the elevation of the pH in the presence of added Cu^{2+}, is only partial and is dependent on the time that elapses before the reversal treatment is effected (see text for details). After Greenwald (92).

of Cu^{2+} added), the deactivation was reversed by 40–43%, and the extent of the reversal was markedly dependent on the time that the enzyme was kept at the low pH (see Fig. 5). These results indicate that in addition to the loss in copper, presumably via a protonation of the functional groups that bind the copper to the protein, a secondary slower process was occurring that prevented reversal of the deactivation. Presumably this slower secondary process was an unfolding of the polypeptide chain of the protein. The 60% deactivated species of the enzyme was found to be very similar to the native enzyme in three characteristics, i.e., the visible spectrum, the pH activity optimum, and the apparent K_m value.

The inhibition of ascorbate oxidase activity by a large number of agents has been a feature of many of the investigations indicated in Table I. However, these studies have not involved the isolated and purified enzyme. They have been concerned, for the most part, with the inhibitory (and activating) effect of various agents on the ascorbate oxidase activity of respiring plant tissue. The action of most of the agents on the activity of the isolated enzyme was extensively reviewed in 1963 (10).

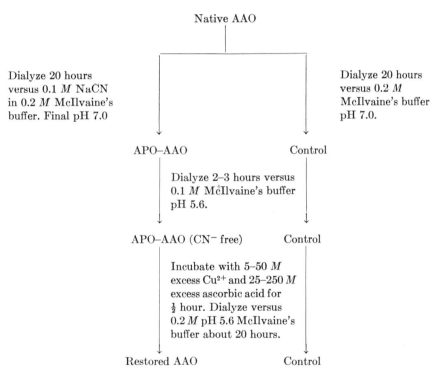

FIG. 6. Procedure for the preparation of apoascorbate oxidase (APO–AAO) and for its restoration to active enzyme (AAO). After Penton (113).

VI. The Apoenzyme

It has been known for a long time that dialysis of ascorbate oxidase against cyanide causes a loss in copper and activity. However, the resulting inactive apoenzyme has received very little attention because until recently it has not been possible, except with crude preparations, to restore the copper and the activity to the protein. An accumulation of experimental observations led us a while ago to reinvestigate this problem in terms of Cu^+ rather than Cu^{2+} for the restoration of activity and copper content. It has been found that apoenzyme derived from the purified oxidase can be restored to almost full catalytic activity, blue color, and copper content by treatment with Cu^+; large excesses of Cu^+ are not required (94, 113). The use of Cu^{2+} results in the partial rebonding of copper, but little or no recovery of activity.

The procedure employed is outlined in Fig. 6 and some of the results are given in Table V. The blue color of the enzyme, characterized by an absorption band in the visible region of the spectrum at 608 mμ, is lost when the copper is removed via the dialysis against cyanide. The resulting apoenzyme is an essentially colorless protein. Restoration of the activity

TABLE V

PERCENTAGE ACTIVITY AND COPPER REMAINING IN SAMPLES OF
APOASCORBATE OXIDASE[a, b]

Before treatment with cuprous ion		After treatment with cuprous ion	
% Activity	% Copper	% Activity	% Copper
1.1	0.0	49.1	52.0
0.6	6.1	79.4	97.2
0.0	4.3	81.5	83.8
0.0	18.1	97.7	82.5
0.0	27.6	84.1	114.0
0.9	3.6	81.2	97.2
2.2	15.4	91.4	92.9
0.0	11.4	55.2	51.4
0.9	11.8	67.1	72.2
0.0	0.0	82.1	70.2
0.0	8.1	86.7	84.6
1.7	0.0	73.4	85.7

[a] Compared with identically treated native ascorbate oxidase.
[b] After Penton (113).

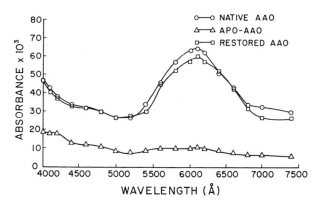

Fig. 7. The visible spectra of native, apo-, and restored ascorbate oxidase (AAO). The original native enzyme had a specific activity of 2470 units per milligram and a copper content of 0.37%. The spectra were determined on a Beckman DU spectrophotometer using a 0.2 M McIlvaine's buffer (pH 5.6) solution of the protein. The protein concentration was $5 \times 10^{-6} M$. After Penton (113).

and copper by the procedure outline in Fig. 6 also restores the visible spectrum of the native enzyme (see Fig. 7).

The ability to restore the apoenzyme to the holoenzyme opens up another experimental approach to elucidating the nature of the copper-protein bonds in the enzyme. Investigations of free functional groups in the apoenzyme and their disappearance on restoration of activity should provide information concerning the ligands involved in bonding the copper. In this connection it is of particular interest to note that the blue color and the activity are not restored equally by a given amount of Cu^+ (see Fig. 8). This fact, and particularly the shape of the restoration curve, suggest that all eight copper atoms of the enzyme are not functionally equivalent. It has been pointed out earlier in the discussion of inactivation that evidence exists to support the view that at least two of the copper atoms are not involved in the activity or blue color of the enzyme. This point will be discussed further in a following section of this paper dealing with the state of the copper in the enzyme.

Another interesting point concerns the stability of the apoenzyme. As can be seen from the data in Table VI the apoenzyme on aging loses its ability to be restored to active enzyme. The freshly prepared apoenzyme has been found by amperimetric titration with silver ion to contain about 10 free —SH groups per mole (94). On the aging the —SH groups disappear. It may be recalled that the native enzyme has no free —SH groups, but the urea-treated enzyme loses its copper and exposes 10–12 free —SH groups (88). The native and fully active enzyme is not inhibited by p-CMB,

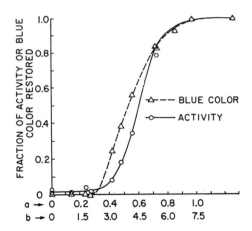

Fig. 8. The recovery of blue color and activity when apoascorbate oxidase is treated with cuprous ion (Cu²⁺ plus substrate or reducing agent). (a) Fraction of total copper added to apoenzyme. (b) Moles of cuprous ion added per mole of enzyme. The data are the average of determinations involving two different apoenzymes prepared as described in Fig. 6 from ascorbate oxidase samples having specific activities of 2180 and 2340 units per milligram and initial copper contents of 0.31% and 0.39% respectively. Both apoenzymes showed a very slight activity but contained no measurable copper (see text for additional details). After Penton (113).

TABLE VI

RESTORATION OF APOASCORBATE OXIDASE WITH COPPER AND
REDUCING AGENT[a]

Apoenzyme	Age (days)[b]	Activity[c] (%)	Copper[c] (%)
Before adding copper	0	1.7	0.0
After adding copper	0	73.4	85.7
	5	33.1	66.7
	13	24.6	59.2
	21	10.9	45.6
	28	6.3	23.7

[a] After Penton (113).

[b] The native enzyme was dialyzed against cyanide overnight. The next day the cyanide was removed by dialysis for about 3 hours. At this point the apoenzyme was considered to be "zero days old."

[c] The activity and copper values are based on the assignment of 100% activity and copper to the control samples which showed no deterioration during the time periods in this experiment.

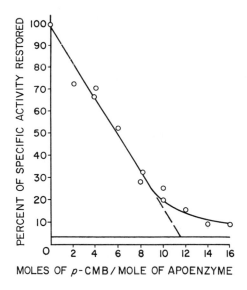

FIG. 9. Prevention of restoration of activity to apoascorbate oxidase by treatment with p-CMB. The experiment was performed twice, using two samples of enzyme having a specific activity of 2470 units per milligram and a copper content of 0.37%. The apoenzymes (see Fig. 6) were incubated with p-CMB for 18 hours at 5° before the restoration of activity was attempted by the addition of cuprous ion in the usual manner. The systems contained about 0.7 mg of protein per milliliter. A part of each apoenzyme sample, not treated with p-CMB, was restored as a control. The untreated apoenzyme had about 3% of the activity of the fully restored control. The activity of the control apoenzyme is used as the base line of this figure. After Penton (113).

but as can be seen from Fig. 9 treatment of the apoenzyme with p-CMB prevents the restoration of activity by the addition of Cu⁺. It is significant, however, that the p-CMB-treated apoenzyme retains much of its capacity to bind copper. Consequently it has been concluded (94) that the primary copper-binding group in ascorbate oxidase is not sulfur, but that —SH groups are involved in maintaining a conformation of the protein polypeptide chain so that the copper atoms are properly oriented for function as activity sites.

VII. The State of the Copper

As pointed out earlier, recent findings have suggested that all of the copper in ascorbate oxidase is not equivalent in respect to valence state, color, and oxidase activity. Consequently an investigation was undertaken utilizing three different valence-specific copper chelating agents to determine the valence nature of the copper in the oxidase (105). The three

TABLE VII

EVIDENCE FOR A MIXED VALENCE STATE OF THE PROSTHETIC COPPER IN ASCORBATE
OXIDASE BY CUPROUS ASSAY WITH COLORIMETRIC REAGENTS[a]

Enzyme condition	Percentage of total prosthetic copper reacting as Cu^+ with the reagents		
	Cuproine +EDTA	Bathocuproine[b] +EDTA	Bathocuproine[c] +Cuprizone
Denatured[d]	23	23	27

[a] After Poillon and Dawson (105).

[b] Applied as the water-soluble, sulfonated, sodium salt.

[c] A simultaneous determination of Cu^+ and Cu^{2+}.

[d] In all three cases, the enzyme was acidified with HCl to completely dissociate prosthetic copper; the inclusion of EDTA prevented reduction of Cu^{2+} by exposed —SH groups.

agents employed were cuproine and BCS (both Cu^+ specific (114)) and cuprizone (Cu^{2+} specific (115)). The effect of these three reagents was determined both on the acid-deactivated and the native enzyme. During the assay of the acidified enzyme, precautions were taken to ensure the maintenance of the exact copper valence state present at the moment of dissociation from the protein. This was successfully accomplished by including in the cuprous assay system sufficient EDTA to instantly complex all Cu^{2+} released, thereby rendering them unavailable for possible

TABLE VIII

SHOWING THE COMPLETE UNREACTIVITY OF EITHER Cu^+ OR Cu^{2+} IN NATIVE ASCORBATE
OXIDASE WITH VALENCE-SPECIFIC REAGENTS AT pH 7.2[a]

	Reagent	
	Bathocuproine	Cuprizone
Specificity	Cu^+	Cu^{2+}
A at λ_{max} in 10 hours	0.005[b]	0.002[c]

[a] After Poillon and Dawson (105).

[b] Reagent applied to 1160 molar excess relative to total prosthetic copper; theoretical $A_{480} = 0.330$.

[c] Reagent applied to 460 molar excess relative to total prosthetic copper; theoretical $A_{600} = 0.250$.

subsequent *in situ* reduction by the 10–12 sulfhydryl groups exposed on denaturation of the apoenzyme.

In Table VII are shown the results of such Cu^+ assays with either cuproine or bathocuproine alone, as well as the simultaneous determination of both Cu^+ and Cu^{2+} by combined bathocuproine–cuprizone assay. These results clearly establish a mixed valence state for the prosthetic copper released from the denatured enzyme. The ratio of 75% Cu^{2+} to 25% Cu^+ found corresponds to 6 Cu^{2+} and 2 Cu^+ per enzyme molecule.

As can be seen in Table VIII the native enzyme was totally unreactive when either the Cu^+-specific reagent, bathocuproine, or the Cu^{2+}-specific reagent, cuprizone, was applied in large molar excess at physiological pH. This complete lack of reactivity of the prosthetic copper in the native enzyme can presumably be attributed either to a steric interference of the protein's tertiary structure, which prevents penetration of both reagents to the copper sites, or to full saturation of the coordination positions of both types of copper by their respective protein ligands.

However, it was found that during oxidase function the 25% cuprous fraction did react with the bathocuproine reagent to form a stable 1:1 complex directly on the enzyme. This finding provides direct evidence for a modification of the protein's conformation during catalytic function, such as to expose the previously inaccessible cuprous sites to the reagent. A comparative study of this bathocuproine-modified enzyme with the native enzyme made possible an evaluation of the precise role played by each type of copper during oxidase function. The results presented in Table IX clearly show that the 25% cuprous fraction is *not* directly involved in either the blue color or oxidase activity of the enzyme.

Initially, the systems 1–4 shown in the table contained the same amounts of enzyme and substrate which allowed rapid aerobic function at pH 5.6; system 5 contained an equivalent amount of resting enzyme (i.e., no substrate present) and was included as a control. Systems 1 and 3 show the effect of oxygenation on the bathocuproine-modified enzyme, while systems 2 and 4 show the effect of oxygenation on the native enzyme. From the A_{480}, values, as shown in column 6 of the table, it can be seen that systems 1 and 3 contained enough bathocuproine to fully complex the 25% cuprous fraction directly on the functioning enzyme. After a 3-hour incubation under the prescribed initial conditions, pure oxygen was bubbled into systems 3 and 4 to regenerate the oxidized form of the enzyme. It is to be noted that this oxygenation fully restored the blue color in both the modified and native cases, as shown by the A_{605} for systems 3 and 4 relative to the control system 5. It should also be noted that the A_{480} in system 3 remained unchanged after oxygenation, relative to system 1 which was unoxygenated. Hence, the 25% cuprous fraction which was complexed by the

TABLE IX

SHOWING THE NONINVOLVEMENT OF THE 25% Cu⁺ FRACTION OF ASCORBATE OXIDASE IN EITHER BLUE COLOR OR OXIDASE ACTIVITY AT pH 5.8[a]

System[b] (5.0 ml)	Oxidase Cu (μg)	BCS (mg)	AH$_2$ (mg)	Final treatment[c]	A_{480}	A_{605}	Final color	Recovery after exhaustive dialysis Activity (%)	Prosthetic Cu (%)
1	14.4	2.82	5.28	Unoxygenated	0.051[d]	0.010	Yellow	—	95
2	14.4	None	5.28	Unoxygenated	0.002	0.004	Colorless	—	99
3	14.4	2.82	5.28	Oxygenated	0.048[d]	0.058	Green	92	109
4	14.4	None	5.28	Oxygenated	0.003	0.058	Blue	91	109
5	14.4	2.82	None	Control	0	0.060	Blue	86	108

[a] After Poillon and Dawson (105).

[b] Systems 1–4 were aerobic, so that normal oxidase functions occurred, i e , substrate presumably totally oxidized very rapidly.

[c] After 3 hours incubation at refrigerator temperature systems 3 and 4 were oxygenated by bubbling pure O$_2$ into them; this treatment regenerated the characteristic blue color.

[d] Corresponds to approximately 20% of the total prosthetic copper reactive as Cu⁺ by BCS complexation during oxidase function, assuming Cu⁺: BCS stoichiometry of 1:1.

TABLE X

Summary of the Heterogeneity of the Prosthetic Copper in Ascorbate Oxidase and the Unique Role of Each Type in the Over-all Behavior of the Enzyme[a]

Copper type	Valence state	Role
Functional	75% Cu^{2+} (6 atoms/mole)	Blue color and oxidase activity
Nonfunctional	25% Cu^+ (2 atoms/mole)	Produces H_2O_2 by a slow, secondary copper catalysis during normal oxidase function
	Ratio of Cu^{2+} to Cu^+ = 3:1	

[a] After Poillon and Dawson (100, 105).

bathocuproine reagent cannot be directly involved in the enzyme's blue chromophore at 605 mμ.

In order to determine whether the same type of relationship existed between the cuprous component and the oxidase activity of the enzyme, systems 3 and 4 were exhaustively dialyzed against phosphate-citrate buffer at pH 5.8. It can be seen from column 9 in the table that essentially full activity was recovered in both systems. Since system 3 had approximately one quarter of its prosthetic copper tied up in the stable cuprous bathocuproine complex, it can be concluded that this same 25% cuprous fraction does *not* participate directly in the enzyme's oxidase activity. The unique role played by each type of prosthetic copper in the over-all behavior of ascorbate oxidase is summarized in Table X.

Recently a sample of the highly purified oxidase (specific activity, 3400 units per milligram, copper content 0.33%) has been examined in the EPR apparatus by Beinert. In a personal communication he has reported that the native enzyme in its oxidized state exhibits two superimposed signals accounting for about 75–80% of the total copper in the form of two different Cu^{2+} species; one comprising about 25% and the other about 50%. The remainder of the copper is Cu^+. Although this is a preliminary result, and involves only one specimen of the enzyme, the substantial agreement with the chemical findings described above seems worthy of emphasis.

VIII. Molecular Properties

Most of the investigations that have been concerned with the structural features of purified ascorbate oxidase, such as the color, the nature of the copper bonds as studied using radioactive ^{64}Cu, the amino acid composition, the stability, homogeneity, and molecular weight of the protein, the possible role of —SH groups, etc. have been relatively recently reviewed (10). However, some very recent observations concerning conformational changes in the protein, and dissociation of the protein into subunits under certain conditions, seem appropriate for consideration.

An ultracentrifugal investigation has been made of the alterations that occur in the protein of purified ascorbate oxidase that are associated with the removal of the copper under acidic conditions, and also under basic conditions (116). Another paper reports sedimentation velocity studies on the reduced and inactivated enzyme, and the apoenzyme after removal of copper by dialysis against cyanide (93).

In the first investigation (116) a number of samples of the purified oxidase were acidified to pH 3.6 at 0°. A rapid bleaching and loss of copper occurred during a 30-minute to 3-hour incubation period. The sedimentation pattern of each sample, taken in the analytical ultracentrifuge at 0°, revealed a mixture of two slower components (S_{20} = 4.4 and 6.3) and some faster sedimenting (apparently aggregated) material. A control sample of the native enzyme showed only one component with an S_{20} = 6.1. Within moderately short times at pH 3.6 and 0° the amount of 6.3 S material (presumably the native enzyme) decreased and the 4.4 S component increased. After longer times (6–12 hours) the fast sedimenting (aggregated) material appeared and the amount of 4.4 S began to decrease. Copper and activity assays of the bleached enzyme, after removal of the dissociated copper ions with Chelex resin, consistently showed greater loss of activity (about 95%) than copper (about 83%). It was suggested that the nonparallel relationship of the copper and activity, also observed by Penton (94, 113), may result from the fact that catalytic function requires the concerted and cooperative interaction of prosthetic copper atoms in groups of two or more.

Raising the pH of the native enzyme at 0° to pH 10–11 resulted in a clear, colorless, stable solution without loss in bound copper. The activity of the alkali-treated enzyme was about 25% that of the untreated enzyme and remained stable for long periods of time. Examination of the alkali-treated enzyme in the ultracentrifuge revealed a single boundary sedimenting at 2.8 S. However, direct molecular weight determinations revealed some heterogeneity of the sample. The major component was calculated to have an M_Z of about 65,000 and the other component (comprising less than 15% of the protein) an M_Z of about 110,000. It was concluded that the 2.8 S component, having a molecular weight of 65,000, was a subunit arising by dissociation of the native enzyme under alkaline conditions. Thus the native enzyme appears to be composed of more than one polypeptide chain.

The identity of the 2.8 S component as a subunit of 65,000 molecular weight allowed the tentative conclusion that the 4.4 S component observed in acid solution was an uncoiled or unfolded conformation form of the enzyme, not a dissociated subunit. It is of particular interest that dissociation of the enzyme and loss of blue color occur in the alkali-treated enzyme without loss of copper. Apparently the unique folding of the polypeptide chains in the native enzyme has much to do with the characteristic blue color and the oxidase activity.

It may be recalled that the enzyme's 25% Cu+ fraction could be complexed by BCS during oxidase function and that the fully active enzyme could be regenerated by subsequent oxygenation without disturbing the Cu+-BCS chromophore (105). It was therefore of interest to determine whether or not the BCS-modified enzyme behaved analogously to the native enzyme in terms of copper dissociation at pH 3.6. From the data shown in Table XI it is apparent that in the BCS-modified enzyme, the 25% Cu+ fraction is completely stabilized against dissociation at pH 3.6. This is in direct contrast with the native enzyme, which loses all of its copper under identical conditions (room temperature) in about 7 hours.

In the second investigation (93) experiments were performed to compare the sedimentation patterns of native (oxidized) enzyme with (a) bleached (reduced) enzyme in the presence of excess substrate under

TABLE XI

STABILIZATION OF THE 25% Cu+ IN ASCORBATE OXIDASE AT
pH 3.6 BY COMPLEXING WITH BCS[a,b]

Time at pH 3.6	Cu content (μg/ml)	Protein (mg/ml)	% Cu	% of original Cu remaining
10 min	1.54	0.75	0.20	55
5 hr	0.58	0.70	0.08	22
20 hr	0.50	0.62	0.08	22

[a] After Clark, Poillon, and Dawson (116).

[b] A sample of ascorbate oxidase (specific activity, 2450 units/mg and copper content 0.36%) was modified with BCS in the presence of ascorbic acid at pH 5.6 as previously described (105). After oxygenation, the green enzyme solution was dialyzed against McIlvaine's buffer, pH 5.6, to remove excess BCS, substrate, and oxidation products. The solution was then acidified to pH 3.6 room temperature (26°). The assays were made after removing dissociated copper by equilibration with Chelex resin.

anaerobic conditions, (b) enzyme which, while functioning, had been
substantially inactivated by H_2O_2 addition under aerobic conditions, and
(c) apoenzyme prepared by dialysis against cyanide. The ultracentrifugal
analyses showed all of the proteins to have essentially identical sedimentation coefficients. The data indicated that gross structural changes in the
protein moiety had not occurred under the different conditions to which
the enzyme had been exposed. This point is of particular significance in
respect to the copper-free apoenzyme because it strongly suggests that the
prosthetic copper does not have a direct role in maintaining the conformational structure of ascorbate oxidase.

IX. Summary

In this review, particular attention has been given to the results and conclusions of investigations, completed during the past 6 years, that have been
primarily concerned with the chemistry of the isolated and purified copper
protein, ascorbate oxidase. The reader is also provided with a complete
bibliography of the publications, appearing during the same period, that
have been concerned mainly with the metabolic function of the enzyme in
a wide variety of plants and microorganisms.

New information concerning the purification, characterization, specificity, and reaction intermediates of the enzyme is followed by a presentation
of new data and ideas involving the enzyme's inactivation, deactivation,
and inhibition. Such studies have provided important clues for an improved understanding of the nature and mode of action of the enzyme,
particularly in regard to the role of its prosthetic copper. The development of a technique for preparing the copper free apoenzyme and restoring it
to essentially full activity and copper content provides a promising out-
look for continuing investigations of the structural features of the copper-
protein bond.

A discussion of the state of copper in the enzyme reviews recent investigations employing valence-specific copper chelating agents. These
studies, and a recent EPR observation, have revealed that the copper in
the native (oxidized) enzyme exists in a mixed valence state; $Cu^{2+}:Cu^+ =$
$3:1$. The experiments with chelating agents have shown that the eight
copper atoms of the enzyme molecule are not structurally and functionally equivalent. Only six of the atoms, those in the Cu^{2+} state, are involved in the color and activity of the enzyme. The other two atoms, in the
Cu^+ state, appear to have no enzymatic function.

The review concludes with a discussion of the molecular properties of the
enzyme. Recent ultracentrifugal investigations have established a molec-

ular weight of 134,000–140,000 for the native enzyme and have indicated that when the copper is removed under acidic conditions a conformational change (presumably unfolding) in the protein occurs. When exposed to alkaline pH the enzyme appears to dissociate into subunits. The apoenzyme has the same sedimentation pattern and coefficient as the native enzyme, and no gross structural change appears to occur in the enzyme as the result of its reduction by substrate and inactivation by H_2O_2.

ACKNOWLEDGMENTS

The author wishes to give credit and express his sincere appreciation and gratitude to all the graduate students and postdoctoral associates who have collaborated with him in investigations on ascorbate oxidase during the past 25 years. They are H. G. Steinman, W. H. Powers, S. R. Ames, M. F. Mallette, M. Joselow, W. B. Tarpley, G. Cohen, R. J. Magee, N. Benhamou, D. M. Kirschenbaum, G. R. Stark, J. Dayan, B. W. Greenwald, W. N. Poillon, Z. Penton, J. B. Wilson, and P. W. Tang. He is especially indebted to Mr. Stanley Lewis for his loyal and skillful service in the isolation and purification of the enzyme during the entire period.

REFERENCES

1. Dawson, C. R., and Magee, R. J., *in* S. P. Colowick and N. O. Kaplan (eds.), "Methods in enzymology," Vol. II, Academic Press Inc., New York, 1955, p. 831.
2. Racker, E., *Biochim. Biophys. Acta*, **9**, 577 (1952).
3. Cohen, G., Ph.D. thesis, Columbia University (1954).
4. Szent-Györgyi, A., *Biochem. J.*, **22**, 1387 (1928).
5. Tauber, H., *Ergebn. Enzymforsch.*, **7**, 301 (1938).
6. Dawson, C. R., and Mallette, M. F., *in* M. L. Anson and J. T. Edsall (eds.) "Advances in protein chemistry," Vol. II, Academic Press Inc., New York, 1945, p. 224.
7. Dawson, C. R., *in* W. D. McElroy and B. Glass (eds.), "Copper metabolism," The Johns Hopkins Press, Baltimore, 1950, p. 18.
8. Dawson, C. R., and Tarpley, W. B., *in* J. B. Summer and K. Myrbäck (eds.), "The enzymes," Vol. II, Part I, Academic Press Inc., New York, 1951, p. 491.
9. Dawson, C. R., *Ann. N. Y. Acad. Sci.*, **88**, 353 (1960).
10. Stark, G. R., and Dawson, C. R., *in* P. D. Boyer, H. Lardy, and K. Myrbäck (eds.), "The enzymes," Vol. VIII, Academic Press Inc., New York, 1963, p. 297.
11. Osaki, S., Walter, C., and Frieden, E., *Biochem. Biophys. Res. Communs.*, **12**, 1 (1963).
12. Osaki, S., McDermott, J. A., and Frieden, E., *J. Biol. Chem.*, **239**, 3570 (1964).
13. Hayashi, N., *Bitamin*, **19**, 64, (1960).
14. Morell, A. G., Aisen, P., and Scheinberg, I. H., *J. Biol. Chem.*, **237**, 3455 (1962).
15. Vasiléva, L. A., *Izvest. Moldavsk. Filiala, Akad. Nauk S.S.S.R.*, **5**, 51 (1958).
16. Pankratova, E. M., *Fiziol. Rastenii, Acad. Nauk S.S.S.R.*, **7**, 584 (1960).
17. Plotnikova, N. I., *Uch. Zap. Tomsk. Gos. Univ.*, **44**, 190 (1962).
18. Kropacheva, F. G., *Materialy Nauchn. Konf. Omskogo Gos. Ped. Inst. Omsk. Sb.*, p. 181 (1963).
19. Mitsui, S., and Miyawaki, K., *Nippon Dojo-Hiryogaku Zasshi*, **31**, 343 (1960).
20. Fric, F., and Majernik, O., *Phytopathol. Z.*, **50**, 17 (1964).

21. Mertz, D., *Dissertation Abstracts*, **20**, 4501 (1960).
22. Zinovév, L. S., and Naumova, N. P. *Rostovye Veshchestva i ikh Rolĭ Protses. Rosta i Razvitiya Rastenii, Akad. Nauk S.S.S.R., Vsesoyuz. Botan. Obshchestvo, Materialy Kollok.*, *Leningrad*, p. 61 (1959).
23. Petinov, N. S., and Malysheva, K. M., *Fiziol. Rastenii, Akad. Nauk S.S.S.R.*, **7**, 553 (1960).
24. Mertz, D., *Am. J. Botany*, **48**, 405 (1961).
25. Serova, Z. Y., *Dokl. Akad. Nauk Belorussk. S.S.R.*, **6**, 805 (1962).
26. Funderburk, H. H., Jr., and Davis, D. E., *Weeds*, **11**, 101 (1963).
27. Grebinskii, S. O., Iovleva, N. D., and Popovich, I. V., *Biol. Deistvie Radiatsii, Lĭosk. Gos. Univ.*, **1**, 84 (1962).
28. Vorisek, V., *Sb. Vysoke Skoly Zemedel. Brne. Rada A*, **2**, 197 (1963).
29. Mertz, D., *Plant Physiol.*, **39**, 398 (1964).
30. Kovalskaya, E. M., *Fiziol. Ustoichivosti Rastenii (Moscow, Akad. Nauk S.S.S.R.) Sbornik*, p. 668 (1960).
31. Gütmanis, K., *Latvijas PSR Zinātnu Akad. Vēstis*, **3**, 73 (1959).
32. Key, J. L., *Plant Physiol.*, **37**, 349 (1962).
33. Dobrolyubskii, O. K., *Dokl. Akad. Nauk S.S.S.R.*, **128**, 1080 (1959).
34. Dobrolyubskii, O. K., and Ryzha, V. K., *Biokhim. Vinodeliya, Sbornik*, **6**, 171 (1960).
35. Dobrolyubskii, O. K., *Sadovodstvo Vinogradarstvo i Vinodelie Moldavii*, **15**, 26 (1960).
36. Dobrolyubskii, O. K., and Slavvo, A. V., *Fiziol. Rastenii, Akad. Nauk S.S.S.R.*, **8**, 355 (1961).
37. Dobrolyubskii, O. K., and Ryzha, V. K., *Fiziol. Rastenii, Akad. Nauk S.S.S.R.*, **9**, 53 (1962).
38. Dobrolyubskii, O. K., *Dokl. Akad. Nauk S.S.S.R.*, **114**, 1174 (1962).
39. Dobrolyubskii, O. K., *Fiziol. Rastenii, Akad. Nauk S.S.S.R.*, **10**, 319 (1963).
40. Mininberg, S. V., *Visn. Kiivśk Univ., Ser. Biol.*, **1**, 42 (1964).
41. Mininberg, S. V., *Pratsi. Botan. Sadu, Kiivśk. Dersh. Univ.*, **26**, 81 (1962).
42. Henke, O., *Phytopathol. Z.*, **47**, 314 (1963).
43. Belkin, N. I., *Effektivnost Udobr. v Usloviyakh Moldavii Sb.*, **2**, 192 (1962).
44. Gukova, M. M., and Faustov, V. V., *Dokl. Mosk. Selśkokhoz. Akad. im K. A. Timiryazeva*, **70**, 37 (1961).
45. Vines, H. M., and Oberbacher, M. F., *Plant Physiol.*, **38**, 333 (1963).
46. Vines, H. M., and Oberbacher, M. F., *Proc. Florida State Hort. Soc.*, **75**, 283 (1962).
47. Nultsch, W., *Angew. Botan.*, **33**, 163 (1959).
48. Nagata, Y., *Gifu Daigaku Nogukufu Kenkyu Hokoku*, **12**, 145 (1960).
49. Tomiyama, K., Takakuwa, M., Takase, N., and Sakai, R., *Phytopathol. Z.*, **37**, 113 (1960).
50. Govorov, P. M., and Torgovkina, E. E., *Sb. Nauchn. Rabot., Vses. Biokhim. Obshchestvo Yakutsk. Otd. Akad. Nauk S.S.S.R., Yakutsk*, p. 25 (1963).
51. Mitsui, S., and Miyawaki, K., *Nippon Dojo-Hiryogaku Zasshi*, **31**, 403 (1960).
52. Yoshida, T., and Takahashi, J., *Nippon Dojo-Hiryogaku Zasshi*, **31**, 423 (1960).
53. Fujimura, K., Kawabata, M., Osaki, K., and Kyoto, S. I., *Japan Potassium Symp., Papers 3rd Japan Potassium Congr., Tokyo*, p. 26 (1959).
54. Fejer, D. F., and Petrasovich, I., *Acta Botan. Acad. Sci. Hung.*, **9**, 1 (1963).
55. Fujimura, K., Osaki, K., and Ikeda, S., *Mem. Research Inst., Food Sci., Kyoto Univ.*, **20**, 44 (1960).
56. Yenson, M., *Bull. Fac. Med. Istanbul*, **20**, 216 (1959).
57. Dvorak, M., *Biol. Plant., Acad. Aci. Bohemoslov.*, **5**, 287 (1963).

58. Spurr, H. W., *Dissertation Abstracts*, **22**, 1790 (1961).
59. Spurr, H. W., Hildebrandt, A. C., and Riker, A. J., *Phytopathology*, **52**, 1079 (1962).
60. Gutmanis, K., *Tautsaimnieciba Derigie Angi, Latvijas PSR Zinatnu Akad. Botan. Darzs.*, **2**, 167 (1963).
61. Okuntsov, M. M., and Aksenova, O. F., *Fiziol. Ustoichivosti Rastenii (Moscow, Akad. Nauk S.S.S.R.) Sbornik*, p. 113 (1960).
62. Guenther, G., *Ber. Deut. Botan. Ges.*, **72**, 25 (1959).
63. Recalde, L., and Carlos Blesa, A., *Anales. Edafol. Agrobiol. (Madrid)*, **20**, 378 (1961).
64. Sapozhnikova, E. V., *Tr. 1-oi [Pervoi] Vses. Knof. po Biol. Aktivnym Veshchestvam Plodov i Yagod, Sverdlovsk*, p. 80 (1961).
65. Serova, Z. Y., *Dokl. Akad. Nauk Belorussk. S.S.R.*, **5**, 405 (1961).
66. Vrublevskaya, K. G., *Uch. Zap. Tomskii Gos. Univ.*, **44**, 208 (1962).
67. Mache, R., *Compt. Rend.*, **256**, 1583 (1963).
68. Hampton, R. E., *Phytopathology*, **53**, 497 (1963).
69. Parshikov, V. M., *Dopovidi Akad. Nauk Ukr. S.S.R.*, p. 338 (1958).
70. Booth, V. H., and Constable, B. J., *Biochem. J.*, **76**, 206 (1960).
71. Chemodanova, E. I., *Voprosy Vitamin., Altaisk. Gosudarst. Med. Inst.*, p. 287 (1959).
72. Mayer, A. M., *Physiol. Plantarum*, **11**, 75 (1958).
73. Palmer, R. D., and Porter, W. K., *Weeds*, **7**, 511 (1959).
74. Bella, F., Kiszel, M., and Gellert, K., *Elelmezesi Ipar*, **14**, 294 (1960).
75. Gopalachari, N. C., *Indian J. Exptl. Biol.*, **1**, 98 (1963).
76. Aksenov, N. P., *Fiziol Rastenii, Akad. Nauk S. S. S. R.*, **10**, 166 (1963).
77. Mattison, N. L., *Kompleksn. Izuch. Fiziol. Aktivn. Veshchestv. Nizshikh Rast. Akad. Nauk S.S.SR., Botan. Inst.*, p. 107 (1961).
78. Newcomb, E. H., *Physiol. Plantarum*, **13**, 459 (1960).
79. Kolesnikov, P. A., and Einor, L. O., *Ukr. Botan. Zh.*, **18**, 46 (1961).
80. White, G. A., and Smith, F. G., *Nature*, **190**, 187 (1961).
81. White. G. A., and Smith, F. G., *Plant Physiol.*, **37**, 742 (1962).
82. Lillehoj, F. B., and Smith, F. G., *Proc. Iowa Acad. Sci.*, **69**, 193 (1962).
83. Volk, W. A., and Larsen, J. L., *Biochim. Biophys. Acta*, **67**, 576 (1963).
84. Mitina, V. S., and Rubin, V. I., *Trudy Saratov. Med. Inst.*, **26**, 254 (1959).
85. Tokuyama, K., Clark, E. E., and Dawson, C. R., *Biochemistry*, **4**, 1362 (1965).
86. Dunn, F. J., and Dawson, C. R., *J. Biol. Chem.*, **189**, 485 (1951).
87. Magee, R. J., and Dawson, C. R., *Arch. Biochem. Biophys.*, **99**, 338 (1962).
88. Stark, G. R., and Dawson, C. R., *J. Biol. Chem.*, **237**, 712 (1962).
89. Kirschenbaum, D. M., Ph. D. thesis, Columbia University (1956).
90. Kirschenbaum, D. M., and Dawson, C. R., *Biochim. Biophys. Acta*, **73**, 655 (1963).
91. Dayan, J., and Dawson, C. R., unpublished observations.
92. Greenwald, B. W., Ph. D. thesis, Columbia University, (1962).
93. Clark, E. E., Poillon, W. N., and Dawson, C. R., *Biochim. Biophys. Acta*, **118**, 82 (1966).
94. Penton, Z. G., and Dawson, C. R., *in* T. E. King, H. S. Mason, and M. Morrison (eds.), "Oxidases and related redox systems," John Wiley and Sons, Inc., New York, 1965, p. 222.
95. Yamazaki, I., and Piette, L. H., *Biochim. Biophys. Acta*, **50**, 62 (1961).
96. Nakamura, T., *Biochem. Biophys. Res. Communs.*, **2**, 111 (1960).
97. Yamazaki, I., *J. Biol. Chem.*, **237**, 224 (1962).
98. Sack, K. A., Staudinger, Hg., and Zubrzycki, Z. J., *Biochem. Z.*, **335**, 177 (1961).

99. Tokuyama, K., and Dawson, C. R., *Biochim. Biophys. Acta*, **56**, 427 (1962).
100. Poillon, W. N., and Dawson, C. R., *Biochim. Biophys. Acta*, **77**, 37 (1963).
101. Sternman, M. D., and Foster, J. F., *J. Am. Chem. Soc.*, **78**, 3652 (1956).
102. Norman, C. L., and Doody, E., *J. Am. Chem. Soc.*, **76**, 221 (1954).
103. Faller, I. L., Urquhart, J. M., and Klotz, I. M., *J. Phys. Coll. Chem.*, **54**, 18 (1950).
104. Fernelius, W. C., Gonick, E., and Douglas, S., *Technical Report to O.N.R.*, Oct. 15, 1959.
105. Poillon, W. N., and Dawson, C. R., *Biochim. Biophys. Acta*, **77**, 27 (1963).
106. Pauling, L., "The nature of the chemical bond," 2nd ed., Cornell University Press, Ithaca, New York, 1948.
107. Wells, A. F., "Structural inorganic chemistry," 2nd ed., Oxford University Press, 1945.
108. Cannan, R. K., Palmer, A. H., and Kibrick, A. C., *J. Biol. Chem.*, **142**, 803 (1942).
109. Laskowski, M., and Scheraga, H. A., *J. Am. Chem. Soc.*, **76**, 6305 (1954).
110. Steinhardt, J., and Zaiser, E. M., *Advances in Protein Chemistry*, **10**, 151 (1955).
111. Frieden, C., and Alberty, R. A., *J. Biol. Chem.*, **212**, 859 (1955).
112. Koshland, D. E., *Advances in Enzymology*, **22**, 25 (1960).
113. Penton, Z., Ph. D. thesis, Columbia University (1964).
114. Diehl, H., and Smith, G. F., "The copper reagents," G. Frederick Smith Chemical Co., Columbus, Ohio, 1958, p. 39.
115. Peterson, R., and Bollier, M., *Anal. Chem.*, **27**, 1195 (1955).
116. Clark, E. E., Poillon, W. N., and Dawson, C. R., *Biochim. Biophys. Acta*, **118**, 72 (1966).

DISCUSSION

DR. AISEN: The agreement between the chemical and physical methods for determining the valence state of copper in native protein is very striking. Nonetheless, it is difficult for me to be confident that the electronic structure of copper after it's knocked off the acid-denatured protein is essentially unaltered. I will, therefore, ask for comment from two sources, Dr. Beinert and Dr. Hemmerich, on this problem, which is of great interest to me.

DR HEMMERICH: I think I am not in agreement that bathocuproine can be assigned as a valence-specific agent. It has analytical specificity, in that it gives a red color for its cuprous compound, but it also has a distinct affinity toward Cu^{2+}, which, however, doesn't lead to a colored complex.

On the other hand, if you add even a real valence-specific agent to a copper protein, the pattern of Cu^{2+} to Cu^+ might be changed, because of the fact that mercaptide may be present. You cannot make a conclusion from the chemical determination.

DR AISEN: I agree with you. You would say, then, that the agreement between the chemical and spin resonance studies is fortuitous.

DR. BEINERT: I don't think I have much more to add. I have always maintained in recent years that the chemical determination of valences of iron and copper, the metals with which we are mainly concerned, is just not safe for reasons Dr. Hemmerich has pointed out. They may in this case agree, but they may also not agree. It is true that integration of the EPR signal gave us a recovery of cupric copper right around 80% of total copper in ascorbate oxidase, in agreement with chemical determinations, and I think from our experience that we do better than having an error of 20% with copper.

DR. AISEN: Do you know any examples, Dr. Beinert, where there is a striking disagreement between the chemical and the physical methods of determination?

DR. BEINERT: Well, cytochrome oxidase is a case where the EPR signal just simply shows only 40% of the copper as cupric copper, unless you denature the enzyme, whereas the chemical determination shows all as cupric.

DR. MORELL: The chemical determination in the presence of p-CMB shows only 25% of the copper in ceruloplasmin in the cuprous state while EPR shows that approximately 50% is cupric.

DR. AISEN: There is no disagreement here if we say that we are detecting minimal rather than absolute amounts of Cu^{2+}. It's always possible that because of exchange interactions you won't get all the Cu^{2+} by the spin resonance.

DR. SCHEINBERG: Nobody thinks there is more than 50% cupric copper in ceruloplasmin, and this is an example of what you are saying, that there is an unavoidable error inherent in chemical methods. It's really incidental whether they indicate too much or too little cupric copper; EPR and proton relaxation rate studies in several laboratories agree that approximately 50% of the copper is cupric.

DR. AISEN: There is no evidence that there isn't more than 50% cupric copper in ceruloplasmin, but on the other hand, if I wish to say that 25% of the copper is cupric but coupled, nobody can prove me wrong now.

DR. SCHEINBERG: I thought one of the big reasons the proton relaxation studies were done was that any broadening of the EPR line that might make it difficult to integrate would not apply to a PRR study. That was one of the reasons why we were quite confident that there is not more than 50%.

DR. BLUMBERG: The purely hypothetical conjecture that Dr. Aisen raised was that, of the 50% of the copper atoms in ceruloplasmin that we were not observing at all in studying the EPR and proton relaxation rate, some might exist formally as a cupric-cupric pair spin-coupled together. There are many inorganic examples of this. The pairs could be completely magnetically inert, and chemically inert as far as the valence state determination is concerned. It's not detected as cuprous. It's not detected by EPR. It might just be there as baggage. But I repeat that it is a hypothetical conjecture.

DR. AISEN: I meant to keep it hypothetical, but it would be diamagnetic nevertheless by both the EPR and proton relaxation studies.

DR. DAWSON: I would like to defend one aspect of the chemical method, or at least reemphasize a couple of things. First, the native protein does not react with bathocuproine. The only time you get a reaction, a formation of this complex, is when the enzyme is functioning. When the enzyme functions, a lot of things get exposed. This is when you get radioactive exchange. This is when you get hydrogen peroxide damage. Presumably things that are not available in the resting enzyme become available.

We have demonstrated that if you leave EDTA out in the cuprous assay, you indeed do get cuprous values that are larger. You can do a time curve on this, vary the amount of EDTA and vary the time, and actually show that something is happening to the copper that is removed. In the presence of a large excess of EDTA, you go right back down to a zero point which is the 25% value.

There is no agreement on my score at all against the concept that things might be happening to this copper when it comes off the protein. This is very obvious to any chemist, I believe. But I think our data, particularly since in one example it is supported by EPR measurements, makes me feel a lot more confident about the valence determination.

DR. CURZON: Cuprous copper may be higher in the absence of EDTA, perhaps because EDTA is itself interfering with the determination of cuprous copper. It would tend to cause cuprous copper to change to cupric because of the high stability of the Cu^{2+}–EDTA complex.

DR. FRIEDEN: I think there is a major discrepancy in the chemical and EPR method for hemocyanin. My recollection is that EPR shows no signal, but the chemical method consistently has given positive results for Cu^{2+} according to Klotz and Klotz [Science, **121**, 477 (1955); **122**, 559 (1955)].

DR. AISEN: I think that is not necessarily correct. This is an argument that Dr. Williams was in in Science [**122**, 558 (1955)] 10 years ago and maybe we could direct it to him.

DR. WILLIAMS: You have no method for "valence" in these complexes. There isn't a method for valence states of the kind you are trying to establish; that's all. There never was one, and there never will be one. What is the valence of Cu in a *diamagnetic* cluster of two copper ions of any formal charge you like?

DR. AISEN: So we are back to 10 years ago.

DR. FRIEDEN: We have for a long time contended that the word "preferential" would be better to describe the Cu^+ and Cu^{2+} reagents; that's probably what people mean. Some years ago we were actually able to identify and study the Cu^{2+} complex of neocuproin, 2, 9-dimethyl-1, 10-phenanthroline, which, of course, is very strongly preferential for Cu^+. But you can certainly see the other complex.

DR. FRIEDEN: Everybody is so careful about eliminating copper ion when they use ascorbate as substrate, and for this the use of Chelex is a great advantage. As I recall it was introduced by Morell, Aisen, and Scheinberg [J. Biol. Chem, **237**, 3455 (1962)]. I wonder if we have perhaps not been neglecting to take a careful look at the presence of iron. This was raised in connection with ceruloplasmin some years ago by Dr. Curzon [Biochem. J., **79**, 656 (1961)], who observed the intense stimulation by iron on the activity of ceruloplasmin toward the aryl diamine substrates. Very recently we have observed a 20-fold stimulation of Fe^{2+} on the ascorbate oxidase activity of ceruloplasmin. I wonder if there has been anything observed about the presence of the ferrous ion in the ascorbate oxidase system.

DR. DAWSON: We have not looked for it.

DR. CURZON: I was interested in the effect of mild acid pH on removing copper from ascorbate oxidase. Was this reversible?

DR. DAWSON: Yes, they are reversible in part. It depends on how long you wait before you attempt to reverse it and on how much additional copper you put in. Up to a certain point it can be reversed.

DR. CURZON: I had very similar results with ceruloplasmin. Again a pK of 3.8 or 3.7 is involved [*Biochem. J.*, **151,** 97 (1965)].

DR. MASON: I would like to ask Dr. Dawson a question. Dr. Yamazaki several years ago showed by EPR that ascorbate oxidase removes one equivalent from ascorbate as the first step. You represented the first step in your Fig. 1 as a 2-equivalent oxidation, I would like to ask what your reservations are about the results of the EPR studies. I would like to comment that since the oxidation is a 1-equivalent oxidation, presumably only a single copper atom is reduced on the enzyme. If I understand the new spin resonance results correctly, there are six active atoms of copper, and there are two kinds of copper among those six atoms. I would like to suggest that in the mechanism of enzyme action one atom of this copper removes a single reducing equivalent from ascorbate, and two atoms transfer the reducing equivalent to oxygen. Two such three-atom centers are present.

DR. DAWSON: I have no reservations on that score at all. I agree completely. As a matter of fact, I did not give the mechanism. I simply gave the over-all reaction products isolated. We have published in dissertation form a mechanism that is completely in agreement with the one-electron study. I think the data there are perfectly sound and reasonable.

Preliminary Remarks on Polyphenoloxidase

H. S. MASON

It is interesting that at the present time no single ligand of copper in any copper enzyme has been identified. Thus the basic information required to understand how copper proteins act is not at hand. If a state of mind can characterize this meeting, it is that copper proteins have a wide range of function for structural reasons which are not understood.

Polyphenoloxidase, or tyrosinase, is a cuprous protein that certainly belongs in this class of mysterious catalysts. The enzyme is a very interesting one for many reasons. It has been known since 1896, when the expression "oxidase" was first used by Bertrand to describe it.

It is the enzyme responsible for the formation of the brown, red, and tan pigments—melanins—which occur in the skin, eyes, and feathers of animals throughout the phylogenetic scale, and its action is connected with grave social, medical, and economic problems.

In addition, it is an enzyme which Kubowitz (1) established as containing essential copper by removing the copper, showing that the activity was lost, and then putting the copper back in and showing that activity was regained. With our present day knowledge of the relationship between protein conformation and catalytic activity, we recognize that this experiment shows only that copper is associated with the over-all activity, but not that it is necessarily at the active site of the enzyme.

A large amount of effort has been expended on the study of polyphenol oxidase from many biological points of view; these studies have been repeatedly and extensively reviewed. The broad picture at the present time is, very briefly, this: In the presence of polyphenol oxidase, catechols are dehydrogenated and monophenols are hydroxylated. The relationship between the dehydrogenase, or catecholase, activity, and the hydroxylase, or cresolase, activity is unknown and continues to be actively debated. According to the Columbia school (2) and others, both activities are catalyzed by the enzyme. According to the school of Onslow and Robinson (3) the hydroxylase activity is not due to the enzyme molecule itself but to hydroxylation of monophenols by the orthoquinonoid product of catecholase action. Our second speaker, Dr. Kertesz, is a contemporary exponent of this idea (4).

Purifications of polyphenolase from mushroom, broad bean, *Neurospora*, potato, melanoma, and insects have all been achieved. It has been shown that isotyrosinases exist in many of these species. They can be demonstrated by starch or acrylamide gel electrophoresis, but the structural basis of isoenzymatic differences is unknown. Mushroom isotyrosinases can be interconverted, and *Neurospora* tyrosinase undergoes rapid shifting between monomer and tetramer.

The existence of unlike subunits, one largely cresolase-active and the other catecholase-active, combining in different proportions, has been advanced as an explanation of the differences that have been observed among the multiple forms of tyrosinase. Like ascorbate oxidase, discussed this morning by Dr. Dawson, polyphenoloxidase undergoes reaction in activation. Recent work has indicated that this may be due to a combination of product quinone with enzyme protein, and our first speaker, Dr. Brooks, will deal with this subject.

On the matter of mechanism of this enzyme a very great deal of speculation has appeared in print. When catechol is oxidized by polyphenoloxidase, the electron spin resonance spectrum of *o*-benzosemiquinone is observed (5). Such a free radical can be produced in two ways: (1) removal of one reducing equivalent from the substrate; or (2) equilibration of fully reduced and fully oxidized substrate.

$$AH_2 \rightarrow AH\cdot + H\cdot \text{ or its equivalent} \tag{1}$$

$$AH_2 \rightarrow A + 2H\cdot \text{ or its equivalent} \tag{2}$$

$$AH_2 + A \rightleftarrows 2AH\cdot$$

Mechanism (1) represents direct catalysis of free-radical formation, and mechanism (2) represents a two-equivalent oxidation to A, followed by a one-equivalent equilibration to two semiquinone molecules.

Thus, when a free radical is detected in the course of oxidase action, it does not always mean that the reaction is a one-equivalent oxidation-reduction.

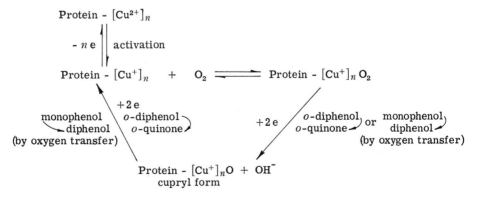

Fig. 1. Relationship between oxygen, electron donors, oxygen acceptors, and poly phenoloxidase intermediates. From Mason (6).

In the case of polyphenoloxidase it has been shown that the equilibration (mechanism 2) is the source of the observed free radicals, and that the polyphenol oxidase catalyzes the donation of two reducing equivalents from substrate and the acceptance of four reducing equivalents by oxygen. o-Benzoquinone is, as far as we can tell, the first product of polyphenolase action.

In the hydroxylation of monophenols by polyphenoloxidase atmospheric oxygen is incorporated into the substrate. The hydroxylation occurs *ortho* only to pre-existing phenol hydroxyl groups, and high catecholase and cresolase enzymes can be separated from one another. Cresolase and catecholase functions of the enzyme are reciprocally inhibited competitively by catechol and cresols, respectively. In my opinion this evidence tends to confirm the concept of a biphasic oxidation of monophenols and catechols dependent upon the active sites (Fig. 1).

At the moment the major problems in the chemistry of this enzyme include, first, discovering the basis of the difference between the isozymes; second, determining the number of copper atoms at the active sites and their ligands; and, third, detecting catalytic intermediates, the characteristics of which may explain the mechanism of the catalytic reactions.

REFERENCES

1. Kubowitz, F., *Biochem. Z.*, **299,** 32 (1939).
2. Nelson, J. M., and Dawson, C. R., *Advances in Enzymology*, **4,** 99 (1944).
3. Onslow, M. W., and Robinson, M. E., *Biochem. J.*, **22,** 1327 (1928).
4. Califarno, L., and Kertesz, D., *Enzymologia*, **6,** 233 (1939).
5. Mason, H. S., Spencer, E., and Yamazaki, I., *Biochem. Biophys. Res. Communs.*, **4,** 236 (1961).
6. Mason, H. S., *in* "Action mechanisms of some iron and copper-protein oxidases," Conference on Oxidative Metal Enzymes, Tokyo, 1957.

Aspects of Tyrosinase Chemistry[*][†]

DAVID W. BROOKS‡ AND CHARLES R. DAWSON

Department of Chemistry,
Columbia University,
New York, New York

Tyrosinase plays a rather unique role in nature because it can catalyze two different aerobic oxidation reactions. The enzyme was originally named because of its ability to catalyze the aerobic oxidation of the monophenolic amino acid tyrosine (1). Tyrosinase also shows marked catalytic activity in the oxidation of several other monophenolic substrates. Furthermore tyrosinase catalyzes the aerobic oxidation of o-dihydric phenols or catechols. It has been recognized for many years that tyrosinase is a copper protein (2) and a discussion of its chemical properties is therefore appropriate at this symposium.

Much of the early work concerning tyrosinase was performed by John M. Nelson and his students at Columbia University where ever since there has been a research group studying this enzyme.

I. General Considerations

A. Types of Activity

To provide an adequate background for the topics to be presented in this paper we shall first present a brief account of only those properties of tyrosinase that are directly concerned. Another treatment of the problems of tyrosinase chemistry appears elsewhere in this symposium (3).

The monophenolic and diphenolic activities of the enzyme have been termed cresolase and catecholase activity, respectively (4). These names were chosen because p-cresol and catechol are customarily used as laboratory substrates for the enzyme. Reliable techniques have been developed for the assay of both the cresolase and catecholase activities of tyrosinase preparations (5, 6). For any enzyme sample a particular ratio of the catecholase to cresolase activity may be determined. (One unit of either activity is defined as the amount of enzyme needed to catalyze the uptake of 10 μl

* This investigation was supported by grants from the U.S. Public Health Service (AM–3200 and AM–06994).

† Taken in part from the Doctoral Thesis of D. W. B.

‡ National Science Foundation Predoctoral Fellow in Chemistry, 1961–1965. Present address: Postdoctoral Research Associate, Department of Chemistry, Columbia University, New York, New York.

343

of O_2 per minute under optimal conditions.) Three general classes of preparations have been described on the basis of the catecholase to cresolase activity ratio (7). High cresolase preparations (cat.:cres. = 1–10) are usually dark in color and possess relatively low catecholase specific activities. Intermediate preparations (cat.:cres. = 11–40) are usually less colored and possess somewhat higher catecholase specific activities. High catecholase preparations (cat.:cres. > 40) are almost colorless and have the highest catecholase specific activities (on the order of 4,000 cat. units/mg). Several reports exist describing the purification of these various sorts of enzyme specimens (8). Quite recent reports have been devoted to the description of a polydispersity observed in tyrosinase preparations (9, 10, 11), and the possibility that several tyrosinase isozymes exist is being actively explored.

However, we wish to emphasize that no workers have yet been able to describe a satisfactory reproducible method for the isolation of a tyrosinase specimen which can be used for chemical exploration. Using various preparations, which may be classified according to the activity ratio scheme given above, two sets of experiments have been performed in these laboratories. Both of these programs yielded data which are useful in discussing the relationship between catecholase and cresolase activity. Moreover, both of these programs were concerned with tyrosinase copper, and are therefore of particular interest to this symposium.

Herein we have also reported the results of a third experimental program concerning an interesting aspect of tyrosinase chemistry. In addition to the catalytic oxidations there is one other phenomenon of particular interest associated with tyrosinase. During the course of catechol oxidation tyrosinase specimens are observed to undergo a rapid irreversible loss of activity. Since this activity loss is entirely associated with the catalytic oxidation it has been called "reaction inactivation" (12). There has been some conjecture concerning the mechanism of the inactivation reaction and the fate of enzyme copper in inactivated enzyme samples. Below we have described some recent work concerning the inactivation phenomenon.

B. Exchange Experiments Involving [64]Cu

A few years ago Dressler and Dawson reported the results of several experiments that indicated that copper–protein bonds are weakened during the catalytic function of tyrosinase (13, 14). The purpose of these experiments was to determine whether enzyme-bound copper can exchange with nonbound radioactively labeled copper in a reaction system. Enzyme samples were allowed to incubate with buffer and several substrates for a fixed period of time. The substrates (4-t-butylphenol, 4-t-butylcatechol,

TABLE I
SUMMARY OF TYPICAL EXCHANGE DATA

Substrate	Type of preparation	
	High-catecholase prep.	High-cresolase prep.
A catechol	55% exchange	30% exchange
A monophenol	30% exchange	10% exchange

4,5-dimethylphenol, and 4,5-dimethylcatechol) were chosen so that the oxidation products (the corresponding substituted o-benzoquinones) would be sufficiently stable so as not to produce interfering secondary products in the system. The number of equivalents of labeled copper added to the system was equal to the number of equivalents of protein-bound copper. Relatively small amounts of substrate were added, and incubation periods were sufficiently long so as to allow for complete oxidation of all the substrate added. Reaction mixtures, after incubation, were passed through columns of ion exchange resin which removed all of the free (nonprotein-bound) copper. The resulting effluents were then assayed for radioactivity and total copper. With these data the extent of exchange between bound and unbound copper could readily be determined. In all cases the extent of exchange in the functioning system was corrected for similar exchange with the resting system under comparable conditions (i.e., identical except for substrate). The enzyme preparations underwent relatively little exchange while resting (nonfunctional). However, as indicated by the data in Table I, a significant exchange of the bound copper in the enzyme occurred when the two types of enzyme were allowed to function catalytically on monophenolic and catecholic substrates, and it is particularly to be noted that the high cresolase enzyme showed a significantly lower exchange with both substrates.

On the basis of this evidence Dressler and Dawson suggested that two types of activity centers might exist on the enzyme, one each for the two types of catalytic ability. The cresolase sites were pictured as having "nonexchangeable" copper atoms as compared with the catecholase sites. The catechol sites were assumed to be "little or not at all" involved in the oxidation of monophenols. It has long been assumed that the oxidation of monophenols to o-benzoquinones proceeds via a catecholic intermediate (15), as in Eq. (1). Dressler and Dawson implied in their report that the oxidation of monophenols need not involve catechol intermediates as had long been thought. This matter is still very much in question (16, 17).

$$\text{(1)}$$

However, the possibility that these experiments suggest, namely that two chemically quite different types of copper atoms may coexist in the tyrosinase molecule, is indeed of interest to this symposium. This idea certainly merits further investigation.

C. Deactivation Studies

The second study referred to above was carried out by Coopersmith and Dawson (18, 19). These workers performed several deactivation experiments with the enzyme. The ones of particular interest concern the effect of hydrogen ion concentration on the resting enzyme. Tyrosinase samples were incubated with buffers of decreasing pH for fixed periods of time. The incubation mixture was then passed through an appropriate cation exchange resin, and the effluent was analyzed for copper content and both catecholase and cresolase activities. It was observed that the cresolase activity was lost at higher pH values than the catecholase activity. It was also observed that the loss of catecholase activity paralleled the loss of copper from the enzyme moiety. This result was interpreted in terms of a two-site enzyme model, and it was suggested that protonation of some group at a cresolase site occurred causing loss of cresolase activity. It appeared, however, that the copper from either type of site was equally susceptible to displacement by hydrogen ion.

These workers also observed that excess cupric ions inhibited cresolase activity. This inhibition was readily reversed by passing the mixture through a column containing an appropriate cation exchange resin. Catecholase activity was apparently unaffected by the presence of excess cupric ion. Furthermore, it was determined that in the presence of urea solutions, both of the tyrosinase activities disappeared with concurrent loss of protein-bound copper, and the deactivation was not reversed by removing urea and incubating with cupric ions.

Perhaps the most important result of this study which concerns us at this time is that all of the data obtained could be satisfactorily rationalized in terms of a tyrosinase model possessing two different activity sites on the same protein.

D. Reaction Inactivation

The contribution of the present authors concerns the tyrosinase reaction inactivation phenomenon. Very recently it has been suggested again, on the basis of new experimental data, that o-quinones are responsible for the observed tyrosinase reaction inactivation phenomenon (20). We have reviewed all of the available data concerning this subject, and have concluded that the suggested inactivation mechanism is probably correct (21). We have also demonstrated that, during the course of the reaction inactivation, copper is lost from the enzyme moiety.

Wood and Ingraham have shown that monophenolic substrate molecules become covalently bonded to the enzyme during a tyrosinase-catalyzed oxidation (20). They proposed that a nucleophilic group in the vicinity of the enzyme activity site underwent a Michael-type addition to the quinone molecules formed at that site, and thereby rendered the enzyme nonfunctional. (Such nucleophilic addition to quinone molecules has been extensively described (22).) Our present interest is to examine and attempt to rationalize all available data in terms of this quinone addition mechanism.

1. Reaction Kinetics

The reaction kinetics of enzymatic catechol oxidations have been the subject of some controversy (23, 24). We have recently reconsidered the question of reaction kinetics (21) and concluded that, regardless of the apparent order of the enzyme in an over-all reaction inactivation experiment, the order with respect to enzyme for any of the individual inactivation reactions must be first order. Once this is agreed upon we may accept the kinetic scheme proposed by Ingraham (25) with some slight modifications. This modified scheme is shown in Eqs. (2–6).

$$E + O_2 \rightarrow E_{ox} + H_2O \qquad (2)$$

$$E_{ox} + C \rightleftharpoons E_{ox}C \qquad (3)$$

$$E_{ox}C \rightleftharpoons EQ \qquad (4)$$

$$EQ \rightleftharpoons E + Q \qquad (5)$$

$$EQ \rightarrow (EQ)' \text{ inactive} \qquad (6)$$

(E = reduced enzyme, E_{ox} = oxidized enzyme, C = catechol, Q = o-quinone, and EQ' = inactive or partially active enzyme–quinone adduct.)

The most important point of this mechanism is that an enzyme–quinone product complex is assumed to be capable of breaking up to regenerate active enzyme and quinone, or the complex may form an inactive enzyme–quinone adduct. It has recently been demonstrated (21) that the observed kinetics of inactivation may be accounted for on the basis (a) that the enzyme is a heterodisperse system of tyrosinase molecules with each of the different molecular species suffering inactivation at a different rate, or (b) that a sequential mechanism is operative involving different nucleophilic species surrounding the active site of a monodisperse enzyme. In the latter case, each of the several possible enzyme–quinone adducts might be assumed to be a modified enzyme capable of catalyzing catechol oxidations albeit at different rates.

2. Modification of Substrate

It has been observed that o-quinone molecules with blocked 4 and 5 ring positions are relatively stable in aqueous systems because they do not undergo the facile nucleophilic addition reactions characteristic of o-benzoquinone (26). When 4,5-substituted catechols are used as substrates in tyrosinase-catalyzed oxidations, the usual extensive reaction inactivation is not observed (26). This observation is consistent with the quinone addition mechanism.

3. Influence of Substrate Concentration and Rate of Oxidation

It has recently been observed that the extent of reaction inactivation is quite independent of both the rate of oxidation and the initial substrate concentration (21). A fixed amount of enzyme is capable of catalyzing a fixed amount of substrate oxidation. The extent of oxidation depends on the total amount of enzyme–quinone product complex that is formed during the course of oxidation. This total amount of enzyme–quinone complex depends only on the amount of product formed. A certain fraction of the time, the irreversible inactivating reaction takes place, and the rest of the time the enzyme is regenerated. These experimental observations are consistent with the proposed mechanism.

4. Effect of Ascorbic Acid

Measurements of the inactivation phenomenon indicate that variations in the ascorbic acid concentration used for the reduction of the enzymatically produced quinone have little effect on the extent of reaction inactivation (27, 28). Since the proposed mechanism is based on an enzyme–quinone complex being critically involved in the inactivation reaction, this observation may seem inconsistent. Ascorbic acid might be expected to effect the amount of this species and therefore effect the total amount of inactivation. Thus, in terms of the addition inactivation mechanism one must suppose that ascorbic acid has no effect on this crucial intermediate, but reacts only with nonprotein-bound quinone.

5. Early Work of Nelson

Finally, we must determine whether the early inactivation experiments of Nelson and co-workers (29) can be explained in terms of the quinone addition mechanism. In a typical experiment these workers manometrically measured the total oxygen absorbed during the inactivation of a given amount of tyrosinase in the presence of a certain amount of catechol. They then repeated the experiment using the same amount of enzyme but added the catechol in two increments such that the first increment was not sufficient to account for the oxygen uptake originally observed. They then allowed the system to stand for a period of time before adding the second increment of catechol. They assumed that during this incubation period the enzyme was exposed to the quinones produced during the oxidation of the first catechol increment. Thus, when they added the second increment of catechol and obtained a total oxygen uptake for the two increments that was similar to the total uptake observed in the original experiment, they concluded that quinones (or other oxidation products) were not responsible for the inactivation phenomenon.

Although these early observations appear at first examination not to conform to the proposed quinone addition inactivation mechanism, the following consideration casts them in an entirely different light, such that they provide supporting argument rather than contradiction. The consideration just mentioned is based on the fundamental and logical premise that the effective local concentration of quinone at the active site of the functioning enzyme is undoubtedly much higher than the quinone concentration at or near the active site of the nonfunctioning tyrosinase molecule. o-Benzoquinone is a very labile molecule subject to rapid destruction by reaction with nucleophilic agents such as buffer anions and water (22). Thus, when the quinone is first formed and is still bound at the active site, it has the highest local concentration relative to the nucleophilic groups of the protein in the vicinity of the active site. Inactivation of the enzyme by covalent bonding, via the addition of one of these nucleophilic groups to the quinone, is most probable at this time, i.e., before the quinone leaves its site of formation. Once the quinone diffuses away from the protein surface [as would be the case in the nonfunctioning enzyme system of Nelson and co-workers (29)] the nucleophilic character of the aqueous solvent would be expected to completely overshadow the interaction of the enzyme protein with the quinone. The reaction of the solvent with the quinone would reduce the concentration of the quinone so rapidly that the protein–quinone interaction would be insignificant.

E. Copper Loss

Perhaps more pertinent to the interests of this symposium is the observation that some of the enzyme's copper is lost during reaction inactivation. The special techniques described below were developed in order to utilize large quantities of the enzyme in the oxidation reaction so that copper determinations would be experimentally feasible. This was accomplished by using a large volume reaction system with diluted enzyme, so as to maintain a reasonable rate of oxidation of the substrate (catechol), and then reconcentrating the enzyme after the oxidation was completed. The concentrating technique chosen included chromatography on DEAE cellulose columns.

The quantity of particular interest was the ratio of copper to protein in the enzyme sample. For a given sample, if some of the enzyme molecules had lost their copper during the reaction for whatever reason, then the ratio of copper to protein for the whole sample would decrease. It was a measure of this copper-to-protein ratio of a sample both with and without reaction inactivation that was determined.

II. Experimental

A. Materials

Reagents. All chemicals used were of the highest purity commercially available and were used without further purification. All water was obtained by distillation in a Corning glass still.

Glassware. All glassware was made copper free by rinsing first with chromic-sulfuric cleaning mixture, and then several times with copper-free water.

DEAE Cellulose Columns. DEAE cellulose was prepared for chromatography by washing with 0.5 M NaOH, and then washing with water until neutral. Two DEAE cellulose columns of 6 cm height were prepared and equilibrated with buffer (300 ml, McIlvaine's, pH 6.2, 0.0067–0.0133 M).

Reaction Mixtures. The following materials were added to a 600 ml reaction vessel in the order indicated: 20 ml buffer (McIlvaine's, pH 5.8, 0.15–0.3 M), ascorbic acid (several increments, initially 7.0 ml of a solution containing 40 mg/ml), enzyme (1.0 ml of a stock solution, usually about 10,000 catecholase units), and water (100 ml). Two reaction mixtures were prepared identically. To one of these solid catechol was added to initiate the reaction. The other reaction mixture contained no catechol and was used as a control. Both of the reaction systems were constantly stirred while in a bath maintained at about 15–20° by the addition of ice.

B. Assay

Reaction Course. There was no convenient way of determining the exact extent of the reaction at any particular time. Manometric techniques were not feasible because oxygen diffusion was always the rate-limiting process. However, once all the ascorbic acid in the system had been indirectly oxidized (via quinone reduction) the characteristic yellow color of quinone started to appear. The immediate addition of more ascorbic acid (in measured increment) allowed the reaction to proceed as desired. After it was judged by these criteria that the reaction had proceeded with the indirect oxidation of about 700 mg of ascorbic acid, Chelex resin was added to both of the systems to complex any ionic copper that had been liberated from the enzyme protein during its catalytic function. Both Chelex-containing mixtures were stirred for 5 minutes and then filtered through glass wool. The filtrates were diluted to a total volume of about 500 ml so as to reduce their ionic strength and thereby permit the absorption of protein in the solution on to the DEAE cellulose columns. They were then passed through the columns. The columns were washed with the equilibrating buffer described above, which contained sufficient ascorbic acid (about 0.4 mg/ml) to prevent quinone formation during the washing, and then with distilled water. The protein adsorbed onto the columns was then eluted with 0.5 M NaCl, and 3.0 ml fractions were collected.

Blanks. The optical densities of the colored column eluates were measured at 480 mμ in a Beckman DU spectrophotometer to provide a blank correction for the subsequent copper assay.

Copper Assay. Copper assays were performed as follows using essentially the procedure described by Poillon (30): 5.0 ml volumetric flasks containing 0.4 ml of 0.2 M HCl, 0.5 ml of hydroxylamine hydrochloride solution (5 mg/ml), 0.1 ml of BCS reagent (G. F. Smith Co., lot 294, 5.0 mg/ml), and 0.05 ml of a 1% alcoholic phenolphthalein solution were prepared. Then 2.0 ml portions of the column eluate fractions were added, each into one of these volumetric flasks, and the resulting solution was allowed to stand for 20 minutes. The solutions were then titrated with 0.1 M NaOH to a faint phenolphthalein end point. This pink color was discharged by the addition of 1.0 ml of buffer (pH 7.2, McIlvaine's, 0.1–0.2 M), and the result was diluted to 5.0 ml total volume with water. The optical density of the solutions was then measured at 480 mμ in a Beckman DU spectrophotometer, and the result was corrected for the blank.

Protein Assay. Protein was assayed according to the modified Folin procedure (30, 31, 32). Optical densities were measured at 660 mµ with a Beckman DU spectrophotometer.

Protein Control. A reaction mixture containing 200 mg of catechol (the maximal amount used in the inactivation experiments) and all of the other ingredients of the inactivation system except enzyme was passed through a DEAE cellulose column. The column was washed as described above, and then eluted with 0.5 M NaCl solution. Folin tests were performed on the eluate fractions, and the measured optical densities were the same as obtained with blanks. We conclude, therefore, that under the conditions of the protein assay, catechol was not present to interfere with the Folin test.

Protein Recovery. In typical experiments between 80 and 100% of the protein added to the reaction mixture was recovered. The major amount of both copper and protein usually appeared in one of the eluate fractions. In the table of results, the copper-to-protein ratios of this "main tube" are reported. It was possible to measure the ratio of total copper recovered to total protein recovered. In no case when the latter ratios were compared did the result differ significantly from the result of the "main tube" analysis. However, because experimental errors are large in determining very small amounts of both copper and protein, it was felt that the main tube ratio was a more reliable estimate.

C. Results and Discussion

On the basis of the experiments described above, copper-to-protein ratios of main tubes were determined for several different enzyme samples at several different catechol concentrations. The results of these experiments are shown in Table II. The copper-to-protein ratio shown is reported as the corrected BCS 480 mµ optical density divided by the Folin 660 mµ optical density. In every case presented there seems to be a definite decrease in the copper to protein ratio indicating that copper is lost from the enzyme moiety in the functioning enzyme system.

This result is very interesting and leads to some intriguing speculation. It would appear from the evidence presented, that one of the nucleophilic groups on the enzyme which becomes involved in the inactivation reaction is very critical to the maintenance of the integrity of the active site. Once this group forms an adduct with a quinone molecule, enzymatic activity must become lost because copper becomes lost. It was mentioned earlier that when the enzyme is denatured in the presence of urea, a loss of enzyme copper is observed. The particular group involved in the inactivation may be important in maintaining the integrity of the entire enzyme, either by directly bonding enzymatic copper, or by maintaining a steric structure at the active site which allows strong copper binding.

TABLE II

Loss of Copper upon Tyrosinase Inactivation

Expt.	Catechol (mg/100ml)	Enzyme	Cu/Protein Control	Cu/Protein Run	Remarks
A	200	7,560 Catecholase units/ml, 227 cresolase units/ml, 2.77 mg dry wt.	0.85	0.53	Dark enzyme preparation with large 480 mμ correction. Run time was about 2 hr.
B	200	Same as above			Same as above. Protein analyses unavailable. Recovered significantly more copper with control experiment than with run
C	200	11,000 Catecholase units/ml, 86 cresolase units/ml, 3.12 mg dry wt.	0.16	0.05	Very pure enzyme preparation. Almost colorless. 2 hr run time
D	5	Above prep. standing 4 months in cold	0.53	0.23	2 hr run time
E	5	Same as above	0.68	0.21	Same as above, to evaluate reproducibility
F	20	Same as above	0.72	0.12	9 hr run time. Total recovery was poor (about 30%) because of length of run. The Cu-to-protein ratio was determined using integrated values for recovery data
F'	20	Same as above	0.70	0.10	Same as F using main tube Cu-to-protein ratio

D. Comparison with Ascorbate Oxidase

It is interesting to compare the results obtained with tyrosinase with those of another copper protein, ascorbate oxidase. In the latter case copper is not lost from the protein upon inactivation (33). However, a mechanism for the ascorbate oxidase inactivation has been suggested which is quite different from the one suggested for tyrosinase. Ascorbate oxidase has been found to contain eight copper atoms, six of which are in the cupric state and two in the cuprous (30). The former have been shown to be responsible for the enzymatic oxidation of ascorbic acid, while the latter are involved in the secondary nonenzymatic production of small quantities of hydrogen peroxide (34). These small quantities of hydrogen peroxide are believed to be responsible for the reaction inactivation of the enzyme. Such an inactivation mechanism is not in operation with tyrosinase (35).

III. Summary

The results of several experimental programs carried out in these laboratories concerning the chemistry of copper in the enzyme tyrosinase are reviewed. Studies concerning (a) the exchange of radioactive copper with the resting and the functioning enzyme and (b) differences in the susceptibilities of the two enzymatic activities toward pH deactivation are discussed in terms of a two–active site model for tyrosinase. A mechanism, involving the interaction of protein and o-quinone, is discussed in detail for the tyrosinase inactivation reaction. The results of experiments demonstrating that some enzyme copper is lost from the enzyme moiety during catalysis of aerobic catechol oxidation are reported.

REFERENCES

1. Bertrand, G., *Compt. Rend.*, **121,** 166 (1895).
2. Kubowitz, F., *Biochem. Z.*, **299,** 32 (1939).
3. Mason, H. S., this symposium.
4. Nelson, J. M., and Dawson, C. R., *Advances in Enzymology*, **4,** 99 (1944).
5. Mallette, M. F., and Dawson, C. R., *J. Am. Chem. Soc.*, **69,** 466 (1947).
6. Miller, W. H., Mallette, M. F., Roth, L. J., and Dawson, C. R., *J. Am. Chem. Soc.*, **66,** 574 (1944).
7. Mallette, M. F., Lewis, S., Ames, S. E., Nelson, J. M., and Dawson, C. R., *Arch. Biochem.*, **16,** 288 (1948).
8. Dawson, C. R., and Magee, R. J., *in* S. P. Colowick and N. O. Kaplan (eds.), "Methods in enzymology," Vol. II, Academic Press Inc., New York, 1955, p. 831.
9. Smith, J. L., and Krueger, R. C., *J. Biol. Chem.*, **237,** 1121 (1962).
10. Bouchilloux, S., McMahill, P., and Mason, H. S., *J. Biol. Chem.*, **238,** 1699 (1963).
11. Jolly, R. L., Jr., and Mason, H. S., *J. Biol. Chem.*, **240,** PC 1489 (1965).

12. Miller, W. H., and Dawson, C. R., *J. Am. Chem. Soc.*, **63**, 3368 (1941).
13. Dressler, H., and Dawson, C. R., *Biochim. Biophys. Acta*, **45**, 508 (1960).
14. Dressler, H., and Dawson, C. R., *Biochim. Biophys. Acta*, **45**, 515 (1960).
15. Raper, H. S., *Ergeb. Enzymforsch.*, **1**, 270 (1932).
16. Rolland, M., and Lissitzky, S., *Biochim. Biophys. Acta*, **56**, 83 (1962).
17. Kim, K., and Tchen, T. T., *Biochim. Biophys. Acta*, **59**, 569 (1962).
18. Coopersmith, M., Ph. D. dissertation, Columbia University (1962).
19. Coopersmith, M., and Dawson, C. R., unpublished observations.
20. Wood, B. J. B., and Ingraham, L. L., *Nature*, **205**, 291 (1965).
21. Brooks, D. W., Ph. D. dissertation, Columbia University (1965).
22. Dawson, C. R., and Nelson, J. M., *J. Am. Chem. Soc.*, **60**, 245 (1938).
23. Asimov, I., and Dawson, C. R., *J. Am. Chem. Soc.*, **72**, 820 (1950).
24. Ingraham, L. L., Corse, J., and Makower, B., *J. Am. Chem. Soc.*, **74**, 2623 (1952).
25. Ingraham, L. L., *J. Am. Chem. Soc.*, **77**, 2875 (1955).
26. Roth, L. J., Ph. D. dissertation, Columbia University (1944).
27. Scharf, W., and Dawson, C. R., *J. Am. Chem. Soc.*, **80**, 4627 (1958).
28. Ingraham, L. L., *J. Am. Chem. Soc.*, **78**, 5095 (1956).
29. Ludwig, B. J., and Nelson, J. M., *J. Am. Chem. Soc.*, **61**, 2601 (1939).
30. Poillon, W., Ph. D. dissertation, Columbia University (1962).
31. Folin, O., and Ciocalteau, V., *J. Biol. Chem.*, **73**, 627 (1927).
32. Lowry, O., Rosenbrough, N., Farr, A. L., and Randall, R., *J. Biol. Chem.*, **193**, 265 (1951).
33. Joselow, M., Ph. D. dissertation, Columbia University (1949).
34. Tokuyama, K., and Dawson, C. R., *Biochim. Biophys. Acta*, **56**, 427 (1962).
35. Dawson, C. R., and Ludwig, B. J., *J. Am. Chem. Soc.*, **60**, 1617 (1938).

DISCUSSION

DR. G. COHEN: In the experiments of Dressler and Dawson [*Biochim. Biophys. Acta*, **45**, 508, 515 (1960)] the exchange of ^{64}Cu with a phenol substrate was less than the exchange of ^{64}Cu with a catechol substrate. If the phenol were indeed converted to a catechol, then one would expect the same or greater exchange of ^{64}Cu starting with phenol as starting with catechol. Dr. Mason spoke of catecholase activity as involving an hydroxylation. However, hydroxylation to a catechol should result in the same exchange for catechol formed enzymatically as for the same amount of catechol added at the beginning. It would almost look as if the end product is not catechol but a quinone.

DR. BROOKS: There is considerable controversy over whether catechol is in fact the first product of phenol oxidation. Roland and Lissitzky [*Biochim. Biophys. Acta*, **56**, 83 (1962)] said that DOPA is in fact the first product of tyrosine oxidation. Kim and Tchen [*Biochim. Biophys. Acta*, **59**, 569 (1962)] could not find DOPA as the first product of tyrosine oxidation. However, both groups of workers seemed to use comparable techniques.

DR. OSAKI: Can this activity of inactivated tyrosinase be restored by adding Cu$^+$ or Cu^{2+} ?

DR. BROOKS. We have not been successful in restoring the catecholase activities, Portions of the cresolase activities can be restored under appropriate conditions. but it's not a complete reversal. It doesn't have much to do with aging because it's done almost immediately after the experiment is completed.

DR. MASON: Many people have tried to reactivate reaction-inactivated tyrosinase with cupric copper, without succeeding. Covalent bond formation with quinone, and perhaps with amine ligand groups at the active site, would destroy the active site. This seems to me to give a good explanation.

DR. BROOKS: We believe that this is correct. Many attempts have been made to restore activity to reaction-inactivated samples but all have failed. This failure is expected if the active site is completely destroyed.

DR. MORELL: Were any of the experiments with ^{64}Cu carried out under anaerobic conditions?

DR. BROOKS: I don't believe these experiments were ever carried out under anaerobic conditions.

DR. MORELL: I wonder whether the rate of exchange is related to the enzymatic activity or simply to the values of reduced prosthetic copper.

DR. ALBEN: Possible mechanisms by which tyrosinase catalyzes the oxidation of monophenolic compounds have been discussed for many years with insufficient data to distinguish between them. It is now possible to bring these speculations into the sharp focus of mathematical equations of sufficient simplicity that they can be tested against experimental data. These mechanisms should include monphenol and oxygen as reactants, enzyme and o-diphenol at very low concentrations, and a substrate inhibition step by monophenol. The initial velocity–steady state conditions are imposed to facilitate handling of the data.

Most enzyme-catalyzed reactions can be described by the reciprocal form of the Michaelis–Menten equation

$$\frac{1}{v} = \frac{1}{V} + \frac{K_m}{V}\frac{1}{S} \tag{1}$$

where v is initial velocity of the over-all reaction, and V and K_m/V are functions of the nonvaried reactants. This equation requires that all reactants are in high concentration relative to the enzyme and that reactant bound to the enzyme may be neglected. This restriction is violated with tyrosinase, since very low concentrations of diphenol "activate" monophenol oxidation. It is therefore necessary to include a conservation equation for diphenol as well as for enzyme, so that $S_0 = S + (e_1 + e_2 + \cdots)$, where S_0 and S are total and free substrate (diphenol) respectively, and the e terms are concentrations of those forms of the enzyme that contain bound S. The e terms are functions time velocity, so that velocity may be factored and the equation written $S_0 = S + v$ (coef). When S_0 replaces S in Eq. (1), the result is a quadratic in velocity:

$$0 = -\frac{v^2 \text{ (coef)}}{S_0 V} + v\left(\left[\left(\frac{K_m}{V}\right)^* + \text{(coef)}\right]\frac{1}{S_0} + \frac{1}{V}\right) - 1 \tag{2}$$

Equation (2) has the form $ax^2 + bx + c = 0$, which may be solved by the binomial expansion: $x = (-c/b)(1 + ac/b^2 + 2a^2c^2/b^4 + \cdots)$. The first term of the binomial expansion gives an approximate solution to Eq. (2), so that

$$\frac{1}{v} = \left[\left(\frac{K_m}{V}\right)^* + \text{(coef)}\right]\frac{1}{S_0} + \frac{1}{V} \tag{3}$$

The slope in Eq. (3), (K_m/V), is $(K_m/V)^* + \text{(coef)}$, and $K_m = (K_m)^* + \text{(coef)}V$.

Data that we have obtained with mushroom tyrosinase yield straight lines when plotted according to Eq. (3), and the Michaelis constant for catechol has the required dependence upon total enzyme concentration. The data also require that $(K_m/V)^*$ contain a term multiplied by $(1 + K_i I)$ to account for substrate inhibition by monophenol, where I is monophenol concentration and K_i is the association constant for the formation of the inhibited enzyme complex. Several types of mechanisms have been ruled out by the data. The one which remains out of those tested is an ordered three-substrate mechanism in which o-diphenol is not the first substrate to be bound to the enzyme:

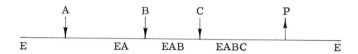

There is not yet sufficient data, however, to further define the reaction sequence. The association constant for substrate inhibition is estimated to be $1.3 \times 10^4 \ M^{-1}$, or $77 \ \mu M$ as a dissociation constant.

Perhaps the most exciting aspect of this kinetic approach is that it allows the concentration of the catalytic center to be calculated from kinetic data for several types of mechanisms, including the one indicated above. This is possible when (coef) in Eq. (3) contains the rate constant for dissociation of enzyme-product complex (Φ_0) which also occurs in V. Thus at very high concentrations of all substrates, the limiting values become: (coef) $= \Phi_0$, $V = E_0/\Phi_0$, and $E_0 = (\Phi_0)(E_0/\Phi_0) = $ (coef) V. E_0 is the total concentration of all catalytic center complexes in the same units of concentration as the substrates. A comparison of monophenolase catalytic center concentration calculated in this manner with analytical data for copper is consistent with four atoms of copper per monophenolase catalytic center for the high catecholase preparations which have been examined. The details of these experiments will be published elsewhere.

DR. HAMILTON: Our interest in tyrosinase stems from our study of a model system. We have been looking at the hydroxylation of a number of aromatic compounds by hydrogen peroxide [Hamilton, G. A., and Friedman, J. P., J. Am Chem. Soc., 85, 1008 (1963); Hamilton, G. A., Friedman, J. P., and Campbell, P. M., ibid, in press; Hamilton, G. A., Hanifin, J. W., and Friedman, J. P., ibid, in press]. This hydroxylation does not take place unless catalytic amounts of ferric ion and catechol are present. We have looked at the kinetics and products of this reaction, and have come to the conclusion that the hydroxylating agent is neither a hydroxyl radical nor a perhydroxyl radical, but a complex of hydrogen peroxide, catechol, and ferric ion. Since it appears that cupric ion can replace ferric ion in the model system, and since a catechol seems to be required for the hydroxylation of monophenols by tyrosinase, we believe that the mechanisms of the enzyme and model hydroxylation reactions may be similar.

Data that we have obtained with synthetic substrates yield straight lines when plotted according to Eq. 13, and the Michaelis constant for sily-chol has the required dependency upon total enzyme concentration. The data also require that $(E)_0/(V)$ curves when multiplied by $(1 + b_1 A_1)/1$ be a constant for substrate inhibition by monoamine], where J is monomolecular concentration and A_1 is the association constant for the formation of the [high]-enzyme complex. Several types of mechanisms have been ruled out by the data. The one which remains out of those tested is an ordered three-substrate mechanism in which sulphacol is not the first substrate to be bound to the enzyme.

$$
E \quad\rightleftharpoons\quad \text{EA} \quad\rightleftharpoons\quad \text{EAB} \quad\rightleftharpoons\quad \text{EABC}
$$

The Copper of Polyphenoloxidase

DENIS KERTESZ

Laboratoire de Biochimie Médicale,
Faculté de Médecine et de Pharmacie,
Marseille, France

I. Optical Absorption Experiments

A. Aromatic Amino Acid Composition

The absorption spectrum of mushroom polyphenoloxidase is well known (1, 2, 3, 4). It shows a very intense and sharp band with a maximum at 282 mμ ($E^{1\%} = 26.92$), and frequently, but not constantly, a low and diffuse band centered around 340 mμ. No other bands are present in the near ultraviolet or visible region of the spectrum. The very high intensity of the absorption at 282 mμ is explained by the high aromatic amino acid content of the enzyme. We have found 10 residues of tyrosine and 11 residues of tryptophan (5) for a minimal molecular weight of 31,800, corresponding to one copper atom per molecule, in reasonable agreement with the recalculated figures of Bouchilloux *et al.* (3). By taking the molar absorption of tyrosine as 1,340, of tryptophan as 5,550, and of cystine (of which we have found two residues) as 150, we obtain the ratio $E_{obs}/E_{calc} = 85,600/74,750 = 1.14$, which is practically equal to the ratio 1.13 found by Wetlaufer (6) for ribonuclease and the ratio 1.12 found by Rickly *et al.* (7) for carbonic anhydrase. There is no difference whatsoever between the absorption spectrum of the holoenzyme and that of the apoenzyme. This insensitivity of the absorption spectrum to the presence or absence of the metal is shared by other copper proteins which contain this metal totally and exclusively in the univalent state (2).

B. Attempts to Detect Complexes of Polyphenoloxidase

Unfortunately, this particular spectrophotometric rigidity is not limited to the insensitivity of the presence or absence of copper. We have made numerous attempts during the past few years to identify spectrophotometrically complexes of polyphenoloxidase with oxygen, with carbon monoxide, and with catechol. In the visible region we were able to use concentrated solutions of the enzyme, corresponding nearly to 1 mM enzyme copper, always without success. No differences have ever been detected in the spectra of the protein in air or in oxygen. No differences were seen in vacuum, in argon, or in carbon monoxide, even after the addition of a substrate amount or an excess of catechol. In the near ultra-violet and especially in the ultraviolet region the high absorption of the enzyme and its substrate did not permit the use of concentrated solutions, at least with the spectrophotometers at our disposal. The highest concentrations used were about 0.01 to 0.2 mM enzyme copper. Of course, the insensitivity of the spectrum of the enzyme to carbon monoxide alone is not surprising. Kubowitz (8) had shown many years ago that the spectrum of potato polyphenoloxidase is the same in air and in carbon monoxide and also that deoxyhemocyanin and carbon monoxyhemocyanin have no absorption bands other than the protein band in the ultraviolet. However, it appeared obligatory to verify whether catechol eventually bound to the enzyme modifies its spectrum or, inversely, if the enzyme (always in strict anaerobiosis or in carbon monoxide) modifies the absorption spectrum of the catechol; in other words, if the half reactions of the enzyme with oxygen or with catechol can be verified spectrophotometrically.

Our negative results do not completely exclude the possibility of finding significant differences in the future, with better spectrophotometers and a better experimental technique. But it may be predicted that these differences will be small and of a different order of magnitude from the spectral reactions of the hemoproteins. The recent finding (9) of a spectrophotometrically identifiable complex of catechol and tyrosinase in the presence of a great excess of cupric chloride cannot be pertinent to the enzymatic activity: it is well known that polyphenoloxidase holoenzyme is fully active with catechol and the effect of extraneous copper is inhibiting because it increases the reaction inactivation.

Recently, we studied the reaction of reduced peroxidase with carbon monoxide (10). We found that the affinity of ferroperoxidase for carbon monoxide is about 10 times lower than that of myoglobin or hemoglobin. After an unsuccessful attempt to displace carbon monoxide from CO-hemoglobin with polyphenoloxidase and with polyphenoloxidase + catechol, we tried to repeat this experiment with reduced peroxidase (11). Although ferroperoxidase, if less than 50% complexed with carbon monoxide, is an extremely sensitive indicator of the CO concentration, the spectrum of a 6.3 μM solution of ferroperoxidase 35% complexed with carbon monoxide remained unchanged after the addition of polyphenoloxidase (Fig. 1). The experiment is obviously complicated by the presence of the dithionite used to reduce the peroxidase, even if it was used as parsimoniously as possible. In fact, the determination of polyphenoloxidase activity, made after the long and rather laborious experiment and after 2 hours' exposure to air, room temperature, peroxidase, and the oxidation products of catechol and dithionite, has shown that only about 12% of the

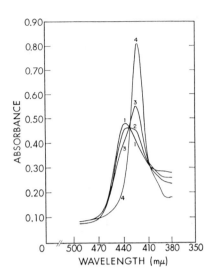

FIG. 1. The effect of addition of polyphenoloxidase and of polyphenoloxidase + catechol to CO-ferroperoxidase. (1) ferroperoxidase; (2) 11% CO-ferroperoxidase + 89% ferroperoxidase; (3) 35% CO-ferroperoxidase + 65% ferroperoxidase; the same result is obtained after the addition of polyphenoloxidase (10.3 μM), and after the further addition of catechol (100 μM); (4) CO-ferroperoxidase. Spectra taken in 0.1 M phosphate buffer, pH 6.8 at 20°.

activity remained. This value is certainly a minimum, and we feel that, even if only this amount of enzyme had combined with carbon monoxide, this should have been shown by a small but clearly visible diminution of the absorption at 423 mμ. However, the only conclusion that can be drawn from this experiment is that if polyphenoloxidase, or polyphenoloxidase + catechol, combines with carbon monoxide at all, their affinity must be very low indeed.

II. Inhibition by Carbon Monoxide

Polyphenoloxidase, however, *is inhibited* by carbon monoxide. The inhibition was discovered by Keilin (12) in 1929 with potato polyphenoloxidase and confirmed by Keilin and Mann (13) in 1938 with the mushroom enzyme. The inhibition of the indirect oxidation of ferrocytochrome c by polyphenoloxidase + catechol (14) is shown in Fig. 2. We have shown earlier that the oxidation of reduced cytochrome c by this system is very similar to its oxidation by cytochrome oxidase. It appears to be a first-order process with respect to reduced cytochrome c and is inhibited by ferricytochrome c (15, 16). The apparent first-order rate constant is a linear

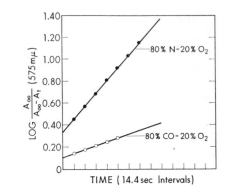

FIG. 2. The inhibition by carbon monoxide of the indirect oxidation of ferrocytochrome c by polyphenoloxidase + catechol. A solution containing 35 μM ferrocytochrome c, 5 μM catechol, and 0.033 M phosphate buffer, pH 6.8, was equilibrated in a tonometer with air or with 80% CO–20% O_2. This was placed in an optical cuvette of 5 cm light path. The reaction was started by adding 0.15 μg of polyphenoloxidase in 5 μl, to a final concentration (as copper) of 2.36 $\times$ 10^{-3} μM.

function of catechol concentration and, for very low concentrations, of the concentration of the enzyme as well (14). We (11) have measured the rate of oxidation from the change in absorbance at 575 mμ, where according to Margoliash and Frohwirt (17) the millimolar extinction coefficient is 0.8 for reduced and 4.2 for oxidized cytochrome c. As the two apparently first-order rate constants are 1.85 $\times$ 10^{-2} sec^{-1} and 0.55 $\times$ 10^{-2} sec^{-1} (Fig. 2), the inhibition is 70%, in perfect agreement with the inhibition which can be calculated from the results of Keilin and Mann (13). If we follow Warburg's reasoning for the calculation of the partition coefficient of his *Atmungsferment* (18) and we make the reasonable assumption that in a mixture of oxygen and carbon monoxide the observed respiration is proportional to the fraction of enzyme not complexed with carbon monoxide n, then the partition coefficient is $K = [n/(1 - n)][CO]/[O_2] = 1.7$. That is, polyphenoloxidase has a greater affinity for oxygen than for carbon monoxide and would be half saturated with each gas in the presence of 37% oxygen and 63% carbon monoxide. According to Yonetani (19) the partition coefficient for cytochrome oxidase is between 5 and 9. Moreover, the affinity of cytochrome oxidase for oxygen is certainly much higher than that of polyphenoloxidase (8, 19, 20, 21). We would have been wiser to attempt the experiment reported in Fig. 1 with cytochrome oxidase.

III. Copper Content and Its Valence State

We have no doubt that, if the necessary precautions against contamination have been taken, polyphenoloxidase from mushroom cultivated

TABLE I

PROPERTIES OF THE FRESH AND THE AGED POLYPHENOLOXIDASE

	Concentration (units/ml)	Dry weight (mg/ml)	Spec. act. (units/mg)	% Cu⁺	% Cu²⁺
Enzyme 1956	90,900	13.3	6,850	0.20	—
Enzyme 1956, aged	54,700	13.1	4,170	0.15	0.05
Enzyme 1957	104,000	15.3	6,800	0.20	—
Enzyme 1957, aged	59,200	15.1	3,940	0.15	0.05
Apoenzyme 1956	480	13.1	37	—	—
Apoenzyme 1957	380	13.9	27	—	—

around Rome contains $0.20 \pm 0.2\%$ copper. If the valence state of this copper is determined as rapidly as possible, all of it appears to be in the univalent form, whether measured with 2,2′-biquinoline in acetic acid or by EPR (22, 4).

A. Aging Effects

It is unfortunate that polyphenoloxidase loses activity even if stored frozen and this inactivation is generally accompanied by a partial oxidation of the copper (23). An example of this aging effect is shown in Table I. The activity and copper content of both preparations were determined shortly after their purification and again after 8 months of storage. During this time both enzyme solutions lost about 40% of their original activity, and 25% of their copper was found in the cupric state. Apoenzyme 1956 was stored as such; apoenzyme 1957 was prepared from the corresponding holoenzyme after 8 months of storage, when 40% of the original activity had already been lost and 25% of the copper had been oxidized.

B. Reconstitution from the Apoenzyme and Copper

The activity to both apoenzymes could be restored by adding 0.15% of Cu^{2+}, and further addition of copper did not increase the activity (Fig. 3). Cu^{2+} added in amounts less than or equal to the original Cu^+ content of the enzyme was found to be reduced to the cuprous state, but excess copper remained cupric (Fig. 4). It may be useful to point out that where copper is not in excess the color development of the cuprous-biquinoline complex is relatively rapid, and it terminates with an unambiguous endpoint. However, in the presence of excess copper the rapid first phase is followed by a slow reaction, so that the amount of the total copper reduced may appear slightly greater than the original cuprous content of the enzyme (Fig. 5).

The conclusions drawn from these experiments were: (a) only the mono-

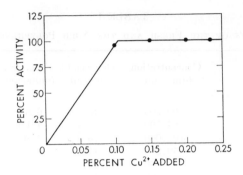

FIG. 3. Restoration of copper to apopolyphenoloxidase. Each sample contained 2.8 mg apoenzyme 1957 (see Table I) in 0.20 ml 0.025 M phosphate, pH 7. The calculated amounts of copper were added with a 5 μl or 10 μl pipette as $CuSO_4$. Activities were determined as in (4).

valent bound copper is active enzymatically; (b) the apoenzyme reduces cupric copper added for its reactivation; (c) the primary cause of the lost activity is an alteration of the protein and not the partial oxidation of the copper since the fraction of activity lost is always greater than the fraction of copper oxidized and since the apoenzyme loses about as much of its potential activity as does the holoenzyme. These conclusions, in their essentials, have been confirmed in the past seven years although the aging and the inactivation of the enzyme appear to be a rather capricious process, the factors of which are difficult to understand. One of our last preparations lost 47% of its original activity after 7 months' storage, although almost all of the original copper, 0.17% out of 0.19%, continued to react as Cu^+ with biquinoline. The apoenzyme required 0.20% copper for its maximal reactivation and again almost all, 0.18%, reacted as Cu^+ with biquinoline.

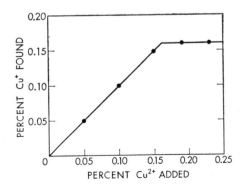

FIG. 4. The reduction of Cu^{2+} by the polyphenoloxidase apoenzyme. Same conditions as in Fig. 3.

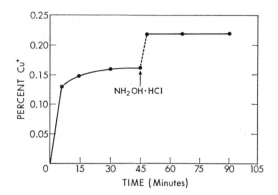

FIG. 5. The development of color by the Cu^+-biquinoline complex in acetic acid, in the presence of excess (0.22%) Cu^{2+}. Same conditions as in Fig. 3.

Our former conclusions must now be modified by adding that not all the Cu^+ bound to the enzyme is necessarily active.

In our earlier reconstitution experiments, we added the calculated amount of copper in a small volume to a relatively concentrated solution of the apoenzyme and after a relatively long contact time the activity with DOPA as substrate was determined manometrically at 37° after 12–15 minutes of equilibration (4). In the spectrophotometric experiments reported we have measured the indirect oxidation of NADH. Under the conditions used the rate of this oxidation is proportional to the concentra-

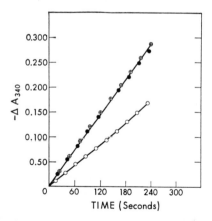

FIG. 6. Restoration of copper to polyphenoloxidase apoenzyme. Apoenzyme 0.92 $\times$ $10^{-2} \mu M$ (see text); 0.12 mM NADH; 0.025 M phosphate, pH 6.8. ●-●-●, 0.92 $\times$ 10^{-2} μM copper (as $CuCl_2$); ⊕-⊕-⊕, 1.84 $\times$ 10^{-2} μM copper; ○-○-○, no copper. The reaction was started by adding 5 μl of catechol to a final concentration of 8.3 μM. Total volume 3 ml; 20°.

tion of the enzyme and to that of the catechol (24). The conditions of the reconstitution were here completely different: the calculated amount of copper was added in a small volume to about 3 ml solution of diluted apoenzyme, the time of contact was short (generally less than 1 minute), and the temperature was 20°. It is evident (Fig. 6) that the effects of 1 and 2 equivalents of copper, respectively, are identical. The control rate without added copper is very high, much higher than it has ever been found in the earlier manometric experiments. However, it may be pointed out that it corresponds to the effect that would have been produced by the presence of less than 1 ng of copper in the whole reaction mixture. Two interesting facts, although they will be more clearly shown in Fig. 7, might be recorded here. The first is that copper may be added to the apoenzyme before or after NADH with equal effect. But copper must be added before the catechol, since copper added after the addition of catechol was found to be ineffective.

In the experiment reported in Fig. 7 the concentration of the apoenzyme was increased 100-fold and the concentration of catechol decreased 18-fold. The enzyme, or more precisely the enzyme's prosthetic copper, is thus present in a greater concentration than the substrate. Although the concentration of the enzyme is 100-fold greater, the control rate is lower than in the preceding experiment, showing that the contamination by copper was in greater part exogenous. The arrow indicates the time of addition of 1

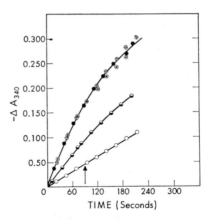

Fig. 7. Restoration of copper to polyphenoloxidase apoenzyme. Apoenzyme 0.92 μM (see text); O–O–O, no copper added; ●–●–●, 0.37 μM copper aded; ⊙–⊙–⊙, 0.92 μM copper added; ⊕–⊕–⊕, 0.92 μM copper added after NADH; ●–●–●, 184 μM copper added. The reaction was stated by adding catechol as in Fig. 6, but to a final concentration of 0.46 μM. The arrow indicates the addition of copper to a final concentration of 0.92 μM. Other conditions as in Fig. 6.

equivalent of copper after the catechol: its inefficiency is evident. When copper was added to the apoenzyme before the catechol, however, the activity increased with the amount of copper until 1 equivalent was added; further addition did not increase the activity, and as was pointed out earlier, it was not reduced by the apoenzyme. It is evident also that copper added before or after NADH was equally effective.

It appears to us that these experiments are in good agreement with and confirm the conclusions drawn earlier. The lack of effect of copper added after the addition of catechol is a new phenomenon, which cannot yet be fully explained. It may be due to the binding of substrate to the apoenzyme at or near the copper-binding site. If so, this binding appears to be quite strong since the addition of excess copper to the enzyme and to the catechol did not restore the activity.

IV. Summary

(a) Complex formation between polyphenoloxidase, oxygen, carbon monoxide, and catechol could not be detected spectrophotometrically. Partition experiments with CO-hemoproteins and polyphenoloxidase were unsuccessful even in the presence of catechol.

(b) Polyphenoloxidase is inhibited by carbon monoxide. The enzyme has a higher affinity for oxygen than for carbon monoxide.

(c) Cu^{2+} added to the apoenzyme is reduced to Cu^+ on reconstitution. Only Cu^+, but not necessarily all Cu^+ bound to the enzyme, is enzymatically active.

ACKNOWLEDGMENTS

The work reported in this paper was done in part at the Research Department of the Istituto Regina Elena, Rome, Italy, in collaboration with Dr. R. Zito and Dr. M. Brunori.

REFERENCES

1. Kertesz, D., and Zito, R., *Nature,* **179,** 1017 (1957).
2. Kertesz, D., and Zito, R., *in* O. Hayaishi (ed.), "Oxygenases," Academic Press Inc., New York, 1962, p. 307.
3. Bouchilloux, S. P., McMahill, P., and Mason, S. H., *J. Biol. Chem.,* **238,** 1699 (1963).
4. Kertesz, D., and Zito, R., *Biochim. Biophys. Acta,* **96,** 447 (1965).
5. Zito, R., and Kertesz, D., unpublished observations.
6. Wetlaufer, D. B., *Advances in Protein Chemistry,* **17,** 304 (1962).
7. Rickly, E. E., Ghazanfar, S. A. S., Gibbons, B. H., and Edsall, J. T., *J. Biol. Chem.,* **239,** 1065 (1965).
8. Kubowitz, F., *Biochem. Z.,* **299,** 32 (1938).
9. Mori, K., Tanabe, H., and Tsutsui, M., *Biochem. Biophys. Res. Communs.,* **14,** 280 (1964).

10. Kertesz, D., Antonini, E., Brunori, M., Wyman, J., and Zito, R., *Biochemistry*, **4**, 2672 (1965).
11. Kertesz, D., Brunori, M., and Zito, R., unpublished observations.
12. Keilin, D., *Proc. Roy. Soc. (London)*, *Ser. B*, **104**, 206 (1929).
13. Keilin, D., and Mann, T., *Proc. Roy. Soc. (London). Ser. B*, **125**, 187 (1938).
14. Kertesz, D., and Zito, R., *Biochim. Biophys. Acta*, **59**, 752 (1962).
15. Smith, L., and Conrad, H., *Arch. Biochem. Biophys.*, **63**, 403 (1956).
16. Minnaert, K., *Biochim. Biophys. Acta*, **50**, 34 (1961).
17. Margoliash, E., and Frohwirt, N., *Biochem. J.*, **71**, 570 (1959).
18. Warburg, O., "Heavy metal prosthetic groups," Clarendon Press, Oxford, 1949, p. 78.
19. Yonetani, T., *in* P. D. Boyer, H. Lardy, and K. Myrbäck (eds.), "The Enzymes," 2nd ed., Vol. VIII, Academic Press Inc., New York, 1963, p. 41.
20. Kertesz, D., *J. Natl. Cancer Inst.*, **14**, 1093 (1954).
21. Ingraham, L., *J. Am. Chem. Soc.*, **79**, 666 (1957).
22. Kertesz, D., *Nature*, **180**, 506 (1957).
23. Kertesz, D., and Zito, R., *Proc. 4th Intern. Biochemistry Congr.* Pergamon Press, London, 1958, p. 65.
24. Kertesz, D., and Azopardi, O., *Compt. Rend. Soc. Biol.*, **154**, 270 (1960).

DISCUSSION

DR. CURZON: Is the ratio of absorption at 300 mμ to the absorption at 280 mμ constant from preparation to preparation?

DR. KERTESZ: Are you speaking of the little shoulder at 290?

DR. CURZON: Yes.

DR. KERTESZ: If you are working with a good spectrophotometer, that is, with a narrow slit width, you will always see it, and always at the same place.

DR. CURZON: I believe you said that this 290 peak is still there, even though the copper is removed?

DR. KERTESZ: Yes, certainly.

DR. CURZON: Now, this does not mean that it is not due to the copper. It could have been due to the copper-containing site oxidizing an adjacent phenolic residue. It occurred to me when I saw your spectrum that it looked quite like the spectra of proteins that have been oxidized themselves by tyrosinase [Yasunobu, K. T., and Dandliker, W. B., *J. Biol. Chem.*, **224**, 1065 (1957); Yasunobu, K. T., Peterson, E. W., and Mason, H. S., *J. Biol. Chem.*, **234**, 3291 (1959)].

DR. KERTESZ: I think that it is simply due to the high tryptophan content.

DR. FRIEDEN: Is the copper ever seen in the Cu^{2+} state in tyrosinase?

DR. KERTESZ: The answer is no, not in a fresh preparation of maximal specific activity.

DR. FRIEDEN: Dr. Mason, is there any Cu^{2+} EPR activity?

DR. MASON: No, there is not.

DR. BROOKS: In our hands, the tyrosinase copper assay using valence-specific reagents has always indicated the presence of 90% cupric copper. This result, obtained with BCS assay (EDTA, p-CMS present) appears to be the only one reporting Cu^{2+}.

DR. MASON: Dr. Kertesz, a very rough calculation shows that there cannot be an absorption maximum in a resting enzyme due to the copper beyond the protein peak having an absorbance larger than 100 per atom of copper per centimeter, since you find the absorption spectra of the apo- and holoenzyme are the same. I wonder if I might ask Dr. Williams whether that is consistent with curpous complexes in general.

DR. WILLIAMS: There are many cuprous copper complexes which do not absorb at wavelengths above 280 mμ.

DR. HEMMERICH: Cuprous copper complexes, when there are no ligands that accept electrons, do not absorb at higher wavelengths than 250 mμ. Only polydentate ligands which accept electrons may have a charge-transfer band extending to the visible region, for example, bipyridine, bathocuproine, or oxinate, but these should not be present in a pure protein.

DR. KERTESZ: I should like to remind you that apohemocyanin and deoxygenated hemocyanin have a similar absorption spectrum.

DR. MASON: Dr. Kertesz has suggested that his apoenzyme contains reducing equivalents, because added cupric copper is reduced by the protein, and the enzyme becomes active. Mr. McMahill of Portland has confirmed that, using EPR spectroscopy.

DR. KERTESZ: I must confess that I haven't succeeded in identifying the reducing groups involved, or in reducing with the apoenzyme anything other than the copper. In our polyphenoloxidase Dr. Zito and I very definitely found no cysteine. We have found two cystines for one copper, but Fling, Horowitz, and Heinemann [*J. Biol. Chem.*, **238**, 2045 (1963)] found none in their *Neurospora* tyrosinase.

DR. MASON: We have had the same experience, but we have done this with EPR and we find that added cupric copper exists as a cupric–protein complex for a short time. The signal is very rapidly lost, and the added cupric copper is reduced. Since cyanide has been used to remove the copper, one wonders whether this isn't a case of the sort that Dr. Hemmerich was discussing this morning, in which you start with a cuprous disulfide, and you simply reverse the oxidation-reduction and pull out cupric copper, leaving sulfide behind. Does that sound reasonable to you, Dr. Hemmerich?

DR. HEMMERICH: Yes, I think it is possible. In any enzyme where you have to postulate an interaction of sulfide or disulfide with copper, you have two possible ways of dissociation. It might dissociate into cuprous copper and disulfide or it might dissociate into cupric copper and mercaptide under suitable conditions, but you cannot say without looking into the enzyme how it *must* dissociate.

Laccase, A Review*

WALTER G. LEVINE†

Department of Pharmacology,
Albert Einstein College of Medicine,
Yeshiva University,
Bronx, New York

I. Historical

To begin the story of laccase, we must go back over 80 years to a paper by Yoshida which appeared in the *Journal of the Chemical Society* in 1883 (1). Considering the embryonic state of biochemical knowledge at that time, the paper engenders great respect for the author as it contains an accurate description of the basis of laccase activity, its substrates, and its probable function. Yoshida systematically examined the chemical properties of a material known as urushi, which is contained in Japanese lacquer. Urushi is the milky secretion, or latex, of *Rhus vernicifera*, the Japanese lac tree. Upon exposure of a thin layer of this substance to moist air at room temperature it darkens rapidly and dries to give a lustrous translucent material which is insoluble in a great variety of solvents. This property is the basis of its use as a furniture finish. Yoshida treated urushi with alcohol and extracted the resulting precipitate with water, thus obtaining three fractions: (a) a material that was alcohol soluble; (b) a gummy material that was alcohol insoluble, but water soluble; and (c) a material that was apparently soluble in neither solvent. Yoshida observed that the alcohol-soluble fraction (or urushic acid as he called it) would not undergo any of the changes characteristic of the original latex. Similarly, the gum frac-

* Supported in part by United States Public Health Service Grant, HE 06450.
† Career Development Awardee of the United States Public Health Service, 5K3–GM–8102.

tion, when added to the urushic acid, did not effect any changes. However, Yoshida reported that fraction (c) acted on urushic acid to bring about the darkening and drying of the lacquer. Fraction (c) contained a nitrogenous substance having "diastatic" (enzymatic) properties. Other known "diastases" of that time (such as those in malt and saliva) had no action on urushic acid. Yoshida observed first, that the interaction of fractions (a) and (c) required moisture and an atmosphere containing oxygen; second, that, during the drying process, oxygen was incorporated into urushic acid; and third, that the "disastatic" material was inactivated by heat. In one concise study carried out when biochemistry was yet in its embryonic stage nearly the entire foundation of the biochemistry of laccase was laid.

A decade later, the nature of the enzymatic activity of the lac tree exudate was further elucidated in a series of papers by Bertrand (2–9), although nowhere in these papers was there any indication that this author was aware of Yoshida's work. Bertrand prepared an alcohol extract of the latex of the Indo-Chinese lac tree (2). He designated this fraction as "laccol" owing to its polyphenolic nature, i.e., it was readily oxidizable to colored substances upon exposure to air, while the heat-labile, enzymatic material contained in the alcohol-insoluble fraction was called "laccase." Bertrand observed that the laccase, when mixed with laccol in the presence of air, elicited immediate and rapid darkening to form a black resinous substance. In the absence of laccase this material did not form. Laccase also reacted with other substances such as gallic acid, pyrogallol, and tannin to form dark products. Like Yoshida, Bertrand also observed the uptake of oxygen during the reaction. He was aware of the considerable autoxidation undergone by polyphenolic substances, but nevertheless noted that the oxygen uptake was greatly enhanced in the presence of laccase.

II. Copper Content and Function

Although it is recognized today that laccase contains tightly bound copper which is essential for enzymatic activity, it was suspected for a number of years that laccase was a manganese enzyme. In the earlier work of Bertrand (8), considerable quantities of manganese were present in his crude laccase preparations and he concluded that the catalytic activity was dependent upon the presence of this metal. Furthermore, the oxidase activity of his enzyme preparation was shown to be greatly accelerated by the addition of small amounts of manganese salts; other metals were ineffective in this respect. However, with the development of improved techniques for enzyme purification as well as refinements in trace metal analysis, the proposed role of manganese was eventually challenged. In 1930, Siminokura (10), using laccase prepared from the Japanese lac tree (*Rhus vernicifera*), found that manganese salts did not affect the enzyme-catalyzed oxidation of pyrogallol. In 1939, Keilin and Mann (11) prepared highly purified laccase from the Indo-Chinese lac tree (*Rhus succedanea*). It had a copper content of 0.154% but no detectable iron or manganese. The copper was nondialyzable and enzymatic activity was found to be proportional to the copper content. Typical copper reagents such as cyanide, H_2S, azide, and diethyldithiocarbamate were inhibitory, although carbon monoxide was without effect, confirming a previous report (10). The latter observation provided an additional means of differentiating laccase from certain other copper-containing oxidases such as tyrosinase and polyphenoloxidase, both of which are inhibited by carbon monoxide and often occur in the same source material as does laccase. The next year Keilin and Mann purified laccase from the Japanese and Burmese lacquer trees (*Rhus vernicifera* and *Melanorrhea usitata*), and the best of these preparations had a copper content of 0.24% (12). Nevertheless, conflicting views on the relative importance of manganese and copper still persisted. Bertrand (13), in 1947, described a *Rhus succedanea* laccase preparation that contained considerable manganese but so little copper that he attributed it to contamination. Furthermore, his active preparations did not possess the blue color that Keilin and Mann associated with their partially purified laccase, and absorption spectra indicated a possible nonprotein nature of the enzyme. The latter particularly was a radical departure from the classical concept of the chemical nature of enzymes. Definitive experiments were carried out in 1948 by Tissieres (14), who was working in Keilin's laboratory. Using *Rhus succedanea* laccase, he was able to remove copper from the protein by treatment with cyanide followed by dialysis, with a resultant loss of catalytic activity. Upon the addition of small amounts of cupric sulfate, activity returned. Restoration of activity was not seen upon the addition of either ferric or manganous ions. Tissieres further observed that during the preparation of laccase, the manganese present in the crude extract quickly disappeared, while the copper content increased with purification and always remained proportional to enzymatic activity as measured using *p*-phenylenediamine as substrate. Thus, unequivocal evidence was offered that laccase is truly a copper enzyme. Omura (15) subsequently extended the observations of Tissieres by demonstrating that in the presence of ascorbate, i.e., under reducing conditions, the tightly bound copper rapidly exchanged with radioactive cuprous ions in the medium. If either the laccase or the copper ions were in the oxidized state, however, little or no exchange occurred. In other experiments (16),

TABLE I

RECONSTITUTION OF *Rhus vernicifera* LACCASE FROM APOLACCASE AND COPPER[a]

	Specific activity	Copper content (%)
Native laccase	7550	0.250
Native laccase + Cu^{2+}	8400	0.249
Native laccase + Cu$^+$	8100	0.265
Apolaccase	190	0.003
Apolaccase + Cu^{2+}	240	0.135
Apolaccase + Cu$^+$	2380	0.182

[a] After Omura (16).

dialysis against cyanide led to a removal of copper from the molecule with a concomitant loss of blue color and enzymatic activity. Although the copper content of this apoprotein could be partly restored by either Cu$^+$ or Cu^{2+}, color and activity were returned by the addition of Cu$^+$ but not by Cu^{2+}. (Table I). The latter observation was at variance with Tissieres' report on restoration of activity with cupric sulfate. Nevertheless, Omura's work did serve to reinforce the concept that laccase was indeed a copper-containing protein and that enzymatic activity was dependent upon copper and no other metal.

Nakamura (27) prepared highly purified laccase from *Rhus vernicifera* and determined its molecular weight to be 120,000, from which he calculated that each molecule contained four atoms of copper. Furthermore, he concluded that in the oxidized enzyme, copper was present in the cupric state and not as a cuprous–oxygen complex. This was inferred from his observations that reduced laccase could be oxidized by ferricyanide under strictly anaerobic conditions and that native laccase was not decolorized by the removal of oxygen. Nakamura also ascertained the role of copper in laccase-catalyzed oxidations (18). Utilizing the dependence of blue color on the cupric state he demonstrated that one molecule of substrate (hydroquinone or ascorbic acid) added anaerobically to a known amount of enzyme would cause a decrease in absorption at 615 mμ, corresponding to a reduction of two atoms of copper. Furthermore, he observed that one molecule of oxygen oxidized four cuprous atoms in reduced laccase. Thus, the following reaction mechanism was proposed for laccase:

$$2 \text{ Cu}^{2+} + \text{Hydroquinone} \rightarrow 2 \text{ Cu}^+ + p\text{-Quinone} + 2 \text{ H}^+ \tag{1}$$

$$2 \text{ Cu}^+ + \tfrac{1}{2} \text{O}_2 + 2 \text{ H}^+ \rightarrow 2 \text{ Cu}^{2+} + \text{H}_2\text{O} \tag{2}$$

Although copper had been shown previously to be essential to laccase this was the first unequivocal demonstration of the actual role of copper in laccase-catalyzed oxidations. This mechanism was similar to the one previously suggested for other copper enzymes (19).

Nakamura then reexamined these findings by studying the magnetic susceptibility of laccase (20). Again his experiments indicated that native laccase copper was all in the cupric state, that reduction to the cuprous form occurred upon the addition of substrate, and, finally, that reoxidation of the copper was brought about by molecular oxygen.

Shortly after this report appeared, Malmström, Mosbach, and Vänngård (21), using laccase prepared from *Polyporus versicolor*, confirmed the existence of Cu^{2+} in laccase, using EPR techniques. They were able to demonstrate that while the addition of substrates (catechol, ascorbate) diminished the laccase cupric signal, the addition of tyrosine, which is not a substrate, had no effect. An extension of these findings is found in a paper by Broman *et al.* (22), who studied the kinetics of the reduction and oxidation of laccase copper during the catalysis of *p*-phenylenediamine oxidation. The rate constants that they observed agreed well with the rate observed for the over-all reaction and confirmed the mechanism proposed by Nakamura (28). Furthermore, through EPR they observed the formation and decay of a free radical species formed by the substrate during the course of the reaction. Broman *et al.* felt that radical formation was due to enzymatic action but that radical decay was due to nonenzymatic mechanisms (22). Nakamura had previously demonstrated a semiquinone as an intermediate during the oxidation of hydroquinone catalyzed by laccase (23). The semiquinone formation resulted from a one-electron transfer from substrate to laccase copper, forming cuprous copper. The next step involved dismutation of the semiquinone, which correlated well with the proposition of Broman *et al.* (22) that radical decay was nonenzymatic. Nakamura dismissed the idea that the semiquinone would be oxidized directly by oxygen. The over-all reaction then appears as follows:

$$HQ \xrightarrow{\text{laccase}} SQ \to 2\ SQ \xrightarrow{\text{nonenzymatic}} Q + HQ \qquad (3)$$

where HQ = hydroquinone; SQ = semiquinone; Q = *p*-quinone. Similar observations concerning free radical formation have been made for ceruloplasmin (22, 24), the copper oxidase of mammalian serum.

More recently, several laboratories have presented evidence that conflicts with some of the earlier findings of Nakamura. Omura (25) prepared highly purified laccases from the Japanese and Indo-Chinese lac trees. The molecular weights were calculated to be 141,000 and 130,000, respectively, and calculations from the copper determinations indicated a copper content ranging from 4.5 to 5.6 atoms of copper per molecule. Blumberg *et al.* (26), using both chemical and EPR measurements, found that *Rhus vernicifera* laccase contained six atoms of copper per molecule. However, only four of these were in the divalent state. Further evidence for the heterogeneity of copper in laccases is found in the work reported by Malmström and his co-workers, who used highly purified laccase from *Polyporus versicolor* (27–30). This enzyme has a molecular weight of 60,000 and contains four atoms of copper per molecule, only two of which are in the cupric state as indicated by EPR measurements.

The nature of the binding of copper within the laccase molecule has not yet yielded to present methods of inquiry. It is known that the copper is nondialyzable. From the appearance of the EPR spectrum of *Polyporus* laccase, Malmström and Vänngård (31) concluded that the copper may be coordinated to nitrogen ligands within the protein. Another area not well investigated is the nature of the enzyme–substrate complex. The existence of Cu^+ within laccase and the high π-electron density of the best substrates have led to the proposal that a Cu^+–π-electron interaction may be involved in complex formation (22); a similar suggestion has been presented for ceruloplasmin (32).

III. Blue Color

Another characteristic of laccases that has fascinated numerous investigators for aesthetic as well as scientific reasons is the deep blue color. It is most appropriate to discuss the blue color at this point because it is believed to be due entirely to the copper bound within the molecule. Although the existence of laccase had been known previous to the turn of the century, it was not until 1939 that Keilin and Mann first commented on this property (11). Undoubtedly, until this time isolation procedures were inadequate to obtain sufficiently pure material in which the color would be apparent. This discovery, together with the lack of inhibition by carbon monoxide, allowed one to distinguish easily between laccase and polyphenoloxidase as the latter is sensitive to carbon monoxide and not endowed with the beautiful blue color.

Keilin and Mann also reported that the blue color of their enzyme preparation disappeared reversibly upon addition of substrates or other reducing substances, and irreversibly upon heating to 60° or acidification. Unfortunately, these authors concluded that the blue color was not due to enzyme copper but instead was attributable to a pigment that contaminated their preparations (12). They were able to obtain some of this pigment

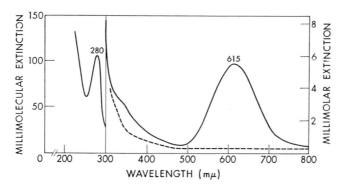

Fig. 1. Absorption spectrum of laccase in phosphate buffer, pH 7.0 and ionic strength 0.2. ——, Native laccase; ------, after the addition of 0.01 M ascorbic acid. Reproduced from *Biochim. Biophys. Acta* (17).

free of the enzyme and reported that it contained neither copper nor protein, but was high in carbohydrate content. They were, however, unable to obtain enzyme free of this pigment. A possible reason for this erroneous conclusion was revealed in the work of Omura, who in the course of purifying *Rhus* laccase (33), separated a second, blue, copper protein which Peisach later named stellacyanin. This blue protein has little or no oxidase activity and is high in carbohydrate content. We have also worked with stellacyanin and have found the color to be far more resistant to the effects of acid than is laccase;[1] again, this was a property of Keilin and Mann's blue pigment. However, in contrast to their blue pigment the material examined by Omura (33) and by ourselves (26) is a copper protein. Furthermore, neither Omura (33) nor Nakamura (27) were able to detect in their laccase preparations a substance which fulfilled the Keilin and Mann description. Perhaps the blue pigment must be relegated to the massive storehouse of unresolved problems.

After the observations of Keilin and Mann, little interest was expressed in the blue color until 1958 when Nakamura (17) published an optical spectrum of *Rhus vernicifera* laccase showing the strong absorption peak at 615 mμ (Fig. 1). This peak, while remaining unchanged in an oxygen-free atmosphere, disappeared upon addition of substrate or other reducing agents under anaerobic conditions. The peak was restored by readmitting oxygen to the system. The blue color remained stable even at pH 2–3 at 37°. However, the possibility of contamination of Nakamura's laccase preparation by the very stable blue protein described by Omura must be considered a possible explanation for this marked stability. Because the 615 mμ peak and the copper content were always linearly related, Naka-

[1] W. G. Levine and J. Peisach, unpublished observations.

mura suggested that the blue color was due to the specific binding of the copper within the enzyme protein. This seemed reasonable in light of the well-known blue color of copper complexes of various amino acids, peptides, and proteins. At the same time, the intensity of the color suggested binding within the laccase protein unlike that seen within any of the simple copper complexes. Based on Nakamura's data, the extinction coefficient per mole of bound copper is 1350 cm^{-1}. The laccase from *Polyporus versicolor* has an extinction coefficient (measured at 610 mμ) per mole of copper of 1000 cm^{-1} (28). This is several orders of magnitude greater than that of copper sulfate and also greater than that of the copper–ammonia complex. Similar observations regarding the intensity of blue color have been made for other copper proteins (e.g., ceruloplasmin (34, 35) and ascorbic acid oxidase (36)).

The question then arises as to which state of copper within the laccase molecule is responsible for the blue color. Hemocyanin has been shown by EPR to contain only Cu^+, whether oxygenated or not (37). On the other hand, deep blue copper proteins have been isolated from *Pseudomonas* (38), *Rhus vernicifera* (26, 33), and *Bordetella* (22, 39, 40). Each of these contains a single cupric atom per molecule. Thus, ostensibly, neither Cu^{2+}, nor Cu^+ nor a $Cu^+ - Cu^{2+}$ pair is *sine qua non* for the blue color of copper proteins. Nakamura (28) demonstrated a linear relationship between 615 mμ absorption and copper content of *Rhus* laccase. Because he believed that laccase copper was entirely in the cupric state he concluded that the color was attributable to Cu^{2+}. The involvement of cupric copper in the chromophoric site was further investigated by Blumberg *et al.* (26). These authors calculated the ratios of absorbance in the red (597–665 mμ, depending on the specific copper protein) per Cu^{2+} for laccase as well as a number of other blue copper-containing proteins (e.g., ceruloplasmin, ascorbate oxidase, cerebrocuproin, plastocyanin, azurin, etc.). The ratios all fell within a fairly narrow range, reinforcing the idea that blue color is dependent upon the cupric state. Blumberg and co-workers (35) also have investigated the relation between blue color and Cu^{2+} in ceruloplasmin, using magnetic resonance techniques. Their data indicate that all cupric atoms, and only cupric atoms, of ceruloplasmin are chromophoric.

Because laccase contains both Cu^+ and Cu^{2+} (25, 26, 29, 30) the question arises as to the possible contribution of Cu^+ to the blue color. Because removal or reduction of Cu^{2+} results in a total loss of color, this contribution could only be as some sort of Cu^+–Cu^{2+} couple. From the appearance of the EPR spectra, it was concluded that, as in ceruloplasmin (29), there is no spin coupling of copper atoms in either *Rhus* (26) or *Polyporus* (29) laccases as there is, for example, in certain solutions of copper uroporphyrin III (41). Furthermore, plastocyanin, which is deep blue, contains two cupric atoms, and EPR studies indicate that the spins of these copper atoms also are not coupled.[2] From what is known of the intense colors of charge-transfer compounds, it is tempting to suggest that this type of Cu^{+}–Cu^{2+} interaction is involved. However, evidence supporting such a concept is lacking.

IV. Occurrence and Substrates

A. Occurrence

Laccase was named for its occurrence in the lac tree (3) while at the same time it is also present in a great variety of plants. It has been found in cabbages, turnips, beets, apples, asparagus, potatoes, pears, mushrooms, and various other vegetables and fungi (2, 5, 6); see also the extensive listing by Franke (42). Other copper oxidases are found in many of the same plants and it is necessary to distinguish them from laccase. Lindeberg (43) identified laccase in the mushroom *Psalliota bispora f. albida* by its ability to oxidize p-phenylenediamine and catechol and to resist inhibition by carbon monoxide. It was differentiated from another polyphenoloxidase which was sensitive to carbon monoxide and which catalyzed the oxidation of catechol but not p-phenylenediamine. In this way, Lindeberg was able to demonstrate that the two enzymes had dissimilar distribution within the fungus. This suggested that they may have different functions. In a like manner, laccase was differentiated from a tyrosinase-like enzyme in various parts of *Agaricus campestris* (44).

Laccase is essentially an extracellular enzyme. Lindeberg and Fåhraeus (45, 46) showed that the wood rotting fungus, *Polyporus versicolar*, when grown under suitable conditions, quantitatively secreted laccase into the growth medium, from which it was readily isolated and purified. In fact, nearly the entire protein content of the medium could be accounted for as laccase. It is interesting that the addition to the medium of substances such as tyrosine and 2,5-xylidine, which are not laccase substrates, was very effective in inducing laccase production. On the other hand, catechol, hydroquinone, and p-phenylenediamine, which are readily oxidized by laccase, showed no such induction effect. Furthermore, those conditions which were most conducive to laccase synthesis were not necessarily optimal for growth of the mold (46). This is exemplified in Table II. With increasing concentration of p-cresol in the growth medium there was little stimulation of growth and even inhibition was seen at high concentrations. Nevertheless, laccase production was greatly enhanced at all p-cresol

[2] Blumberg, W. E., and Peisach, J., personal communication.

TABLE II

INFLUENCE OF INCREASING AMOUNTS OF p-CRESOL ON GROWTH AND LACCASE
PRODUCTION OF Polyporus versicolor[a]

p-Cresol (mmoles/flask)	Mycelial dry weight (mg)	Laccase activity (μl O$_2$/hr)
0	94	51
0.5	105	560
1.0	110	1300
1.5	104	1500
2.0	94	1700
4.0	77	4100
8.0	57	1400

[a] After F°hraeus (46).

concentrations. In fact the best enzyme yields were obtained where growth was partially suppressed. Even total suppression of growth allowed for a small amount of laccase formation.

B. Diphenol Substrates

The original "laccol" of Bertrand was later shown to be a mixture containing four derivatives of catechol with varying degrees of sidechain unsaturation.

The structures were identified as follows (47):

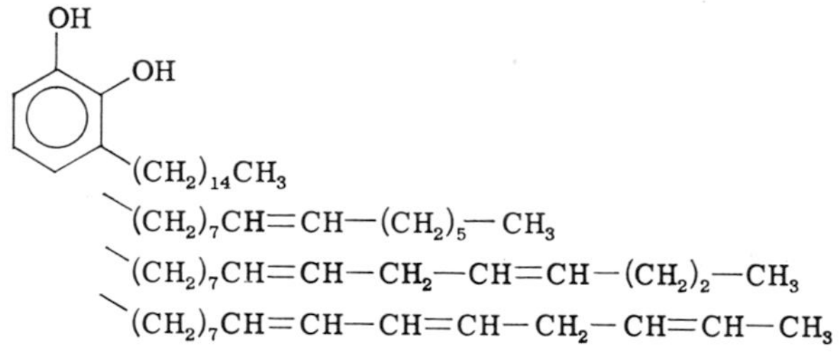

$$
\begin{array}{l}
OH \\
\quad OH \\
\quad\quad (CH_2)_{14}CH_3 \\
\quad\quad (CH_2)_7CH{=}CH{-}(CH_2)_5{-}CH_3 \\
\quad\quad (CH_2)_7CH{=}CH{-}CH_2{-}CH{=}CH{-}(CH_2)_2{-}CH_3 \\
\quad\quad (CH_2)_7CH{=}CH{-}CH{=}CH{-}CH_2{-}CH{=}CH{-}CH_3
\end{array}
$$

The darkening and hardening of lac tree latex is a result of the action of laccase on these substances. Laccase also reacts with a large number of aryl diphenols and diamines. In general the functional groups must have an *ortho* or *para* relationship. Controversy exists concerning the oxidation of *meta* compounds. It has been reported that *Rhus* laccase does not oxidize such substances (9, 48). Phloroglucinol (1,3,5-trihydroxybenzene), on the

other hand, was shown to be oxidized by laccases from *Lactarius piperatus*
(49) and *Polyporus versicolor* (50). Neufeld *et al.* (51) prepared a specific
metapolyphenoloxidase from the fungi *Piricularia oryzae* and *Polyporus
versicolor*. These investigators felt that reports of the oxidation of *meta*
substrates are attributable to such a specific enzyme, which may occur
together with laccase in various plant tissues. This was disputed by Fåhraeus and Ljunggren (50), who felt that, at least for *Polyporus versicolor*,
there was no reason to assume the existence of a particular metapolyphenoloxidase. It was believed by Keilin and Mann that at least two
phenolic or amino functions were required for substrate activity (11, 12).
However, evidence for this is contradictory. Yakushiji (49) found that
laccase from *Lactarius piperatus* catalyzed the oxidation of *p*-cresol, and
Higuchi (52) reported weak oxidation of this substance in the presence of
laccase from Japanese lacquer (biological source not indicated). It should
be pointed out that Yakushiji's enzyme was obtained from a source that is
known to contain more than one copper oxidase, and that the purity of his
preparation is doubtful. More recently Fåhraeus and Ljunggren (40, 50)
have reported the oxidation of a number of monophenols, including *p*-
cresol, in the presence of laccase from *Polyporus versicolor*. It was noted
that, unlike catechol oxidation, *p*-cresol oxidation rapidly diminished in
rate (Fig. 2). Furthermore, in the presence of *p*-cresol the oxidation of
catechol was greatly depressed. The addition of gelatin or Tween 80 to the
reaction mixture containing *p*-cresol protected against this inhibitory
effect and allowed a rapid uptake of oxygen to occur in either the presence
or absence of catechol. In living fungal cultures, this inhibitory effect was

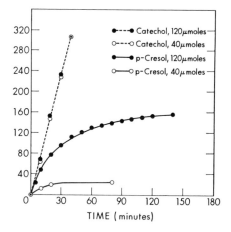

Fig. 2. Oxidation of catechol and *p*-cresol by laccase. After Fåhraeus and Ljunggren
(50).

not seen; thus a protective environment for the enzyme exists naturally. The authors interpreted their results as evidence for the existence of separate sites for monophenolase and diphenolase activity, although other interpretations are possible. This inhibitory effect is reminiscent of the reaction inactivation reported for ascorbic acid oxidase (53) and for tyrosinase (54). The ascorbic acid oxidase inhibition has been attributed to H_2O_2, which forms during the reaction (55), while the tyrosinase inhibition has been attributed to the interaction of enzyme and quinone formed during the oxidation process (56). Whether or not either or both of these mechanisms play a role in the *Polyporus* laccase–*p*-cresol system is not known. The observations of Fåhraeus and Ljunggren may further serve to explain the findings by other authors that laccase does not catalyze the oxidation of monophenols (11, 57). Other reports state that laccase, isolated from either *Polyporus versicolor* or *Rhus vernicifera*, reacts with *p*-cresol, forming a white precipitate; yet no uptake of oxygen is observed (48, 58, 59). The formation of a white precipitate from *p*-cresol also occurs in growing laccase-producing *Polyporus versicolor* (50). Catalytic activity with *p*-cresol and related structures may be dependent upon the source of the laccase. Further investigation into this problem would certainly be of value.

C. Diamine and Other Substrates

The best substrate for laccase, based on V_{max} measurements, is *p*-phenylenediamine (48) (Table III). Keilin and Mann (11) first showed this substance to be rapidly oxidized in the presence of laccase, and, together with hydroquinone, it is commonly used to assay for the enzyme. Activity

TABLE III

REACTION VELOCITIES OF VARIOUS SUBSTRATES WITH *Rhus vernicifera* LACCASE[a]

Substrates	V_{max} ($\mu l\, O_2$/hr/μmole of enzyme)
p-Phenylenediamine	21.70
N,N-dimethyl-*p*-phenylenediamine	17.60
Hydroquinone	7.60
N-Phenyl-*p*-phenylenediamine	3.47
o-Phenylenediamine	3.16
p-Aminophenol	1.04
Catechol	0.95

[a] After Peisach and Levine (48).

toward these substrates is particularly useful in differentiating laccase and tyrosinase, both of which commonly occur together in plant tissues (43, 44). Tyrosinase does not readily oxidize aromatic diamines or diphenols whose functional groups are *para* related. Keilin and Mann (11) observed that crude laccase preparations oxidized ascorbate, but with increasing purity, only indirect oxidation through p-phenylenediamine was possible. Graubard (57) also reported that ascorbate was oxidized only in the presence of a carrier such as catechol. However, the direct oxidation of ascorbate by laccase has been demonstrated by numerous authors (25, 44, 48, 60) even with highly purified enzymes (48, 25). Bertrand (61) has reported that laccase catalyzed the oxidation of cysteine, although this was denied by Graubard (57) and by Tissieres (62). The latter, however, did find that the methyl ester of cysteine was oxidized by laccase at 5–8% of the rate found with p-phenylenediamine. Reduced cytochrome c was reported to be oxidized by laccase from *Russula foetens* (57) and *Rhus succedanea* (63). However, negative results were reported by Nakamura (17) and Tissieres (62). In this regard it must be pointed out that the purity of the *Russula* laccase (57) was questionable, and the *Rhus* laccase (63) was able to oxidize reduced cytochrome c only in the presence of added hydroquinone.

Unlike ceruloplasmin-catalyzed reactions, oxidations catalyzed by *Rhus vernicifera* laccase are not inhibited by chelating agents such as EDTA, 4,5-dihydroxy-m-benzenedisulfonic acid, or diethylenetriaminepentaacetic acid (48). The one exception is that the oxidation of ascorbate is completely inhibited by micromolar concentrations of EDTA. Although ceruloplasmin-catalyzed oxidations are strongly stimulated by low concentrations of Fe^{2+} and Cu^{2+} (64, 65), these metal ions exhibit little or no stimulation in laccase systems (48).

D. Naturally Occurring Substrates

A considerable number of complex polyphenols which occur in various plant tissues have been reported to be oxidized in the presence of laccase. It is therefore tempting to consider that laccase may play a role in the metabolism of these substances. Freudenberg was able to demonstrate both *in vitro* and *in vivo* that, in spruce saplings, the conversion of coniferyl alcohol to lignin is catalyzed by laccase (66). Intermediates in this reaction which have thus far been identified or postulated include dimeric products, free radicals, and quinones. The actual enzymatic reaction, however, is restricted to oxidation of the phenolic group. (Note that this is another monophenolic substrate.) Subsequent reactions including radical interactions, addition reactions, and polymerizations are thought to proceed nonenzymatically. The wood rotting fungi, such as *Polyporus versicolor*, produce laccase and utilize it to break down lignin. Thus the same enzyme, from different sources, may participate in both the synthesis and degradation of lignin. Caution was advised by Higuchi and Ito (67) in attributing

Coniferyl alcohol

lignin biosynthesis only to the action of laccase. These authors demonstrated similarity in the reaction products of coniferyl alcohol formed in the presence of laccase, of phenoloxidase, and of peroxidase. Since these enzymes often occur together it may be difficult to assign to only one of them the key role in lignin biosynthesis. Lindeberg and Holm (68) have suggested that the laccase of certain hymenomycetes plays a role in the oxidation of phenolic substances found in forest soils. The coloration seen upon injury to mushroom fruit bodies has been attributed in part to the action of laccase on naturally occurring polyphenolic substances. The fact that laccase is responsible for the darkening and hardening of *Rhus* latex upon injury to the tree may indicate a protective function for the enzyme. Wosilait and Nason (69) isolated a pyridine nucleotide–quinone reductase from pea seeds and suggested a coupled system with laccase which would function in the plant electron-transport system.

E. Heterogeneity of Laccases

From the above, it is evident that laccase is not a single entity but rather represents a group of closely related enzymes that can be distinguished from each other in several ways. Molecular weights differ considerably. Since the molecular weights of *Rhus* laccases are 130,000 and 141,000 (25) and that of *Polyporus versicolor* is 60,000 (28) it is somewhat dubious that the former represent merely polymeric forms of the latter. Laccases also differ in copper content and in substrate specificity. Concerning the latter, however, more careful evaluation with highly purified enzymes is necessary, particularly in those instances in which the source material contains more than one copper-oxidase. Laccases also differ in their pH dependence. The pH optimum is 6.4 for *Rhus succedanea* laccase, 7.5 for *Rhus vernicifera*, and 4.5 for *Melanorrhea usitata* (25). The pH optimum for *Polyporus* laccase varies with substrate. For catechol and hydroquinone the pH optima have been shown to be 5.0 and 4.0, respectively (50, 45). Even from a single source, nonidentical laccases have been obtained. The laccase obtained by Mosbach (28) from *Polyporus versicolor* showed two forms, designated A and B. They showed similar absorption spectra, copper content, and magnetic properties, but were separable on DEAE–cellulose columns and had different specific activities and carbohydrate content. The possibility cannot be excluded that one or more of these differences may represent a procedural artifact.

From these observations, it is imperative that reference to the enzyme source be made when the properties of a laccase are described. This will avoid the presentation of views that are apparently conflicting, but in truth are not.

V. Summary

Laccase has been known for over 80 years. It has been detected in a great variety of plant tissues, although its occurrence in the animal kingdom has yet to be described. It contains both Cu^+ and Cu^{2+}, and the copper is essential for enzymatic activity. During laccase-catalyzed reactions the copper is alternatively reduced by the substrate and oxidized by molecular oxygen. The Cu^{2+} is probably responsible for the deep blue color and in the presence of reducing agents the color disappears. Similarly upon removal of the copper by treatment with cyanide, the blue color is lost. Laccase catalyzes the oxidation of a large number of aryl diamines and diphenols (e.g., catechol, hydroquinone, *p*-phenylenediamine) as well as ascorbate. The enzymatic activity is not inhibited by chelating agents. Laccases isolated from different sources may vary considerably with respect to molecular weight, pH optima, and substrate spectrum.

REFERENCES

1. Yoshida, H., *J. Chem. Soc.*, **43,** 472 (1883).
2. Bertrand, G., *Compt. Rend.*, **118,** 1215 (1894).
3. Bertrand. G., *Bull. Soc. Chim.*, **11,** 717 (1894).
4. Bertrand, G., *Compt. Rend.*, **120,** 266 (1895).
5. Bertrand, G., *Compt. Rend.*, **121,** 166 (1895).
6. Bertrand, G., *Bull. Soc. Chim.*, **13,** 361 (1895).
7. Bertrand, G., *Compt. Rend.*, **121,** 166 (1896).
8. Bertrand, G., *Bull. Soc. Chim.*, **17,** 619 (1897).
9. Bertrand, G., *Bull. Soc. Chim.*, **15,** 791 (1896).
10. Suminokura, K., *Biochem. Z.*, **224,** 292 (1930).

11. Keilin, D., and Mann, T., *Nature*, **143**, 23 (1939).
12. Keilin, D., and Mann, T., *Nature*, **145**, 304 (1940).
13. Bertrand, D., *Bull. Soc. Chim.*, **29**, 613 (1947).
14. Tissieres, A., *Nature*, **162**, 340 (1948).
15. Omura, T., *J. Biochem.*, **50**, 305 (1961).
16. Omura, T., *J. Biochem.*, **50**, 389 (1961).
17. Nakamura, T., *Biochim. Biophys. Acta*, **30**, 44 (1958).
18. Nakamura, T., *Biochim. Biophys. Acta*, **30**, 538 (1958).
19. Mason, H. S., *Advances in Enzymology*, **16**, 129 (1955).
20. Nakamura, T., *Biochim. Biophys. Acta*, **30**, 640 (1958).
21. Malmström, B. G., Mosbach, R., and Vänngård, T., *Nature*, **183**, 321 (1959).
22. Broman, L., Malmström, B. G., Aasa, R., and Vänngård, T., *Biochim. Biophys. Acta*, **75**, 365 (1963).
23. Nakamura, T., *in* M. S. Blois, H. W., Brown, R. M. Lemmon, R. O. Lindblom, and M. Weissbluth (eds.), "Free radicals in biological systems," Academic Press Inc., New York, 1961, p. 169.
24. Peisach, J., and Levine, W. G., *Biochim. Biophys. Acta*, **77**, 615 (1963).
25. Omura, T., *J. Biochem.*, **50**, 264 (1961).
26. Blumberg, W. E., Levine, W. G., Margolis, S., and Peisach, J., *Biochem. Biophys. Res. Communs.*, **15**, 277 (1964).
27. Malmström, G., Fåhraeus, G., and Mosbach, R., *Biochim. Biophys. Acta*, **28**, 652 (1958).
28. Mosbach, R., *Biochim. Biophys. Acta*, **73**, 204 (1963).
29. Broman, L., Malmström, B. G., Aasa, R., and Vänngård, T., *J. Mol. Biol.*, **5**, 301 (1962).
30. Ehrenberg, A., Malmström, B. G., Broman, L., and Mosbach, R., *J. Mol. Biol.*, **5**, 450 (1962).
31. Malmström, B. G., and Vänngård, T., *J. Mol. Biol.*, **2**, 118 (1960).
32. Levine, W. G., and Peisach, J., *Biochim. Biophys. Acta*, **63**, 528 (1962).
33. Omura, T., *J. Biochem.*, **50**, 394 (1961).
34. Holmberg, C. G., and Laurell, C. B., *Acta Chem. Scand.*, **2**, 550 (1948).
35. Blumberg, W. E., Eisinger, J., Aisen, P., Morell, A. G., and Scheinberg, I. H., *J. Biol. Chem.*, **238**, 1675 (1963).
36. Powers, W. H., Lewis, S., and Dawson, C. R., *J. Gen. Physiol.*, **27**, 167 (1944).
37. Nakamura, T., and Mason, H., *Biochem. Biophys. Res. Communs.*, **3**, 297 (1960).
38. Mason, H. S., *Biochem. Biophys. Res. Communs.*, **73**, 204 (1963).
39. Sutherland, I. W., and Wilkinson, J. F., *J. Gen. Microbiol.*, **30**, 105 (1963).
40. Fåhraeus, G., *Biochim. Biophys. Acta*, **54**, 192 (1961).
41. Blumberg, W. E., and Peisach, J., *J. Biol. Chem.*, **240**, 870 (1965).
42. Franke, W., *Handbuch Pflanzenphysiologie*, **12**, 401 (1960).
43. Lindeberg, G., *Nature*, **166**, 739 (1950).
44. Legrand, G., *Compt. Rend.*, **240**, 249 (1955).
45. Lindeberg, G., and Fahråeus, G., *Physiol. Plantarum*, **5**, 277 (1952).
46. Fåhraeus, G., *Physiol. Plantarum*, **7**, 704 (1954).
47. Sunthankar, S. V., and Dawson, C. R., *J. Am. Chem. Soc.*, **76**, 5070 (1954).
48. Peisach, J., and Levine, W. G., *J. Biol. Chem.*, **240**, 2284 (1965).
49. Yakushiji, E., *Acta Phytochim.*, **10**, 73 (1937).
50. Fåhraeus, G., and Ljunggren, H., *Biochim. Biophys. Acta*, **46**, 22 (1961).

51. Neufeld, H. A., Latterell, F. M., Green, L. F., and Weintraub, R. L., *Arch. Biochem. Biophys.*, **76,** 317 (1958).
52. Higuchi, T., *J. Biochem.*, **45,** 515 (1958).
53. Powers, W. H., and Dawson, C. R., *J. Gen. Physiol.*, **27,** 181 (1944).
54. Miller, W. H., and Dawson, C. R., *J. Am. Chem. Soc.*, **63,** 3368 (1941).
55. Poillon, W. N., and Dawson, C. R., *Biochim. Biophys. Acta*, **77,** 37 (1963).
56. Brooks, D. W., and Dawson, C. R., this symposium.
57. Graubard, M., *Enzymologia*, **5,** 332 (1938).
58. Brown, B. R., and Bocks, S. M., *in* J. B. Pridham (ed.), "Enzyme chemistry of phenolic compounds," Macmillan Company (Pergamon), New York, 1963, p. 129.
59. Benfield, G., Bocks, S. M., Bromley, K., and Brown, B. R., *Phytochem.*, **3,** 79 (1964).
60. Bertrand, D., *Bull. Soc. Chim. Biol.*, **27,** 396 (1945).
61. Bertrand, D., *Bull. Soc. Chim. Biol.*, **29,** 608 (1947).
62. Tissieres, A., *Nature*, **163,** 480 (1949).
63. Bertrand, D., Belval, H., and Legrand, G., *Bull. Soc. Chim. Biol.*, **29,** 607 (1947).
64. Curzon, G., *Biochem. J.*, **79,** 656 (1961).
65. Levine, W. G., and Peisach, J., *Biochim. Biophys. Acta*, **77,** 601 (1963).
66. Freudenberg, K., *Nature*, **183,** 1152 (1959).
67. Higuchi, T., and Ito, Y., *J. Biochem.*, **45,** 575 (1958).
68. Lindeberg, G., and Holm, G., *Physiol. Plantarum*, **5,** 100 (1952).
69. Wosilait, W. D., and Nason, A., *J. Biol. Chem.*, **206,** 255 (1954).

Characteristics of the State of Copper in *Rhus* Laccase[*]

TAKAO NAKAMURA AND YASUYUKI OGURA[†]

Department of Biophysics and Biochemistry,
Faculty of Science,
University of Tokyo,
Tokyo, Japan

I. Introduction

Among the copper proteins thus far isolated from biological materials, laccase is characterized by its high activity in catalyzing the aerobic oxidation of polyphenols, *p*-phenylenediamine, and ascorbic acid. Its electron-transferring activity is thought to be closely related to the electronic state of the copper atom and its ligand groups in the enzyme molecule, but little has been known about the difference in these respects between the enzymatically active and nonactive copper proteins. To get insight into the molecular characteristics of the enzyme, the following experiments were performed using laccases of different origins as well as some organic copper complexes:

(a)   Determination of valence state of copper by EPR spectroscopy and colorimetric methods,

(b)   Examination of localization and delocalization of the unpaired electron (hole) of Cu^{2+} from EPR spectra, and

(c)   Comparison of absorption spectra of laccase with those of other Cu^{2+} complexes, with special reference to the difference absorption at 330 mμ of oxidized and reduced forms.

II. Materials and Methods

Copper Proteins: Rhus vernicifera laccase was purified from the latex samples which were obtained from Ken Shii (two samples), Mao Ba (three samples), and Chu Shi, China, and Ibaraki, Japan. The procedures for purification of the enzyme were the same as described previously (1). *Rhus vernicifera* blue protein was purified from the Ken Shii latex. *Rhus succedanea* laccase was purified from the latex, obtained from Taiwan, by the method described by Omura (2). Ceruloplasmin was obtained from

* This work was supported in part by Public Health Service Research Grant GM 09 795 from the National Institutes of Health.

† Not at meeting.

horse serum by ethanol and ammonium sulfate fractionation, and purified by DEAE–cellulose column chromatography at pH 5.5.

Colorimetric Assay of Copper in the Proteins: The amounts of total copper and cuprous ion in copper proteins were determined colorimetrically by using 2,2′-biquinoline, which is a color-specific chelating agent for cuprous ion. Details of the procedures have been described previously (3).

Electron Paramagnetic Resonance Spectrometry: The EPR spectrometer used was the model JES-3BX X-band instrument of Japan Electron Optics Laboratory Co. Spectra were recorded at liquid nitrogen temperature ($-196°$). Signal strength and g value were determined as described previously (3).

Spectrophotometry: The absorption spectra of copper proteins and Cu^{2+} complexes were recorded with a Cary Model 14 recording spectrophotometer. Copper proteins were dissolved in 0.1 M phosphate buffer, pH 6.8. The spectra of the other Cu^{2+} complexes were recorded at pH 9.0; the concentrations of Cu^{2+} and the complexing agent were 10 mM and 50 mM, respectively, unless otherwise indicated.

Spectrophotometric Measurements by the "Stopped Flow Method": The "stopped flow" experiments were performed according to Chance (4) with a sensitive spectrophotometer combined with a flow system designed by Chance and Legallais (5). Details of the equipment have been described previously (6).

Assay of Polyphenoloxidase Activity: The rate of the polyphenol oxidase reaction was estimated by measuring the consumption of molecular oxygen dissolved in the reaction medium with a Clark oxygen electrode. The reaction mixture contained 20 mM hydroquinone or pyrogallol as substrate and 0.1 M phosphate at pH 7.0, 6.8 or 6.3, or 0.1 M acetate at pH 5.0. Reaction temperature was 25°. For further details of the procedures, see Ref. (3).

III. Results and Discussion

A. Valence State of Copper in *Rhus vernicifera* Laccase

By using a magnetochemical method, Nakamura (7) has shown that copper in *Rhus vernicifera* laccase (Ken Shii) was in the cupric form. On the other hand, Blumberg *et al.* (8) found only 70% of the copper in *Rhus vernicifera* laccase in the cupric form by EPR measurements. In the present work, the Cu^{2+} content of the enzyme samples was re-examined by EPR and colorimetric methods. Other quantitative measurements were also performed on the enzyme samples, and the results obtained are summarized in Table I.

TABLE I

COPPER ANALYSIS, SPECTROMETRY, AND ACTIVITY OF LACCASE PREPARATIONS

Laccase	Ken Shii-I	Ken Shii-II	Chu Shi	Mao Ba-I	Mao Ba-II	Mao Ba-III	Ibaraki
Cu^{2+} by biquinoline method (%)	89	90	73	71	47	42	80
Cu^{2+} by EPR (%)	91	—	75	80	57	—	72
A_{615}/mM total Cu	1.44	1.46	1.41	1.59	1.49	1.43	1.44
A_{615}/mM Cu^{2+}	1.62	1.66	1.92	2.24	3.20	3.41	1.80
Activity[a]/total Cu (sec^{-1})	4.2	4.1	3.2	2.6	2.2	1.9	6.5
Activity[a]/Cu^{2+} (sec^{-1})	4.8	4.6	4.4	3.7	4.8	4.5	8.2

[a] Turnover number of laccase copper reacting at pH 7.0 with hydroquinone as substrate.

The Cu^{2+} contents of the *Rhus vernicifera* laccase preparations were estimated by the biquinoline method as the difference between the amount of total copper and that of Cu^+ (designated as Cu^+-detected). The ratio of Cu^{2+} (designated as Cu^{2+}-detected) to total copper was obtained as a reproducible value in repeated measurements using the same enzyme sample, but the values differed according to the origin of the latex samples.

The laccase samples of different origins were found to give essentially the same EPR spectra. Cu^{2+} contents of these laccase samples were estimated from their EPR spectra (see Fig. 1c), and the ratios of Cu^{2+} to total copper thus obtained were found to be in good agreement with those obtained by colorimetry.

All preparations of *Rhus vernicifera* laccase were found to have the same absorption maximum at 615 mμ and the same value for A_{280}/A_{615} as reported previously (1). From the data of copper analysis, which was carried out by the biquinoline method, the values of the extinction coefficient at 615 mμ were calculated on the basis of the contents of total copper and Cu^{2+}. The results obtained are presented in Table I. It was found that the absorption at 615 mμ is proportional to the content of total copper, but not to the estimated amount of Cu^{2+}. On the other hand, the oxidized-minus-

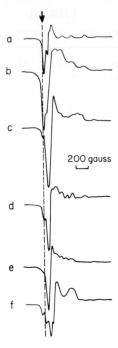

Fig. 1. Derivative curves of the EPR spectra of laccase and other copper complexes. Temperature, $-196°$; field modulation, 6.6 Gauss; the magnetic field decreases from left to right. Each sample contained 10–20 µg of copper, and the arrow indicates $g = 2.0036$. a, Cu^{2+}-citrate; b, Cu^{2+}-glutamate; c, *Rhus vernicifera* laccase, d, *Rhus succedanea* laccase; e, horse ceruloplasmin; f, *Rhus vernicifera* blue protein.

reduced extinction coefficient difference at the absorption shoulder at 330 mµ was found to be proportional to the Cu^{2+} content (see Table II and Fig. 2a.

The activities of these enzyme preparations were determined with hydroquinone as substrate at pH 7.0, and it was found that the activity

TABLE II

Cu^{2+} Content and Oxidized minus Reduced Extinction Coefficient Difference of *Rhus vernicifera* Laccase at 330 mµ

Laccase	Ken Shii-I	Chu Shi	Mao Ba-III
Percentage Cu^{2+} by biquinoline method	89	73	42
ΔA_{330}/mM Cu^{2+}	0.77	0.79	0.78

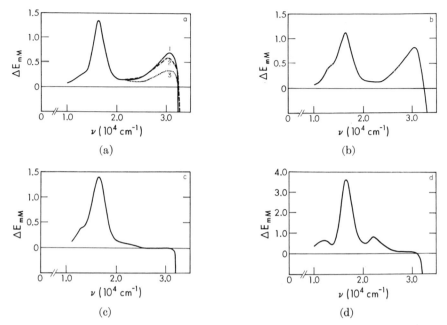

FIG. 2. Oxidized-minus-reduced absorption difference spectra of copper proteins. The reduced form was obtained by adding ascorbic acid to the protein solution. a, *Rhus vernicifera* laccase (1, Ken Shii-I; 2, Chu Shi; 3, Mao Ba-III). b, *Rhus succedanea* laccase. c, Horse ceruloplasmin. d, *Rhus vernicifera* blue protein.

values (turnover number of the enzyme copper) of the different preparations of *Rhus vernicifera* laccase of Chinese origin were almost proportional to their Cu^{2+} contents.

In a preliminary experiment, the change of absorbance at 615 mμ in a solution of *Rhus vernicifera* laccase was followed after a small volume of a concentrated solution of hydroquinone was rapidly mixed with the enzyme. As seen in Fig. 3a the absorbance at 615 mμ quickly decreased to a level corresponding to the Cu^{2+} content of the enzyme sample, and after a steady state period, the enzyme was totally reduced with exhaustion of molecular oxygen. Using the stopped flow method, an enzyme solution previously reduced by an excess of hydroquinone was mixed with a solution containing molecular oxygen, and the change of absorbance at 615 mμ was recorded. As may be seen in Fig. 3b, the absorption at 615 mμ immediately appeared and reached a level which corresponded to the Cu^{2+} content of the enzyme, and after a steady state period the enzyme was again brought back to the reduced form by the exhaustion of dissolved molecular oxygen. The turnover number of the enzyme copper, which was calculated from the kinetic curve in Fig. 3b according to Chance's formulas

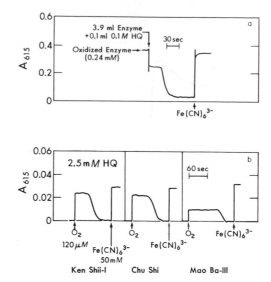

FIG. 3. Reaction of laccase with hydroquinone at pH 7.0 followed by change of optical density at 615 mμ.a, Aerobic addition of hydroquinone to the oxidized form of *Rhus vernicifera* laccase (Chu Shi). For the details of the experiment, see text. Temperature, 13°. b. "Stopped flow" experiment with laccase at 16.5°. The arrows indicate the time of introduction of oxygen or ferricyanide into the solution of enzyme in the reduced form. The relative values of ΔA_{615} in the steady state of the reaction are given as the percentage of those obtained by adding ferricyanide to the reduced enzyme.

Origin of latex	Ken Shii-I	Chu Shi	Mao Ba-III
Total conc. of laccase Cu(μM)	23	23	26
Steady state $\Delta A_{615}\%$	86	76	38
Cu$^{2+}\%$ by cuproine method	89	73	42
Turnover number (min^{-1}) from			
{kinetic curve	21	19	23
{overall reaction (Cu^{2+} basis)	23	22	24

(9), was in good agreement with that obtained from over-all reaction measurements with an oxygen electrode under the same experimental conditions. The data presented in Fig. 3 and Tables I and II show that both Cu^{2+}-detected and Cu^{+}-detected represent blue chromophores in the oxidized form of laccase, but that the copper which was detected as cuprous in the oxidized form of the enzyme does not participate in the enzymatic activity. The blue color of the Cu^{+}-detected rapidly disappeared upon addition of the substrate, and it reappeared when acted upon by ferricyanide, but not when exposed for a short time to molecular oxygen. The color of Cu^{2+}-detected could also be reduced on addition of the substrate, but it was readily oxidized by oxygen. The distinctive characteristic of the

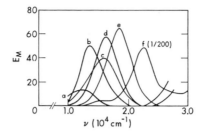

FIG. 4. Absorption spectra of Cu^{2+} chelates. a, $CuSO_4$ in 0.25 M H_2SO_4; b, Cu^{2+}-citrate; c, Cu^{2+}-imidazole (pH 5); d, Cu^{2+}-glutamate; e, Cu^{2+}-ethylenediamine; f, Cu^{2+}-diethyldithiocarbamate. For curve f, scale reading of E_M should be multiplied by a factor of 200.

active Cu^{2+}-detected copper is its absorption at 330 mμ. Its relation to the enzymatic activity will be discussed later. In *Rhus vernicifera* laccase, the ratio of Cu^{2+}-detected to total copper varied from 40 to 90%, depending on the origin of the samples, but there seems to be no evidence for the existence of a Cu^{+}-Cu^{2+} pair in laccase molecule, as has been suggested by Broman *et al.* (10) in the case of *Polyporus* laccase.

B. Electronic State of Copper in *Rhus* Laccase as Compared with Those of Some Other Cu^{2+} Complexes

The difference absorption spectra of oxidized and reduced forms and the EPR spectra of laccase and some other Cu^{2+} complexes were examined (Figs. 1, 2, and 4), and the data obtained are summarized in Table III. The turnover number of these complexes estimated from over-all reaction measurements are also shown.

There was a single and symmetric peak in the visible absorption spectra of simple Cu^{2+} chelates (Fig. 4) coordinated with O or N ligands. This may indicate a symmetrical Cu–ligand configuration in these Cu^{2+} chelates. A distinct hyperfine splitting of the $g_{||}$ signal was observed in the EPR spectra of these complexes (Fig. 1a, b),[1] suggestive of a high degree of localization of the unpaired electron to the nucleus of copper atom. Only a very weak polyphenoloxidase activity was observed with the Cu^{2+} chelates of this structure.

In the absorption spectra of *Rhus vernicifera* laccase and *Rhus succedanea* laccase (Fig. 2a, b), a shoulder at 760–780 mμ was observed in addition to the peak at 615 or 609 mμ, which may indicate that in these enzymes the ligand configuration around the copper atom is slightly distorted. Com-

[1] Similar results have been obtained by H. S. Mason and T. Nakamura, unpublished observations.

TABLE III

SUMMARY OF THE ACTIVITY MEASUREMENTS, COPPER ANALYSIS, EPR, AND SPECTROPHOTOMETRIC DATA FOR LACCASES AND OTHER COPPER COMPLEXES

Compound	Turnover number (sec^{-1}) [a]	Cu^{2+} by cuproine method (%)	g_m	$g_{\|}$	$A_{\|}$ (cm^{-1}) [b]	Absorption maximum (mμ) [c]
Cu^{2+}-citrate	10^{-4}(5.0)	—	2.06[d]	2.27[d]	0.014[d]	740
Cu^{2+}-glutamate	10^{-3}(5.0)	—	2.07	2.25	0.015	615
Cu^{2+}-ethylenediamine	10^{-3}(5.0)	—	2.07	—	0.017	548
Rhus vernicifera laccase (Ken Shii-I)	60(6.8)	89	2.07	2.30	0.004	(780), 615, (330)
Rhus succedanea laccase	208(6.3)	79	2.06	2.21	0.007	(760), 609, (330)
Horse ceruloplasmin	0.01(6.8)	80	2.06	2.20	0.006	(770), 608
Rhus vernicifera blue protein	0.5(6.8)	100	2.09	2.30	<0.002	850, 608, 450[e]
			$g_{\perp} = 2.02$		$A_{\perp}{}^{b} = 0.006$	

[a] Turnover number of copper measured with pyrogallol as substrate. The pH values of the reaction media are shown in parentheses.
[b] Hyperfine splitting constant.
[c] In the range of 300–1,000 mμ. Absorption shoulders are shown in parentheses.
[d] Similar results have been reported by Malmström and Vänngård (12).
[e] Data given by Omura (13).

parison of the position of the main peak of the visible absorption of the enzyme with those of Cu^{2+} chelates (11) (Fig. 4) leads us to infer that the copper in laccase is probably coordinated with N and O atoms. The hyperfine splitting constant $A_{||}$ of laccase (Fig. 1c, d) was found to be smaller than those of simple Cu^{2+} chelates, and this suggests a moderate delocalization of the unpaired electron of Cu^{2+} in laccase. A similar result has been obtained by Malmström and Vänng°rd for *Polyporus* laccase (12). Blumberg *et al.* (8) have measured the EPR spectra of *Rhus* laccase and *Rhus* blue protein, and reported values of g_x, g_y, and g_z. In their paper the $g = 2.00$ signal was ascribed to the g_x absorption; however, it may have been caused by an enzyme-bound free radical.

A salient feature of the absorption spectra of *Rhus* laccase is a shoulder at 330 mμ. In the case of *Rhus vernicifera* laccase, the oxidized-minus-reduced difference extinction at this wavelength was found to be proportional to the amount of the active Cu^{2+}-detected copper in the enzyme (Table II and Fig. 2a). *Rhus succedanea* laccase, with a higher turnover number than of *Rhus vernicifera* laccase, was characterized by a remarkable absorption at 330 mμ, which may be seen in the difference spectrum of the enzyme.

The absorption spectrum and EPR spectrum of horse ceruloplasmin were found to be quite similar to those of *Rhus* laccase, except that there was no distinct absorption at 330 mμ (Figs. 1c, e and 2a, c). The polyphenol-oxidase activity of this protein was very low. Considering that the presence of the 330 mμ band in *Rhus* laccase is probably due to the existence of a specific Cu^{2+} chelate configuration, it may be that the presence of this configuration is one of the necessary conditions for the activity of polyphenol oxidase.

There are at least three absorption peaks in the visible region in the case of *Rhus vernicifera* blue protein (13) (Fig. 2d). As has been discussed by Brill, Martin, and Williams (11), there seems to be a ligand configuration of low symmetry in this protein molecule. Blumberg *et al.* (8) gave an estimation of both $A_{||}$ and $A_\perp$ values for this protein, but in our measurements, the hyperfine splitting of the blue protein in the $g_{||}$ signal (Fig. 1f) was too small to allow the estimation of the splitting constant. The hyperfine splitting in the $g_\perp$ signal, on the other hand, was found to be well resolved, in accordance with the result reported by Blumberg *et al.* (8). The hyperfine splittings in the $g_\perp$ signal were obscure in the case of other Cu^{2+} chelates and copper proteins. These facts suggest that, in *Rhus vernicifera* blue protein, the unpaired electron of the Cu^{2+} is in a localized state in the $g_\perp$ signal, and in a delocalized state in the $g_{||}$ signal. This protein also lacked a distinct band at 330 mμ, which may account for the weakness of its oxidase activity (13).

IV. Summary

(1) It was demonstrated by colorimetric as well as EPR measurements that the oxidized form of *Rhus vernicifera* laccase contains both Cu^{2+} and Cu^+ ions. The ratio of Cu^{2+}-detected to total copper varied (40–90%) in samples of latex collected from various districts. The absorption maximum at 615 mμ and a shoulder at 780 mμ, invariably found in the enzymes of different origins, were proportional to the content of total copper in the enzyme. Enzyme activity was found to parallel the content of the cupric form and not that of total copper. The extinction difference (oxidized minus reduced) of the enzyme at 330 mμ was also proportional to the amount of Cu^{2+}-detected.

(2) By comparison of the EPR spectra of the laccases of *Rhus vernicifera* and *Rhus succedanea* with those of simple Cu^{2+} chelates, it was inferred that the unpaired electron of the Cu^{2+} ion was in a moderately delocalized state. The absorption spectra of these enzymes seem to indicate that the ligand field around Cu^{2+} is in a slightly distorted configuration. The absorption band at 330 mμ, which was always present in active laccase samples and absent or weak in other copper proteins such as horse ceruloplasmin or *Rhus vernicifera* blue protein, showing no or only weak laccase activity, and therefore thought to be related to the enzymatic activity, seems to be due to some electronic configuration specific to the laccase molecule. This absorption band has been suspected to be a charge transfer (ligand to cupric ion) band (11). The enzymatically weakly active horse ceruloplasmin showed, however, EPR and optical absorption spectra similar to those of laccase. The blue protein of *Rhus vernicifera* seems to have a markedly distorted ligand configuration as indicated by its absorption spectrum. In *Rhus* blue protein the distribution of the unpaired electron of the cupric ion may be in a delocalized state in the $g_{||}$ EPR signal and in a localized state in the $g_\perp$ signal.

ACKNOWLEDGMENTS

The authors wish to express their gratitude to Prof. H. Tamiya for his valuable criticism of this work. Thanks are also due to the Saito Co. Ltd., Osaka for their kindness in supplying crude latex used in this investigation, and to Japan Electron Optics Laboratory Co. for their valuable assistance in performing the EPR measurements.

REFERENCES

1. Nakamura, T., *Biochim. Biophys. Acta*, **30**, 44 (1958).
2. Omura, T., *J. Biochem.*, **50**, 264 (1961).
3. Nakamura, T., Ikai, A., and Ogura, Y., *J. Biochem.*, **57**, 808 (1965).

4. Chance, B., *in* N. Weissberger (ed.), "Techniques in organic chemistry," Vol. 8, John Wiley & Sons, Inc. (Interscience), New York, 1953, p. 690.
5. Chance, B., and Legallais, V., *Rev. Sci. Instr.*, **22**, 627 (1951).
6. Nakamura, T., and Ogura, Y., *J. Biochem.*, **52**, 214 (1962).
7. Nakamura, T., *Biochim. Biophys. Acta*, **30**, 640 (1958).
8. Blumberg, W. E., Levine, W. G., Margolis, S., and Peisach, J., *Biochem. Biophys. Res. Communs.*, **15**, 277 (1964).
9. Chance, B., *J. Biol. Chem.*, **151**, 553 (1943).
10. Broman, L., Malmström, B. G., Aasa, R., and Vänngård, T., *J. Mol. Biol.*, **5**, 301 (1962).
11. Brill, A. S., Martin, R. B., and Williams, R. J. P., *in* B. Pullman (ed.), "Electronic aspects of biochemistry," Academic Press Inc., New York, 1964, p. 519.
12. Malmström, B. G., and Vänngård, T., *J. Mol. Biol.*, **2**, 118 (1960).
13. Omura, T., *J. Biochem.*, **50**, 394 (1961).

DISCUSSION

DR. BLUMBERG: I have several comments that I would like to make. First, a general comment about the interpretation Dr. Nakamura made concerning the delocalization of the electron and its relation to the g and A values that are measured in EPR spectra. It is true that delocalization of the electron tends to reduce both the A values and the g values. It is true that the g value in the perpendicular direction is always less than it is in the parallel direction, and usually the A value in the perpendicular direction is less than it is in the parallel direction. These two statements don't follow from one another, because delocalization in any direction from the copper atom will lead to reduction of these parameters in all other directions; that is, anything that pokes the wavefunction at one point affects the entire set of parameters. It would be fortunate indeed if EPR results were interpretable in terms of things that are happening at particular points on the cupric ion, as thus we would have some detailed information that we do not have.

The second point I would like to make is to remind Dr. Nakamura that in human ceruloplasmin there is indeed a large absorption in the near ultraviolet. It was reported first by Blumberg, Eisinger, Aisen, Morell, and Scheinberg [*J. Biol. Chem.*, **238**, 1675 (1963)]. It is centered at 332 mμ, and it is very intense. In fact, it is about two-thirds as intense as the visible absorption at 610 mμ.

Third, I would like to make some comments about the EPR spectrum of the blue protein, stellacyanin, from *Rhus vernicifera*.

Figure 1 shows three EPR spectra, each of which is a computer output. The middle curve, B, is the experimental curve read into the computer in order to be read out in this format. It is not processed in any way by the computer. This spectrum is essentially identical to the one presented in Dr. Nakamura's Fig. 1f.

I published some values for g and A [Blumberg, W. F., Levine, W. G., Margolis, S., and Peisach, J., *Biochem. Biophys. Res. Communs.*, **15**, 277 (1964)], at which time I was not very well equipped to do a complete analysis on such asymmetric spectra. Curve A is the best that I can now do in fitting the experimental data. I have intentionally, in order that I can better tell where the peaks and valleys are,

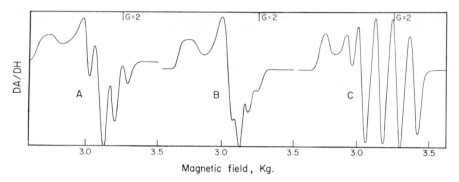

FIG. 1. Computer plots of EPR spectra for stellacyanin (*Rhus vernicifera* blue protein). A. Compouted spectrum using *g* and *A* values given in the discussion. B. Observed spectrum. C. Computed spectrum using *g* and *A* values listed in Table III of Nakamura (this symposium).

used a broadening function a little narrower than would fit the experimental spectrum. I can reduce the height of these valleys by just increasing the broadening. I have never published the *g* and *A* values for that particular spectrum, and I take the opportunity to do so now. Those three *g* values are 2.30, 2.03, and 2.06. *A* values that go with these are 100 Mc/sec, 20 Mc/sec with a large error, and 140 Mc/sec, respectively. In other units to which you may be more accustomed, these are: 0.0033 cm^{-1}, 0.0006 cm^{-1}, and 0.0047 cm^{-1}. The fit is not perfect, but I think it is probably adequate for any computations that one may make on the basis of this spectrum.

You may be wondering what the spectrum on the right is, as it doesn't seem to be related to either of the others. That is the spectrum that one would obtain from a copper complex that had the *g* and *A* values reported by Dr. Nakamura for the blue protein stellacyanin. This shows the drastic importance, when analyzing these complicated spectra, of computing what they would look like if they indeed had the values one is intending to report in the literature. Because they are very complicated, it is easy to go wrong by just looking at the peaks and reading off some numbers without actually doing the computation.

DR. BRILL: What did you do about line width variations?

DR. BLUMBERG: The line width was taken as a constant throughout, although it certainly can vary from one end of the spectrum to the other. That can be put in arbitrarily.

The fourth point that I want to comment upon is that Dr. Nakamura asserted that in my analysis of the laccase EPR spectrum, I had been confused by the presence of the free radicals which he reported. I am indeed confused by many things, but, in the words of the late Senator McCarthy, I know a radical when I see one.

DR. NAKAMURA: In the EPR spectra of *Rhus* laccase I found that the spike at *g* = 2.00 was stronger when the enzyme sample was impure. Even after reducing the enzyme, the spike did not completely disappear, while the copper signal disappeared. So it was assumed that the spike was caused by an enzyme-bound free radical.

Dr. MALMSTRÖM: I would like to say a few words about some recent work that Dr. Vänngård and I have been doing on the effects of increased pH on the spectral properties of fungal laccase. It shows some interesting new properties of this enzyme. and also it might throw some light on some differences in the EPR spectra of different preparations of laccase. We have found with the fungal enzyme that the strong absorption with a maximum at 610 mμ can be reversibly bleached by an increase in pH. If the pH is raised from 6 to 9, the color is almost completely bleached. This only takes a matter of minutes. When this same solution is brought back to pH 6, almost all of the color returns. We thought this might be due to one of two causes, either that we are destroying the specific bonding of the cupric ions or that we are reducing the cupric ion on changing pH.

We tried to see whether, when the color was lost, there was also a reduction of copper. The results were not quite conclusive. There was a loss of EPR intensity but it didn't correlate with the loss of color; thus some cupric copper appears to be reduced, but not all the cupric copper. I think this can be explained if we reinterpret the actual EPR spectra observed. It has the characteristic narrow hyperfine lines that we have reported earlier for this enzyme [*J. Mol. Biol.*, **12**, 118 (1960)], and which have also been reported for ceruloplasmin by ourselves and by Blumberg *et al.* [*J. Biol. Chem.*, **238**, 1675 (1963)]. However, there is an extra peak which suggests that we have a superposition of two EPR spectra. In fact, when we record the spectrum at the high pH, it turns out that what is left is mainly the signal from this superposed second spectrum. At pH 9 the EPR shows a spectrum with a wide hyperfine splitting, and there is only a little of the first signal remaining. This, then, shows that the loss of color on changing the pH is due to a reduction of cupric copper, but it is only a reduction of that part of the cupric copper which gives the characteristic narrow hyperfine splitting.

We have also found that in all our preparations of fungal laccase we also have superimposed signals which vary from preparation to preparation, but correspond in this case to about 40% of the total cupric content. I wonder if a similar superposition of signals may not also account for some of the alleged differences between fungal laccase and other laccases.

I haven't had an opportunity to see whether this would fit Dr. Nakamura's recent EPR spectra, but we have reexamined the spectra reported by Blumberg *et al.* [*Biochem. Biophys. Res. Communs.*, **15**, 277 (1964)]. We think that we can interpret it as having one component which really has the characteristics we have reported for the fungal laccase. I would like to ask Dr. Blumberg if he thinks that really the different types of laccase have one component which gives similar spectra to the one reported, and whether the one he has reported is partly a superposition from two forms of cupric ion.

Dr. BLUMBERG: I wouldn't be surprised if the spectra that we got could be interpreted quite well in the manner suggested by Dr. Malmström. I first tried to interpret this spectrum in terms of a single axial copper site, and found that that gave a very poor fit. Thus I was forced to go to the more complicated rhombic fitting procedure, where I got a reasonably good fit with the data.

The reason that we were fairly confident that there was only one site was that we tried several preparations and they all seemed to have the same structure, so it appeared that there was just one signal. I will analyze the EPR spectrum using your techniques, to see whether the superimposed signals give a better fit. If this is true, it would attest to the very careful techniques of the Einstein group as they presented the very same artifacts in each preparation.

DR. HEMMERICH: Can we be sure that it's a reduction and not a narrowing of the distance between two cupric ions, which I do not favor.

DR. MALMSTRÖM: We cannot be sure of that. All we see is a loss of the optical and EPR absorption intensities. The losses behave as though color were related only to the part of the EPR spectrum which gives the narrow hyperfine splitting.

DR. HEMMERICH: What is the donor of the electrons?

DR. MALMSTRÖM: We don't know. Probably not water anyhow.

DR. BRILL: I think all you are seeing is the change in the redox potential for sulfhydryl oxidation with pH, which is what we have seen in the case of *Pseudomonas* blue protein, which I will discuss later.

DR. HEMMERICH: That's what I wanted Dr. Malmström to say; but he refuses.

DR. MALMSTRÖM: We don't have any evidence that allows us to make that conclusion yet. We can guess at it.

DR. PEISACH: The hyperfine structures in the spectra presented by Dr. Nakamura were even more complex than those that were shown by Dr. Malmström. Dr. Nakamura, did you pass your protein solution through Chelex resin or some other absorption resin to remove nonspecifically bound copper?

DR. NAKAMURA: I purified the enzyme by passing it through a column of Amberlite CG–50, which is a cation exchange resin. I don't think that there is any copper inpurity.

DR. PEISACH: I must disagree, because we also purified *Rhus vernicifera* laccase with Amberlite CG–50, and, after concentration by ultrafiltration, we passed the protein solution through Chelex. We always find a blue ring on the top of the column which we think is due to a copper impurity.

I would like to make a statement about the enzyme activity of the *Rhus vernicifera* blue protein, which we call stellacyanin by permission of Dr. Omura. We purified this blue protein much further than it was purified before, and we find no enzyme activity with PPD.

DR. DAWSON: How about ascorbic acid?

DR. PEISACH: It reduces it confirming the findings of Omura [*J. Biochem.*, **50,** 394 (1961)].

DR. BRILL: I wish to discuss some of the experiments with the blue protein from *Pseudomonas aeruginosa* which Dr. Hanna J. Maria has conducted in my laboratory [*Nature*, **209,** 1023 (1966)]. The data of Fig. 2 bear directly upon Dr. Nakamura's contention that the blue color of *Rhus* laccase is proportional to the total amount, $Cu^+ + Cu^{2+}$, of copper ion. *Pseudomonas* blue protein contains one copper per molecule from which, in the cupric state, arises a distinctive EPR signal [Mason, H. S., *Biochem. Biophys. Res. Communs.*, **10,** 11 (1963)]. In alkaline solution (pH 8 to 12), a bleaching reaction occurs which takes weeks to come to completion. In parallel with this decolorization, the EPR signal decreases, Since the EPR line width and shape

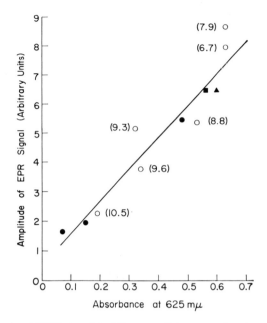

FIG. 2. Amplitude of EPR signal (arbitrary units) versus absorbance at 625 mμ. O, No urea, the number next to each point is the pH of the solution; ■, 2.55 M urea; ▲, 5.1 M urea; ●, 7.7 M urea. All urea solutions at pH 6.8. Protein concentration 2×10^{-4} M in all solutions. (Courtesy of *Nature*.)

remain unchanged, the amount of cupric ion present is proportional to the amplitude of the EPR signal, and the ordinates of Fig. 2 are a measure of the amount of copper in the cupric form. The abscissas are the absorbance at the wavelength of the peak of the visible band. The line of least squares deviation from the experimental points passes through the origin, within experimental error. We conclude that the *color is strictly proportional to the amount of cupric ion* present, as was found for ceruloplasmin. [Blumberg, W. E., Eisinger, J., Aisen, P., Morell, A. G., and Scheinberg, I. H., *J. Biol. Chem.*, **238**, 1675 (1963)]. At a high concentration of urea, bleaching also occurs, the intensities of optical and magnetic absorption being related in the same way as for pH decolorization.

The color of the alkaline bleached protein can be instantly restored by ferricyanide, and restored slowly by lowering the pH. The effects of 7.7 M urea are irreversible.

Reduction of the cupric ion to cuprous in basic solution could arise either from (a) the decrease in the redox potential of sulfhydryl groups with increasing pH, these groups acting as reductants in the reaction

$$2 \text{ Cu}^{2+}\text{-protein-SH} \rightarrow \text{Cu}^+\text{-protein-S-S-protein-Cu}^+ + 2 \text{ H}^+$$

or an increase in the redox potential of the cupric-cuprous coupled due to a change in the environment of the metal ion attending a conformational change in the protein

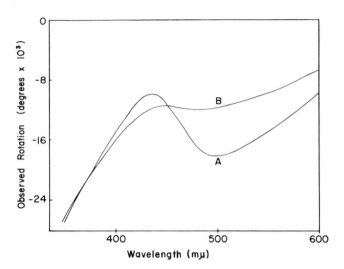

FIG. 3. Optical rotatory dispersion curves. *A*, pH 7.9; *B*, pH 9.6. Protein concentration 2×10^{-4} *M* in both cases. (Courtesy of *Nature*.)

at high pH. We are now examining experimentally the chemical implications of the first scheme. The second possibility appears unlikely in view of the constancy of the EPR line width and shape at high pH and because of the striking observation that the optical rotatory dispersion of the protein moiety (below 280 mμ) is the same at pH 8 and 10. To the extent that the optical rotatory dispersion in the ultraviolet is a measure of the *secondary structure of the protein*, this structure *is unchanged upon a change in the valence of the copper ion*.

Bleaching the protein with urea does change the ultraviolet optical rotatory dispersion. The more negative values so produced indicate less helical structure. It remains to be determined whether the copper is simply reduced to the cuprous state, or released from the protein as well by strong urea.

There is a large Cotton effect associated with the visible band of the blue protein, as shown by curve I (pH 7.9) of Fig. 3, which diminishes as the protein decolorizes, curve II (pH 9.6). Clearly the *cupric ion is in an asymmetric environment*, a finding consistent with predictions from related physicochemical properties [Brill, A. S., Martin, R. B., and Williams, R. J. P., *in* B. Pullman (ed.), "Electronic aspects of biochemistry," Academic Press Inc., New York, 1964, p. 519].

DR. WILLIAMS: Does this protein have a 330 mμ band?

DR. BRILL: It does not.

DR. PEISACH: Plastocyanin, which we studied, *does* have a 330 mμ band. Dr. Blumberg has looked at plastocyanin, stellacyanin, ceruloplasmin, and *Rhus vernicifera* laccase at Albert Einstein College, and they all have Cotton effects in the visible region.

In addition, I would also like to make a comment about your finding concerning the relative stability of the chromophoric site of the *Pseudomonas* blue protein. You mentioned that you raise the pH and you let it sit around for weeks.

DR. BRILL: It is stable at pH 11.5, for weeks, but not forever.

DR. PEISACH: Nothing lasts forever. We came across a phenomenon with stellacyanin, at a low pH. The protein can be added to a final HCl concentration of 6M, and there is a very finite time–the order of 10 or 20 seconds–before the blue color disappears. I thought this might indicate that the chromophoric site in this protein may be very deeply imbedded within it.

DR. FRIEDEN: I want to point out an interesting correlation. We have summarized various copper enzyme systems, the number of copper atoms per mole of enzyme, and whether water or peroxide is formed [Frieden, F., Osaki, S., and Kobayashi, H., *J. Gen. Physiol.*, **49,** 213 (1965)]. Except for one or two, all the copper systems which produce hydrogen peroxide have only one copper per molecule, and all the others, including the enzymes that we talked about tonight, have four or more. It would be interesting if there were any enzymes that had two atoms of copper.

It's interesting also to notice, as Dr. Mason has pointed out in one of his early reviews [*Adv. in Enzymol.*, **19,** 79 (1957)] that it is wasteful and probably undesirable to have a great deal of peroxide being formed. It apparently indicates that the copper enzymes producing peroxide have been relegated to minor pathways, in contrast to the probably greater significance of the enzymatic processes leading to water.

The Role of Plastocyanin in NADP Photoreduction by Chloroplasts*

S. KATOH† AND ANTHONY SAN PIETRO‡

Charles F. Kettering Research Laboratory,
Yellow Springs, Ohio

I. Plastocyanin as a Chloroplast Component

Plastocyanin, a nonautoxidizable copper protein, was first discovered in a green alga, *Chlorella ellipsoidea* (1). The subsequent findings that this copper protein is ubiquitous among various plants and algae and that its concentration in chloroplasts is comparable to that of cytochrome *f* suggested a possible role for plastocyanin in the photosynthetic electron-transfer chain of chloroplasts (2).

Evidence in support of this postulation has been reported. Nieman *et al.* (3) demonstrated that photoxidation of reduced cytochrome *c* in detergent-treated chloroplasts requires a chlorophyll-containing particle and a soluble protein. The characteristics of the soluble protein are identical with those of plastocyanin (4, 5). Kok *et al.* (6) showed that light of wavelengths greater than 690 mμ is effective in promoting this photoxidation. Thus, only photosystem I is involved. Plastocyanin stimulated the rate of photoxidation in very weak light as well as strong light, thereby increasing the quantum yield. With light of long wavelength quantum yields of unity (1 photon per electron equivalent) were obtained (5).

Other photoreactions involving only photosystem I include the reduction of substances whose oxidation-reduction potentials are lower than zero Volt, using the ascorbate-DPIP[1] couple as electron donor (7, 8). Plastocyanin is also necessary for these photoreductions (9, 10). Using *Scenedesmus* cells grown in a copper-deficient medium, Bishop (11) observed that the ability of these cells to photoreduce CO_2 with molecular hydrogen was much lower than that observed with normal cells. In contrast, their capacity to use quinone as the oxidant in a Hill reaction was only slightly depressed by copper deficiency.

* Contribution No. 205 of the Charles F. Kettering Research Laboratory. This research was supported in part by a research grant (GM 10129) from the National Institutes of Health, United States Public Health Service.

† On leave from the Department of Biochemistry and Biophysics, Faculty of Science, University of Tokyo, Tokyo, Japan.

‡ Not at meeting.

[1] The abbreviations used are DPIP, 2,6-dichlorophenolindophenol; CMU, *p*-chlorophenyl-1,2-dimethylurea.

A light-induced absorption change around 600 mμ in various green plants was observed by de Kouchkovsky and Fork (12). They ascribed this absorption change to the oxidation-reduction of the plastocyanin present in chloroplasts. The additional observation that far red light (713 mμ) was more effective than red light (651 mμ) in promoting the oxidation of plastocyanin, while red light accelerated the decay time of oxidation, indicated that plastocyanin couples the two photochemical systems of photosynthesis.

Evidence consistent with this hypothesis was recently reported by Katoh and Takamiya (13), who showed that sonic treatment of chloroplasts resulted in almost complete abolition of NADP photoreduction activity whereas the Hill activity with ferricyanide or DPIP was only slightly modified (see below). Addition of a small amount of plastocyanin to the sonicated chloroplasts effectively restored the NADP photoreduction activity. It was suggested, therefore, that the transfer of electrons from photosystem II to photosystem I was disrupted by sonication, and that plastocyanin acts as an intermediary electron carrier between the two photosystems. The restoration of NADP photoreduction by plastocyanin, in the presence of sonicated chloroplasts and ascorbate as the electron donor, was also reported by Davenport (14).

It is the purpose of this paper to describe recent observations on the role of plastocyanin in photoreactions of sonicated chloroplasts, especially NADP photoreduction.

II. Materials and Methods

A. Chloroplasts

Chloroplasts were prepared from fresh spinach leaves obtained from a local market. Some of the experiments were carried out with *Brassica* chloroplasts. Broken chloroplasts were prepared as described previously (10). For sonication, the broken chloroplasts were suspended in 0.05 M phosphate, pH 7.8, containing 0.4 M sucrose and 0.01 M NaCl, at a concentration of about 300 μg of chlorophyll per milliliter. They were sonicated in the cold in a Raytheon 10 Kc/sec sonic oscillator operated at full power.

B. Hill Reaction Assays

Hill reactions were carried out in cuvettes having an optical path of 1 cm which were illuminated with a 150 Watt tungsten lamp through a water filter of 7 cm thickness. Light intensity was about 3000 foot candles. Photoreduction of the Hill oxidants was measured spectrophotometrically with a Beckman model DU spectrophotometer at the following wave-lengths: 610 mμ for DPIP; 420 mμ for ferricyanide; and 340 mμ for NADP. All experiments were carried out at room temperature (about 22°).

Each reaction mixture contained, in a final volume of 3 ml, 30 μmoles of NaCl, chloroplasts (or chloroplast fragments) equivalent to about 30 μg of chlorophyll, 200 μmoles of buffer and an electron acceptor, either 2.1 μmoles of ferricyanide, 0.1 μmole of DPIP or 0.5 μmole of NADP and a saturating amount of both ferredoxin (15) and flavoprotein having trans-hydrogenase activity (16). Phosphate and Tris buffer were used together for the pH range of 5.7 to 8.7. In other experiments, glycine–NaOH or citrate–phosphate were the buffers used. The pH of the reaction mixture was measured immediately after the reaction.

C. Photoreduction with Ascorbate and DPIP

Reactions were carried out anaerobically using a Thunberg-type cuvette. Illumination was provided as described above with the exception that a red glass filter (no transmission below 650 mμ) was placed in front of the cuvette for the measurement of methyl red and FMN photoreduction. Absorption changes were measured spectrophotometrically at 340 mμ for NADP, 430 mμ for methyl red, 610 mμ for indigo carmine, and 450 mμ for FMN. The reaction mixtures were the same as those for the Hill reaction and, in addition, contained 3 mμmoles of CMU, 20 μmoles of ascorbate, and 0.2 μmole of DPIP. The amount of electron acceptor added was either 0.08 μmole of methyl red, 0.08 μmole of indigo carmine, or 0.5 μmole of NADP. Ascorbic acid was neutralized just before addition.

III. Results

A. Effect of Sonication Time on NADP Hill Reaction

In a previous study, the time course for the change in activity of chloroplasts during sonic oscillation was measured at the optimal pH for the Hill reaction with nonsonicated chloroplasts (13). It has now been found that the effect of sonication time on NADP photoreduction activity varies dramatically depending on the pH at which the activity is assayed. Figure 1 shows the relationship between the rate of photoreduction of NADP, measured at pH 7.0 and 8.0, and the time of sonication of the chloroplasts. It is seen that the ability of chloroplasts to catalyze the photoreduction of NADP was almost completely lost after one minute of sonication. However, the activity was restored in part by the addition of plastocyanin and the degree of restoration was dependent upon the time of sonication and

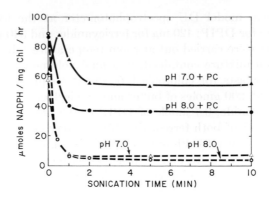

FIG. 1. Effect of sonication time on Hill reaction with NADP. Small aliquots of the chloroplast suspension were removed from the sonicator at various times. Where indicated, 3.5 mμmoles of plastocyanin (PC) were added. Chloroplast concentration equivalent to 22.5 μg of chlorophyll (Chl).

pH. At pH 7.0, the rate increased at first, went through a maximum, and then reached a level of activity which was independent of the time of sonication. In other experiments, it was shown that the rate was maximal within 10–25 seconds of sonication. On the other hand, the rate of reduction of NADP measured at pH 8.0 with plastocyanin showed only an initial decrease until a constant activity, independent of sonication time, was reached.

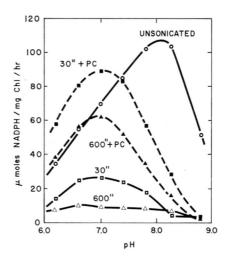

FIG. 2. Effect of pH on NADP photoreduction. Untreated chloroplasts (○); chloroplasts sonicated for 30 seconds (□) and 600 seconds (△). Plastocyanin (PC), 3.5 mμmoles. Chloroplasts equivalent to 22.5 μg of chlorophyll (Chl).

B. Effect of pH on NADP Hill Reaction

The pH dependence of NADP photoreduction by untreated chloroplasts, and chloroplasts sonicated for 30 seconds or 10 minutes, is illustrated in Fig. 2. The activity of the untreated chloroplasts showed optimal activity at pH 8.0. Sonication of the chloroplasts for 30 seconds caused a considerable reduction in activity; the remaining activity was optimal around pH 7.0. After sonication for 10 minutes, the activity was very low and independent of pH between 6.2 and 8.8. The addition of plastocyanin to the sonicated chloroplasts increased the rate of reduction at each pH tested. Although the activity restored is higher with the chloroplasts treated for 30 seconds, the pH dependence was the same for both preparations, i.e., the restored activity was optimal at pH 7.0.

C. Effect of Plastocyanin Concentration

Figure 3 shows the effect of plastocyanin concentration on the restoration of NADP photoreduction by chloroplasts which were sonicated for 10 minutes. Activity was determined at pH 7.0. The rate of reduction increased with increasing plastocyanin concentration and reached a maximal rate in the presence of 2×10^{-9} mole of the protein. This amount of plastocyanin corresponds to about one-twelfth the amount of chlorophyll in the reaction mixture on a molar basis.

Figure 4 shows a typical time course of NADP photoreduction by the sonicated chloroplasts with and without addition of plastocyanin. The reaction proceeds linearly for at least 3 minutes. It can be calculated from the data for 3 minutes that, in the presence of 3.5×10^{-9} mole of plasto-

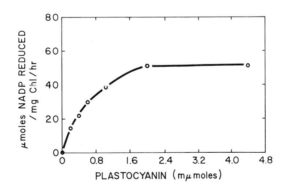

FIG. 3. Effect of plastocyanin concentration on NADP photoreduction by sonicated chloroplasts. Chloroplasts were sonicated for 10 minutes. Activity was measured at pH 7.0. Chloroplast fragments in each reaction mixture were equivalent to 22.5 μg of chlorophyll (Chl).

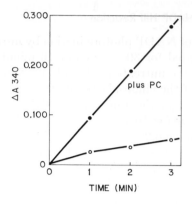

FIG. 4. Time course of NADP photoreduction by sonicated chloroplasts in the presence and absence of plastocyanin. Chloroplasts were sonicated for 10 minutes and activity determined at pH 7.0. Plastocyanin (PC), 3.5 mμmoles. Chloroplast fragments equivalent to 54.5 μg of chlorophyll.

cyanin, an additional 106×10^{-9} mole of NADP was reduced. It is clear, therefore, that the function of plastocyanin in this reaction is a catalytic one.

D. Effect of Sonication Time on Solubilization of Plastocyanin

The observation that plastocyanin functions catalytically in restoring NADP photoreduction by sonicated chloroplasts suggests that plastocyanin is an essential constituent of the electron-transfer system of chloroplasts. Dissociation of plastocyanin from the electron-transfer system by sonication would result in a severe inhibition of NADP photoreduction by chloroplasts. Davenport (14) reported recently that a substantial amount of plastocyanin was solubilized from pea chloroplasts by 30 minutes of sonication. This possibility was, therefore, examined further by comparing the extent of dissociation of plastocyanin and the loss of NADP photoreduction activity when chloroplasts are sonicated for various times.

Five chloroplast suspensions, each containing 70 mg of chlorophyll, were sonicated for 0, 0.5, 1.5, 4, and 10 minutes, respectively. After removal of a small sample for the determination of activity, the sonicates were brought to 40% saturation with ammonium sulfate and chloroplasts (or chloroplast fragments) removed by centrifugation. The precipitates were washed by centrifugation with 0.01 M phosphate buffer, pH 7.5, containing ammonium sulfate equivalent to 40% saturation. The supernatant solutions were combined and dialyzed extensively against a large amount of 0.01 M phosphate buffer, pH 7.5. The dialysate was then applied to a small column (1 × 10 cm) of DEAE–cellulose. The charged column was washed

TABLE I

EFFECT OF TIME OF SONICATION OF SPINACH CHLOROPLASTS ON NADP PHOTOREDUCTION
ACTIVITY AND SOLUBILIZATION OF PLASTOCYANIN[a]

Sonication time (minutes)	Activity of NADP Hill reaction $\left(\dfrac{\mu\text{moles NADPH/hr}}{\text{mg chlorophyll}}\right)$	Plastocyanin solubilized (mμmoles)
0	78	64
0.5	46	172
1.5	15	203
4.0	3	236
10.0	3	237

[a] Hill activity with NADP was determined at pH 8.0 in the absence of plastocyanin. For experimental conditions, see text.

with 0.05 M phosphate buffer, pH 7.5, and the protein was eluted with 0.2 M of the same buffer. Plastocyanin concentration in each eluate was determined spectrophotometrically (2).

The results obtained are summarized in Table I. NADP photoreduction activity at pH 8.0, and without the addition of plastocyanin, decreased rapidly with increasing time of sonication. At the same time, plastocyanin was rapidly brought into solution from the sonicated chloroplasts. It was found that a significant amount of the protein was detected in the supernatant from the nonsonicated chloroplasts, probably owing to the treatment of the chloroplasts with a very high concentration of ammonium sulfate. Apart from the plastocyanin dissociated by this treatment, the effect of sonication on the inactivation of NADP photoreduction and solubilization of plastocyanin are comparable. Both effects are apparent, and significant, within the shortest time of sonication used and complete within 4 minutes. The molar ratio of chlorophyll to copper of the plastocyanin thus solubilized is approximately 300. This value is consistent with that obtained by the acetone treatment of the chloroplasts (2).

E. Effect of Sonication Time on NADP Photoreduction with Ascorbate and DPIP

These experiments were extended further to the photoreduction of NADP with the ascorbate–DPIP couple as the electron donor. In this reaction, the oxygen-evolving system was inhibited by 10^{-6} M CMU. It

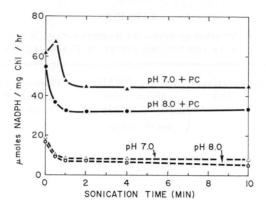

FIG. 5. Effect of sonication on NADP photoreduction with ascorbate and DPIP Plastocyanin (PC), 3.5 mμmoles. Chloroplasts equivalent to 24.5 μg of chlorophyll (Chl).

has been suggested previously that this photoreduction reaction requires plastocyanin for maximal activity (10).

Figure 5 shows the effect of sonication of chloroplasts on the photoreduction of NADP with ascorbate and DPIP. The responses observed were similar to those for the Hill reaction with respect to the restorative effect of plastocyanin and pH (Fig. 1). In the absence of plastocyanin, the rates of reduction at pH 7.0 and 8.0 were low with the untreated chloroplasts and were further decreased by sonication. On addition of plastocyanin, the rate of NADP reduction at pH 7.0 showed an initial spike before it reached a level which was unaltered by prolonged treatment; in contrast, the rate measured at pH 8.0 only decreased without showing any initial rise.

F. Effect of pH on NADP Photoreduction with Ascorbate and DPIP

The effect of pH on NADP photoreduction by the ascorbate–DPIP system was determined before and after sonic oscillation of chloroplasts for 10 minutes (Fig. 6). With untreated chloroplasts, the pH-activity curve was rather complex. In addition to the main peak with a maximum at pH 7.0, there was a shoulder at pH 8.0–8.4. A stimulatory effect of plastocyanin was apparent at each pH tested. After sonication, little activity was observed between pH 6.0 and 8.8; the addition of plastocyanin increased the activity almost to the original level. The activity thus restored showed a pH dependence identical with that of untreated chloroplasts except for the loss of the shoulder at alkaline pH.

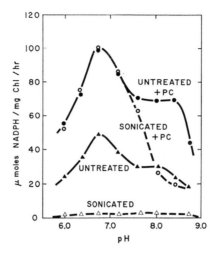

FIG. 6. pH dependence of NADP photoreduction by untreated or sonicated chloroplasts with ascorbate and DPIP. Plastocyanin (PC), 2.5 mμmoles. Chloroplasts equivalent to 31 μg of chlorophyll (Chl). Time of sonication, 10 minutes.

G. Effect of Sonication on Photoreduction of Methyl Red

The mechanism of photoreduction of methyl red, indigo carmine, and FMN with ascorbate and DPIP as the electron donor is considered to be similar to that for NADP photoreduction, except that the latter requires ferredoxin and transhydrogenase. It was expected, therefore, that the effect of sonication on these photoreductions would be similar to that ob-

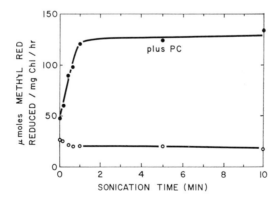

FIG. 7. Effect of sonication time on methyl red photoreduction with ascorbate and DPIP. Activity was determined at pH 7.0. Plastocyanin (PC), 2.5 mμmoles. Chloroplasts equivalent to 38.0 μg of chlorophyll (Chl).

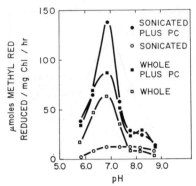

Fig. 8. pH dependence of methyl red photoreduction by untreated or sonicated chloroplasts. Plastocyanin (PC), 2.5 mμmoles. Chloroplasts equivalent to 32.0 μg of chlorophyll (Chl). Time of sonication, 10 minutes.

served for the photoreduction of NADP. This appears to be true for methyl red photoreduction (Fig. 7). In the absence of plastocyanin, sonication is somewhat inhibitory. On the other hand, sonic oscillation of chloroplasts significantly increases the activity in the presence of plastocyanin.

The pH profile of methyl red photoreduction is also similar to that of the NADP system (Fig. 8). The only difference noticed between the two was that the rate of methyl red photoreduction in the presence of plastocyanin did not decrease after the initial rise, as was observed for NADP photoreduction

H. Effect of Sonication on Indigo Carmine and FMN Photoreduction

Hinkson and Vernon showed previously that sonication of chloroplasts for 10 minutes severely inhibited the photoreduction of indigo carmine with

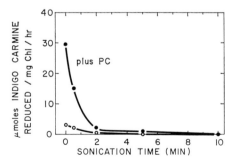

Fig. 9. Effect of sonication time on indigo carmine photoreduction with ascorbate and DPIP as electron donor. Plastocyanin (PC), 2.5 mμmoles. Chloroplasts equivalent to 31.5 μg of chlorophyll (Chl).

the ascorbate–DPIP system; a lesser inhibition was observed with the Hill reaction with DPIP as oxidant (17). This was confirmed in the present study. The results presented in Fig. 9 show that the stimulating effect of plastocyanin, apparent on the indigo carmine reducing activity of the untreated chloroplasts, decreased with time of sonication. No restoration effect of the protein was observed with chloroplasts sonicated for 10 minutes. This was also the case of FMN photoreduction. The ability of the ascorbate–DPIP couple to sustain FMN reduction was completely and irreversibly abolished by sonication.

I. Effect of Sonication on Ferricyanide Photoreduction

The nature of the change in Hill activity with ferricyanide caused by sonication of chloroplasts depends upon the pH of assay system. As can be

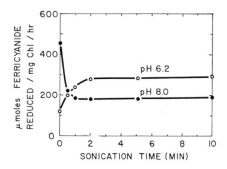

FIG. 10. Effect of sonication time on Hill activity with ferricyanide as oxidant. Chloroplasts equivalent to 32.0 μg of chlorophyll (Chl).

seen in Fig. 10, the activity measured both at pH 7.8 and 6.0 was effected by the time of sonication for times less than 2 minutes; for longer times of sonication the activity remained at a constant level. The direction of the change in activity brought about by a brief exposure of the chloroplasts to sonic waves was, however, opposite at the two pH's. The rate of reduction increased at pH 6.0 and decreased at pH 7.8. In contrast to NADP photoreduction, there was no decrease in activity after the initial rise at the acidic pH

J. Effect of pH on Ferricyanide Photoreduction

The pH optimum for ferricyanide photoreduction was at pH 8.0 with the untreated chloroplasts, but shifted to the acid side, pH 6.0, upon sonication of the chloroplasts (Fig. 11). The maximal activity with sonicated chloroplasts was always lower than that of the untreated chloroplasts.

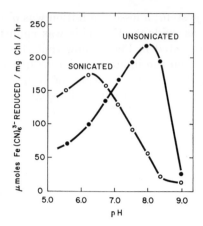

FIG. 11. pH dependence of Hill activity with ferricyanide by chloroplasts untreated or sonicated for 10 minutes. Chloroplasts equivalent to 30.5 μg of chlorophyll (Chl).

Plastocyanin was without effect on ferricyanide reduction with either the untreated or the sonicated chloroplasts

The effect of sonication on the Hill activity with DPIP was quite similar to that with ferricyanide, except that pH optimum of the former reaction by sonicated chloroplasts was not established because of a change in color of the dye at acidic pH's.

IV. Discussion

It has been clearly established that sonic treatment of chloroplasts causes marked changes in their capacity to catalyze various photoxidation-reduction reactions. The changes induced by sonication are quite different depending on the nature of the electron acceptors and donors employed. They could be classified into three groups in the following manner.

(a) *Hill reaction with ferricyanide and DPIP.* Sonication decreased but did not abolish the activity, and caused a shift of the optimal pH to the acid side; plastocyanin was without effect.

(b) *Hill reaction with NADP, and photoreduction of NADP and methyl red with ascorbate and DPIP.* Sonication inactivated the activity almost completely; plastocyanin restored activity.

(c) *Photoreduction of indigo carmine and FMN with ascorbate and DPIP.* Complete and irreversible loss of activity by the sonication.

These observations would indicate that sonic treatment induced several kinds of modifications in the electron-transfer system of the chloroplasts.

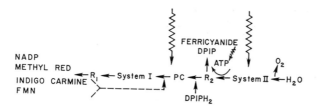

Fig. 12. Proposed electron transfer pathway of chloroplasts. The wavy arrows indicate sites which may be susceptible to alteration by sonication.

This is illustrated schematically in Fig. 12, where systems I and II represent the two primary photoacts in the terminology of Duysens (18). R_1 is a strong reductant which is capable of reducing NADP (or ferredoxin) and it is reduced by system I using an electron provided by system II or reduced DPIP.

A. Blockage of Electron Transfer between Systems I and II

Sonic oscillation of the chloroplasts would block the electron transfer between the two systems, so that sonicated chloroplasts are unable to photoreduce NADP using water as the hydrogen donor. Sonicated chloroplasts could photoreduce ferricyanide or DPIP via a weak reductant, R_2, produced by system II and capable of reducing substances of high oxidation-reduction potential.

The dissociation of plastocyanin from the chloroplasts paralleled the inactivation of NADP photoreduction during the first few minutes of sonic treatment. The addition of a catalytic amount of plastocyanin to the sonicated chloroplasts restored the activity. It is, therefore, inferred that the inactivation of NADP photoreduction in the sonicated chloroplasts is due to the dissociation of plastocyanin, an essential catalyst in the photo-reducing system, from the electron-transfer chain. The mechanism of photoreduction of methyl red with ascorbate and DPIP seems to be the same as that of NADP. On the other hand, the complete and irreversible inactivation of indigo carmine and FMN photoreduction upon sonication of chloroplasts was unexpected, since these photoreductions exhibit characteristics identical in many respects to that of NADP or methyl red photoreduction (7, 10). However, the highly oxidizable nature of reduced indigo carmine and FMN, but not of reduced NADP and methyl red, should be taken into consideration. A tentative explanation is that, although indigo carmine and FMN could be reduced by R_2, accumulation of the reduced forms of the dyes would not take place because of a rapid reoxidation reaction catalyzed by a site uncovered in the sonicated chloroplasts. In fact, it has previously been observed that chloroplasts, on sonication, manifest a capacity to photoxidize added substances (13).

B. Uncoupling of Electron Transfer from Phosphorylation

That sonic treatment of chloroplasts causes other kinds of modification in the electron-transfer system of chloroplasts is apparent in the case of ferricyanide photoreduction. This reduction might, at least, be catalyzed by system II alone in sonicated chloroplasts. The sonication-induced change consisted of a decrease in the rate of reduction at alkaline pH and an increase at acidic pH. A similar change in the pH dependence of ferricyanide photoreduction was reported to occur when the Hill reaction was uncoupled from phosphorylation by the addition of an uncoupler or treatment of chloroplasts by detergent (19, 20, 21). Recently, Gressel and Avron showed that photophosphorylation was much more sensitive than the Hill reaction to sonic oscillation of chloroplasts (22). It seems likely, therefore, that the rapid change in pH dependence of ferricyanide photoreduction observed in sonicated chloroplasts is due to dissociation of the electron-transfer system from the phosphorylation mechanism.

However, an uncoupling mechanism alone is insufficient to explain the change in ferricyanide photoreduction, since the maximal activity obtained at the respective optimal pH values were always lower after sonication than before. Uncoupling of the Hill reaction would increase the rate of reduction beyond that of the original system. This difference between the rate of reduction by the sonicated and untreated chloroplasts becomes more marked when activity is determined in the presence of the phosphorylation cofactors.[2] In addition, Izawa and Good (23) found that, although the rate of ferricyanide reduction without addition of an uncoupler is usually higher in sonicated chloroplasts than in untreated chloroplasts, the stimulated activity observed in the presence of uncoupler was decreased markedly by sonication. They suggested, therefore, that sonic treatment of chloroplasts severely damaged some part of the Hill reaction mechanism; at the same time, the Hill reaction was more completely uncoupled from phosphorylation.

C. Modification of System II

We have also observed that ferricyanide photoreduction in sonicated chloroplasts differs from that in untreated chloroplasts in respect to dependence of the rate of reaction on the concentration of ferricyanide and intensity of actinic light.[2] It seems from these data that system II itself underwent some modification by sonication.

[2] Unpublished data.

Wessels (24) reported that the electron transfer to NADP from reduced DPIP was not associated with phosphorylation. Therefore, the increased rate of photoreduction of NADP and methyl red by ascorbate and DPIP does not appear to be due to an uncoupling from phosphorylation. An alternative explanation for this stimulation is that sonication of chloroplasts increases the accessibility of added substances, electron donors or acceptors, to the reaction site or sites of the chloroplasts by decreasing the permeability barrier or by exposing a new reaction site in the chloroplasts.

In this connection, it is worthwhile to mention another marked effect of sonication on chloroplasts, that is, fragmentation of their lamellae structure. All the sonication-induced changes in photoreduction activity noted herein were complete within the first minute or two of sonication. Thereafter, no appreciable change was observed in the activity remaining with times of sonication of up to 10 minutes. Fragmentation of chloroplasts undoubtedly proceeds throughout the period of sonication. These findings indicate that the increase in photoreduction activity, especially NADP reduction with ascorbate and DPIP, is not due simply to an increase in available surface area, that is, a decrease in the size of the chloroplast fragments. Following the initial rapid change in activity, the residual activity is apparently independent of the continuing decrease in particle size of the chloroplast fragments caused by sonication, until at least a critical size, determined by Thomas *et al.* (25), is reached.

V. Summary

The effect of plastocyanin on various photoreduction activities of sonicated chloroplasts was studied. Activity for NADP photoreduction by the Hill reaction system or the ascorbate–DPIP system was almost completely inactivated by a few minutes of sonication. Accompanying this inactivation, a rapid and complete solubilization of plastocyanin from the chloroplasts was observed. Addition of catalytic amount of plastocyanin effectively restored the NADP photoreduction activity, but the restored activity showed a pH dependence somewhat different from that of the original activity.

The effects of sonication and addition of plastocyanin on methyl red photoreduction with ascorbate and DPIP as the electron donor were essentially similar to those observed for NADP photoreduction, whereas indigo carmine and FMN photoreduction were completely and irreversibly inhibited by sonication. Sonication of chloroplasts did not abolish the Hill activity with ferricyanide as oxidant, although the pH dependence of the reaction was modified significantly.

ACKNOWLEDGMENTS

The advice and suggestions of Dr. L. P. Vernon in the preparation of this manuscript are gratefully acknowledged.

REFERENCES

1. Katoh, S., *Nature*, **186,** 533 (1960).
2. Katoh, S., Suga, I., Shiratori, I., and Takamiya, A., *Arch. Biochem. Biophys.*, **94,** 136 (1961).
3. Nieman, R. H., Nakamura, H., and Vennesland, B., *Plant Physiol.*, **34,** 262, (1959).
4. Katoh, S., and Takamiya, A., *Plant and Cell Physiol.*, **4,** 335 (1963).
5. Kok, B., Rurainski, H. J., and Harmon, E. A., *Plant Physiol.*, **39,** 513 (1964).
6. Kok, B., Hoch, G., and Cooper, B., *Plant Physiol.*, **38,** 274 (1963).
7. Vernon, L. P., and Hobbs, M. O., *Arch. Biochem. Biophys.*, **72,** 25 (1957).
8. Hoch, G., and Martin, I., *Arch. Biochem. Biophys.*, **102,** 430 (1963).
9. Katoh, S., and Takamiya, A., *in* B. Kok and A. T. Jagendorf (eds.), "Photosynthetic mechanisms of green plants," National Academy of Science, National Research Council, Washington, D.C., 1963, p. 262.
10. Katoh, S., and Takamiya, A., *J. Biochem.*, (*Tokyo*) **58,** 396 (1965).
11. Bishop, N. I., *Nature*, **204,** 401 (1964).
12. de Kouchkovsky, Y., and Fork, D. C., *Proc. Natl. Acad. Sci.*, **52,** 232 (1964).
13. Katoh, S., and Takamiya, A., *Biochim. Biophys. Acta.*, **99,** 156 (1964).
14. Davenport, H. E., *in* A. San Pietro (ed.), "Non-heme iron proteins: role in energy conversion," Antioch Press, Yellow Springs, Ohio, 1965, p. 115.
15. San Pietro, A., and Lang, H. M., *J. Biol. Chem.*, **231,** 211, (1956).
16. Keister, D. L., San Pietro, A., and Stolzenbach, F. E., *J. Biol. Chem.*, **235,** 2989 (1960).
17. Hinkson, J. W., and Vernon, L. P., *Plant Physiol.*, **34,** 268 (1959).
18. Duysens, L. N. M., Amesz, J., and Kamp, B. M., *Nature*, **190,** 510 (1961).
19. Krogman, D. W., Avron, M., and Jagendorf, A. T., *Plant Physiol.*, **34,** 272 (1959).
20. Stiller, M., *Biochim. Biophys. Acta*, **94,** 53 (1965).
21. Neumann, J., and Jagendorf, A. T., *Biochim. Biophys. Acta*, in press.
22. Gressel, J., and Avron, M., *Biochim. Biophys. Acta*, **94,** 31 (1965).
23. Izawa, S., and Good, N. E., *Biochim. Biophys. Acta.*, **109,** 372 (1965).
24. Wessels, J. S. C., *Biochim. Biophys. Acta*, **79,** 640 (1964).
25. Thomas, J. B., Blaauw, O. H., and Duysens, L. M. N., *Biochim. Biophys. Acta*, **10,** 230 (1953).

DISCUSSION

DR. BEINERT: I have two questions: first, I don't think you mentioned anything about the specificity of plastocyanin in NADP photoreduction. Second I wonder if you would explain what happened to plastoquinone. Is the place that originally was assigned to plastoquinone taken in this scheme by plastocyanin, or where would you put it in your scheme?

DR. KATOH: I tried proteins such as cytochrome c, cytochrome f from algae, and *Rhus* blue copper protein, supplied to us by Dr. Omura, in place of plastocyanin, and without success. I think plastocyanin has a specific function in NADP photoreduction.

I have not done any experiments with plastoquinone, but it is possible that plastoquinone would be placed at R_2 in Fig. 12.

Some Recent Advances in the Field of Amine Oxidases[*]

SAKARI NARA[†] AND KERRY T. YASUNOBU[‡]

Department of Biochemistry and Biophysics,
University of Hawaii,
Honolulu, Hawaii

I. Introduction

Amine oxidases are widely distributed in animals, plants, and bacteria. They catalyze the following reaction:

$$RCH_2NH_2 + O_2 + H_2O \rightarrow R\overset{\overset{\textstyle O}{\|}}{C}H + NH_3 + H_2O_2$$

Several review articles (1–12) have summarized the current status of our knowledge concerning the various amine oxidases. Since these articles have appeared, some significant advances have occurred and they will be the subject of discussion in the present paper.

The first point of importance concerns the nomenclature of the amine oxidases. The older classification of the enzymes as either monoamine oxidase or diamine oxidase is no longer tenable. This characterization of the amine oxidase was based on the apparent fact that the monoamine oxidases were inhibited by iproniazid while the diamine oxidases were inhibited by isoniazid but not by iproniazid. The recent papers by McEwen on the human plasma amine oxidase (13) and Yamada *et al.* on *Aspergillus niger* amine oxidase (14) have shown that these enzymes are inhibited by both isoniazid and iproniazid. Therefore, it appears that the various amine oxidases should be named as follows: (a) Source of enzyme; (b) cellular localization of the enzyme; and (c) followed by the general term, amine oxidase, e.g., beef liver mitochondrial amine oxidase. A second possible method for classifying the amine oxidase is based on the nature of the prosthetic groups of the enzymes as will be shown subsequently in this article.

From the increasing data dealing with the various amine oxidases it is becoming evident that, in all likelihood, all amine oxidases will turn out to be copper proteins. Table I lists some of the amine oxidases which have been sufficiently purified to establish their copper-protein nature.

The third major advance that has occurred is the reported solubilization

[*] Supported in part by research grant NIH–MH–10380.

[†] Present address: Chemical Laboratory, Hokkaido Gakugei University, Hachimancho, Hokodate, Japan.

[‡] Not at meeting.

TABLE I

THE COPPER CONTENT OF VARIOUS AMINE OXIDASES

Enzyme	Cu content (%)	Reference
1. Beef plasma amine oxidase	0.09	(22)
2. Pea seedling amine oxidase	0.08–0.09	(18)
3. Pig plasma amine oxidase	0.1	(21)
4. *Aspergillus niger* amine oxidase	0.07–0.08	(14)
5. Hog kidney amine oxidase[a]	—	(23)
6. Beef liver mitochondrial amine oxidase[b]	0.05	Present paper

[a] Enzyme judged to be 80% pure by ultracentrifugal analysis.
[b] The purity of enzyme has not been rigorously established.

and purification of mitochondrial amine oxidase (15). As has been stressed in some of the review articles (5, 6), our knowledge concerning the physico-chemical properties of the mitochondrial amine oxidases is nil owing to the fact that the enzyme is located within the mitochondria and is difficult to purify.

II. Beef Liver Mitochondrial Amine Oxidase

Research on the purification of beef liver mitochondrial amine oxidase has been in progress in our laboratory for the past 4 years, and we wish to discuss these results in subsequent portions of this paper. However, ultra-sonication, a technique used by other workers for the solubilization of rat brain mitochondrial (16) and rat liver mitochondrial amine oxidases (15), did not give rise to good yields of water-soluble preparations when applied to beef liver mitochondria.

A. Purification of the Enzyme

This topic will not be discussed in detail here. In essence, the mito-chondria were purified by the Schneider and Hogeboom procedure (17) and disrupted with a Potter-Elvejhem homogenizer and then by treatment with Triton X-100. The solubilized protein was then fractionated with ammonium sulfate, and the fraction precipitating between 25 and 45% saturation was collected. The enzyme was dissolved in buffer and absorbed on alumina C_γ. After elution from the gel, the enzyme was passed through Sephadex G-25 and then chromatographed on DEAE–cellulose. The enzyme was then purified on a hydroxyapatite column which yielded two

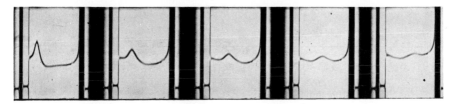

Fɪɢ. 1. Sedimentation pattern of the purified beef mitochondrial amine oxidase at a concentration of 0.6 mg per milliliter. Photographs were taken at 8.4, 16.4, 24.4, 32.4, and 40.4 minutes after reaching top speed (59,789 rpm at 24°).

fractions, both having amine oxidase activity. Depending on the batch of mitochondria, sometimes a water-soluble preparation was derived by this purification procedure while, with other preparations, the enzyme still required detergent to be soluble. The preparations were about 52-fold purified on the basis of specific activity measurements.

A detailed study of the homogeneity of the enzyme has not been made. However, as shown in Fig. 1, the ultracentrifuge pattern of the purified enzyme showed only one main component. It should be pointed out that a part of the asymmetry of the peak is due to the fact that detergent cannot be completely removed from the enzyme. The detergent undoubtedly forms micelles and can be detected on the tailing edge of the main component in the sedimentation patterns. However, the following points can be made: (a) The copper content of the enzyme is in the range expected for amine oxidases (14, 18–23); (b) heme proteins either appear to be present in low concentrations or are absent according to the spectrum of the purified enzyme; (c) a rough check of the sedimentation coefficient of the purified enzyme yielded a sedimentation coefficient of 10.5 (uncorrected), which is in the range observed for other amine oxidases (21, 24), i.e., a molecular weight of about 2–3×10^5. At any rate, it should be pointed out that the enzyme is sufficiently pure for detailed spectral studies in order to determine the prosthetic groups or for mechanistic studies.

B. Substrate Specificity

Gorkin (25) has recently demonstrated that rat liver mitochondria contain two types of amine oxidases. One oxidized p-nitrophenylethylamine while the other oxidized m-amino-p-hydroxybenzylamine. Thus, it was of interest to determine whether the enzyme isolated in our laboratory was the well-known mitochondrial amine oxidase whose specificity has been studied in some detail. As shown in Table II, the purified enzyme oxidized all of the reported substrates of the mitochondrial enzyme (4, 6).

TABLE II

Substrate Specificity of Purified Enzyme[a]

Substrate	Relative activity
1. Monoamines	
a. Tyramine	100
b. Benzylamine	73
c. Dopamine	60
d. Tryptamine	53
e. 5-Hydroxytryptamine	46
f. Heptylamine	41
2. Catecholamine	
a. Norepinephrine	17
6. Diamines	
a. Cadaverine	0
b. Histamine	0
c. Agmatine	0
d. Trimethylenediamine	0
4. Polyamines	
a. Spermine	0
b. Spermidine	0

[a] The enzyme activity was determined with the Conway microdiffusion apparatus. The outer chamber contained enzyme, specific activity 2,500, and 0.1 M potassium phosphate buffer, pH 7.4, in a total volume of 1 ml. The central chamber contained 1 ml of 2% boric acid with one drop of bromcresol green. The mixture was allowed to react for 30 minutes at 22°. Then 1 ml of saturated K_2CO_3 solution was added and the mixture was allowed to stand for 1 hour at 33°. The borate solution was titrated with $3.07 \times 10^{-3} M$ H_2SO_4. Each determination was run in duplicate.

III. The Prosthetic Groups of the Enzyme

A. The Metallic Component

Recent studies have demonstrated that numerous amine oxidases are copper proteins. Therefore, our initial efforts were directed towards investigating the effect of known copper chelating agents on the activity of beef liver mitochondrial amine oxidase. It should be pointed out that other investigators have investigated the effect of chelating agents on the enzyme, but either the enzyme preparations were crude or only a few chelating agents were tried (25, 26). The results with the purified enzyme are summarized in Table III. The order of inhibitory effectiveness was: cuprizone > 8-hydroxyquinoline > neocuproine > o-phenanthroline > sodium diethyldithiocarbamate > 2,2'-bipyridine. The results are somewhat similar to that reported for beef plasma amine oxidase (20) although an approxi-

TABLE III

INHIBITION BY METAL CHELATING AGENTS[a]

Chelator	Final concentration	Inhibition (%)
1. None	—·	0
2. Cuprizone	3×10^{-4}	76
3. Neocuproine	3×10^{-4}	33
4. 8-Hydroxyquinoline	3×10^{-3}	90
	3×10^{-4}	48
5. Sodium diethyldithiocarbamate	3×10^{-3}	24
6. o-Phenanthroline	3×10^{-4}	19
7. 2, 2'-Bipyridine	3×10^{-3}	10
8. EDTA	3×10^{-3}	0
9. NaN$_3$	3×10^{-2}	0
10. NaCN	3×10^{-2}	0

[a] The enzyme was assayed using the standard kynuramine assay (27). 0.1 ml of partially purified enzyme, specific activity 2400 was preincubated for 15 minutes with 0.3 ml of chelating agents at 26° before assay.

mate 10-fold excess of inhibitor is required to produce the same degree of inhibition, and the order of inhibitory effectiveness of the chelating agents was: cuprizone > o-phenanthroline > 8-hydroxyquinoline > sodium diethyldithiocarbamate > 2,2'-bipyridine.

Relationship between copper content and specific activity. For purposes of demonstrating that copper is essential for enzymatic activity, the copper content and specific activity[1] of nine different purified preparations of the enzyme were determined. As shown in Fig. 2, there appears to be a direct proportionality between copper content and specific activity. It might also be pointed out that another copper protein present in mitochondria, namely, cytochrome c oxidase, appears to be either absent or present in minute quantity, as indicated by spectral studies of the purified enzyme.

Investigation of other possible metallic components. Although detailed studies on this point are planned, thus far microchemical analysis of the dry ashed enzyme for iron by the o-phenanthroline method (28) indicates that iron is not an essential metal of the enzyme. Preliminary investigations of the trichloracetic acid treated enzyme supernatant fraction by EPR techniques indicate that copper is the only metal released in significant

[1] The activity of the enzyme was determined using benzylamine as the substrate and the enzyme was assayed using the spectrophotometric method previously described (22). The specific activity is defined as units per milligram of protein throughout the paper unless otherwise specified.

TABLE III

Inhibition by Metal Chelating Agents[a]

Chelator	Final concentration	Inhibition (%)
1. None	—	0
2. Cuprizone	3×10^{-4}	76
3. Neocuproine	3×10^{-4}	33
4. 8-Hydroxyquinoline	3×10^{-3}	90
	3×10^{-4}	48
5. Sodium diethyldithiocarbamate	3×10^{-3}	24
6. o-Phenanthroline	3×10^{-4}	19
7. 2, 2'-Bipyridine	3×10^{-3}	10
8. EDTA	3×10^{-3}	0
9. NaN$_3$	3×10^{-2}	0
10. NaCN	3×10^{-2}	0

[a] The enzyme was assayed using the standard kynuramine assay (27). 0.1 ml of partially purified enzyme, specific activity 2400 was preincubated for 15 minutes with 0.3 ml of chelating agents at 26° before assay.

mate 10-fold excess of inhibitor is required to produce the same degree of inhibition, and the order of inhibitory effectiveness of the chelating agents was: cuprizone > o-phenanthroline > 8-hydroxyquinoline > sodium diethyldithiocarbamate > 2,2'-bipyridine.

Relationship between copper content and specific activity. For purposes of demonstrating that copper is essential for enzymatic activity, the copper content and specific activity[1] of nine different purified preparations of the enzyme were determined. As shown in Fig. 2, there appears to be a direct proportionality between copper content and specific activity. It might also be pointed out that another copper protein present in mitochondria, namely, cytochrome c oxidase, appears to be either absent or present in minute quantity, as indicated by spectral studies of the purified enzyme.

Investigation of other possible metallic components. Although detailed studies on this point are planned, thus far microchemical analysis of the dry ashed enzyme for iron by the o-phenanthroline method (28) indicates that iron is not an essential metal of the enzyme. Preliminary investigations of the trichloracetic acid treated enzyme supernatant fraction by EPR techniques indicate that copper is the only metal released in significant

[1] The activity of the enzyme was determined using benzylamine as the substrate and the enzyme was assayed using the spectrophotometric method previously described (22). The specific activity is defined as units per milligram of protein throughout the paper unless otherwise specified.

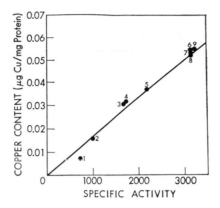

FIG. 2. Relationship between copper contents and specific activities of various purified mitochondrial amine oxidase. Benzylamine was used as the substrate and the standard spectrophotometric enzyme assay was used (20) in all studies unless otherwise noted. Specific activity is defined as units per milligram of protein.

quantities (29) and that Fe, Mn, Co, and Mo are not present in significant quantities.

Valence state of copper in the enzyme. As shown in Table IV, when the valence state of the copper was checked by the chemical method of Felsenfeld and Printz (31) as modified by Griffiths and Wharton (32), most of the copper was in the cupric state. Detailed studies are planned to further con-

TABLE IV

VALENCE STATE OF COPPER IN ENZYME

Experiment	Protein (mg)	$Cu^{2+} + Cu^+$ (mμ moles)	Cu^+ (mμ moles)
1. Cuprizone[a]	1.14	3.7	—
2. Biquinoline[b]	1.14	—	0
3. $Na_2S_2O_4$[b] biquinoline	1.14	—	3.8

[a] One milliliter of enzyme (1.14 mg/ml, 0.1 M phosphate buffer pH 7.4, specific activity 2,500) was denatured by the addition of 2 N HCl and 20% trichloracetic acid. The supernatant was analyzed for total copper by the method of Peterson and Bollier (30).

[b] To 1.0 ml aliquots of the enzyme solution containing 1.14 mg of protein were added 30 μmoles of phosphate buffer (KH_2PO_4–K_2HPO_4), pH 7.4, and about 1 mg of sodium dithionite to give a final volume of 0.8 ml. The copper was determined by first adding 0.2 ml of 0.2 M EDTA and 1×10^{-3} M p-chloromercuriphenylsulfonic acid followed by 1.4 ml of 0.1%, 2,2′-biquinoline in glacial acetic acid. After addition of 1.4 ml of ethanol, the mixture was centrifuged for 10 minutes at 15,000 $\times$ g. The absorbance at 540 mμ was determined by the method of Griffiths and Warton (32).

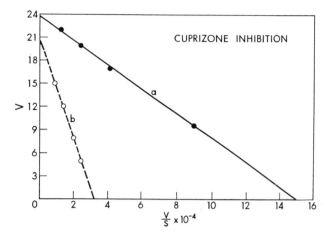

FIG. 3. Inhibition of beef liver mitochondrial amine oxidase by cuprizone. (a) control, (b) $5 \times 10^{-5} M$ cuprizone. Substrate was benzylamine.

firm the results by EPR spectroscopy. Preliminary investigations demonstrate that the valence of the copper is not changed by the addition of substrate but is readily reducible by sodium dithionite (29). The results are identical to that reported for beef plasma amine oxidase (33), and galactose oxidase (34).

Type of inhibition produced by cuprizone. When cuprizone was used as an inhibitor of the enzyme, as shown in Fig. 3 mixed inhibition, i.e., partially competitive and partially noncompetitive, was observed. On the other hand, cuprizone was shown to be a competitive inhibitor of beef plasma amine oxidase. The recent report of McEwen (13) has shown that cuprizone is a mixed inhibitor of human plasma amine oxidase.

The Michaelis–Menten constant K_m, using benzylamine at pH 7.4, was determined to be $2.3 \times 10^{-4} M$ as contrasted to a value of $1.5 \times 10^{-3} M$ for the beef plasma amine oxidase (22). McEwen has reported, again with benzylamine as the substrate, that K_m is equal to $3.3 \times 10^{-4} M$ for human plasma amine oxidase (35).

B. Flavin as a Possible Prosthetic Group

One of the most striking differences between crystalline plasma amine oxidase and purified mitochondrial amine oxidase is the color of the enzymes. The plasma enzyme is pink while the purified mitochondrial enzyme is bright yellow. As shown in Figs. 4A and 4B the mitochondrial enzyme shows a maximum at 410 mμ and shoulders at about 450 and 480 mμ. The spectrum of the enzyme resembles that reported for the crystalline beef plasma

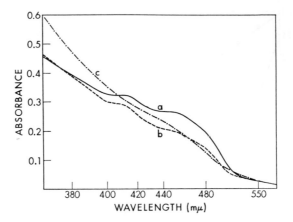

Fig. 4A. Absorption spectra of various forms of purified mitochondrial amine oxidase (specific activity, 3200; enzyme concentration, 3.5 mg/ml in 0.1 M phosphate buffer, pH 7.4). (a) Native enzyme; (b) substrate-reduced enzyme (1 mg solid tyramine) after 1 minute; and (c) copper-free enzyme. The copper-free denatured enzyme was obtained by treating enzyme with 20% trichloracetic acid, centrifugation, solution by addition of 2 M KOH, and then adjustment of pH to 8.0 by the addition of 2 M HCl.

amine oxidase (maximum at 410 and about 480 mμ) and the flavoprotein sarcosine dehydrogenase (maxima at 410–412 mμ and a shoulder from 430–460 mμ) (36).

During the purification of the enzyme, the ratio of absorbance at 410 mμ

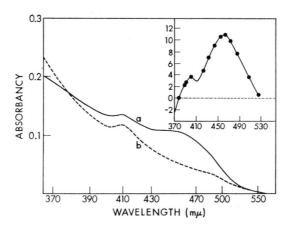

Fig. 4B. Absorption spectra of oxidized and reduced forms of beef mitochondrial amine oxidase and the difference spectrum. The enzyme (1.75 mg/ml, specific activity 3,400) was dissolved in 0.1 M phosphate buffer, pH 7.4. (a) Native enzyme; (b) sodium dithionite (1 mg) reduced enzyme.

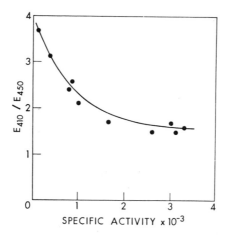

FIG. 5. The ratio of extinction coefficients at 410 mμ and 450 mμ for different preparations of purified mitochondrial amine oxidases.

(copper) to that at 450 mμ (flavin) was measured. The results are shown in Fig. 5 and demonstrate that this ratio decreased during the purification procedure and approached a constant value. The lack of direct proportionality can be attributed to the presence of heme proteins during the early stages of enzyme purification, especially cytochrome c.

More direct evidence was obtained concerning the flavoprotein nature of the enzyme in the following manner. The enzyme was precipitated with trichloracetic acid, which liberated insignificant quantities of flavins. The denatured enzyme was dissolved in base and after pH adjustment, digested with trypsin as described by Wilson and King (37). The difference spectrum (oxidized minus the reduced forms) of the peptide liberated is shown in Fig. 6. The fluorescence spectra of the peptide also resembled that of flavins. If the enzyme is a flavoprotein, it appears that the flavin is covalently bonded to the enzyme.

Assuming that the mitochondrial amine oxidase is a flavoprotein, evidence was sought concerning its involvement in catalytic activity. When the substrate, tyramine, was added either aerobically or anaerobically to the purified enzyme, there was a decrease in absorption in the region 370–500 mμ (see Fig. 4A) and the difference spectra (native enzyme minus enzyme with substrate) resembled the difference spectrum of the oxidized minus the reduced form of the enzyme. Finally, the spectra of the copper-free enzyme (see Fig. 4B) and the sodium dithionite-reduced enzyme are shown in Fig. 4B, which suggests that the maximum at 410 mμ may be due to the presence of copper.

That the mitochondrial amine oxidase is a flavoenzyme is in agreement

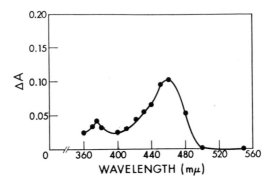

Fig. 6. Difference spectrum (oxidized minus reduced) of flavopeptide isolated by tryptic digestion. The peptide was obtained from the trichloracetic denatured enzyme. For the experiment, 2 ml of enzyme (specific activity 2,650 in 0.1 M phosphate buffer, pH 7.4) was denatured by the addition of 1.0 ml of 20% trichloracetic acid. The solution was centrifuged and 3 ml of 0.1 M phosphate buffer, pH 7.4 was added. The pH was adjusted to 8.0 and about 0.5 mg of crystalline trypsin was added. The reaction was allowed to proceed for 4 hours at 40°. The reaction was terminated by the addition of 1.0 ml of 20% trichloracetic acid and centrifuged. The supernatant was extracted with 3.5 ml of ether three times and the spectrum recorded.

with the findings of Hawkins (38). Rats which were fed riboflavin-deficient diets showed a decrease in hepatic amine oxidase activity. Homogenates of the liver from these rats did not respond to additions of FMN or FAD. Since the results from our laboratory suggest that the flavin is covalently linked to the enzyme, the addition of FMN or FAD would not be expected to reactivate the enzyme without the addition of an energy source.

The flavin may be playing the role of the hydrogen acceptor, i.e., a reaction similar to that proposed for D-amino acid oxidase (39). Some of the possible roles of metals in metalloflavoproteins are described in a review by Mahler (40).

C. Essential Sulfhydryl Groups

As reported by some investigators (38, 41), mitochondrial amine oxidase appears to be inhibited by sulfhydryl reagents. The effect of p-CMB was therefore tested on the enzyme. The point of 50% inhibition under the experimental conditions tested was 5×10^{-6} M and when the nature of inhibition was studied, mixed inhibition was observed. The lack of inhibition by arsenite and the high concentrations of Cd^{2+} required for inhibition argue against the presence of vicinal sulfhydryl groups. The fact that the enzyme is purified may account for the lack of agreement of K_I values reported by Barbato and Abood (26).

TABLE V

SOME PROPERTIES OF AMINE OXIDASES

Amine oxidase	Molecular weight	$S_{20,w}$	Prosthetic group	Valence state of Cu	Essential —SH	Isoelectric point	$E_{1\text{cm},280}^{1\%}$	Specific activity	Isoniazid inhibition	Iproniazid inhibition	CN^- inhibition	References
Beef plasma	260,000	9.6[a]	4 Cu 2 Pyr–PO$_4$[b]	Cu^{2+}	No	4.5	9.5	550$_{25°}$	Yes	No	Yes	(12, 20, 22, 23, 24)
Hog kidney	—	8.05	Cu Pyr–PO$_4$[b]	—	No	Acidic	—	—	Yes	No	Yes	(23)
Aspergillus niger	—	—	Cu Pyr–PO$_4$[b]	—	No	Acidic	11.8	10,000$_{20°}$	Yes	No	Yes	(14)
Pig plasma	190,000	—	4 Cu Pyr–PO$_4$[b]	Cu^{2+}	No	Acidic	—	—	Yes	No	Yes	(21)
Beef liver mitochondria	—	10.4[a]	Cu Flavin[c]	Chiefly Cu^{2+}	Yes	Acidic	—	3,000$_{25°}$	No	Yes	No	This paper
Pea seedling	—	—	Cu Pyr–PO$_4$[b]	Cu^{2+}	No	Acidic	—	—	Yes	No	Yes	(18, 19)

[a] Uncorrected.
[b] Shown thus far to be pyridoxal-like (Pyr) substance.
[c] Additional data desirable confirming flavin nature of enzyme.

433

IV. Comparative Properties of Amine Oxidases

Some of the properties of the various amine oxidases are summarized in Table V. The physicochemical properties of the enzymes have not been determined in detail. However, there are certain interesting conclusions that can be drawn. As with the majority of copper proteins, the various amine oxidases probably have an acidic isoelectric point. The copper appears to be mainly in the cupric state.

V. Summary

For beef liver mitochondrial amine oxidase, the following generalizations can be made:

(a) The enzyme is a copper protein in which the copper is mainly in the cupric state.

(b) The evidence to date suggests that this enzyme may be a flavoenzyme in which the flavin is covalently bonded to the enzyme.

(c) The enzyme has essential sulfhydryl groups which are not vicinal.

In addition, from the results of the previous investigators the following can be concluded:

(d) The enzyme is able to oxidize amines in which the amino group is in the terminal carbon atom of the substrate. Unsubstituted, monosubstituted, and disubstituted (methyl) amine derivatives, but not trisubstituted derivatives (6), can be substrates of the enzyme.

(e) There is a three-point attachment of substrate to enzyme. The points of attachment include the hydrogen attached to the nitrogen and adjacent carbon atoms and the side chain of the substrate (42, 43).

(f) Molecular oxygen is converted to H_2O_2 and the oxygen in the carbonyl group of the product arises from the solvent, water (44).

(g) The unprotonated form of the substrate is probably oxidized by the enzyme (35).

(h) In contrast to the other amine oxidases, the enzyme is not inhibited by high concentrations of substrate. This finding rules out multiple substrate binding sites on the enzyme.

It should be pointed out that the flavoprotein nature of the enzyme must be reinvestigated with an enzyme preparation that has been rigorously proven to be homogeneous by the various physicochemical methods. Nevertheless, it is the hope of the authors that the conclusions cited above will be of aid to other investigators who are studying the various amine oxidases.

REFERENCES

1. Zeller, E. A., *Advances in Enzymology*, **2**, 93 (1942).
2. Zeller, E. A., *Pharmacol. Revs.*, **11**, 387 (1959).

3. Schayer, R. W., *Physiol. Revs.*, **39**, 116 (1959).
4. Zeller, E. A., *in* J. B. Sumner and K. Myrbäck (eds.), "The enzymes," 1st ed., Vol. II, Academic Press Inc., New York, 1951, p. 536.
5. Zeller, E. A., *in* P. D. Boyer, H. Lardy, and K. Myrbäck (eds.), "The enzymes," 2nd ed., Vol. VIII, Academic Press Inc., New York, 1963, p. 313.
6. Blaschko, H., *in* P. D. Boyer, H. Lardy, and K. Myrbäck (eds.), "The enzymes," 2nd ed., Vol. VIII, Academic Press Inc., New York, 1963, p. 337.
7. Blaschko, H., *Advances in Comparat. Physiol. Biochem.*, **1**, 67 (1962).
8. Tabor, H., Tabor, C. W., and Rosenthal, S. M., *Ann. Rev. Biochem.*, **30**, 579 (1961).
9. Zeller, E. A., *in* J. H. Quastel and R. M. Hochester (eds.), "Metabolic inhibitors," Vol. IV, Academic Press Inc., New York, 1963, p. 53.
10. Zeller, E. A., *Ann. Rev. Pharmacol.*, **3**, 9 (1963).
11. Blaschko, H., *Pharmacol. Revs.*, **4**, 415 (1952).
12. Yasunobu, K. T., and Yamada, H., "Proc. symp. chem. and biol. aspects of pyridoxal catalysis, Rome, 1962," The Macmillan Company (Pergamon), New York, 1963, p. 453.
13. McEwen, C. M., Jr., *J. Biol. Chem.*, **240**, 2003 (1965).
14. Yamada, H., Adachi, O., Kumagai, H., and Ogata, K., *Memoirs of the Research Institute for Food Science, Kyoto University*, **26**, 21 (1965).
15. Guha, S. R., and Krishna Murti, C. R., *Biochem. Biophys. Research Communs.*, **18**, 350 (1965).
16. Seiden, S. L., and Westley, J., *Biochim. Biophys. Acta*, **58**, 363 (1962).
17. Schneider, W. C., and Hogeboom, G. H., *J. Biol. Chem.*, **183**, 123 (1950).
18. Mann, P. J. G., *Biochem. J.*, **79**, 623 (1961).
19. Hill, J. M., and Mann, P. J. G., *Biochem. J.*, **85**, 195 (1962).
20. Yamada, H., and Yasunobu, K. T., *J. Biol. Chem.*, **237**, 1511 (1962).
21. Buffoni, F., and Blaschko, H., *Proc. Roy. Soc. (London), Ser. B.*, **161**, 153 (1964).
22. Yamada, H., and Yasunobu, K., *J. Biol. Chem.*, **237**, 3077 (1962).
23. Mondovi, B., private communication.
24. Yamada, H., Gee, P., Ebata, M., and Yasunobu, K. T., *Biochim. Biophys. Acta*, **81**, 165 (1964).
25. Gorkin, V. Z., *Nature*, **200**, 77 (1963).
26. Barbato, L. M., and Abood, L. G., *Biochim. Biophys. Acta*, **67**, 531 (1963).
27. Weissbach, H., Smith, T. E., Daly, J. W., Witkop, B., and Udenfriend, S., *J. Biol. Chem.*, **235**, 1160 (1960).
28. Peterson, R. E., *Anal. Chem.*, **25**, 1137 (1953).
29. Nara, S., Piette, L., and Yasunobu, K. T., unpublished observations.
30. Peterson, R. E., and Bollier, M. E., *Anal. Chem.*, **27**, 1195 (1955).
31. Felsenfeld, G., and Printz, M. P., *J. Am. Chem. Soc.*, **81**, 6259 (1959).
32. Griffiths, D. E., and Wharton, D. C., *J. Biol. Chem.*, **236**, 1857 (1961).
33. Yamada, H., Yasunobu, K. T., Yamano, T., and Mason, H. S., *Nature*, **198**, 1092 (1963).
34. Blumberg, W. E., Horecker, B. L., Kelly-Falcoz, F., and Peisach, J., *Biochim. Biophys. Acta*, **96**, 336 (1965).
35. McEwen, C. M., Jr., *J. Biol. Chem.*, **240**, 2011 (1965).
36. Hoskins, D. D., and Bjur, R. A., *J. Biol. Chem.*, **239**, 1856 (1964).
37. Wilson, D. F., and King, T. E., *J. Biol. Chem.*, **239**, 2683 (1964).
38. Hawkins, D. D., and Bjur, R. A., *Biochem. J.*, **51**, 399 (1952).
39. Frieden, C., and Velick, S. F., *Biochim. Biophys. Acta*, **23**, 439 (1957).
40. Mahler, H., *Advances in Enzymology*, **17**, 233 (1956).
41. Friedenwald, J. S., and Hermann, H., *J. Biol. Chem.*, **146**, 411 (1942).

42. Belleau, B., Fang, M., Burba, J., and Moran, J., *J. Am. Chem. Soc.*, **82,** 5752 (1960).
43. Belleau, B., and Burba, J., *J. Am. Chem. Soc.*, **82,** 5751 (1960).
44. Smith, T. E., Weissbach, H., and Udenfriend, S., *Biochemistry*, **1,** 137 (1962).

DISCUSSION

Dr. McEwen: I would like to make just three brief points. The first is that I entirely agree with Dr. Nara's statement that the classification of amine oxidases is extremely difficult at this time. However, I do believe that there is some use in the terms monoamine oxidase and diamine oxidase, particularly when two distinct activities occur in the same tissue at the same time—for example, in human serum and plasma [McEwen, C. M. Jr., *J. Lab. Clin. Med.*, **64,** 540 (1964)].

Second, because Dr. Nara has compared the substrate specificity of his prepara-

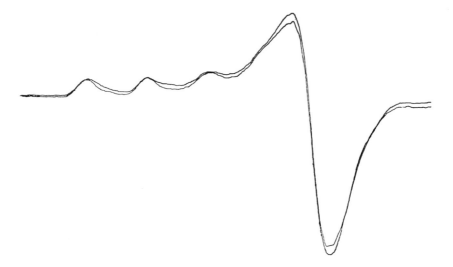

Fig. 1. EPR spectra of diamine oxidase of pig kidney in the presence and absence of putrescine. 0.4 mM enzyme of 90% purity [B. Mondovì, A. Finazzi, M. I. Giarhieri, and G. Rotilio, *Abstr. 6th Inter. Congr. Biochem., New York*, **4,** 112 (1964)] was dissolved in 0.020 ml of 0.05 M phosphate of pH 7.4 in an anaerobic cell. Lower curve: before addition of putrescine; upper curve: 1 minute after addition of 0.01 ml of a 0.5 M neutralized putrescine hydrochloride solution. The spectra were recorded at a microwave power of 10 mWatt, modulation amplitude of 6 Gauss, scanning rate of 200 Gauss/min, and a temperature of $-160°$. The difference seen in the hyperfine lines at low field (left) was reproduced in different samples with putrescine, cadaverine, or histamine as substrate. The separation of the hyperfine lines at low field is 149 Gauss and $g_m = 2.06$. According to unpublished experiments of B. Mondovì, R. E. Hansen and H. Beinert.

The flattening of the hyperfine lines at low field (left) was seen consistently in all samples when the substrate putrescine, cadaverine, or histamine was added, but the small difference in intensity at the main peak could be due to the error introduced by volume measurements on dilution with substrate.

tion with the specificity of the monoamine oxidase of human serum, I would like to point out that the factors governing the substrate specificities of amine oxidases may be very complex [McEwen, C. M. Jr., *J. Biol. Chem.*, **240**, 2011 (1965)]. For this reason I am unable to make any definite statement on the comparison of the two enzymes in this respect. The fact that Dr. Nara has detergent in his assay system makes me wonder whether this may possibly account for some of the differences between the two enzymes. However, although the two enzymes do appear to attack similar substrates I feel the relative rates of oxidation for the various amines are sufficiently dissimilar to make them entirely different enzymes.

Last, I would like to point out that the recent publication by Campello, Tabor, and Tabor [*Biochem. Biophys. Res. Communs.*, **19**, 6 (1965)] is probably the best evidence that flavins may be prosthetic groups in amine oxidases. Their data indicate that the amine oxidase of *Serratia marcescens* may be resolved and reconstituted with FAD.

DR. BEINERT: Would you, Dr. Nara, clarify something for us—as far as I am aware, flavin has not been found in some amine oxidases. The plasma amine oxidase purified by your group and the diamine oxidase that we have obtained from Dr. Mondovì in Rome have no flavin, but they both have pyrodoxal phosphate. It would be interesting if some needed flavin and some did not.

DR. McEWEN: This is the point that Dr. Nara was making—that it is far more realistic to classify amine oxidases as to whether pyridoxal phosphate or flavin is present.

DR. BEINERT: What is the electron acceptor in those that don't have flavin and where the copper obviously is not reduced?

DR. PEISACH: No prosthetic group other than copper has been found in galactose oxidase, either.

DR. BEINERT: We have had a look at diamine oxidase of hog kidney with EPR spectroscopy, and we find that all the copper is cupric. The spectrum shown in the Fig. 1 may be better resolved than the spectrum you have shown. In the oxidized enzyme we get very nice hyperfine lines with spacing of 149 Gauss. We have some very faint narrowly spaced ($\Delta_H \simeq 10$ Gauss) hyperfine structure in the main peak. On the addition of substrate the copper signal is not diminished, but it is slightly changed. This is very reproducible with histidine, putrescine, and cadaverine. Some way or other the copper sees the substrate. Whether it comes directly in contact with it or not, we cannot say. There may be a change in the protein brought about by substrate which the copper feels. Certainly the narrow (10 Gauss) hyperfine structure is there, whether the substrate is or not, and this stems therefore from groups of the protein and not from the substrate.

DR. MASON: I think that the changes which Dr. Beinert observed in the presence of substrate suggest a change of symmetry rather than a change of ligands, and that would mean a change of conformation of the protein. That could take place by having the substrate bind at a place away from the copper atom.

DR. HAMILTON: It is now apparent that several enzymes which catalyze the over-all reaction

$$R_2 CHNH_2 + O_2 + H_2O \rightarrow R_2 CO + NH_3 + H_2O_2$$

require pyridoxal phosphate and a metal ion (usually copper) as cofactors. Although some of the enzymes have been obtained in relatively pure form the mechanism by which the hydrogen is transferred from the amines to oxygen is still not known. In an attempt to obtain some information about the mechanism of the enzymatic reactions we have searched for a model reaction which has characteristics similar to the enzymatic reactions, and whose kinetics and stoichiometry could be readily studied.

In 1954, Ikawa and Snell [*J. Am. Chem. Soc.*, **76**, 4900 (1954)] reported that amino acids are deaminated to α-ketoacids and ammonia when heated to $100°$ in air in the presence of pyridoxal and certain metal ions such as Cu^{2+}, Fe^{3+}, or Co^{2+}. We hoped to find a reaction whose kinetics could be studied at room temperature by conventional Warburg manometry. Thus, we looked for oxygen uptake in several survey experiments, all with pyridoxal present but with a number of different amines, several different metal ions, and various pH's. We found that with Mn^{2+} and pyridoxal as catalysts, oxygen readily reacted with a number of amines, especially amino acids. Some typical reactions and controls are shown in Fig. 2. In this case, alanine is the amine being oxidized. With either Mn^{2+} or pyridoxal absent from the reaction mixture very little oxygen reacts even after an hour. With no alanine present some oxygen reacts but after a few minutes the reaction is completed. Accompanying this reaction is a change in color of the solution from the yellow of pyridoxal to dark brown. The dark color is characteristic of Mn^{3+} solutions and it is

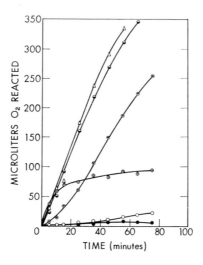

FIG. 2. The oxidation of alanine by oxygen. All experiments were carried out at $25.0°$ in a Tris buffer at pH 8.1 with an oxygen pressure of 0.2 atm. The concentrations of the reactants unless specified otherwise were: pyridoxal, 0.005 M; Mn^{2+}, 0.005 M; and alanine, 0.04 M. $\triangle$, Initiated by adding Mn^{2+}; $\ominus$, initiated by adding pyridoxal; $\odot$, initiated by adding alanine; $\oplus$, no alanine present and initiated by adding Mn^{2+}; $\bigcirc$, no pyridoxal present and initiated by adding Mn^{2+}; $\bullet$, no Mn^{2+} present and initiated by adding pyridoxal.

believed that the oxygen which reacts in the absence of alanine oxidizes Mn^{2+} to Mn^{3+}. This reaction stops when 1 mole of oxygen has reacted per 4 moles of initial Mn^{2+}. The oxidation of Mn^{2+} to Mn^{3+} is somewhat interesting since it does not occur until the Mn^{2+} is mixed with pyridoxal. When alanine is present in the reaction mixture the solutions also rapidly become darkly colored and thus, presumably, Mn^{3+} rather than Mn^{2+} is the catalyst for the alanine oxidation. As can be seen in Fig. 2 less oxygen reacts when the reaction is initiated with alanine; in that case Mn^{2+} is already oxidized to Mn^{3+} at zero time. When the reaction is initiated by adding Mn^{2+} or pyridoxal some of the oxygen uptake is caused by the oxidation of the Mn^{2+} to Mn^{3+}.

In the experiments shown in Fig. 2 the alanine is present in large excess. If limiting amounts of alanine are present the uptake of oxygen stops when 1 mole has reacted per mole of alanine (determined after subtracting the amount of oxygen which reacts in the absence of alanine). In addition, we found that for every mole of oxygen which reacts with alanine 1 mole of pyruvic acid is formed. We also have shown that ammonia is present after the alanine is oxidized. If the reaction is a model for amine oxidases then another product should be hydrogen peroxide. However, we have not yet been able to show that hydrogen peroxide is formed although the stoichiometry of the reaction would indicate that it should be formed. Catalase has no effect on the rate of oxygen uptake or on the observed stoichiometry. If hydrogen peroxide is added to the reaction mixture it appears to react. Thus, apparently the Mn^{3+} catalyzes the reaction of hydrogen peroxide with some component in the system (possibly the Tris buffer). This is an aspect of the reaction which requires further study. Tentatively, however, the model reaction appears to have the same stoichiometry as the enzymatic reactions.

The rate of uptake of oxygen due to oxidation of alanine is approximately proportional to the alanine concentration, the Mn^{2+} concentration, and the pyridoxal concentration, but is essentially independent of the oxygen pressure from 0.2 to 1.0 atm. Also, the rate is increased as the pH is increased and the reaction is inhibited by EDTA. However, the reaction is not affected by free-radical inhibitors such as phenol, 2,4-dimethylphenol, and so on. This indicates that the oxidation is not a free-radical chain reaction. There is a marked deuterium isotope effect on the rate of oxygen uptake as glycine is oxidized five to six times more rapidly than 1 , 1-dideuteroglycine. Lactic acid or 1-methylalanine does not react with oxygen under conditions where alanine reacts readily. Salicylaldehyde is a much poorer catalyst than pyridoxal for the reaction; pyridoxine is not a catalyst for the reaction and it does not react with oxygen; pyridoxamine does react with oxygen when manganous ion and alanine are present but a precipitate is formed under these conditions. In the oxidation of alanine with pyridoxal as catalyst no precipitate is formed. Thus, probably pyridoxamine is not an intermediate in the pyridoxal-catalyzed oxidation.

These results and others are consistent with the mechanism for the model oxidation outlined in Fig. 3. The formation of intermediates I and II from alanine, Mn^{3+}, and pyridoxal is similar to what has been proposed in the past to explain pyridoxal-catalyzed reactions of amino acids. In the present case it is suggested that II or some intermediate like II can complex with a molecule of oxygen to give III. Since metal ions are capable of transferring electrons by overlap of their d-orbitals with the

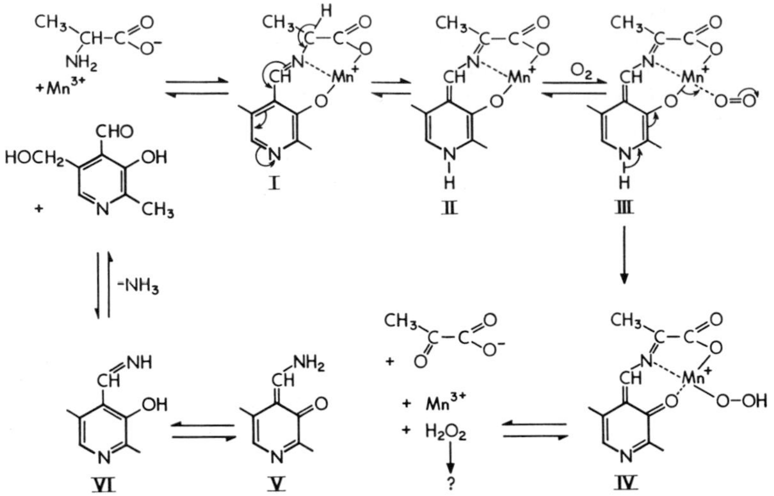

FIG. 3. Possible mechanism for the model oxidation.

p-orbitals of the ligands, the transformation of III to IV should occur readily. This transformation involves the transfer of a proton from the nitrogen of the pyridoxal through the solvent to the oxygen, and the transfer of electrons through the conjugated system and the metal ion to the oxygen. Intermediate IV has the oxygen converted to the oxidation level of hydrogen peroxide, and thus, the rest of the complex has been oxidized by two electrons. One would expect IV to be in equilibrium with pyruvic acid, Mn^{2+}, hydrogen peroxide, and V which is a tautomer of the Schiff base of pyridoxal with ammonia (VI). VI would be expected to give pyridoxal and ammonia rapidly. The hydrogen peroxide presumably reacts in some unknown way with some component in the system.

It is proposed that the mechanism of the enzymatic oxidations of amines is similar to that suggested for the model oxidation. The enzymes are different from other pyridoxal enzymes because a metal ion is required as well as pyridoxal phosphate, whereas metal ions are not required for most pyridoxal enzymes. The proposed mechanism requires the presence of a metal ion to complex with molecular oxygen and the phenolic oxygen of pyridoxal, and transfer electrons from the pyridoxal to the oxygen. It would be expected that a number of metal ions would have these properties and in the presence of an enzyme presumably copper has these properties to the best extent.

The model and enzymic reactions differ in another respect. Amino acids appear to be the best substrates for the model oxidation whereas simple amines are the usual substrates for the enzymatic reactions. Probably amino acids react more readily in the model reaction because they form stronger complexes with metal ions and thus intermediates such as I, II, III, etc. will be more stable. For the enzymatic reactions the additional complexing ability of the carboxyl group probably is not necessary because the enzyme can aid in binding the substrate at the active site. The negative charge on the carboxyl may also be necessary to partially neutralize the higher positive charge on the manganic ion so that it can complex with oxygen more readily.

Dr. WILLIAMS: In fact I think you would expect a very big change in any property of the Mn^{3+} if you put on either oxygen or hydrogen peroxide. This would be equivalent to a very big change in the oxidation state around the metal ion, and what one would expect if copper were going through this would be a very remarkable change in signal.

Dr. HAMILTON: This is only a momentary intermediate. In our model, the rate-limiting step is apparently the removal of the proton from the alanine.

Dr. WILLIAMS: Well, If the intermediate is not there in sufficient amount, you can't see it, and then you won't get the change in signal. I agree with that.

Dopamine—β—Hydroxylase: A Copper Enzyme

M. GOLDSTEIN*

Department of Psychiatry and Neurology,
Neurochemistry Laboratories,
New York University School of Medicine,
New York, New York

I. The Catalytic Hydroxylation of Dopamine

The biogenesis of norepinephrine involves the oxidation of phenylalanine to tyrosine, the catalyzed conversion of tyrosine to DOPA by tyrosine hydroxylase, the decarboxylation of DOPA to dopamine[1] by DOPA decarboxylase, and the β-hydroxylation of dopamine to norepinephrine by dopamine-β-hydroxylase. The β-hydroxylation of dopamine had been demonstrated *in vitro* (1, 2, 3, 4), as well as *in vivo* (5, 6). The enzyme was solubilized from bovine adrenal medulla particles by treatment with a detergent and subsequently purified by conventional methods of protein fractionation (7, 8).

Dopamine-β-hydroxylase is a mixed function oxidase that catalyzes the conversion of dopamine to norepinephrine according to the following equation (7).

$$\text{Dopamine} + \text{Ascorbate} + O_2$$

$$\rightarrow \text{Norepinephrine} + H_2O + \text{Dehydroascorbate}$$

The enzyme requires ascorbic acid or a catechol as cofactor (9). Fumarate and related dicarboxylic acids markedly stimulate the enzymatic β-hydroxylation (7). Recently it was found that fumarate stimulates the enzymatic β-hydroxylation at low substrate concentration but has no effect on the enzymatic activity at high substrate concentration. Fumarate lowers the K_m but does not change the V_{max} (10). Studies are now in progress to determine whether fumarate changes the configuration of the enzyme. The stimulation of dopamine-β-hydroxylation by adenosine triphosphate and by catalase has been shown to be due to an effect of these substances on the enzyme stability (8, 9). Peroxidase also protects the enzyme from inactivation during the incubation period (10). It is conceivable that

* Research Career Development Awardee of the United States Public Health Service, Grant No. 5–K3–MH–14,1918–04. Supported by the grant of USPHS No. MH–02717 and by the grant of the National Science Foundation, No. GB–3176.

[1] The abbreviations used are: dopamine, 3,4-dihydroxyphenylethylamine; epinine, 3,4-dihydroxyphenylethylmethylamine; disulfiram, tetraethylthiuram disulfide; DTC, diethylidithiocarbamate; PRR, proton relaxation rate.

peroxidase, which is present in salivary glands and other sympathetically innervated tissues, protects the enzyme from inactivation by peroxides *in vivo* in the presence of ascorbate or other substrates.

The enzyme is nonspecific and catalyzes the β-hydroxylation of many phenylethylamines and phenylpropylamines (9, 11, 12, 13, 14). The wide substrate specificity of this enzyme suggests that it may have a more general function with respect to the biosynthesis of biogenic amines than just the formation of norepinephrine.

II. Inhibition of Dopamine-β-Hydroxylase

Inhibitors of dopamine-β-hydroxylase can be classified as two types of compounds, compounds which are structurally related to phenylethylamine and compounds which are chelating agents.

A. Compounds Structurally Related to Phenylethylamine

The relative nonspecificity of the enzyme suggested that compounds which are not substrates might act as inhibitors. The α-aminoacetophenone analogs of epinephrine and norepinephrine, adrenalone and arterenone, proved to be potent inhibitors of the enzyme *in vitro* and *in vivo* (15). A Lineweaver–Burk plot indicates that the inhibition by α-aminoaceto-phenones is of a competitive nature. In Table I are shown the activities of some phenylethylamines as substrates and their α-aminoacetophenone analogs as inhibitors of dopamine-β-hydroxylase. Primary amines are better substrates than the corresponding secondary amines, but secondary amines are more potent inhibitors than the corresponding primary amines. N-(3,4-Dichlorophenylethyl) isopropyl amine shows weak activity as a substrate but its β-keto analog is a potent inhibitor. Another discrepancy between the interaction of aminoacetophenones and the interaction of substrates with the enzyme is the effect of pH: the enzyme activity is optimal at pH 5.5, while α-amino acetophenones exhibit their maximum inhibition at pH 6.4. Benzylhydrazines and benzyloxyamines which are isosteric with substrates of dopamine-β-hydroxylase are active as competitive inhibitors of the hydroxylating enzyme (16).

B. Chelating Agents

The effects of various chelating agents on dopamine-β-hydroxylase activity are shown in Table II. All the tested chelating agents, and especially those with a high affinity for binding with copper, were effective inhibitors of dopamine-β-hydroxylase (8, 17, 18, 19). The inhibition of the enzymatic activity by the tested chelating agents can be reversed by

TABLE I

COMPARISON OF PHENYLETHYLAMINE DERIVATIVES AS SUBSTRATES AND
α-AMINOACETOPHENONE DERIVATIVES AS INHIBITORS OF DOPAMINE-β-HYDROXYLASE

Substrate ϕ—CH$_2$—CH$_2$—amino	Relative activity	Inhibitor ϕ—C—CH$_2$—amino $\overset{\|}{\underset{O}{}}$	% Inhibition at 2 × 10^{-4} M
3,4 OH, NH$_2$ (dopamine)	100	3,4 OH, NH$_2$ (arterenone)	45
3,4 OH, NHCH$_3$ (epinine)	16	3,4 OH, NHCH$_3$ (adrenalone)	50
3,4 OH, NHCH$\overset{\diagup\text{CH}_3}{\diagdown\text{CH}_3}$	—	3,4 OH, NHCH$\overset{\diagup\text{CH}_3}{\diagdown\text{CH}_3}$	80
4 OH, NH$_2$ (tyramine)	100	4 OH, NH$_2$	—
4 OH, NHCH$\overset{\diagup\text{CH}_3}{\diagdown\text{CH}_3}$		4 OH, NHCH$\overset{\diagup\text{CH}_3}{\diagdown\text{CH}_3}$	12
3,4 Cl, NHCH$\overset{\diagup\text{CH}_3}{\diagdown\text{CH}_3}$	5–10[a]	3,4 Cl, NHCH$\overset{\diagup\text{CH}_3}{\diagdown\text{CH}_3}$	40

[a] The β-hydroxy product was not isolated, but the relative activity was determined from the inhibition studies.

Fe^{2+} or Co^{2+}. However, the inhibition by DTC or by disulfiram was not reversed by addition of Fe^{2+}, Co^{2+}, or Cu^{2+}. At a concentration of 2 × 10^{-4} M, Cu^{2+} inhibits the enzymatic activity 60 to 80% (19). The inhibition of the enzymatic activity by the tested chelating agents can also be reversed by a 24 hour dialysis against phosphate buffer, pH 7.8. The variation of the preincubation time of the chelating agent with the enzyme has no effect on the extent of the inhibition. Also, the extent of the inhibition does not depend on the concentration of cofactor. Of considerable interest is the finding that tropolones are inhibitors of dopamine-β-hydroxylase (17). The restoration of activity upon addition of Fe^{2+} or Co^{2+} ions, and the inhibition by colchiceine, which has no acyloin structure, but not by

TABLE II

INHIBITION OF DOPAMINE-β-HYDROXYLASE WITH CHELATING AGENTS

Chelating agent	Activity (%)
EDTA, 10^{-4} M	60
o-Phenanthroline, 10^{-5} M	30
8-Hydroxyquinoline, 10^{-5} M	40
2,2'-Bipyridine, 10^{-5} M	30
3-Ethoxy-2-oxobutyraldehydebisthiosemi-carbazone, 10^{-5} M	50
4-Isopropyltropolone, 10^{-5} M	25
Colchiceine, 10^{-5} M	30
Colchicine, 10^{-5} M	100
Sodium diethyldithiocarbamate, 10^{-6} M	25
Disulfiram, 10^{-6} M	<10

colchicine, which does have the acyloin structure, suggests that the enzymatic inhibition by tropolones is due to their metal chelating properties. In this connection it is noteworthy that tropolone has a high affinity for copper (20).

The very high sensitivity to inhibition by tropolones, DTC, and disulfiram suggested that dopamine-β-hydroxylase is a copper protein (17, 18). The inhibition of dopamine-β-hydroxylase by Cu^{2+} (19), the inactivation of the enzyme by peroxides (9), and the finding that the metal is tightly bound to the protein (17, 18) have also been cited as indirect evidence that dopamine-β-hydroxylase is a copper protein.

III. Absorption Spectra of Copper Disulfiram Chelates

To learn more concerning the mechanism of inhibition by disulfiram, the possible reduction of disulfiram to DTC by ascorbate was studied. In the absence of ascorbate the disulfiram-copper chelate shows an absorption maximum at 425 mμ. Immediately after addition of ascorbate a shift in the absorption maximum to 450 mμ as well as an increase in the absorbance was observed. The latter was identical with the spectrum of an authentic copper-DTC chelate (Fig. 1). Thus, the copper-disulfiram complex is completely reduced by ascorbate to a copper-DTC complex under the conditions which exist in an incubation reaction. The absorption spectrum in the visible region of a highly purified dopamine-β-hydroxylase[2] in the

---

[2] Dopamine-β-hydroxylase was purified by a modification of the previously described procedure A (8). The enzyme was eluted from the DEAE column with a gradient of increasing NaCl concentration.

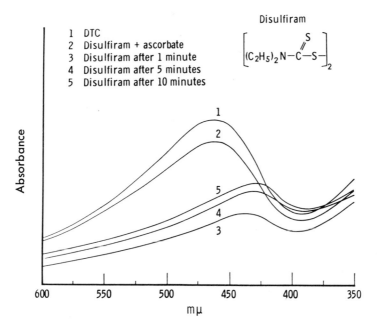

Fig. 1. Absorption spectra of copper–disulfiram and copper–diethyldithiocarbamate chelates.

presence of disulfiram and ascorbate was essentially identical to that of copper-DTC complex (10).

IV. Relationship of Copper to Activity: State of the Copper

It is evident from Table III that on purification of dopamine-β-hydroxylase there is an increase in activity proportional to the increase in copper content. Analysis of the valence of copper by the method of Felsenfeld (21) shows that approximately 80% of the copper is in the cupric state (8). The EPR spectrum of dopamine-β-hydroxylase in the resting state shows a large signal attributable to Cu^{2+} and a small signal attributable to Fe^{3+} (22). The magnetic parameters for copper are found in Table IV. These values are typical for oxygen coordinated Cu^{2+} and show some deviation from a square planar configuration. The EPR spectrum of dopamine-β-hydroxylase was studied under four experimental conditions (22): (1) resting (Fig. 2), (2) in the presence of dopamine, (3) in the presence of ascorbate, (4) under conditions of active hydroxylation with dopamine, ascorbate, and fumarate.

In the presence of dopamine, the EPR spectrum is virtually unchanged, yet in the presence of ascorbate the EPR signal, attributable to Cu^{2+}, is

TABLE III

The Content of Cuprous Copper and Total Copper in the Enzyme Preparations
at Different Purification Stages

Purification stage	Specific activity[a] (units/mg protein[b] $\times 10^{-2}$)	Cu$^+$	Cu$^+$ + Cu^{2+}
		(μg/mg protein)	
Ammonium sulfate I	0.77	<0.05	<0.05
First DEAE-cellulose column	22.00	0.15	0.80
Second DEAE-cellulose column	32.70	0.25	1.25
Second DEAE-cellulose column Procedure A[c] (8)	140.00	0.30	1.60

[a] Recently, higher specific activities as presented in the above table were obtained by addition of a more effective crystalline catalase preparation to the incubation mixture.

[b] A unit enzyme is defined as the amount of enzyme that catalyzes the formation of 1 μmole of norepinephrine per minute at optimum conditions.

[c] The enzyme was purified by a modification of the previously described procedure A (8). The enzyme was eluted from the DEAE–cellulose column with a gradient of increasing NaCl concentration.

diminished by 60%. Furthermore, with ascorbate, a small signal at $g = 2$ is seen which is due to the presence of ascorbate free radical. The amount of radical represented by this signal is far less than the quantity of reduced Cu^{2+}. The EPR spectrum obtained under conditions of enzymatic hydroxylation shows that 30% of the divalent copper was reduced compared to the sample under resting conditions. The Fe^{3+} signal remains unchanged

TABLE IV

Magnetic Parameters for Copper in Dopamine-β-Hydroxylase

System	g_z	g_x	g_y	$A_{||}$(Mc/sec)	Cu^{2+} total Cu
Dopamine hydroxylase	2.26	2.08	2.05	540	1.0
Dopamine hydroxylase + dopamine	2.26	2.08	2.06	550	1.0
Dopamine hydroxylase + ascorbate	2.25	2.09	2.06	—[a]	0.4
Dopamine hydroxylase + dopamine + ascorbate + fumarate	2.27	2.09	—[a]	670	0.7

[a] Unresolved.

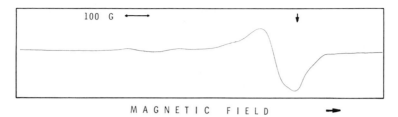

Fig. 2. EPR absorption derivative spectrum of dopamine-β-hydroxylase, 2°K. The vertical arrow denotes $g = 2$.

under all experimental conditions. PRR data for dopamine-β-hydroxylase under various conditions are given in Table V. These data suggest that copper in this enzyme is specifically bound on the enzyme surface probably accessible to a single water molecule in contrast to the three or four water molecules which are accessible to Cu^{2+} unspecifically bound to nucleic acids (23) or to proteins (24). Furthermore, it appears from these data that ascorbate reduces enzymatic copper. Also of interest is the finding that dopamine does not change the PRR of the enzyme copper and thus it does not bind to the copper directly. When an enzyme–ascorbate mixture is

TABLE V

PROTON RELAXATION RATES FOR DOPAMINE-β-HYDROXYLASE

System[a]	$\Delta R/C$[b] (sec^{-1}/μgCu/ml)	ϵ[c]
Cu^{2+} in H_2O	0.0096	1
Cu^{2+} nonspecifically bound[d]	0.077	8.0
Dopamine-β-hydroxylase	0.023	2.4
Dopamine-β-hydroxylase + dopamine + catalase	0.023	2.4
Dopamine-β-hydroxylase + dopamine + catalase + ascorbate	0.017	1.8
Dopamine-β-hydroxylase + dopamine + catalase + ascorbate + fumarate	0.021	2.2

[a] The amounts of additives were 16 μmoles dopamine, 20 μmoles ascorbate, 20 μmoles fumarate, and 400 units catalase. The enzyme contained 35 μg Cu in an initial volume of 0.45 ml.

[b] $\Delta R/C$ is the difference between the relaxation rate of the system under study and that of pure H_2O under the same conditions, divided by the concentration of paramagnetic ions.

[c] ϵ is the enhancement of the relaxation rate of the system under study over that of the same concentration of Cu^{2+} in H_2O.

[d] For example on DNA or on ceruloplasmin.

supplemented with dopamine and fumarate the partially reduced copper signal is reoxidized as indicated by an increase in PRR to a value slightly less than that for the resting enzyme.

Both the EPR and PRR data show that the addition of dopamine does not change the valence of copper, nor is there any binding of substrate directly to the copper. Partial reduction of the divalent copper by ascorbate is evidenced by EPR and PRR data.

V. Studies on the Mechanism of Enzymatic β-Hydroxylation

The finding that phenylethylamine is a substrate for the hydroxylating enzyme (9, 11) ruled out a postulated mechanism in which the catechol grouping plays an essential role in enzymatic β-hydroxylation (25).

It has also been suggested that an oxygenated derivative of the substrate, perhaps a hydroperoxide, is first formed as an intermediate during the enzymatic β-hydroxylation. This intermediate is then reduced by ascorbate or by the catechol group of the substrate to the β-hydroxylated product (13).

From the EPR and PRR studies (22), as well as from the chemical analysis of copper in purified dopamine-β-hydroxylase preparations (8, 26), it became obvious that copper is involved in the catalytic activity of the enzyme and that copper undergoes reduction before enzymatic β-hydroxylation, and partial reoxidation during enzymatic reaction. On the basis of the EPR and PRR data, the mechanism presented in Fig. 3 has been postulated for the enzymatic β-hydroxylation in the presence of ascorbate.

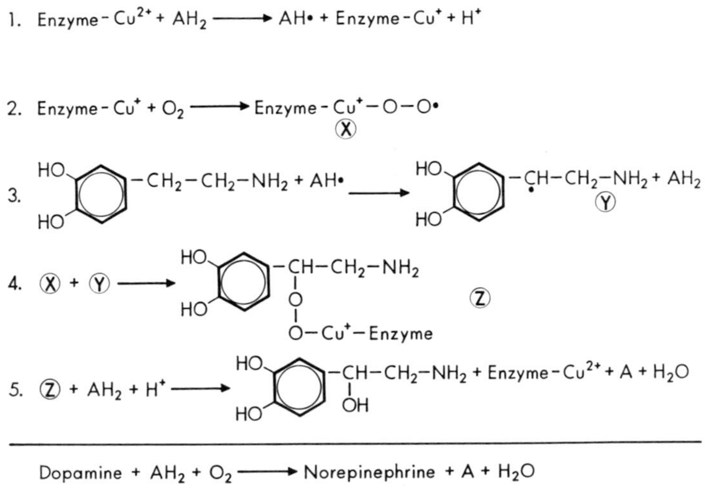

FIG. 3. The postulated mechanism for enzymatic dopamine-β-hydroxylation. Abbreviations: AH_2 = ascorbate; $AH\cdot$ = ascorbate free radical; A = dehydroascorbate.

The first step in this mechanism, the reduction of Cu^{2+} by ascorbate and the formation of ascorbate free radical, was evidenced by the EPR data (22). However no evidence had been obtained as to whether a dopamine free radical is formed or whether dopamine can react directly with the reduced enzyme intermediate, or whether a ternary enzyme–oxygen–substrate complex is formed.

The recent finding that the reduced enzyme catalyzes the β-hydroxylation in the absence of ascorbate (26) now suggests that dopamine reacts with the reduced enzyme and that the function of ascorbate is only to reduce the cupric copper of the enzyme. In this mechanism, it is still essential to remove the hydrogen from the β-carbon of the substrate (25). Whether this is done by ascorbate free radical or by a reduced enzyme intermediate, the main features of the hydroxylation mechanism do not change. In both instances, a substrate free radical is probably formed.

The role of ascorbate radical, which is formed upon the addition of ascorbate to the enzyme, still remains obscure. A dismutation of ascorbate radical to ascorbate and dehydroascorbate could not be reconciled with the occurrence of a substrate-dependent oxidation of ascorbate to dehydroascorbate during the enzymatic β-hydroxylation (7). This suggests that after reducing the enzyme the ascorbate radical remains bound in a way which prevents dismutation.

Although it was recently reported that the reduced enzyme catalyzes the enzymatic β-hydroxylation in the absence of ascorbate (26), it was of interest to reinvestigate these findings under different experimental conditions. In the previous work the enzyme was reduced with ascorbate and the excess of ascorbate was removed with ascorbate oxidase (26). Since ascorbate oxidase is inactivated by peroxide, it was conceivable that not all of the ascorbate was oxidized by ascorbate oxidase. It should also be pointed out that some of the ascorbate radical which is formed by addition of ascorbate to the hydroxylating enzyme is not oxidized by ascorbate oxidase (27). More recently it was shown that cysteine also reduces the cupric copper of the enzyme, (27) and therefore the enzymatic β-hydroxylation was investigated in a system which does not contain ascorbate and ascorbate oxidase. Upon addition of cysteine to the hydroxylating enzyme and removal of the excess cysteine with p-CMB, the reduced enzyme catalyzes the enzymatic β-hydroxylation of ^{3}H-tyramine without addition of ascorbate. This finding confirms that the reduced enzyme catalyzes the enzymatic β-hydroxylation in the absence of ascorbate (26) and demonstrates that other reducing agents can also serve as cofactors. The essential role of cuprous copper is also evident from the finding that the enzymatic β-hydroxylation of the reduced enzyme is inhibited by carbon monoxide (10, 28).

The present studies have established that copper is at the active site of the enzyme and is directly involved in the mechanism of the enzymatic β-hydroxylation. However, the mechanism by which copper takes part in the binding of the oxygen and the substrate to the enzyme surface still remains obscure.

Finally, as an attractive hypothesis for the mechanism of dopamine-β-hydroxylase stimulation by fumarate, the possibility should be considered that during the reduction of the cupric copper of the enzyme some bonds between the ligands and copper are broken and fumarate then stabilizes the enzyme configuration.

VI. Summary

Dopamine β-hydroxylase is a copper-containing protein. The enzyme activity is inhibited by various chelating agents, especially by those which have high affinity for binding with copper. The ratio of copper to protein increases with the purification stage. Evidence was obtained from the EPR and PRR studies that ascorbate reduces the cupric copper of the enzyme and that the copper undergoes reduction and oxidation during the enzymatic β-hydroxylation. A mechanism for the enzymatic β-hydroxylation is postulated.

REFERENCES

1. Hagen, P., *J. Pharmacol. Exptl. Therap.*, **116,** 26 (1956).
2. Goodal, McC., and Kirschner, N., *J. Biol. Chem.*, **226,** 213 (1957).
3. Neri, R., Hayano, M., Stone, D., Dorfman, R. J., and Elmadijan, F., *Arch. Biochem. Biophys.*, **60,** 287 (1956).
4. Kirschner, N., *Fed. Proc.*, **18,** 261 (1959).
5. Goldstein, M., Friedhoff, A. J., Simmons, C., and Prochoroff, N. N., *Proc. Soc. Exptl. Biol. Med.*, **103,** 137 (1960).
6. Sjoerdsma, A., Leeper, L. C., Terry, L. L., and Udenfriend, S., *J. Clin. Invest.*, **38,** 31 (1959).
7. Levin, E. Y., Levenberg, B., and Kaufman, S., *J. Biol. Chem.*, **235,** 2080 (1960).
8. Goldstein, M., Lauber, E., and McKereghan, M. R., *J. Biol. Chem.*, **240,** 2066 (1965).
9. Levin, E. Y., and Kaufman, S., *J. Biol. Chem.*, **236,** 2043 (1961).
10. Goldstein, M., unpublished data.
11. Goldstein, M., and Contrera, J. F., *Experientia*, **17,** 447 (1961).
12. Goldstein, M., and Contrera, J. F., *J. Biol. Chem.*, **237,** 1898 (1962).
13. Bridgers, W. F., and Kaufman, S., *J. Biol. Chem.*, **237,** 526 (1962).
14. Creveling, C. R., Daly, J. W., Witkop, B., and Udenfriend, S., *Biochim. Biophys. Acta*, **64,** 125 (1962).
15. Goldstein, M., Musacchio, J. M., Kenin, M. C., Contrera, J. F., and Rice, M. D., *Biochem. Pharmacol.*, **11,** 809 (1962).
16. Nikodijevic, B., Creveling, C. R., and Udenfriend, S., *J. Pharmacol. Exptl. Therap.*, **140,** 224 (1963).
17. Goldstein, M., Lauber, E., and McKereghan, M. R., *Biochem. Pharmacol.*, **13,** 1103 (1964).

18. Green, A. L., *Biochim. Biophys. Acta*, **81,** 394 (1964).
19. Goldstein, M., and Contrera, J. F., *Experientia*, **18,** 334 (1962).
20. Bryant, B. E., Fernelius, W. C., and Douglas, B. E., *J. Amer. Chem. Soc.*, **75,** 3784 (1953).
21. Felsenfeld, G., *Arch. Biochem. Biophys.*, **87,** 247 (1960).
22. Blumberg, W. E., Goldstein, M., Lauber, E., and Peisach, J., *Biochim. Biophys. Acta*, **99,** 188 (1965).
23. Eisinger, J., Shulman, R. G., and Szymanski, B. M., *J. Chem. Phys.*, **36,** 1721 (1962).
24. Blumberg, W. E., Eisinger, J., Aisen, P., Morell, A. B., and Scheinberg, I. H., *J. Biol. Chem.*, **238,** 1675 (1963).
25. Senoh, S., Creveling, C. R., Udenfriend, S., and Witkop, B., *J. Amer. Chem. Soc.*, **81,** 6236 (1959).
26. Friedman, S., and Kaufman, S., *J. Biol. Chem.*, **240,** PC 552 (1965).
27. Blumberg, W. E., Goldstein, M., and Peisach, J., unpublished data.
28. Kaufman, S., *Pharmacol. Rev.*, **18,** 61 (1966).

DISCUSSION

DR. SCHEINBERG: Dr. Beinert showed a very small change in hyperfine structure in diamine oxidase on addition of substrate. Was there really no change in the hyperfine structure upon the addition of substrate to your enzyme?

DR. GOLDSTEIN: Not as far as we could tell.

DR. BRILL: Dr. S. Friedman has looked at this system, in my laboratory, at a higher signal-to-noise ratio, and there is no change in hyperfine structure.

DR. MASON: If hydroxylation can proceed without ascorbate, then the stoichiometry of the reaction with one oxygen inserted into the molecule, and presumably one reduced to water, cannot occur as there is no source of reducing equivalents for the reduction step. Therefore you must come to the conclusion that to conserve the oxygen the actual stoichiometry is one oxygen hydroxylating two substrate molecules. Alternatively, the enzyme was reduced in your experiments, and turned over only once.

DR. FREEMAN: Is there any precedent for a metal-activated reaction that requires three consecutive steps to take place at the catalytic metal center? Is there, indeed, any conclusive experimental evidence that the substrate is *ever* attached to the metal atom in any of the enzymes discussed at this symposium? Assuming that this evidence exists, the statistical probability of *three* participant molecules reaching the metal site in the correct order does not seem very high.

DR. GOLDSTEIN: In the pyruvate kinase system, as well as some other Mn^{2+} requiring enzymes, ternary complexes of enzyme, substrate, and ATP are formed, mediated by the metal ion.

DR. ALBEN: Certainly tyrosinase is an excellent example of a three-substrate mechanism.

DR. CAUGHEY: With regard to Dr. Freeman's point about things getting very crowded near a metal ion in mechanisms that are often proposed—if we consider that the metal ion is chelated to the protein, then the suggestion that *several* reactants enter into the inner sphere to become directly bonded to the metal ion often appears most unlikely stereochemically. In many such cases electron transfer appears more likely to involve a pathway *through* an atom already bound to the metal ion (outer-sphere mechanism) rather than to require ligand exchange (inner-sphere mechanism).

DR. FREEMAN: Mechanisms which require a series of reactants to become sequentially attached at the same reactive site on the protein are open to an additional objection. Any molecule which interacts with the enzyme presumably fits into some sort of hole in the protein structure. This hole ought to have just the right size, and a hole into which an oxygen molecule is going to fit isn't also going to have the right size for dopamine.

DR. MASON: It's dismaying how little direct proof there is for the existence of any intermediates. No oxidases have been detected in intermediate reaction states.

Helix pomatia Hemocyanins[*]

R. LONTIE AND R. WITTERS†

Laboratory of Biochemistry,
University of Louvain,
Louvain, Belgium

The hemocyanins of the edible snail have a molecular weight of 9×10^6 and show a characteristic dissociation (1, 2). With a copper content of 0.23% they are able to bind oxygen reversibly. Several topics have been investigated since earlier reviews (3–5). The sedimentation and diffusion coefficients have been determined for the two components and the pH stability region compared for the oxy- and apohemocyanins. The decrease of the copper absorption bands has been followed as a function of time and their regeneration with reducing agents studied. The expulsion of oxygen by thiocyanate and thiourea has been examined. Copper can be restored to apohemocyanin when added as the chloride complex or, preferably, as the acetonitrile complex of Cu^+.

I. Molecular Weight and pH Stability Region

Brohult and Borgman (6) recognized the presence of two components in the hemolymph of *H. pomatia* by a partial dissociation in 1 *M* NaCl at pH 5.2. The separation of the two hemocyanins was achieved by preparative ultracentrifugation in 1 *M* NaCl at pH 5.7 (7); the α-hemocyanin (75%) dissociates into halves under these conditions; the β-hemocyanin (25%) does not. The two components are immunologically different, as shown by double diffusion in agar.[1] A study on 48 snails did not reveal any individual variation in the ratio of the two hemocyanins (8).

The sedimentation and diffusion coefficients are given in Table I for both hemocyanins.[2] They are more reliable for β-hemocyanin owing to its greater purity and stability. The ratio of the molecular weights of β-hemocyanin at pH 5.7 and 8.1 indicates a dissociation into tenths instead of into eighths (1, 2). Electron micrographs have also shown a fivefold axis for the cylindrical molecule (9). Our preparations of the less stable α-hemocyanin still contain a few percent of a smaller component. The determin-

* We wish to thank the Nationaal Fonds voor Wetenschappelijk Onderzoek and the Fonds voor het Collectief Fundamenteel Onderzoek for several research grants, and the Instituut tot Aanmoediging van het Wetenschappelijk Onderzoek in Nijverheid en Landbouw for several graduate fellowships.

† Not at meeting.

[1] D. Roosels, G. Préaux, and R. Lontie, unpublished data.

[2] R. Witters, and R. Lontie, unpublished data.

TABLE I

THE SEDIMENTATION COEFFICIENT, DIFFUSION COEFFICIENT, AND MOLECULAR WEIGHT
OF α- AND β-HEMOCYANIN OF *H. pomatia*[a]

Hemocyanin	pH	$S^\circ_{20,w}$	$D_{20,w}$	M
α	5.69	104.25 S	1.126 F	8,690,000
	8.04	19.02 S	1.822 F	990,000
β	5.69	105.78 S	1.100 F	9,030,000
	8.12	18.77 S	1.992 F	890,000

[a] Wholes at pH 5.7, tenths at pH 8.1.[2]

ation of the sedimentation and diffusion coefficients of α-hemocyanin is likely to be disturbed by the equilibrium between wholes and halves, suggested by the decreasing values of the sedimentation coefficient of the wholes at low protein concentrations.[3] The diffusion coefficient, calculated from the sedimentation data by the method of Fujita (10), amounts to 1.08 F for β-hemocyanin, in good agreement with the figure of Table I.[3] For α-hemocyanin, the same method yields a diffusion coefficient of 1.90 Fick units, which is much higher than the directly measured value, indicating a possible heterogeneity of the α-component.

The pH stability region has been determined in the Spinco Model E analytical ultracentrifuge.[2] The percentages of wholes, halves, and tenths are plotted as a function of pH in Fig. 1. For both components the tenths reach a concentration of 50% at the same pH values: 3.9 and 7.9. For the α-hemocyanin the dissociation proceeds via halves, for which a maximum concentration is found at pH 4.2 and 7.8. These data agree with the sedimentation diagrams obtained before at the critical pH values (4), and with the pH stability regions determined by light scattering (5). The electron microscope shows no difference in the stability region between α- and β-hemocyanin and clearly demonstrates for the α-hemocyanin a dissociation into halves perpendicularly to the fivefold axis (9).

The dissociation of the apohemocyanins has been compared on the alkaline side of the pH stability region and shows a still more pronounced difference between the α- and β-components.[2] The dissociation of β-apo-hemocyanin is quite similar to that of β-hemocyanin, though it occurs at a slightly lower pH value (7.7 instead of 7.9). For α-apohemocyanin, however, halves at an average concentration of 75% are already observed from pH 6.6 to 8.2. The dissociation into tenths of the remaining wholes

[3] G. Brauns, R. Witters, and R. Lontie, unpublished data.

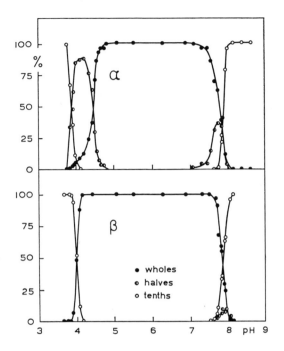

Fig. 1. The pH stability region of α- and β-hemocyanin of *H. pomatia*, determined in the analytical ultracentrifuge at 20°, ionic strength 0.15, about 1 hour after dilution of the solutions. The percentages were calculated from the areas corrected for radial dilution.

and halves is only halfway at pH 8.2. This delayed formation of tenths for α-apohemocyanin had previously been observed by light scattering (5).

II. Aging and Regeneration of the Copper Absorption Bands

Besides the usual protein band at 278 mμ, the absorption spectrum of the oxyhemocyanins of *H. pomatia* shows two so-called copper bands at 346 and 580 mμ. The contribution of light scattering to the extinction is considerable, owing to the very high molecular weight (11). In order to reduce this contribution the spectrum is usually measured at an alkaline pH just outside the stability region, where the dissociation into tenths is complete (7).

Both copper bands decrease with time, depending on storage conditions (12). Some typical curves are represented on Fig. 2. The aging is much more pronounced for α- than for β-hemocyanin. For fresh hemocyanin the major copper band at 346 mμ has a maximum value of 0.345 for the ab-

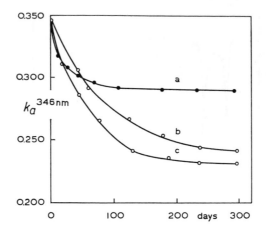

Fig. 2. Decrease at 4° of the copper band at 346 mμ. (a). Untreated *H. pomatia* hemolymph, pH 8.2. (b) Hemocyanin stored in acetate buffer, pH 5.7, *I* 0.10. (c) Hemocyanin stored as a precipitate with ammonium sulfate at half saturation.

sorbance (k_a) of an 0.1% solution. The absorbance k_a has been corrected for light scattering effects as previously described (7).

On aging a signal of Cu^{2+} is found by EPR, while no such signal is given by fresh preparations (13). The decrease of the copper bands is accomp-

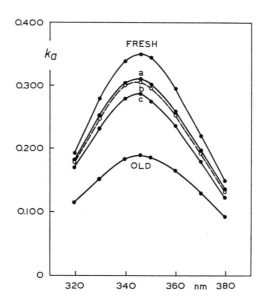

Fig. 3. Regeneration at pH 5.7 of 4-year-old *H. pomatia* hemocyanin with (a) hydroxylamine/Cu = 10, after 24 hours, (b) hydrogen peroxide/Cu = 10, the maximal value after 2 hours, (c) cysteine/Cu = 50, after 24 hours.

TABLE II

REGENERATION OF THE COPPER BAND AT 346 Mμ BY REDUCING
AGENTS AT pH 5.7 AFTER 24 HOURS[a]

Reducing agent	Reducing agent/Cu	Absorption coefficient	Percentage of the initial copper band
Hydroxylamine	10	0.310	89
Hydrogen peroxide[b]	10	0.306	87
Cysteine	50	0.286	82
Ferrocyanide	10	0.248	71
Hydrogen sulfite	10	0.242	69
Dithionite	10	0.232	66
Hydrazine	10	0.216	62
(None)	—	0.190	54

[a] Average concentration of the *H. pomatia* hemocyanin was 1.1 g/liter.

[b] For hydrogen peroxide the indicated maximal value is reached after 2 hours.

anied by a lowering of the oxygen capacity, a decrease of the free thiol groups, and a reduction of the color developed with 2,2'-biquinoline in glacial acetic acid.

The aged copper bands can be regenerated slowly with cysteine and more rapidly with hydrogen peroxide, and at the same time (13), the Cu^{2+} EPR signal disappears. A slow but complete regeneration is also obtained with hydroxylamine[4] (Fig. 3). A constant absorbance k_a is reached after 24 hours, depending on the hydroxylamine concentration. A practically complete regeneration is obtained from a ratio of hydroxylamine to copper of 10. The copper bands are also regenerated slowly by other reducing agents such as hydrazine, ferrocyanide, sulfite, and thiosulfate (Table II).

III. The Expulsion of Oxygen by Thiocyanate and Thiourea

Small amounts of thiocyanate reduce the intensity of the copper bands (Fig. 4). A limit of 23% of their original value is reached after a few minutes for a thiocyanate-to-copper ratio of 5000. A corresponding liberation of oxygen is found in the Warburg apparatus. On dialysis the copper bands are completely recovered (14).

A similar but slightly slower effect was found with small thiourea concentrations (Fig. 4). A fast and completely reversible step is followed by a slow secondary and irreversible reaction. The copper bands decrease to a limiting value of 10% for a thiourea-to-copper ratio of 2000. Copper is not

[4] B. Peeters, and R. Lontie, unpublished data.

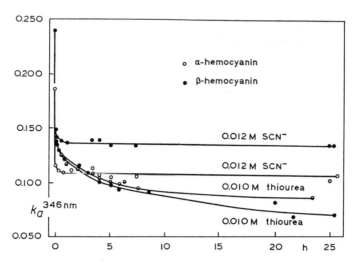

FIG. 4. The action of thiocyanate and thiourea on α- and β-hemocyanin of *H. pomatia* in borate buffer, pH 8.08, I 0.08, protein concentration about 1.5 g/liter. Thiocyanate/Cu = 210, thiourea/Cu = 180.

removed, as shown by determinations according to the method of Zuckerkandl (15). The slightest substitution of thiourea markedly reduces the oxygen expulsion (16).

The following substances were found to be inactive: azide, thiosulfate, iodide, acetonitrile.

IV. Removal of Copper and Reconstitution

The essential copper cannot be removed from hemocyanin by EDTA or ion-exchange resins. It does not exchange with radioactive Cu^{2+} (17).

Copper becomes accessible to chelating agents only on denaturation. The reaction with sodium diethyldithiocarbamate increases with denaturation by urea, as do the viscosity and the solubility at the isoelectric point (18).

Under circumstances that do not denature *H. pomatia* hemocyanin, 10% of the copper reacts with sodium diethyldithiocarbamate (18). This quantity could depend on the aging of the preparation. The percentage remains constant in the pH stability region and increases only in a fairly acid or alkaline medium, where the protein is denatured.[5] With *Cancer pagurus* hemocyanin, however, no copper reacts with diethyldithiocarbamate in the undenatured protein (19).

The binding of copper seems to be stabilized by the conformation of the

[5] N. Griffé, and R. Lontie, unpublished data.

protein. Copper also inhibits the partial hydrolysis of the protein with trypsin and chymotrypsin. The enzymatic hydrolysis of the apohemocyanin proceeds indeed faster and further than that of the native hemocyanin. The hydrolysis of α-hemocyanin is also more rapid than that of the β-component (20).

Apohemocyanin can only be prepared without any appreciable denaturation of the protein by cyanide treatment (21). Cu^+ is removed with cyanide at pH 8.2 in the presence of Ca^{2+} (5) in order to extend the region of stability (22). The possibility of a secondary reaction, caused by cyanide and the Cu^{2+} present in aged hemocyanin, has been considered. No evidence for such an effect has yet been found by amino acid determinations or by experiments with model mixtures.

An important proof for the valence of copper in hemocyanin is afforded by the fact that the reconstitution from apohemocyanin can only be obtained with Cu^+. All the experiments with Cu^{2+} have failed. The chloride complex $CuCl_2^-$ has mainly been used for the fixation of copper, which is carried out under hydrogen or nitrogen, owing to the rapid oxidation of Cu^+ in the air (21). A much more stable complex of Cu^+ with acetonitrile (23) allows a practically quantitative reconstitution directly in the air (24). The copper bands are recovered to the extent of 95%, and the preparations again reversibly bind oxygen.

V. Summary

The α- and β-hemocyanins of *Helix pomatia* have a molecular weight of 9×10^6. Both dissociate into tenths at the same pH values (50% dissociation at pH 3.9 and 7.9). This dissociation proceeds via halves for α-hemocyanin only.

The copper bands decrease on storage, and at the same time Cu^{2+} appears. They can be regenerated with traces of hydrogen peroxide, cysteine, or hydroxylamine.

Oxygen is expelled reversibly with thiocyanate and, at least for the initial reaction, with thiourea.

The reaction of copper with sodium diethyldithiocarbamate is parallel to the denaturation by urea.

Hemocyanin can be reconstituted quantitatively from apohemocyanin with the acetonitrile complex of Cu^+, even in air. The reconstituted preparation reversibly binds oxygen.

REFERENCES

1. Eriksson-Quensel, I. B., and Svedberg, T., *Biol. Bull.*, **71**, 498 (1936).
2. Brohult, S., *Nova Acta Regiae Soc. Sci. Upsaliensis*, **12**, No. 4 (1940).

3. Lontie, R., *Mededel. Vlaam. Chem. Ver.*, **16,** 110 (1954).
4. Lontie, R., *Behringwerk-Mitt.*, **32,** 64 (1957).
5. Lontie, R., *Clin. Chim. Acta*, **3,** 68 (1958).
6. Brohult, S., and Borgman, K., "The Svedberg 1884–1944," Almqvist and Wiksell, Uppsala and Stockholm, 1944, p. 429.
7. Heirwegh, K., Borginon, H., and Lontie, R., *Biochim. Biophys. Acta*, **48,** 517 (1961).
8. Lontie, R., Brauns, G., Cooreman, H., and Vanclef, A., *Arch. Biochem. Biophys.*, Suppl., **1,** 295 (1962).
9. van Bruggen, E. F. J., Wiebenga, E. H., and Gruber, M., *J. Mol. Biol.*, **4,** 1 (1962).
10. Fujita, H., *J. Chem. Phys.*, **24,** 1084 (1956).
11. Lontie, R., Dessent, M., and Heirwegh, K., *Mededel. Koninkl. Vlaam. Acad. Wetenschap. Belg.*, **13,** 1 (1951).
12. Heirwegh, K., and Lontie, R., *Nature*, **185,** 854 (1960).
13. Heirwegh, K., Blaton, V., and Lontie, R., *Arch. Intern. Physiol. Biochim.*, **73,** 149 (1965).
14. Rombauts, W., and Lontie, R., *Arch. Intern. Physiol. Biochim.*, **68,** 695 (1960).
15. Zuckerkandl, E., *Bull. Soc. Chim. Biol.*, **34,** 1164 (1952).
16. Rombauts, W., and Lontie, R., *Arch. Intern. Physiol. Biochim.*, **68,** 230 (1960).
17. Joselow, M., and Dawson, C. R., *Science*, **121,** 300 (1955).
18. Griffé, M., and Lontie, R., *Arch. Intern. Physiol. Biochim.*, **69,** 594 (1961).
19. Zuckerkandl, E., *Bull. Soc. Chim. Biol.*, **41,** 1629 (1959).
20. Brauns, G., and Lontie, R., *Arch. Intern. Physiol. Biochim.*, **68,** 211 (1960).
21. Kubowitz, F., *Biochem. Z.*, **299,** 32 (1938).
22. Brosteaux, J., *Naturwiss.*, **16,** 249 (1937).
23. Hemmerich, P., and Sigwart, C., *Experientia*, **19,** 488 (1963).
24. Lontie, R., Blaton, V., Albert, M., and Peeters, B., *Arch. Intern. Physiol. Biochim.*, **73,** 150 (1965).

DISCUSSION

DR HEMMERICH: You spoke about the deoxygenation with thiourea in the second phase of Fig. 4. Can this be reversed when hydroxylamine is the reagent?

DR. LONTIE: This has not been tried yet. Thiourea might be oxidized to form-amidine disulfide. We would now like to add formamidine disulfide to hemocyanin, but perhaps this is too strong an oxidizing agent. There may be some intermediate reagent.

DR. JØRGENSEN: I would just like to suggest, since all of you feel that cyanide is one of the best ways of removing copper, also looking at some of the sulfur-containing ligands. The point is that, for instance, dithiocarbamates are not very good, because they dissociate at biological pH into nasty things like carbon disulfide. But dialkyldithiophosphates can stand any pH for many, many hours, and I would suspect that they would very strongly bind copper. However, there is one snag. The complexes with heavy metals are soluble in organic solvents, but not in water, so I suggest that you might substitute sulfonic groups or betaines for the alkyl groups to make them more soluble. In that case I think you would have the nearly ideal case of something binding heavy metals extremely strongly and being independent of pH.

DR. LONTIE: Thank you very much for this suggestion, but I would just like to answer with another question. What do you think about the possible reaction of your substance with disulfides? When we remove the copper, we worry even with cyanide that we are doing something to some disulfide groups of the protein.

DR. JØRGENSEN: I don't think it will be very reactive.

DR. KERTESZ: You remember, Dr. Lontie, that polyphenoloxidase and hemocyanin, after that classical paper of Kubowitz [*Biochem. Z.*, **299,** 32 (1938)], can be deprived of their copper by cyanide. Polyphenoloxidase ordinarily is deprived of its copper not by cyanide, but by hydrocyanic acid. It is very easy to dialyze at 0.01 M HCN and remove practically all the copper. I have the impression that in octopus hemocyanin copper is more strongly bound. It must be dialyzed against strong solutions of hydrocyanic acid.

DR. LONTIE: I would be surprised if the acid removed copper. I would rather be in favor of cyanide ion, and you still have to dialyze it for quite some time against fresh cyanide solutions.

DR. MASON: I think that Dr. Kertesz is right, because the pK of HCN is around 9. Certainly at physiological pH we must be using mostly HCN.

DR. LONTIE: But that is the reason we tried to go up to pH 8.5, to have a little more cyanide.

DR. SCHUBERT: The pK is about 9, but the stability constant of cuprous cyanide is of the order of 10^{15}, so you have an ample region for direct complexing with the copper. I have one question about the apoprotein. Have you experimented with how long you can wait before reconstituting? In other words, is there an aging effect, or something of that sort?

DR. LONTIE: Well, we have just started worrying about that now, so I have no definite answer. We are trying to find out, for instance, if the protein regenerated by a reducing agent becomes really native hemocyanin again.

The Binding of Carbon Monoxide by Hemocyanin*

W. VANNESTE† AND H. S. MASON

Department of Biochemistry,
University of Oregon Medical School,
Portland, Oregon

A fundamental property of hemocyanin which is under dispute is whether or not it binds carbon monoxide (1–4). Root examined the oxygen dissociation curve of hemocyanin in the presence of carbon monoxide and concluded that carbon monoxide combines with hemocyanin in a ratio of one molecule per two copper atoms; the half-saturation pressure (*Limulus* hemocyanin) was 120 mm, compared with 6 mm for oxygen (3). On the other hand, Rawlinson found that no compound of carbon monoxide with hemocyanin could be detected even at a partial pressure of approximately 760 mm (4) (*Palinurus vulgaris* hemocyanin). Rawlinson's negative result has been frequently cited in theoretical discussions of the active site of hemocyanin (5, 6).

In this study, the question of carbon monoxide binding by hemocyanin has been reexamined using a method which employs ^{14}C-labeled carbon monoxide (7). We found that a compound is formed between CO and the hemocyanin of the Pacific crab, *Cancer magister.*

I. Experimental Methods

A. Materials

Hemocyanin was prepared from the hemolymph of the Pacific crab, *Cancer magister,* by an ultracentrifugal method already described (8). The hemocyanin so obtained was ultracentrifugally homogeneous, $s_{20,w} = 25 \times 10^{-13}$ sec; molecular weight, 950,000; copper content, 0.157–0.178%, equivalent to 24–26 atoms of copper per molecule of protein. In determining copper an appropriate quantity of hemocyanin solution was dried at 105° in a Kjeldahl flask. After addition of 0.2 ml concentrated sulfuric acid, heating was started as in the Kjeldahl nitrogen procedure. A few drops of 30% H_2O_2 were occasionally added until destruction was complete. The walls of the flask were rinsed twice with 5 ml of water during the digestion. The

* This study was supported in part by grants from the American Cancer Society and the National Institutes of Health.

† Fulbright Scholar, on leave from the University of Ghent, Ghent, Belgium, at the University of Oregon Medical School. Present address: University of Ghent, Ghent, Belgium. Not at meeting.

contents of each flask were transferred quantitatively to a 10 ml volumetric flask containing 0.1 ml glacial acetic acid, 1 ml 3 × 10⁻³ M BCS, and 10 mg ascorbic acid. The pH was adjusted to 4.5 with ammonia solution and the total volume made up to 10 ml. The optical density at 483 mμ was measured after standing for 30 minutes. The same procedure was applied simultaneously to an equal amount of the buffer and the final absorbance so obtained was used as a blank. The extinction coefficient 12.25 mM^{-1} cm⁻¹ for the copper complex was derived from a standard curve based upon solutions prepared from analytical grade metallic copper.

B. Radiochemical Analysis for CO

A detailed description of this method will be published elsewhere (7); the following brief description provides the principal operations of the method, which has already been applied to the determination of CO binding by cytochrome oxidase (9). In this procedure, the carbon monoxide gas is collected and its radioactivity is determined directly by scintillation counting. In another published procedure utilizing ¹⁴CO for the study of carbon monoxide binding by cytochrome oxidase (10), the CO is oxidized to CO_2, the radioactivity of which is then determined in solution. A hemocyanin solution (4.0 ml) of known copper content (0.5–1 mM) in 0.05 M Tris buffer, pH 6.8, containing 0.01 M Ca^{2+}, was deoxygenated in a 50 ml flask by 8–10 quick evacuations and flushings with pure N_2. The sample was shaken lightly for 3 minutes during each cycle to assist the removal of O_2. The anaerobic hemocyanin solution was then equilibrated for 30 minutes at 0° with a mixture of ¹⁴CO, CO, and N_2. The partial pressure of the total CO in this mixture was known. Two 1.3 ml samples of the liquid phase were withdrawn and mixed with 0.2 ml of alkaline ferricyanide (16% $K_3Fe(CN)_6$, 1 M KOH) in closed vessels under N_2. An aliquot of the gas phase containing the CO released by this treatment was transferred to specially constructed counting vials containing 2 g Pilot B beads as scintillator and counted in a Packard Tricarb scintillation counter. The measured counting rate was proportional to the sum of the physically dissolved and chemically bound CO present in the hemocyanin sample. The procedure was simultaneously carried out under identical conditions, except for CO partial pressure, on equal concentrations of hemoglobin and methemoglobin. The ratio of the difference in counting rates obtained to the hemoglobin concentration was used as a conversion factor to calculate the sum of the concentrations of dissolved and bound CO in the hemocyanin samples. To find the part of this sum due to CO in solution (and from this, the carbon monoxide bound to the hemocyanin), it was assumed that the amount of carbon monoxide in solution is independent of the nature and concentration of the protein present in a given buffer. The solubility of carbon monoxide at 0° in buffer containing known amounts of hemoglobin was determined, and the result was applied to the case of hemocyanin. Identical samples of hemoglobin solutions were equilibrated with different partial pressures of carbon monoxide at pressures sufficiently high to saturate the hemoglobin with carbon monoxide. A plot was made of the counting rates obtained from these samples by the procedure described above as a function of partial pressure of carbon monoxide, and straight lines were obtained in conformity to Henry's law. The intercept of this plot, counting rate at 0 mm Hg, corresponded to hemoglobin-bound carbon monoxide. Since the hemoglobin concentration was known, this intercept calibrated the counting rate in terms of molarity of CO in the original solution. The slope of the plot then yielded the value of the molarity of physically dissolved carbon monoxide per millimeter pressure of the gas in the buffer used in these experiments. Three separate determinations gave 173, 194, and 191 μM carbon monoxide dissolved at 0° per 100 mm Hg of CO, for an average of 18.6 μM CO per mm Hg pressure.

In a typical experiment with hemocyanin, a sample containing 463 μM copper was equilibrated with partial pressures of carbon monoxide ranging from 17.9 to 152 mm Hg. The total counting rate observed at each of these pressures was converted by means of a factor obtained from the hemoglobin experiments into molarity of the total carbon monoxide in the hemocyanin solution. From this was subtracted the estimated molarity of the dissolved carbon monoxide to give the molarity of carbon monoxide in chemical combination with the hemocyanin. These values ranged from 28.4 to 119.6 μM, according to the partial pressure of the CO.

II. Results

If it is assumed that there is only one type of CO-binding site on the hemocyanin molecule, that the affinity of all the sites for CO is the same, and that there is no interaction between sites in such a manner that the binding of one molecule of CO affects the affinity of any other site for CO, then a simple equilibrium relationship should hold:

$$\text{Site} + \text{CO} \rightleftharpoons \text{Site—CO} \tag{1}$$

If [S] is the concentration of free CO-binding sites, [S—CO] is the concentration of occupied CO-binding sites, and K_D is the dissociation constant of the above relationship (Eq. (1)), then,

$$K_D = \frac{[\text{S}][\text{CO}]}{[\text{S—CO}]} \tag{2}$$

where [CO] is the concentration of dissolved CO, and then

$$1/[CO] = \frac{[S]}{K_D[S{-}CO]} = \frac{[S]_{tot} - [S{-}CO]}{K_D[S{-}CO]} \quad (3)$$

where

$$[S]_{tot} = [S] + [S{-}CO] \quad (4)$$

whence

$$1/[CO]_{dissolved} = [S]_{tot}/K_D[CO]_{combined} - 1/K_D \quad (5)$$

If the underlying assumptions hold, we should expect a straight line relationship between $1/[CO]_{dissolved}$ and $1/[S{-}CO]$, with an intercept of $-1/K_D$ on the y axis. When the binding sites are half-saturated, $[S] = [S{-}CO]$, and $[CO] = K_D$, which thus corresponds to the half-saturation

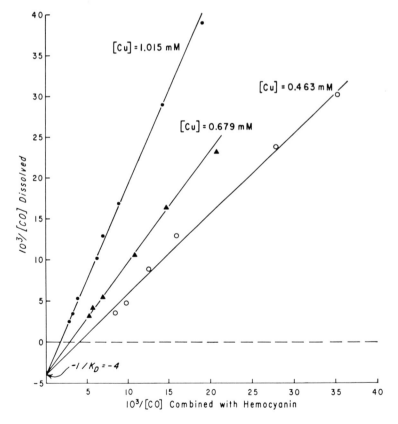

FIG. 1. Binding of CO yy *Cancer magister* hemocyanin. Relationship between hemocyanin concentration, CO (dissolved) concentration, and CO-hemocyanin concentration.

TABLE I

Dissociation Constants K_D for the CO–Hemocyanin Reaction, Half-Saturation Pressures ($P_{50\%}$) and Copper-to-Carbon Monoxide Ratios Observed from Three Sets of Experiments with *Cancer magister* Hemocyanin

Hemocyanin Cu concentration (μM)	Measured CO-binding sites (μM)	Cu/CO$_{bound}$	K_D (μM)	$p_{50\%}$ (mm)
463	244	1.90	150	134
679	337	2.01	250	134
1015	580	1.75	250	134
Average	—	1.88	—	—

pressure of the hemocyanin. A plot of these relationships for three experiments is shown in Fig. 1.

The results from these experiments is summarized in Table I. The average number of copper atoms required to bind one molecule of CO is 1.88, slightly less than 2; $K_D = 250 \mu M$, equivalent to a half-saturation pressure of 134 mm. It is interesting that in another series of experiments it was found that 1.84 atoms of copper are required (on the average) to bind one molecule of O_2 (11).

III. Discussion

Our results establish the binding of carbon monoxide to hemocyanin. The ratio of total copper in hemocyanin to total carbon monoxide bound averaged 1.88 atoms per molecule or somewhat less than two atoms per molecule. This result may be due to experimental error since it is only 6% different from the ideal figure of 2 atoms Cu per molecule. It is possible, however, that a few binding sites require only one copper atom per molecule of CO bound. In any case, the half-saturation pressure for this hemocyanin, 134 mm, is almost identical to the half-saturation pressure, 120 mm, observed by Root for *Limulus* hemocyanin (3).

The hypothesis that the O_2- and CO-binding site of hemocyanin contains, in general, two copper atoms is reinforced by our results. On the other hand, it must be remembered that the observed ratio of binding is an average and that one copper atom may comprise the binding site while another atom plays some essential but different role such as the determination of conformation. Direct chemical or physical evidence for the two-copper site hypothesis is required to support the essentially statistical results reported here.

ACKNOWLEDGMENT

We wish to thank C. Simo for providing the samples of hemocyanin and checking them spectrophotometrically. Mrs. M. Vanneste kindly determined the copper concentrations of hemocyanin solutions.

REFERENCES

1. Craifaleanu, A. D., *Boll. Soc. Nat. Napoli*, **32**, 141 (1919).
2. Dhere, C., and Schneider, A., *J. Physiol. Path. Gen.*, **20**, 34 (1922).
3. Root, A., *J. Biol. Chem.*, **104**, 239 (1934).
4. Rawlinson, W. R., *Australian J. Exptl. Biol. Med. Sci.*, **18**, 131 (1940).
5. Ingraham, L. L., *J. Chem. Ed.*, **41**, 66 (1964).
6. Williams, R. J. P., *Proc. Vth Internat. Congr. Biochem.*, **4**, 133 (1963).
7. Vanneste, W. H., unpublished observations.
8. Thomson, L. C. C., Hines, M., and Mason, H. S., *Arch. Biochem. Biophys.*, **83**, 88 (1959).
9. Vanneste, W. H., *Biochem. Biophys. Res. Communs.*, **18**, 563 (1965).
10. Gibson, Q. H., Palmer, G., and Wharton, D. C., *J. Biol. Chem.*, **240**, 915 (1965).
11. Simo, C., Ph. D. thesis, University of Oregon Medical School (1965).

DISCUSSION

DR. PETERS: May I ask an extremely elementary question which I'm sure that I ought to know? If you put these animals into a high concentration of CO, how long does it take them to die, or do they not die?

DR. MASON: I'm afraid I don't know the answer to that extremely elementary question.

DR. JØRGENSEN: With a little bit of oxygen they ought to survive—with a mixture of oxygen and CO.

DR. AISEN: That assumes that the function of hemocyanin is to transport oxygen, and that nothing else is going to be affected significantly by the CO. It is perfectly conceivable that an enzyme system will be attacked.

DR. CAUGHEY: It might be pertinent to mention here that hemocyanin can have as a function the reduction of oxygen in the course of oxygen binding. For CO binding reduction of CO by hemocyanin need not be proposed, so CO binding in itself may not be related to the need for two coppers at the active site. CO could be bound to one copper whereas oxygen may require bonding to two atoms of copper.

DR. SCHUBERT: It's interesting to know that oxygenated hemocyanin is resistant to the action of ionizing radiation as well as to H_2O_2 and organic peroxides, but the deoxygenated form is terribly sensitive [Schubert, J., and Westfall, W. M., *Nature.*, **197**, 1096 (1962)]. It would be interesting to learn whether the CO complex behaves the same as the deoxygenated form.

DR. NAKAMURA: Dr. Mason, is there any absorption peak with your CO-hemocyanin?

DR. MASON: Miss Simo observed no absorption peaks with CO hemocyanin.

DR. JØRGENSEN: That means that the peak at 550 mμ flatly disappears when you put the CO on?

DR. MASON: That's correct.

DR. JØRGENSEN: How interesting! And the 345 mμ as well?

DR. MASON: Yes, that's correct. Only the protein peak is left.

DR. YONETANI: Is the CO binding photodissociable?

DR. MASON: We haven't tried photodissociation of the CO compound. That would be an interesting experiment to try. It could be done with light of a high energy.

DR. YONETANI: Where is your absorption maximum?

DR. MASON: Actually, toward the ultraviolet. We did try a laser flash on oxyhemocyanin, but there weren't enough calories per second being thrown into the solution to make a detectable difference.

Do you have high-intensity sources that produce something in the order of 10^{18} photons per second in the region of 550 mμ?

DR. YONETANI: No.

DR. AISEN: Dr. Mason, what was the wavelength of the laser?

DR. MASON: It was a red beam at 833 mμ.

DR. AISEN: That's too far away, isn't it?

DR. MASON: I hoped there would be enough absorption on the side of the absorption band around 600 mμ.

DR. KERTESZ: If I remember well, Warburg has attempted to dissociate carbonmonoxyhemocyanin by light, and he stated that it could not be done (Warburg, O., "Heavy metal prosthetic groups," Clarendon Press, Oxford, 1949, p. 81).

DR. MASON: That is true.

DR. WILLIAMS: This paper has raised some problems which I'm sure Dr. Mason realizes, but, in his disinclination to speculate, he has rather left the fun out of his paper and has given us just the meat.

The conventional way of writing oxygen binding is

$$\text{Cu—O}{=}\text{O—Cu} \qquad \text{Cu—} \overset{\text{O}}{\underset{\text{O}}{\|}} \text{—Cu} \qquad or \qquad \text{O}{=}\text{O—Cu}$$

There are only certain of these geometries, of course, which are satisfactory from the point of view of CO binding. For instance, these forms of CO binding are highly improbable:

$$\text{Cu—C}{=}\text{O—Cu} \qquad and \qquad \text{Cu—} \overset{\text{C}}{\underset{\text{O}}{\|}} \text{—Cu}$$

We never see CO bound like oxygen in a bridge. But there is the other form of CO binding as a bridge, like this:

$$\overset{\displaystyle \text{O}}{\underset{\displaystyle \text{C}}{\|}}$$
$$\diagup \quad \diagdown$$
$$\text{Cu} \qquad \text{Cu}$$

I have drawn these with lots of bonds, but it doesn't really matter. I think I'm right in saying that this too is not known in cuprous chemistry. It's only known in the heavy transition metals. Thus, if this form turned up in copper chemistry in these proteins, it would be the only example known of it. Again if this is the structure there is no room for the oxygen in the structure Cu—O=O—Cu; there is only room for the structure:

$$\text{Cu}-\overset{\text{O}}{\underset{\text{O}}{\|}}-\text{Cu}$$

I think it is now Dr. Mason's job to find out whether the CO is bound to one or two coppers.

DR. MASON: Dr. Williams, we have observed the nitric oxide compound of hemocyanin. I wonder whether this would throw any light on the problem you raise.

DR. WILLIAMS: How is it as to color?

DR. MASON: It's greenish.

DR. WILLIAMS: That's fine, because $CuNO^+$ is blue. It's quite likely that nitric oxide will oxidize copper first to give Cu^{2+} which then combines with NO to give $Cu^+ NO^+$. It's a well-known blue compound.

DR. MASON: And it's also interesting that the NO compound of hemocyanin has a very distinct EPR spectrum, with lots of hyperfine structure. However, we can't

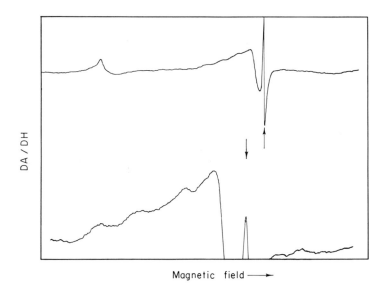

FIG. 1. EPR spectrum of concentrated serum of *Homarus americanus*. Upper trace: wide field sweep showing the Cu^{2+} absorption on the right on either side of the $g = 2.0$ marker signal and a small absorption at $g = 4.3$ which is due to Fe^{3+}. Lower trace: region of hyperfine structure of the Cu^{2+} signal taken at higher gain and less field sweep. Spectra observed at 1.5°K.

tell whether that's due to copper-nitrogen interaction or to copper-copper inter-action, which is what we hoped to find.

DR. BLUMBERG: I would like to present some data about hemocyanin. Dr. Lontie told you that the hemocyanin he had shows no EPR when it's fresh, but under various kinds of maltreatment the EPR signal will arise. We have looked at some hemocyanins (*Limulus* and *Busycon*) furnished by Dr. Felsenfeld which he had had around in his refrigerator for some years. I assume that's some kind of maltreat-ment, but those didn't show any EPR signal.

Dr. Scheinberg went to a fish market in New York and picked up some very fresh *Homarus americanus* (lobsters) and brought them to the laboratory. We very gently extracted the serum and were very careful to give it no maltreatment, except we had to concentrate it a little by centrifuging. We didn't add or subtract anything except supernatant, and we looked at it within hours after the lobster had been swimming around in the sea water. We saw the EPR signal shown in Fig. 1. This signal corresponds to roughly one quarter of the total amount of copper present, and it is a spectrum which looks somewhat like ceruloplasmin and somewhat like the narrow signal of laccase that Dr. Malmström reported. There is a little iron at $g = 4.3$. We didn't try to purify it from any contaminants. I don't know whether this represents the native state of hemocyanin in *Homarus americanus* or whether this protein is especially labile toward this type of denaturation. This experiment was done a long time ago, and we have never continued the study. I wish my Einstein colleagues would renew their interest in this problem, because work on *Homarus americanus* is delightful for several reasons.

Wilson's Disease, A Review

J. M. WALSHE

Department of Experimental Medicine,
University of Cambridge,
Cambridge, England

Wilson's disease, like most other inborn errors of metabolism, is a rare disease inherited in a recessive manner. Bearn (1) has calculated that the general gene frequency rate is of the order of 1/500, assuming always that there is but a single abnormal allele; this gene frequency should result in a disease incidence of 1/1,000,000 of the population. However, the rarity of this disease bears no relationship to its importance for during the last two decades, as I hope to show, research into this condition has resulted in our present understanding of both normal and abnormal copper metabolism in man.

I. History

Neither time nor space permit a detailed review of the history of Wilson's disease though there are case reports to be found in the neurological literature dating back to the latter half of the last century which can, with some confidence, be diagnosed retrospectively as examples of this condition. The historical aspects have been admirably reviewed recently by Bearn and Kunkel (2), Boudin and Pepin (3), and Cumings (4) and it is not necessary to do more than mention the major milestones here. Wilson in 1911 (5) originally referred to the disease which now bears his name as "progressive lenticular degeneration, a familial nervous disease associated with cirrhosis of the liver." He described four cases of his own and selected six reports from the earlier literature as conforming to the same clinical picture; however, he failed to appreciate the significance of the corneal pigment rings earlier described by Kayser (6) and Fleischer (7) in patients with "pseudosclerosis." Hall (8) brought these aspects of the story together in a monograph published in 1921 and introduced the name "hepatolenticular degeneration" which is still commonly used. The first hint that copper might be implicated came as early as 1913 when Rumpel (9) reported finding excess of the metal in the liver and this abnormality was later shown to apply to the brain also (10–13). It was, however, Cumings (14) in 1948 who put beyond further doubt the association of copper with the liver and brain lesions of Wilson's disease. He suggested the therapeutic use of the chelating agent BAL in this disease; this had originally been introduced by Peters, Stocken, and Thompson (15) for arsenical war gas poisoning. The year 1948 was indeed a vintage one for Wilson's disease for two other important publications appeared. Holmberg and Laurell (16) described the isolation and characterization of a copper protein in normal serum which, because of its blue color, they named ceruloplasmin; they showed that it contained 8 atoms of copper per molecule and had a weak oxidase activity for amines such as p-phenylenediamine and epinephrine. The increased urinary excretion of copper by patients with Wilson's disease, and also its enhancement after the administration of BAL, was first reported at this time (17). The design of the BAL molecule by Peters' team in Oxford and the realization of its possibilities in the treatment of Wilson's disease by Cumings unquestionably opened the gates to the great flood of research into the pathogenesis and treatment of this rare condition which has not yet spent its force.

II. Clinical Features

A. Case Material

I shall return to the question of the biochemical lesion and treatment later for I must now summarize the main clinical features of the disease.

In discussing these I will draw mainly on my personal experience rather than on published case reports which are readily available (Fig. 1). Although Wilson's disease is generally believed to fall mainly in the province of the neurologist an analysis of the findings in 50 patients of whom I have case histories shows that 31 first had signs of hepatic involvement, 17 presented with neurological symptoms, one with schizophrenia, and one with the Fanconi syndrome. The average age of onset was 13.4 years with a range from 6 to 39 years. These 50 cases comprised 41 sibships: 27 were male and 23 female. The average age of onset in females, 11.7 years, was younger than in the males, 14.7 years. As has been pointed out elsewhere in an analysis of 25 cases (18) the age of onset is younger in patients with

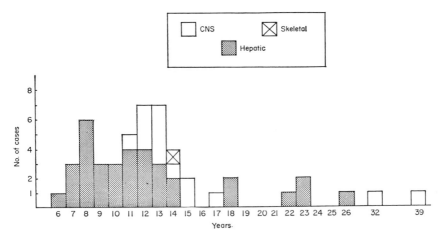

Fig. 1. Age at onset of first symptoms in 50 patients with Wilson's disease classified according to the principally involved organ.

hepatic symptoms (mean 11 years) than in those with neurological symptoms (mean 17 years). The explanation was then offered that the difference was in some way related to puberty with the increased secretion of steroid hormones. The significance of a mixed hepatic and hemolytic type of jaundice as an early symptom has also been confirmed by the finding of three more cases in whom repeated severe hemolytic crises required transfusion. No less than 15 of the 31 patients presenting signs of hepatic disease died of subacute hepatic necrosis. This high mortality does not in fact indicate that these cases are particularly resistant to treatment for seven were only diagnosed either at post-mortem examination or retrospectively when further cases of Wilson's disease were later found among the surviving siblings; of the eight others three were in the terminal stage of the illness when the diagnosis was first made, three were very ill, and two died of hemorrhage from esophageal varices. Four cases were diagnosed as asymptomatic younger siblings during the course of screening studies; these were found to have hepatosplenomegaly and abnormal liver function studies. All have remained well on prophylactic treatment. Eight of the remaining 12 cases later went on to develop neurological signs before the diagnosis was made, while four were rendered symptom free with treatment. In the untreated patients the course of the hepatic illness tended to progress rapidly to fluid retention, portal hypertension, and death either from hemorrhage or hepatic coma. There was nothing specifically characteristic about the illness, but the pathology of the liver is rather typical with pigment granules, glycogen nuclei, fatty changes, and intracellular deposition of copper in the parenchymal cells only (19, 20).

B. Physical Findings

The neurological picture was more varied: The commonest initial complaint was deteriorating performance at school particularly in handwriting and difficulty of speech; this was almost invariably found to be associated with a small spastic tongue which could scarcely be protruded beyond the lips. Tremor was a variable symptom, in some cases so wild as to lead to a diagnosis of hysteria and one patient was subjected to a course of convulsive therapy for this reason. Tremor of the head and trunk was found even at rest in severe cases but was more common when the patient was excited or embarrassed and was more often revealed only on purposive movement. This sequence was particularly true of tremor and ataxia of the limbs. Parkinsonian type of tremor and variable rigidity were also found and a mixture of Parkinsonism and cerebellar ataxia was rather characteristic of the disease. Dystonia, choreiform posture, and sudden jerky spontaneous movements were seen in five patients and in two were very severe, occurring even in sleep. The textbook neurological picture of the disease leading to flection deformities, incontinence, virtual anarthria, drooling, helplessness, and screaming has now been almost eliminated by earlier diagnosis and effective treatment.

Many patients when first seen have a rather typical facial expression with retraction of the upper lip and drooling giving them a foolish appearance belying their natural intelligence which is often retained until quite late in the illness. Mental impairment is not a symptom of early Wilson's disease, and many of the children are of above average intelligence. The Kayser–Fleischer corneal ring is probably always present when neurological symptoms develop, but may be only a crescent seen at the top of the cornea. Later it also appears inferiorly and then slowly spreads outward before finally meeting laterally to complete the ring. It may not be present in asymptomatic younger siblings. Under adequate treatment the ring disappears slowly in the reverse order, going first laterally, then inferiorly, and finally also superiorly so that the cornea may become quite clear even under slit lamp examination. Cataracts have not been seen in any patient. One girl of 13 years, with a choreiform syndrome, was correctly diagnosed when she was noted to have green deposits in her lens capsule and vitreous humor.

No new abnormalities have been recorded among these patients. No true blondes were seen, patients having either sandy or brown hair only. Azure lunulae (21) also have not been observed; neither have abnormalities of skin pigmentation. Only one patient has had initial complaints referable to his skeleton and he has been reported in detail elsewhere (22). Fourteen other patients have been subjected to detailed radiological examination of the skeleton and all showed some abnormalities which may be summarized as follows: osteoporosis, 4; various cartilage abnormalities, 25; bone cysts, 3. Mental subnormality was seen in two patients, but whether this was due to the Wilson's disease or to another independent genetic abnormality cannot be determined. In view of the unsatisfactory family backgrounds in both cases the latter explanation would seem more likely. The picture of schizophrenia with delusions was seen in two cases and in one was the presenting complaint. Clinical evidence of renal disease was not seen except in one patient suffering from vitamin D overdosage, but inability to acidify the urine and reduced ammonia formation were common findings. Renal glycosuria was seen in less than half the cases, but two showed fructose, pentose, and other reducing substances, in addition to glucose, in their urines.

C. Laboratory Studies

Other routine laboratory investigations revealed no characteristic pattern of abnormality that has not already been described. Thrombocytopenia was rather common, the mean platelet count on 25 patients being 156,000/mm.[3] Low levels of plasma fibrinogen were seen in 8 out of 19 cases examined with the mean value for the group, 220 mg/100 ml, on the lower limits of normal. Of the various tests of liver function employed the serum transaminases were the most useful in the early stages, particularly in screening asymptomatic younger siblings. In these they were frequently considerably elevated, returning slowly to normal with treatment. Urine copper excretion was raised in all but one case when first seen and serum copper and serum ceruloplasmin levels were low in all but three; one of these had recently completed a course of estrogens which may, at least in part, have accounted for the high level. The second is of some interest as he had a normal ceruloplasmin concentration when first examined on the death of his elder sister; three years later he developed signs of subacute hepatic necrosis, and at this time his serum ceruloplasmin concentration was found to be over 50 mg/100 ml, falling to 21 mg/100 ml a few days before his death from hemorrhage and liver failure. The concentration of copper in his brain (22.4 μg/g wet weight) and liver (203 μg/g wet weight) was considerably elevated as had been found in the brain from his elder sister (57.8 μg/g wet weight); he must be presumed to have had Wilson's disease although he never had Kayser–Fleischer rings. The third patient was also the younger sibling of a typical patient with disease. Despite a normal ceruloplasmin concentration he was found to have hepatomegaly; eventually he developed Kayser–Fleischer rings and was also found to have a reduced rate of incorporation of radiocopper into his ceruloplasmin. At no time did he have symptoms of liver disease nor did biochemical tests of liver show more than minor abnormalities.

III. Copper Metabolism

A. Previous Studies

1. Normal Copper Metabolism

Certain aspects of copper metabolism in Wilson's disease have necessarily been touched upon in both the historical and clinical sections. Normal copper metabolism has been reviewed by Van Ravestyn (23), Adelstein and Vallee (24), Scheinberg and Sternlieb (25), and Cartwright and Wintrobe (26) but it is necessary to refer briefly to their conclusions before proceeding to discuss the abnormal copper storage of Wilson's disease. The normal daily diet contains from 2 to 5 mg copper. Studies with the radioactive isotope ^{64}Cu have shown that up to 80% of orally administered copper is recovered in the stools, less than 1% in the urine, and only negligible amounts in the sweat (27). Very much smaller amounts were recovered after intravenous administration. The fate of the radiocopper after absorption or intravenous administration has also been followed. When given by the oral route radiocopper appeared rapidly in the plasma reaching a peak at about 2 hours (28) at which time it was found bound to serum albumin (29, 27). A secondary peak appeared at or after 24 hours by which time the radiocopper had been incorporated into ceruloplasmin. The radiocopper has also been detected in the liver (27) and it has been estimated that as much as 90% of the dose may be present in that organ (30, 31). Studies in patients with bile duct drainage have shown that approximately 10% of injected radiocopper was excreted in the bile, which is the principal route of excretion of the metal, in 24 hours (32).

Copper retained in the body is incorporated in a number of copper proteins in brain, liver, and red cells as well as in the enzymes tyrosinase, ceruloplasmin, and cytochrome c oxidase (25). The normal serum copper concentration varies from 90 to 150 μg/100 ml and 90% of this is present in ceruloplasmin. Less than 50 μg are excreted daily in the urine. In pregnancy and many chronic diseases the concentration of copper in the serum rises due to a rise in the ceruloplasmin concentration. The function of this somewhat enigmatic protein has been discussed in this symposium by Dr. Scheinberg. The total content of copper in the body is probably less than 150 mg (25, 26) of which 10–15 mg is present in the liver and 10 mg in the brain; in the pigmented areas of the brain the copper concentration may be considerable, figures as high as 404 μg/g dry weight having been recorded for the locus ceruleus (33).

2. Copper Metabolism in Wilson's Disease

The abnormal handling of copper in Wilson's disease can now be compared with these normal metabolic pathways. The accumulation of copper in the brain and liver of patients has already been referred to; it is now known also that the metal accumulates in abnormal amounts in the kidneys (34, 35). Paradoxically the concentration of copper in plasma is much reduced (36) and this is always secondary to a low level of ceruloplasmin (36, 37). At the same time the urine copper is markedly elevated and may reach figures as high as 1 mg daily. Much of the plasma copper is not bound to ceruloplasmin and is presumably more readily available for excretion by the kidneys and for diffusion into the tissues. The concentration of copper in the red cells appears to be normal (34) despite the occurrence of hemolytic crises, although there is no published data on erythrocyte copper levels at the time of hemolysis. I have studied one patient shortly after hemolysis in whom the red cell copper was on the lower limits of normal (89 μg/100 ml) and the uptake of radiocopper by the cells was reduced.

Much information has in fact been obtained by the use of ^{64}Cu in the study of this disease although the short half-life of this isotope (12.8 hours) rather limits its usefulness. Bearn and Kunkel (29), who were first to use ^{64}Cu, showed in Wilson's disease that the fecal loss of copper was reduced compared with normals and the urinary loss increased but not sufficiently so to compensate for differences in stool excretion. These observations have been confirmed by Matthews (28) and by Cartwright's group (27). The transport of radiocopper in the plasma is also abnormal in Wilson's disease with delayed or absent incorporation of the metal into ceruloplasmin (29). This defect is also partly present in the heterozygotes, so that calculation of the ratio of radioactivity in the plasma at 24 hr/2 hr has been used as a test to identify these individuals (38). This defect of incorporation of copper in to ceruloplasmin also seems to be present in these rare but puzzling cases of Wilson's disease with normal or near normal concentrations of ceruloplasmin (51, 52). The distribution of copper in the body is also different. Cartwright's group (27) found reduced counting rates over the liver and Osborn and Walshe have shown that there is in fact a greatly reduced percentage uptake in that organ (30, 31) which is not simply due to dilution of ^{64}Cu in the body pool of that metal. More recent studies have suggested that this is due not to prior saturation of binding sites for copper in the liver but to a genetically determined absence or deficiency of an enzyme system normally used for concentrating copper from the plasma and incorporating it into ceruloplasmin (39). Calculation of the ratio of activity per gram of liver with that per gram of plasma also shows quite different pictures for patients and controls. In control subjects the ratio was 24.9 at 2 hours, falling to 20.9 at 24 hours. In patients, on the other hand, the ratio was only 11.0 at 2 hours but had risen to 81.9 at 24 hours. Despite this apparent considerable rate of uptake in the Wilson's disease liver, the total amount of copper in the liver still remains low, partly because of the low levels of plasma radioactivity from which the liver must concentrate the radioisotope and partly, also, because the 2-hour levels of radioactivity in the liver were so greatly below normal. Studies with the scintiscanner have shown in addition there is concentration of copper in the kidneys in Wilson's disease patients, substantiating an observation originally made by Sass-Kortsak (40) and confirmed by Osborn and Walshe (52). The difference in handling of injected radiocopper by the liver of controls compared with patients can be demonstrated within minutes of injection by making graphic recordings of radioactivity appearing in the liver and thigh. The normal subjects show a sharp rise in radioactivity over the liver followed by a slow steady climb whereas the patients, after the initial peak, commonly show a slow decline although in some the level may remain constant (Figs. 2 and 3). These findings have been put on a quantitative basis by comparing liver with thigh counting rates. In normal subjects at 15 minutes the ratio liver:thigh is in excess of 2.0 while in patients it has never exceeded 1.2 and may fall as low as 0 5, the mean for 10 patients being 0.8 (39). This pattern of delayed liver uptake of in-

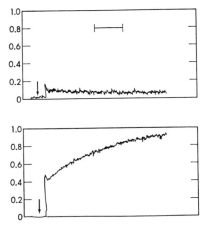

Fig. 2. The uptake of ^{64}Cu by the liver (lower tracing) and the thigh (upper tracing) immediately after injection (arrow on the left) of the radioisotope into a control subject. The horizontal mark indicates a scale of 5 min.

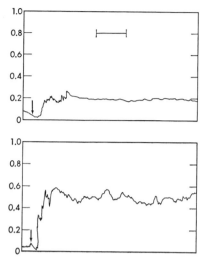

FIG. 3. The uptake of ^{64}Cu by the liver (lower tracing) and thigh (upper tracing) in a patient with Wilson's disease. Note the entirely different pattern from that shown by the control subject in Fig. 2. The horizontal mark indicates a scale of 5 min.

jected ^{64}Cu is remarkably constant for patients with Wilson's disease whether they have predominantly hepatic or neurological signs and whether they are untreated or have been successfully "decoppered" (39, 41).

There are no reports of the detection of radiocopper in the brain. After extensive searches Osborn and I have not found any evidence of concentrations in the head for periods up to 48 hours after injection. We have also observed that much of the injected copper cannot be accounted for at 2 hours in the normal subject unless the assumption is made that all extracellular fluid contains the radioisotope at the same concentration as the plasma and all the intracellular fluid at the same level as the red cells. Even this somewhat outrageous assumption does not account for all the radiocopper in the patients so that one must assume that there are other localized sites of concentration such as the kidneys (32). At 24 hours the picture is different and the assumption that the radiocopper is evenly distributed throughout the intra- and extracellular compartments leads to a marked calculated excess in normals. This was to be expected as by 24 hours most of the plasma copper is bound to ceruloplasmin and is not available for diffusion into the tissues. In the patients at 24 hours the assumption accounts for all the injected copper. It would seem therefore that immediately after injection labeled copper finds its way into most fluid compartments in the body. The normal individual can readily recall it from these, concentrating it in the liver and incorporating it into cerulo-

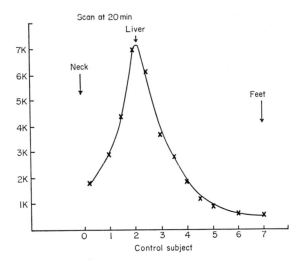

FIG. 4. Profile of whole body radioactivity in a normal subject 20 minutes after the I.V. injection of 168 μC ^{64}Cu. The patient was lying along the horizontal axis with the head on the left. Height of the curve on the vertical axis is equivalent to the radioactivity at any given point. Note the peak over the liver where most of the activity is concentrated. After Osborn, Pope, and Walshe (42).

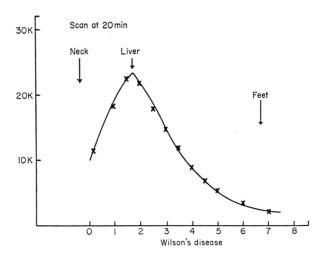

FIG. 5. Profile of whole body radioactivity in a patient with Wilson's disease 20 minutes after the I.V. injection of 335 μC ^{64}Cu. Note the peak is very much broader and less well localized to the liver than in the normal subject shown in Fig. 4. After Osborn, Pope, and Walshe (42).

plasmin. Patients lack this hepatic uptake mechanism so that copper remains in the tissues and is only slowly withdrawn to the liver.

Whole body scanning with very sensitive crystal detectors has confirmed the rapid deposition of copper in the normal liver and has shown a more diffuse peak in most patients with Wilson's disease (Figs. 4 and 5). This picture of copper uptake and distribution can be significantly modified by prior administration of penicillamine (42), a point which will be discussed further in the section on therapy.

3. Amino Acid Metabolism in Wilson's Disease

So much for the disturbances of copper transport and metabolism. It is now necessary to mention briefly the vexed question of protein and amino acid metabolism, for Uzman has seriously questioned the role of copper as the toxic agent in the pathogenesis of Wilson's disease. In 1948 he and Denny-Brown reported finding aminoaciduria in a patient with Wilson's disease (43) and in an otherwise normal sibling and suggested that this was the primary defect in the disease. Later Uzman and Hood described another family with aminoaciduria and peptiduria in both patients and healthy siblings (44) and they suggested that copper was deposited in tissues as stable copper-peptide complexes, the peptides themselves being formed by abnormal tissue proteolytic enzymes. Later still Uzman (45) and his associates, working with biopsy tissue, claimed they could show the presence of the abnormal peptide in liver extract by paper electrophoresis and on dialyzing this extract against copper-containing buffer solutions they were able to show that the extract of Wilson's disease liver had a much higher afinity for copper than did the normal. Uzman himself claimed that "no one seriously attributes" the development of hepatic cirrhosis or nervous system involvement "to copper intoxication per se" (46). However, Stein, Bearn, and Moore (47) found abnormal amino acid excretion by the kidneys in only five of six patients with Wilson's disease and showed that this was secondary to a renal lesion. They also found an excess of conjugated amino acids in the urine but the abnormality was less than for free amino acids. The renal lesion was later confirmed and shown (48) to consist of a tubular lesion with some degree of glomerular involvement. Bearn and his co-workers believed this to be due to the effect of copper on the kidneys and not the effect of an abnormal gene.

Earlier I strongly criticized Uzman's view on the pathogenesis of Wilson's disease (49) and recent unpublished studies in which normal and Wilson's disease brain and liver extracts were dialyzed against radiocopper solutions showed no increased affinity for the metal by Wilson's disease tissue (Fig. 6). This is certainly in keeping with the *in vivo* finding that the liver of

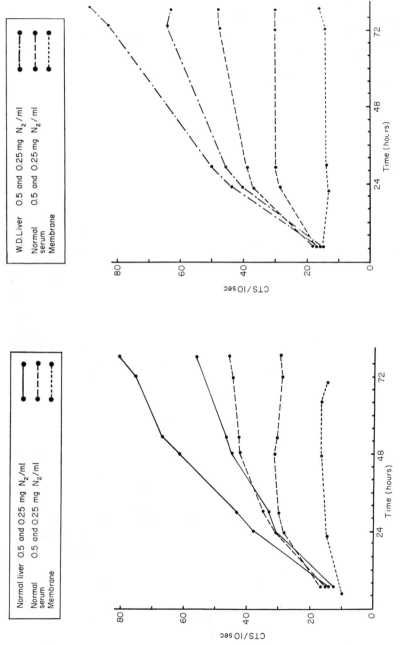

Fig. 6. Uptake of ^{64}Cu by extracts of soluble proteins from a normal liver (left) and from a patient with Wilson's disease (right). The extracts were standarized for nitrogen content and the rate of copper uptake was compared with that by normal serum standardized to the same nitrogen content. Empty dialysis membrane was also run with each set of samples. The radioactivity of the buffer for the normal liver was 0.113 mμC/ml and for the Wilson's disease liver 0.137 mμC/ml. Counting rates are expressed as 10^3/10 sec.

patients with Wilson's disease takes up less rather than more copper than the normal. Furthermore, copper is a well-known enzyme poison (50), and it is difficult to believe that the accumulation of large amounts of metal in the cells would not, sooner or later, lead to enzyme inhibition and tissue necrosis. I have previously suggested (53) that copper, with its well-known affinity for —SH, might oxidize glutathione and thus block the entry of pyruvate into the tricarboxylic acid cycle. Experimental studies with pigeon brain *in vivo* and *in vitro* undertaken with Peters (54, 55) which are reported at this symposium have shown that copper by its action on lipoic acid did block the oxidation of pyruvate in mitochondrial preparations. However, *in vivo* copper appears to attack not this system but the membrane ATPase. Copper is thus a powerful poison for at least two brain enzyme systems, damage to either of which, in man, would certainly lead to severe disease. The therapeutic action of chelating agents can thus best be explained in terms of removal of copper and reactivation of —SH enzyme systems rather than by some unknown action on proteolytic enzymes of undetermined specificity. It should be mentioned also that a careful chromatographic separation of both liver (56) and brain (57) proteins has failed to confirm the presence of a specific protein abnormality in Wilson's disease.

The other vexed question is the role of ceruloplasmin in the pathogenesis of Wilson's disease. The physiological role of this protein is still not known (58) and some of the difficulties in the theory that deficiency of ceruloplasmin is the primary genetic defect in Wilson's disease have recently been discussed (59). Certainly it is possible to lead a reasonably normal life without this protein as shown by many patients who have been adequately treated with penicillamine (41). On the other hand patients with undoubted Wilson's disease may have normal or near normal values for plasma ceruloplasmin when first seen (60) and I have earlier referred to three such cases.

B. Recent Studies on the Pathogenesis of Wilson's Disease

So much for the two principal theories which have in the past contended for the star role in the pathogenesis of Wilson's disease. It would seem that the theory of an abnormal tissue protein still lacks supporting evidence or confirmation, and the ceruloplasmin theory, though at first attractive, has failed to stay the course. There is, however, an alternative hypothesis. It has been suggested (31, 32, 39) that the primary defect is a deficiency or absence of a specific mechanism in the liver for concentrating copper from plasma and incorporating it into ceruloplasmin. This evidence has been summarized already and the theory accounts for most of the observed facts. Injected copper is rapidly cleared from plasma into the extracellular fluid space and into most cells of the body with a particular affinity for liver and kidney. In the untreated patient less than 10% is lost in the urine in 72 hours and only about 5% in the stools (27). The rest achieves a dynamic equilibrium between liver, plasma, extracellular fluid, and cells with a small bias in favor of the liver so that over the course of some days most of the injected metal will appear in that organ but some will be present in other fluid compartments depending on the relative affinity of the proteins for copper. Once present in the tissues copper accumulates in various proteins, as has been shown for brain (57). In time enzyme systems come to be involved, including the membrane ATPase and the lipoic acid–pyruvate oxidase system. In the liver this leads to cirrhosis, in the brain to the death of neurones, particularly in the basal ganglia, in the kidneys to tubular damage, and in the cornea to typical pigment rings. I suggest that when copper accumulates slowly it affects principally pyruvate oxidase leading to the "pseudosclerotic" type of illness while in those cases with a rapid accumulation of the metal in the brain it is the membrane ATPase which bears the brunt of the injury leading to the more bizzare picture of wild incoordination, spontaneous movements, and postural abnormalities. In the kidneys copper attacks the renal tubular enzymes mediating the reabsorption of glucose, amino acids, phosphates, and urates and also the ammonia formation and acidification mechanisms. The ability of copper to attack membrane ATPase offers a particularly attractive explanation of the hemolytic crises as a breakdown of the sodium pump would clearly be disastrous for the red cells. As further facts come to light this theory will, I have no doubt, require modification if not abandonment but if it stimulates further useful research it will have served its purpose. There is, at present, no information as to the enzyme system in normal liver which concentrates copper, and the dialysis studies I have referred to were not designed to detect an enzymatically mediated mechanism but to search for specific copper-binding proteins.

IV. Therapy

A. Copper-Binding Agents

Untreated Wilson's disease runs a course which, in the great majority of cases, is one of progressive deterioration leading to death in a few years. In some the illness is more acute with high swinging fever and in these the course is very much shorter. When the illness presents as hepatic failure in children death may occur in a matter of weeks. There is, however, a small residue of cases, commonly presenting later in life with predominantly neurological signs, who may survive, more or less disabled, for many years (61). The untreated case, though now rare, is still seen when diagnosis has been long delayed and these still confirm the older reports of an illness progressing by rather uneven stages and occasional remissions to increasing disability. The introduction of BAL by Cumings (14) for the treatment of Wilson's disease has unquestionably benefited many patients (62, 63, 64) though it was noted that the clinical response could be out of proportion to the amount of copper mobilized (64). Later it was found that the cupriuretic response rapidly fell off and many patients became biochemically and clinically resistant (65) and toxic reactions were not uncommon (66). EDTA, though it promoted a considerable increase in urinary copper excretion (34), proved disappointing therapeutically (35) as did attempts to restore the blood ceruloplasmin level to normal either by injecting purified ceruloplasmin (67) or by the administration of estrogens (68).

Search for a new chelating agent active by mouth led to the introduction of penicillamine, 2,2-dimethylcysteine (53). Early studies showed that in the majority of cases it promoted a considerably greater excretion of copper than either BAL or EDTA (53, 30) (Fig. 7) and it was recommended, on this evidence, that penicillamine should be given a long-term trial in the management of Wilson's disease. As L-penicillamine had previously been shown to have antipyridoxine action (69) it seemed preferable to use the

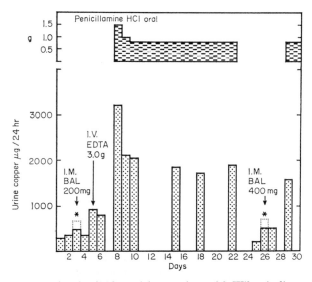

FIG. 7. Copper excretion (μg/24 hours) in a patient with Wilson's disease before treatment and after BAL, EDTA, and penicillamine. Dotted line shows result obtained by method of Cartwright et al. (34). Reproduced from *The American Journal of Medicine* (53).

D-isomer. Preliminary reports (70, 71, 72) all suggested that penicillamine, though relatively slow in action, generally led to marked clinical remission of the neurological, and in some cases the hepatic, signs (73). A more detailed study by Sternlieb and Scheinberg (74) showed excellent results in patients with predominantly neurological lesions but less satisfactory response for the hepatic and psychiatric disturbances. On the other hand Denny-Brown (63) reported almost unreservedly bad results with the use of BAL and penicillamine, only one of his 18 patients maintaining an early improvement and 12 dying of the disease despite continued treatment. It is difficult to assess these results, however, as no treatment schedule is given. For comparison with these reports I have selected 27 patients from my own records who have been seen regularly during the course of treatment for periods of up to ten years and in all these cases it has been possible to cooperate with their local physicians on the treatment program. Four of these cases are asymptomatic younger siblings of proven cases, in all of which the diagnosis has been established by biochemical and radiochemical tests. They have been under surveillance for periods of three to six years on a dose of 600–1350 mg D-penicillamine daily, remaining symptom-free and developing normally. In all cases the liver function tests have returned to normal. Four patients had purely hepatic signs when first seen, one with additional severe hemolysis, and two with gross fluid retention. All have done well and are now symptom-free and require no salt restriction in their diets. Their penicillamine dosages vary from 1000 to 1800 mg daily. Fourteen patients had predominantly neurological signs when first seen. Three gave previous histories of episodes of jaundice, severe in one case. Nine of these patients have had an excellent response so that they would virtually pass as normal; three have some residual disability but are able to lead normal independent lives. Two patients who have been on treatment for just a year are already showing improvement although one of these had been almost totally disabled by tremor for 16 years. One patient, a girl whose symptoms started at the age of 12, had had repeated courses of BAL. She had made a very satisfactory response initially but later relapsed despite further treatment. She had severe dystonic disease with spontaneous movements when first seen. She responded to D-penicillamine, 1350 mg daily, but after 4 months she had a severe relapse with continuous movements in her sleep and totally disabling tremor by day. Her penicillamine dose was increased to 2700 mg daily and after another month she started to improve. Now, 2 years later, she leads a normal life being able to ride a bicycle, swim, and attend school. Her present penicillamine dose is 1800 mg (Fig. 8). One patient has an I.Q. of 70; despite an improvement in his electroencephalogram there has been an increase in his I.Q. only to 83; he has a very unsatisfactory family background and there may well be another genetic defect. The dose range in this group was from

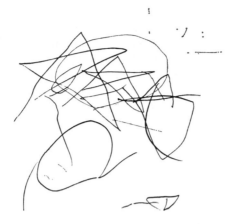

FIG. 8. Handwriting of N.Y., a patient with Wilson's disease: (upper) after one year of intermittent treatment with BAL, and (lower) again after 26 months of treatment with D-penicillamine HCl, 1800 mg daily.

900 to 1800 mg daily, except for the case mentioned in some detail above. Finally mention must be made of five patients who died. Two of these had severe febrile reactions with increasing jaundice each time penicillamine was administered and were clearly intolerant of the drug. Both ran acute febrile courses, one dying in 9 months of hepatic failure the other in 18 months of a mixed neurological and hepatic syndrome. The third patient presented at the age of 12 years the typical picture of dystonic Wilson's disease. Over a period of 3 years she followed a relentless downhill course apparently uninfluenced by treatment with penicillamine, BAL, or estrogens. Retrospectively it would seem that she was undertreated as her dose of penicillamine never exceeded 1200 mg and for much of the time was only 900 mg daily. Post-mortem examination revealed extensive subcortical cavitation in the brain and active cirrhosis which had given rise to no symptoms in life. In view of more recent experience I would now recommend a dose of at least 2000 mg penicillamine daily for this type of case. The remaining two patients both died shortly after the diagnosis was made and treatment started so that it could scarcely have influenced the illness. One, a girl of 13 years, died of hemorrhage from esophageal varices 2 weeks after starting treatment (she had previously been subjected to a gastric transection for hemorrhage). The other, a girl of 11 years, presented with an acute febrile illness, cachexia, and wild tremor. When the diagnosis was made she was already in the terminal dystonic stage of Wilson's disease and she died of aspiration soon after starting treatment.

In summary the results of treatment of 27 patients with Wilson's disease with D-penicillamine in doses up to 2700 mg daily has led to a good or very good clinical response in 12 of 14 patients with predominantly neurological signs and some early improvement in the other two, a good clinical response in four with hepatic disease and the reversal of abnormal liver function tests in four asymptomatic siblings. Finally, five cases died: three of these must be considered as therapeutic failures, although one was probably inadequately treated.

Other agents which have been recommended in the treatment of Wilson's disease are zinc sulfate (75) and sodium diethyldithiocarbamate (76) but my own experience with the latter drug has been disappointing.

B. Clinical Pharmacology of Penicillamine

Penicillamine has been associated with a number of reports of toxic reactions, the most serious being optic neuritis (77) and the nephrotic syndrome (78, 79). DL-Penicillamine has been incriminated in most of these reactions and in at least one case this was shown to be a result of its anti-pyridoxine action (77). Recently it has been demonstrated that in very large doses the D-isomer can reproduce the biochemical effects of pyridoxine deficiency in rats (80, 81), and an antipyridoxine effect for D-penicillamine has recently been described in man (82). There have also been reports of bone marrow depression (74), and it has been suggested that depletion of other trace metals besides copper might lead to anemia and other deficiency states. In the present series, in which D-penicillamine only has been used, no patient has suffered renal damage nor has there been any evidence of bone marrow depression. Although, as has already been mentioned, thrombocytopenia is common this has not been rendered more severe by treatment. One patient did develop a generalized purpuric rash after a single test dose of penicillamine but this was not associated with a further fall in her platelet count, already severely depressed. The question of iron

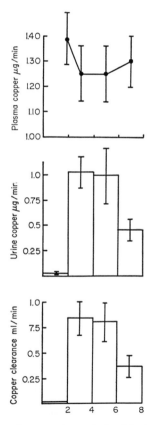

FIG. 9. Endogenous copper clearance in control subjects (mean of 10 determinations on 7 subjects; Two standard errors are shown above and below the mean). 600 mg D-penicillamine HCl was given immediately after the end of the first 2 hour collection period. Reproduced from *Clinical Science* (41).

deficiency and anemia has been investigated in some detail (83). The mean serum iron at the start of treatment in 10 patients was 116.5 µg/100 ml and 19 months later was 108.8 µg/100 ml, while the hemoglobin level varied from 13.4 to 12.9 g/100 ml. During this period the mean serum copper had fallen from 45.3 to 18.4 µg/100 ml. It has also been found that although penicillamine can significantly lower the serum copper levels it does not cause any change in the concentration of copper in hair (84), thus suggesting that it is only excess metal, stored and not required, which is removed from the body. The problem of pyridoxine deficiency has also been investigated in 16 patients who have been on treatment for periods up to 10 years. In two only, following a tryptophan load, were tryptophan

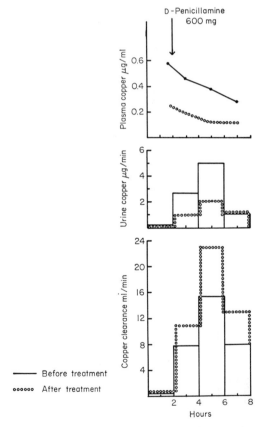

Fig. 10. Endogenous copper clearance in patients with Wilson's disease (mean of 9 determinations) before the start of treatment and again after an average of 8 months of treatment with penicillamine. 600 mg D-penicillamine HCl was given at the end of the first collection period. Reproduced from *Clinical Science* (41).

metabolites found in the urine in excess of the normal range. It must be admitted that the two patients who suffered the severe febrile reactions already described were not investigated by this technique but the onset of symptoms so closely followed the start of treatment that these could scarcely have been conditioned deficiency states and were presumably sensitivity reactions.

It has been shown that the mode of action of penicillamine depends upon its ability to render plasma copper more readily available for diffusion across a semipermeable membrane (85, 86) *in vitro* and across the glomerular membrane *in vivo* with a consequent fall in the plasma copper concentration and a rise in the renal clearance of the metal (41) (Fig. 9). It has also been shown that the decreased cupriuretic effect recorded on long-term penicillamine therapy is due not to drug resistance but to decreased body stores of excess copper (41) (Fig. 10). In studies with radiocopper it has also been shown that the administration of penicillamine shortly before injection of the isotope results in a different pattern of uptake and excretion of the metal (42). In the normal individual a single dose of penicillamine increased radioisotope excretion in the urine from less than 1% to 35% in 24 hours and in a patient with Wilson's disease from around 3% to 86% in 28 hours. It was observed that within half an hour of injection of the radiocopper, when a prior dose of penicillamine had been given, the main site of concentration was in the bladder, an organ which had never previously been outlined in these studies (Fig. 11). Moreover the body profile of radioactivity, in relation to the liver peak, in both the control and the patient remained very much more easily delineated for

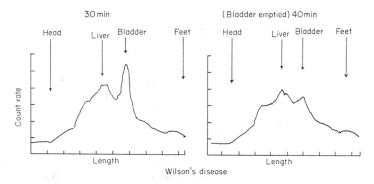

FIG. 11. Profile of whole body radioactivity in a patient with Wilson's disease 30 minutes after injection of 429μC ^{64}Cu (left) and at 40 minutes (right). The patient had taken 600 mg D-penicillamine HCl shortly before the start of the study. Note the large bladder peak on the left which disappears after voiding; note also the poor localization of copper in the liver. After Osborn, Pope, and Walshe (42).

periods of up to 24 hours after administration of the ^{64}Cu if penicillamine
was given first. Indeed in the control subject the pattern of whole body
activity and reduced liver uptake mimicked the pattern of untreated
Wilson's disease in which the liver is unable to concentrate copper, thus
permitting it to diffuse more readily into the tissues and to be excreted
more rapidly by the kidneys.

V. Summary

This then is the story I have had to unfold of a genetically determined
disease in which copper accumulates in the tissues, principally the liver,
brain, and kidneys. The mechanism of copper deposition is probably the
result of the deficiency or absence of a specific copper-concentrating enzyme
system in the liver leaving the metal more readily available to diffuse into
other tissues. The excess copper attacks enzymes, particularly membrane
ATPase and pyruvate oxidase. Copper accumulation can be reversed and a
large degree of useful function restored by administration of the chelating
agent D-penicillamine.

REFERENCES

1. Bearn, A. G., *in* J. M. Walshe and J. N. Cumings (eds.), "Wilson's disease: some current concepts," Blackwell's Scientific Publications, Oxford, 1961, p. 118.
2. Bearn, A. G., and Kunkel, H. G., "Ergebnisse d. inn. Medizin N.F.," Vol. 7, Springer-Verlag Berlin, 1956, p. 149.
3. Boudin, G., and Pepin, B., "Dégénérescence hépatolenticulaire," Masson et Cie, Paris, 1959.
4. Cumings, J. N., "Heavy metals and the brain," Blackwell's Scientific Publications, Oxford, 1959.
5. Wilson, S. A. K., *Brain*, **34,** 295 (1911/12).
6. Kayser, B., *Klin. Mbl. Augenheilk*, **40,** 22 (1902).
7. Fleischer, B., *Klin. Mbl. Augenheilk*, **41,** 489 (1903).
8. Hall, H. C., "La dégénérescence hepatolenticulaire. Maladie de Wilson pseudo-sclérose," Masson et Cie, Paris, 1921.
9. Rumpel, A., *Dtsch. Z. Nervenheilk.*, **49,** 54 (1913).
10. Siemerling, E., and Oloff, H., *Klin. Wschr.*, **i,** 1087 (1922).
11. Vogt, A., *Klin. Mbl. Augenheilk*, **82,** 433 (1929).
12. Haurowitz, F., *Z. Physiol. Chem.*, **190,** 72 (1930).
13. Glazebrook, A. J., *Edinburgh Med. J.*, **52,** 83 (1945).
14. Cumings, J. N., *Brain*, **71,** 410 (1948).
15. Peters, R. A., Stocken, L. A., and Thompson, R. H. S., *Nature*, **156,** 616 (1945).
16. Holmberg, C. G., and Laurell, C.-B., *Acta Chem. Scand.*, **2,** 550 (1948).
17. Mandelbrote, B. M., Stanier, M. W., Thompson, R. H. S., and Thurston, M. N., *Brain*, **71,** 212 (1948).
18. Walshe, J. M., *Arch. Dis. Child.*, **37,** 253 (1962).
19. Anderson, P. J., and Popper, H., *Am. J. Path.*, **36,** 483 (1960).
20. Schaffner, F., Sternlieb, I., Barka, T., and Popper, H., *Am. J. Path.*, **41,** 315 (1962).

21. Bearn, A. G., and McKusick, V. A., *J. Am. Med. Ass.*, **166,** 904 (1958).
22. Morgan, H. G., Stewart, W. K., Lowe, K. G., Stowers, J. M., and Johnstone, J. H., *Quart. J. Med., N. S.* **31,** 361 (1961).
23. Van Ravesteyn, A. H., *Acta. Med. Scand.*, **118,** 163 (1944).
24. Adelstein, S. J., and Vallee, B. L., *New Engl. J. Med.*, **265,** 892, 941 (1961).
25. Scheinberg, I. H., and Sternlieb, I., *Pharmacol. Revs.*, **12,** 355 (1960).
26. Cartwright, G. E., and Wintrobe, M. M., *Am. J. Clin. Nutrition.*, **14,** 224 (1964).
27. Bush, J. A., Mahoney, J. P., Markowitz, H., Gubler, C. J., Cartwright, G. E., and Wintrobe, M. M., *J. Clin. Invest.*, **34,** 1766 (1955).
28. Matthews, W. B., *J. Neurol. Psychiat.*, **17,** 242 (1954).
29. Bearn, A. G., and Kunkel, H. G., *Proc. Soc. Exp. Biol.*, **85,** 44 (1954).
30. Osborn, S. B., and Walshe, J. M., *Lancet*, **i,** 70 (1958).
31. Osborn, S. B., Roberts, C. N., and Walshe, J. M., *Clin. Sci.*, **24,** 13 (1963).
32. Osborn, S. B., and Walshe, J. M., *Clin. Sci.*, **29,** 575 (1965).
33. Earl, C. J., *in* J. M. Walshe and J. N. Cumings (eds.), "Wilson's disease: some current concepts," Blackwell Scientific Publications, Oxford, 1961, p. 18.
34. Cartwright, G. E., Hodges, R. E., Gubler, C. J., Mahoney, J. P., Daum, K., Wintrobe, M. M., and Bean, W. B., *J. Clin. Invest.*, **33,** 1487 (1954).
35. Bickel, H., Neale, F. C., and Hall, G., *Quart. J. Med.*, **26,** 527 (1927).
36. Bearn, A. G., *Am. J. Med.*, **15,** 442 (1953).
37. Scheinberg, I. H., and Gitlin, D., *Science*, **116,** 484 (1952).
38. Sternlieb, I., Morell, A. G., Bauer, C. D., Combes, B., de Bobes-Sternberg, S., and Scheinberg, I. H., *J. Clin. Invest.*, **40,** 707 (1961).
39. Osborn, S. B., and Walshe, J. M., *Clin. Sci.*, **27,** 319 (1964).
40. Sass-Kortsak, A., personal communication.
41. Walshe, J. M., *Clin. Sci.*, **26,** 461 (1964).
42. Osborn, S. B., Pope, R., and Walshe, J. M., unpublished observations.
43. Uzman, L. L., and Denny-Brown, D., *Am. J. Med. Sci.*, **215,** 599 (1948).
44. Uzman, L. L., and Hood, B., *Am. J. Med. Sci.*, **225,** 392 (1952).
45. Uzman, L. L., Iber, F. L., Chalmers, T. C., and Knowlton, M., *Am. J. Med. Sci.*, **231,** 511 (1956).
46. Uzman, L. L., *Arch. Neurol. Psychiat.*, **77,** 164 (1957).
47. Stein, W. H., Bearn, A. G., and Moore, S., *J. Clin. Invest.*, **33,** 410 (1954).
48. Bearn, A. G., Yu, T. F., and Gutman, A. B., *J. Clin. Invest.*, **36,** 1107 (1957).
49. Walshe, J. M., *Brit. Med. Bull.*, **13,** 132 (1957).
50. Rees, K. R., *in* J. M. Walshe and J. N. Cumings (eds.), "Wilson's disease: some current concepts," Blackwells Scientific Publications, Oxford, 1961, p. 49.
51. Sass-Kortsak, A., Cherniak, M., Geiger, D. W., and Slater, R. S., *J. Clin. Invest.*, **38,** 1672 (1959).
52. Osborn, S. B., and Walshe, J. M., unpublished observations.
53. Walshe, J. M., *Am. J. Med.*, **21,** 487 (1956).
54. Davies, A., Peters, R. A., and Walshe, J. M., *J. Physiol.*, **159,** 32 P. (1961).
55. Peters, R. A., Shorthouse, M., and Walshe, J. M., *J. Physiol.*, **181,** 27 P. (1965).
56. Morell, A., Shapiro, J. R., and Scheinberg, I. H., *in* J. M. Walshe and J. N. Cumings (eds.), "Wilson's disease: some current concepts," Blackwells Scientific Publications, Oxford, 1961, p. 36.
57. Porter, H., *in* J. M. Walshe and J. N. Cumings (eds.), "Wilson's disease: some current concepts," Blackwells Scientific Publications, Oxford, 1961, p. 24.
58. Holmberg, C. G., *in* J. M. Walshe and J. N. Cumings (eds.), "Wilson's disease: some current concepts," Blackwells Scientific Publications, Oxford, 1961, p. 64.

59. Cartwright, G. E., Markowitz, H., Shields, G. S., and Wintrobe, M. M., *Am. J. Med.*, **28**, 555 (1960).
60. Scheinberg, I. H., and Sternlieb, I., *Lancet*, **ii**, 1420 (1963).
61. Seven, M. J., and Johnson, L. A., *in* J. M. Walshe and J. N. Cumings (eds.). "Wilson's disease: some current concepts," Blackwells Scientific Publications, Oxford, 1961, p. 222.
62. Cumings, J. N., *Brain*, **74**, 10 (1951).
63. Denny-Brown, D., and Porter, H., *New Engl. J. Med.*, **245**, 917 (1951).
64. Bearn, A. G., *Am. J. Med.*, **21**, 134 (1956).
65. Denny-Brown, D., *New Engl. J. Med.*, **270**, 1149 (1964).
66. Hollister, L. E., Cull, V. L., Gonda, V. A., and Kolb, F. O., *Amer. J. Med.*, **28**, 623, (1960).
67. Bickel H., *in* J. M. Walshe and J. N. Cumings (eds.). "Wilson's disease: some current concepts," Blackwells Scientific Publications, Oxford, 1961, p. 273.
68. German, J. L., and Bearn, A. G., *J. Clin. Invest.*, **40**, 445 (1961).
69. Kuchinskas, E. J., Horvath, A., and Du Vigneaud, V., *Arch. Biochem.*, **68**, 69 (1957).
70. Walshe, J. M., *Lancet*, **i**, 188 (1960).
71. Scheinberg, I. H., and Sternlieb, I., *Am. J. Med.*, **29**, 316 (1960).
72. Goldstein, N. P., Randall, R. V., Gross, J. B., Rosevear, J. W., and McGuckin, W. F., *Neurology*, **12**, 231 (1962).
73. Sherlock, S., *in* J. M. Walshe and J. N. Cumings (eds.), "Wilson's disease: some current concepts," Blackwells Scientific Publications, Oxford, 1961, p. 182.
74. Sternlieb, I., and Scheinberg, I. H., *J. Am. Med. Ass.*, **189**, 146 (1964).
75. Schouwink, G., "De hepato-cerebrale degeneratie," G. W. van der Wiel and Co., Arnhem, 1961.
76. Sunderman, F. W., Jr., White, J. C., and Sunderman, F. W., *Am. J. Med.*, **34**, 875 (1963).
77. Tu, J., Blackwell, R. Q., and Lee, P. F., *J. Am. Med. Ass.*, **185**, 83 (1963).
78. Yonis, I. Z., and Karp, M., *Lancet*, **ii**, 689 (1963).
79. Adams, D. A., Goldman, R., Maxwell, M. H., and Latta, H., *Am. J. Med.*, **36**, 330 (1964).
80. Asatoor, A. M., *Nature*, **203**, 1382 (1964).
81. Walshe, J. M., and Gibbs, K., *Lancet*, **i**, 175 (1966).
82. Jaffe, I. A., Altman, K., and Merryman, P., *J. Clin. Invest.*, **43**, 1869 (1964).
83. Walshe, J. M., and Patston, V., *Arch. Dis. Child.*, **40**, 651 (1965).
84. Gibbs, K., and Walshe, J. M., *J. Med. Genetics*, **2**, 157 (1965).
85. Walshe, J. M., *Clin. Sci.*, **25**, 405 (1963).
86. Osborn, S. B., and Walshe, J. M., *Clin. Sci.*, **26**, 213 (1964).

DISCUSSION

DR. McEWEN: I would like to know whether decreased immediate copper uptake by the liver is related to the cirrhosis that is present. Is the decreased uptake present in patients who have minimal cirrhosis, and can it therefore be described as a more primary defect?

DR. WALSHE: No, I must confess for a start that I don't do liver biopsies on all these patients: I am not sufficiently ruthless.

But one can get a good assessment of the liver from the patient's clinical condition, and also from the routine laboratory tests of liver function. There does not seem to be any correlation between the uptake patterns of the liver and the degree of liver damage assessed by these techniques. In fact, the last scintiscan on that girl showed no concentration in the liver at all although in a liver biopsy there were minimimal abnormalities: no fibrosis and no necrosis, a little fat in the liver cell and glycogen nuclei. So I think this is a primary part of the lesion, and not a secondary phenomenon following liver damage.

DR. BROMAN: I would like to argue with Dr. Walshe on a couple of points. First, there is an enormous difference between a total absence of ceruloplasmin and a very low ceruloplasmin concentration. The interpretation of the role of this protein would be quite different if it could be shown to be entirely absent in a healthy patient, than if one could show that the protein is always present although sometimes in a concentration that is too low to be measurable with standard methods. In the first case the protein is evidently dispensable, but in the second case it might be indispensable.

DR. WALSHE: Well, this is a gorgeous hypothesis—isn't it?—because if you say that it is too low to be measured, but it is still there, we can never answer your question.

DR. BROMAN: Well, one could, of course, try a better method.

DR. WALSHE: I suppose if you take sufficient serum and concentrate it enough, you will find anything which is normally present, however little there appears to be; but whether, when it is present in such infinitesimal amounts, it is serving any physiological role is another story.

DR. BROMAN: The concentration of certain intermediary metabolites may be very low, although the turnover is rather high. It depends on the balance of production and consumption rates.

DR. WALSHE: Well, if you can tell me what the physiological function is, I'll answer your question.

DR. BROMAN: Suppose it is involved in transport. The fact that it occurs in plasma suggests this. If its function were to transfer copper, or a prosthetic group containing copper, from the liver to the cells, then its concentration could be very low but there could be a substantial transfer of the protein between these extravascular compartments.

DR. WALSHE: Well, this is possible. It is an argument one could carry on all night. You can't prove it or disprove it. It is possible.

DR. BROMAN: But it could be proved by improving the assaying method, as you suggested, by concentrating ceruloplasmin from large amounts of plasma in those cases which appear to be without the protein.

Could I ask another question? What was the uptake of radioactive copper by the liver in Wilson's disease? Did you account for the presence of nonceruloplasmin copper which is high in Wilson's disease, and which could cause a dilution of the administered radioactive copper?

DR. WALSHE: I don't really think this answers the question. If the copper was simply diluted in the body pool, then you would expect it to go to the liver, where the biggest part of the body pool in Wilson's disease is. In Wilson's disease the highest concentration of copper is in the liver, and you would expect the injected isotope to go there, while in a normal individual, where only about 10% of the copper is in the liver, you would not expect very much copper to go there. I don't think this is the explanation.

Dr. Holtzman: We have studied ceruloplasmin from two patients with Wilson's disease. Crystalline ceruloplasmin was prepared from one of these patients. A comparison with ceruloplasmin crystallized from two normal individuals is shown in Table I. The copper content, oxidase activity, electrophoretic mobility, peptide map, amino acid composition, and optical spectrum of the ceruloplasmin from one of these patients is indistinguishable from normal. The few measurements made on the ceruloplasmin from the second patient with Wilson's disease suggest it too is normal. Three possible differences, however, remain to be explored. First, our methods would not detect an amino acid alteration of the minor ceruloplasmin component isolated on hydroxyapatite. Second, an alteration in the carbohydrate composition of ceruloplasmin in Wilson's disease is also possible. Third, some problems remain in our peptide mapping; there could be a hidden alteration. Furthermore, while these maps of tryptic digests show 80% of the total ceruloplasmin, the remaining "core" which remains at the origin of the map could contain an amino acid alteration. If an amino acid or sugar substitution does occur it probably does not involve a change in net charge since electrophoretic mobility of the ceruloplasmins from each patient with Wilson's disease was normal at pH 6.4 and 9.4. A change in the number of sialic acid residues, for example, is excluded.

Work is now in progress on these problems but we would tentatively conclude that the ceruloplasmin from Wilson's disease patients is structurally and functionally (in terms of oxidase activity) normal.

Recently, our attention turned to the factors which determine serum ceruloplasmin concentration when a $5\frac{1}{2}$ year-old female was admitted to the Johns Hopkins Hospital because of acute hemolytic anemia and oliguria following the seventh debridement of burned skin with crystalline copper sulfate over a 9-week period in another hospital. On admission, serum copper was 540 μg/100 ml and serum ceruloplasmin 86 mg/100 ml. The patient was started on D-penicillamine, 1 g/day. By the third day, total serum copper declined to 360 μg/100 ml, but the serum ceruloplasmin had risen to 114 mg/100 ml on the second day and on the third day was 108 mg/100 ml. By the seventh day, the ceruloplasmin level had fallen to 56 mg/100 ml. Although moderate elevation of ceruloplasmin is relatively nonspecific, the extraordinary increase in this patient, together with its rapid fall as copper was removed from the body, suggests that the high serum ceruloplasmin concentration was a direct consequence of elevated body copper. Whether this increased ceruloplasmin protected the patient from more extensive damage we cannot say.

Dr. Sternlieb: Dr. Holtzman, did you check the concentration of ceruloplasmin in other patients with similar injuries. As you know, ceruloplasmin is to some extent an acute phase reactant, and you may encounter as high a concentration of this protein in normal, pregnant women. This can also be the case in a patient with a large wound or with prolonged inflammatory disease as a result of infection.

Dr. Holtzman: This may well be, and we are looking for it. This patient was not acutely burned. The burns were suffered about 10 months before this episode of copper intoxication, but in going over the literature I could not find anything as high as this except that in one study of Cartwright and Wintrobe's [Am. J. Clin.

TABLE I

COMPARISON OF CERULOPLASMIN FROM NORMAL INDIVIDUALS TO THAT FROM TWO PATIENTS WITH WILSON'S DISEASE

	Ceruloplasmin from normal individuals	Ceruloplasmin from E. C. (Wilson's disease)	Ceruloplasmin from J. S. (Wilson's disease)
Molarity of sodium acetate, pH 5.8, at which peak eluted from DEAE Sephadex	0.41–0.43	0.42	0.39
Electrophoresis:			
Na phosphate starch gel, pH 6.4	Single band with oxidase activity	Same mobility as normal	Same mobility as normal
Tris acrylamide gel, pH 9.4	Single band	Same mobility as normal	Same mobility as normal
Crystals	Tetragonal; hexagonal rosette	Same as normal	Crystallization not attempted
Oxidation of p-phenylenediamine (A_{530}^{1cm}/mg/min in 1% NaCl, 1.2 M Na acetate, pH 5.8)	0.183 ± 0.022	0.180	Oxidase activity present
Moles copper/mole ceruloplasmin	8.0	8.1	Insufficient quantity
A_{280}/A_{610} of crystallized ceruloplasmin	23–24	24.3	Insufficient quantity
Spectral analysis 220–730 mμ	Peaks at 280, 612 mμ	Same as normal	Too impure
Amino acid analysis	—	Agree with normal within range of experimental error	Too impure
Tryptic peptide map	—	Same as normal	Too impure

Nutrition, **14,** 224 (1964)] in a pregnant woman, the level was this high. This child had no evidence of either estrogenization or pregnancy.

DR. BEINERT: When was this ceruloplasmin isolated from the patient, before treatment was started or after?

DR. HOLTZAMN: Ceruloplasmin from the first patient was isolated after about one day of penicillamine.

DR. BEINERT: Together with Dr. H. F. Deutsch in Madison we have looked at ceruloplasmin from individual patients with Wilson's disease. We were mainly interested in the quantity of total copper to EPR-detectable copper, and there is no gross difference as comparted to samples from apparently normal individuals. There are small differences which require a lot more work, but there is no striking difference.

DR. BEARN: I suppose one could supplement the chemical evidence from finger-printing by immunological methods. Ceruloplasmin from normal subjects and from Wilson's disease patients could be used as antigens and then we could see whether the antibodies cross react or whether they can absorb each other out. This would be another way of looking at the three-dimensional structure of the protein.

I wonder whether some experiments which we did 12 or 13 years ago might be relevant to the second part of your talk. This was at a time when, rather naively, we thought that these patients were perhaps copper deficient, even though they had a lot of copper in their body. We gave a patient with Wilson's disease very large amounts of copper sulfate by mouth over a period of several weeks. The serum copper rose very, very strikingly— went up above 200 μg/100 ml—and the serum ceruloplasmin also went up, but not so strikingly. The patient continued to go down-hill and died fairly soon thereafter. It is quite apparent that although we increased the serum ceruloplasmin concentration, we also increased, disproportionately, the copper loosely bound to albumin and so I am afraid we probably did more harm than good. Now, I gave myself the same treatment, and I had some increase in serum copper and a very slight increase in ceruloplasmin.

DR. AISEN: Is it possible at these extraordinarily high concentrations that some of the oxidase activity you are seeing is due to the copper?

DR. HOLTZMAN: Well, this bothered us. We pooled the remainder of the serum that we obtained from this patient in the first 7 days. The pool had a ceruloplasmin concentration of 80 mg per 100 ml, still significantly elevated. When we purified ceruloplasmin from this pool, our recovery of ceruloplasmin was about 70— which is the same as we get in our usual procedure.

DR. SCHUBERT: I have always wondered whether the copper enzymes like cytochrome oxidase are involved in Wilson's disease. In experimental animals if you add copper to liver homogenates, you find that marked inhibition of cytochrome oxidase occurs when you reach levels corresponding to that found in Wilson's disease patients. If you add more copper a maximum inhibition of 40% is reached and from there on there is no further inhibition. If this had any bearing on the patients you would assume that there would be a chronic inhibition of cytochrome oxidase, as measured, say, in the liver of the patients. I was wondering whether any of the clinicians had measured cytochrome oxidase and the integrity of the mitochondria from the liver of Wilson's disease patients?

Radiocopper Studies on a Family with Wilson's Disease

NORMAN ASPIN* AND ANDREW SASS-KORTSAK†

University of Toronto and The Research Institute,
The Hospital for Sick Children,
Toronto, Canada

I. Introduction

In spite of considerable effort on the part of many investigators the nature of the basic metabolic defect in Wilson's disease is still obscure. Numerous efforts have been made using radioactive copper to study the handling of copper by individuals afflicted with this disease. Of particular interest are studies which have attempted to describe the movement and distribution of radioactive copper between the various tissues of the body (1, 2, 3). It is of major significance that by these techniques abnormalities were demonstrated not only in homozygous patients but also in heterozygotes (1, 2).

Stimulated by these findings we have been studying the fate of a single intravenous dose of copper in patients with Wilson's disease and in members of their families. In our earlier studies loading doses of 0.5–1.0 mg of copper were used. Lately we obtained a ^{64}Cu preparation of very high specific activity (20 mC/μg) which has enabled us to carry out experiments with tracer doses of the isotope.

II. Case Material and Methods

This paper is a report of such studies made on a patient with Wilson's disease and on four siblings of the patient. The 12 members of this family are listed in the first column of Table I. Columns 2 and 3 list their sex and age respectively and the family members investigated with ^{64}Cu are indicated. The patient (Br.B.) with symptomatic Wilson's disease was not included in the study as he had been under treatment with penicillamine for more than one year. A second patient in this sibship, O.B., was clinically only mildly affected and was not treated with copper-binding agents prior to our study. The four other siblings were clinically normal.

Each subject was given an intravenous injection of ^{64}Cu. Following the injection serial blood samples were taken and the radioactivity was measured in whole blood, in the plasma, and in the ceruloplasmin fractions.

* Department of Medical Biophysics.
† Department of Pediatrics.

TABLE I

FAMILY B. 1964

Initials	Sex	Age (years)
Mr. B.	M	48
Mrs. B.	F	38
R. B.	M	15[a]
F. B.	M	14[a]
B. B.	F	13[a]
Br. B.	M	12
O. B.	M	10[a]
Fr. B.	M	9
An. B.	M	7
A. B.	F	6[a]
K. B.	F	5
D. B.	F	4

[a] ^{64}Cu study.

Urine and stools were collected quantitatively and counted for ^{64}Cu activity. External scintillation probe measurements of activity were made over the head, liver, and thigh of the subjects, and a liver scan was made using the whole body scanner at the Ontario Cancer Institute (4).

High specific activity ^{64}Cu (20 mC/μg) was obtained from McMaster University in Hamilton (5), which enabled these tracer studies to be performed. The radioactive copper was incubated with a sample of the subject's plasma prior to injection, and doses of approximately 15 μC ^{64}Cu per kilogram of body weight containing less than 0.05 μg of inactive copper were used. This is three orders of magnitude less than the total exchangeable plasma copper, the albumin bound fraction of plasma copper, which contained from 50 to 150 μg Cu. All previous human studies with radioactive copper have used loading doses of copper.

III. Results

A. Blood Studies

In Fig. 1 are shown curves which express the percentage of the injected activity remaining in the total plasma compartment as a function of time. In all subjects there is a rapid disappearance of the dose from the plasma so that less than 10% of the total injected activity remains in the plasma after one hour. At later times the plasma activity of subject F.B. increases from a value of 4% at 4 hours to a value of 8% of the injected dose at 77

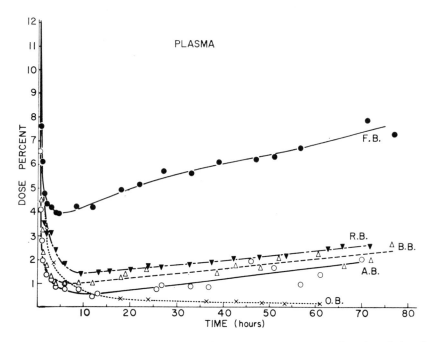

Fig. 1. The percentage of ^{64}Cu in the plasma compartment as a function of time, in hours, after injection.

hours. Subjects A.B., B.B., and R.B. show only a slight secondary rise in activity. In the case of O.B., the patient with Wilson's disease, a secondary rise of plasma activity was not observed.

The differences between the plasma activity of the five subjects at later times can be explained by examination of Fig. 2, which shows the percentage of the dose bound to ceruloplasmin as a function of time after injection. The steady rise in ceruloplasmin activity in subject F.B. corresponds closely in magnitude to the secondary rise in plasma activity seen in Fig. 1. Similarly, the increases in ceruloplasmin activity exhibited by subjects A.B., B.B., and R.B. match closely the slight secondary rise in their respective plasma activities. Subject O.B. shows negligible incorporation of ^{64}Cu into ceruloplasmin (Fig. 2), in keeping with the disappearance of plasma activity seen in Fig. 1.

It has been reported earlier by both Sternlieb *et al.* (6) and our own group (7) that following oral loading doses of radioactive copper individuals who are heterozygous in respect to the gene of Wilson's disease incorporate ^{64}Cu into ceruloplasmin at a lower rate than homozygous normal subjects. Using intravenous tracer doses we have made a similar observation here. Accordingly, we may consider O.B., who shows no incorporation of copper

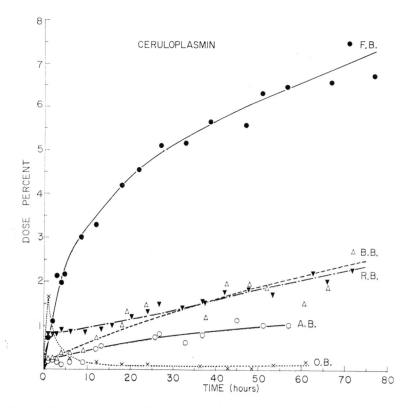

FIG. 2. The percentage of ^{64}Cu in the ceruloplasmin compartment as a function of time, in hours, after injection.

into ceruloplasmin, as homozygously abnormal—a patient with Wilson's disease, for which we have other evidence as well. F.B. has shown relatively fast rate of incorporation of ^{64}Cu into ceruloplasmin, and therefore could be considered homozygously normal. A.B., B.B., and R.B., on the other hand, showed relatively low rates of incorporation, and on the basis of this and the above quoted earlier observations we may consider all three of them heterozygotes.

B. Tissue Distribution and Excretion

Whole body scans following the injection of ^{64}Cu have shown a low level of uniform activity throughout the body with an area of high uptake of activity in the region of the liver. Figure 3 shows a scan of the liver region of subject F.B., whom we consider homozygously normal. This was taken 24 hours after the injection of the dose. A high uptake of ^{64}Cu into the liver can be seen, which is represented as a dark area on the left of the scan. The faint outline of the left kidney suggests that there is also renal uptake of the injected dose. Scans similar to this were obtained in the case of the other individuals. We wish to stress the point that at no time in any of the subjects was there evidence of concentration of activity in any other region.

The extent of the uptake of ^{64}Cu into the liver region has been measured by means of an external scintillation probe. The measurements were corrected for activity emanating from blood in the tissue and also for activity in nonliver tissue in the field of the probe. The corrected data from the liver probe expressed as percentage of the dose in the liver and kidney are plotted against time in Fig. 4. In all subjects there is a rapid initial uptake of activity into the liver. In the case of O.B., the patient with Wilson's

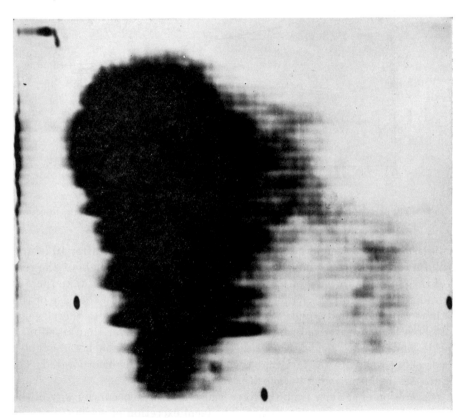

FIG. 3. Radioisotope scan of the upper abdomen of subject F. B. taken 24 hours after the injection of ^{64}Cu with the subject placed in a supine position above the scanner. The two lateral spots indicate the positions of the costal margins and the lower mid-line spot indicates the location of the umbilicus. The dark region on the left represents uptake of activity into the liver, and on the right slight uptake into the left kidney is suggested.

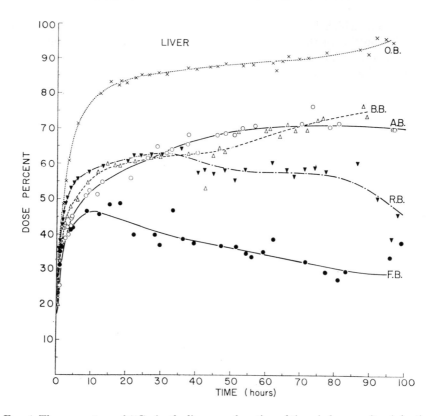

FIG. 4. The percentage of ^{64}Cu in the liver as a function of time, in hours, after injection.

disease, the initial rapid uptake of ^{64}Cu starts to flatten out after 10 hours, and a further slow accumulation of activity continues throughout the rest of the study. In the case of F.B., after 10–15 hours of rapid uptake there is gradual but definite discharge of activity from the liver. In the case of the three remaining individuals whom we consider heterozygotes there seems to be a higher degree of accumulation of ^{64}Cu in the liver than in subject F.B. and also less evidence of a discharge. This finding in heterozygotes correlates well with the fact that these same individuals incorporated ^{64}Cu into ceruloplasmin at a lower rate than normal.

Excretion of activity from the liver is also known to occur, by way of the bile, into the gastrointestinal tract. The fecal excretion of activity in these individuals together with their urinary excretion is shown in Table II. It can be seen here that the lowest fecal excretion occurred in the patient O.B., the highest in the normal homozygote F.B. The three heterozygotes are in between, but while the trend fits the differences already found be-

TABLE II

EXCRETION OF INJECTED ^{64}CU

| Subject | Percentage of dose excreted in 100 hours | |
	Stool	Urine
F. B.	20.6	0.35
A. B.	6.82	0.40
B. B.	17.3	0.51
R. B.	16.5	0.28
O. B.	0.53	1.2

tween the ceruloplasmin excretion of the homozygous normal and the heterozygotes, these differences in fecal excretion are far from significant. The highest urinary excretion was in the patient, but even this amounted to not more than 1.2% of the injected dose.

IV. Discussion

It should be stressed at this point that the results presented here refer to our initial studies with five members of a single sibship with Wilson's disease, and our conclusions are based on a limited amount of data. However, this evidence, together with our previous experiences with loading doses of copper, indicates the following trends:

Patients with Wilson's disease who are homozygously abnormal in respect to the gene which determines this condition do not incorporate measurable amounts of ^{64}Cu into ceruloplasmin from an intravenous tracer dose of this isotope. Throughout the period of observation these individuals accumulate the injected isotope in the liver (and, to a smaller extent, kidney) with no evidence of discharge of activity from the liver. A normal individual gave definite evidence of incorporation of ^{64}Cu into ceruloplasmin. Over the course of a 3-day period 7 to 8% of the dose was bound to ceruloplasmin in the circulating plasma compartment. Moreover, following an initial rapid uptake of ^{64}Cu by the liver there was definite evidence of discharge from the liver in this same normal individual. Individuals who are heterozygous with respect to the gene of Wilson's disease were different from the patient in that they did show definite evidence of incorporation of ^{64}Cu into ceruloplasmin but were also different from normal homozygotes in that the rate of incorporation was much slower. At the end of the 3-day period only 1 to 3% of the dose was incorporated into circulating ceruloplasmin by these individuals. Finally, in the hetero-zygotes the balance between the simultaneous processes of uptake and discharge of activity from the liver was such that in terms of over-all balance they were between the homozygously normal and homozygously abnormal individuals. These observations are in general agreement with the results of our earlier studies with loading doses of copper.

V. Summary

Radioactive copper studies were performed on a patient with Wilson's disease and on four siblings. Following intravenous injection of ^{64}Cu changes of activity in whole blood, plasma, and ceruloplasmin were meas-ured as a function of time. Excreta were collected and assayed for ^{64}Cu activity. Scintillation probe measurements were made over the head, liver, and thigh of the subjects. Analysis of the data enabled a differentiation to be made between individuals homozygously normal, heterozygous, and homozygously abnormal for the gene of Wilson's disease.

ACKNOWLEDGMENTS

The authors wish to thank Dr. J. B. Hanshaw for allowing these studies to be made on patients under his care and the John A. Hartford Foundation for financial support.

REFERENCES

1. Osborn, S. B., Roberts, C. N., and Walshe, J. M., *Clin. Sci.*, **24**, 13, (1963).
2. Osborn, S. B., and Walshe, J. M., *Clin. Sci.*, **27**, 319, (1964).
3. Maytum, W. J., Goldstein, N. P., McGuckin, W. F., and Owen, C. A., *Proc. Mayo Clinic*, **36**, 641, (1961).
4. Baker, R. G., Rotenberg, A. D., Cederlund, J. F., and Johns, H. E., *Can. Med. Assoc. J.*, **87**, 367, (1962).
5. Fritze, K., *Radiochimica Acta*, **3**, 166, (1964).
6. Sternlieb, I., Morell, A. G., Bauer, C. D., Combes, B., de Bobes-Sternberg, S., and Scheinberg, I. H., *J. Clin. Invest.*, **40**, 707, (1961).
7. Sass-Kortsak, A., Glatt, B. S., Cherniak, M., and Cederlund, I., *in* J. M. Walshe and J. N. Cumings (eds.), "Wilson's disease, some current concepts," Blackwells, Oxford, 1961, p. 151.

DISCUSSION

Dr. Sternlieb: Don't you think that your results on the stool excretion point out the fallacy that even a tracer dose is evenly distributed through all copper compartments?

A patient does not retain 99% of the copper he is ingesting. Otherwise he would be loaded with more copper than one usually observes. So obviously he does excrete it, probably as cold copper. If this is true, one has to conclude that the tracer dose is not homogeneously mixed.

Dr. Bearn and Dr. Kunkel [*J. Lab. Clin. Med.*, **45**, 623 (1955)] have shown that there is a difference in the amount of ^{64}Cu excreted by normal subjects and by patients, but this difference was not as shown here.

DR. ASPIN: I tried not to put too much emphasis on the fecal excretion data. We are aware of the difficulties with this method, the fact that some individuals may have 2–3 stools per day while others may have one every 2–3 days, and this is compounded by the problem of looking for a short-lived isotope, and the problem of reabsorption, etc.

However, we have repeatedly observed lower excretion of the label in patients than in controls and these differences tended to be marked.

DR. STERNLIEB: This ought to be emphasized, because the basic assumption is correct; obviously the patients are in positive copper balance, and therefore we know that they are retaining it. However, the figures are misleading, because if you add up the stool copper and the urine copper, the total is 10 times less than that seen in the normal subject.

DR. ASPIN: Perhaps the crux of the matter is that at the moment, we are only in the position to report on tracer studies in five individuals. Studies have been completed this last month on 12 additional individuals, members of two additional families. However, the evaluation of the latter studies is not complete at the present. It is obvious that at this point we cannot make dogmatic statements.

DR. SASS-KORTSAK: May I be permitted to say something in reply to what Dr. Sternlieb has said? It should be realized that the doses of copper that we have given were true tracer and not loading doses and therefore, it is quite possible that only insignificant excretion of the label occurred in 3 days. I don't think this is unusual.

DR. STERNLIEB: This is true, but then you also have to assume that there is not an homogeneous mixing of the copper tracer in the copper compartments. You can't have it both ways.

DR. SASS-KORTSAK: I grant you that you may be right in that, but we have never assumed or said that we have assumed even mixing of the label in all compartments.

DR. STERNLIEB: Then one has to conclude that the tracer studies do not represent an advance from loading studies.

DR. SASS-KORTSAK: In our opinion, Dr. Sternlieb, studies with true tracer doses of copper and the studies with loading doses of copper are two different types of experiments. With tracer doses you can measure transport phenomena without upsetting the over-all balance. On the other hand, with loading doses, the balance is willfully upset but this type of experiment answers the question how in fact a load of copper is handled by the organism. Both types of experiments are necessary because they give answers to different questions. When you look at this from this point of view, it becomes irrelevant whether the two types of studies show similar results or not.

DR. AISEN: Dr. Sass-Kortsak, is there any difference at all between the curves obtained with the tracer doses and the curves obtained with the oral loading doses, for the blood studies?

DR. SASS-KORTSAK: There is very little difference. However, by looking at the results of our small group it seems to us that the difference between heterozygotes and normals is more exaggerated by the tracer technique.

DR. AISEN: I think that perhaps there aren't enough cases to conclude that. Perhaps there would be more overlap with more cases.

DR. SASS-KORTSAK: This is quite possible, it remains to be seen.

DR. WALSHE: These results are not comparable to ours, and I'm not completely sure who is wrong, but Dr. Osborn and I have every confidence in our results. When we studied our first family of two parents and eight children by this technique, hoping to pick up the heterozygote, we thought we could do so. In this experiment, only 7–13 μC of activity, and thus presumably only tracer amounts of carrier, was injected. We have done more studies now, and we are not so sure.

DR. ASPIN: We have also done loading studies similar to your own in the past, using as much as 1 mg of copper injected with the ^{64}Cu and some of these studies agree very well with yours. But, there is one other thing; we have changed our method of calibration for this whole system. Unfortunately, we haven't had a chance to reanalyze all our old data using this new method of calibration to find out whether these old results using loading doses tend to confirm or deny what we have shown here.

DR. WALAAS: I would like to ask if the incorporation of ^{64}Cu represents an exchange of copper in ceruloplasmin, or does it mean that the copper is incorporated into newly synthesized ceruloplasmin?

I was wondering about the mechanism of the biosynthesis of ceruloplasmin. Is the polypeptide chain first formed at the ribosomes, whereupon copper is incorporated, or is the copper incorporated during the biosynthesis at the ribosomal level?

There is one more thing I would like to bring up. Dr. Broman suggested that ceruloplasmin copper is utilized for the biosynthesis of cytochrome oxidase. I wonder if in such studies as Dr. Aspin has mentioned it might be interesting to study the incorporation of copper in cytochrome oxidase from liver.

DR. ASPIN: With our present material, we haven't been able to do that, but I think obviously that these studies just don't give us any answer to that question. I don't think we can say anthing about what is happening in the liver at the moment.

Ceruloplasmin, A Review*

I. HERBERT SCHEINBERG

Department of Medicine,
Albert Einstein College of Medicine, Yeshiva University, and
The Bronx Municipal Hospital Center,
Bronx, New York

I. Introduction

In the late 1940's certain batches of plasma protein fractions in E. J. Cohn's laboratory were noted to be bluish or greenish in color. Further purification of these fractions by Gurd, Kominz, and Oncley was carried out, but before definitive characterization of the component responsible for the blue color could be made a series of papers by Holmberg and Laurell appeared. These, dating from 1947 to 1951 (1–5), elegantly and concisely described a blue plasma protein which was christened "ceruloplasmin." Holmberg and Laurell detailed methods for preparing pure ceruloplasmin, which could be crystallized, from pig plasma; recognized that almost all of the copper in mammalian plasma circulated as part of this protein; defined its copper content, on the basis of analytic results and molecular weight determination, as equivalent to 8 atoms of copper in a molecule of approximately 150,000 molecular weight; characterized it electrophoretically as an alpha globulin; found that its blue color could be reversibly abolished by several reducing agents; and reported that the oxidase activity known to reside in plasma and directed toward polyphenols and polyamines was solely due to the plasma's content of ceruloplasmin. The capstone of physiological significance to their discoveries ironically and undeservedly eluded them. Aware of recent findings that Wilson's disease was associated with abnormalities of copper metabolism, they determined the content of

* This work was supported in part by grants from the National Institute of Arthritis and Metabolic Diseases of the United States Public Health Service (AM–1059) and the Life Insurance Medical Research Fund (G–65–50).

TABLE I

RECENT METHODS OF PREPARATION OF HUMAN CERULOPLASMIN

Year	Ref.	Source	Procedure	pH Range of procedure	Product	
					State	$A_{610}:A_{280}$[a]
1959	(6)	Fraction IV–1 or IV–4 of Cohn	Chromatography on DEAE–cellulose	4.8	Solution	—
1959	(7,8)	Fraction G–2 of Kekwick and MacKay	Ether treatment of crude extract; precipitation at pH 4.8; chromatography on DEAE–cellulose	4.8–7.0	Solution	0.044
1960	(9)	Out-dated blood bank plasma	Chromatography on DEAE–cellulose; precipitation with $(NH_4)_2SO_4$; crystallization from acetate buffer, 0.025 M, pH 5.25	5.2–7.4	Cryst.	0.0465
1962	(10)	Fraction IV–1 of Cohn	Chromatography on DEAE–cellulose; precipitation with $(NH_4)_2SO_4$; crystallization from acetate buffer, 0.025 M, pH 5.25	5.2–7.4	Cryst.	0.0465
1962	(11)	Fraction IV–1 of Cohn	Chromatography on DEAE–cellulose; precipitation with ethanol–chloroform	5.4–7.0	Solution	0.043
1962	(12)	Fraction IV–1 of Cohn	Chromatography on DEAE–cellulose; precipitation with ethanol chloroform; crystallization from acetate buffer 0.01 M	5.2–7.0	Cryst.	0.047
1964	(13)	Retroplacental serum	Chromatography on DEAE–Sephadex and hydroxyapatite; gel filtration on Sephadex G–100	6.8	Solution	0.042

[a] This ratio appears to be the best single index of purity of ceruloplasmin. Preparations in the author's laboratory crystallized by the modifications of the method of Deutsch have had values as high as 0.048.

ceruloplasmin in the plasma of a patient with this disease hoping to find it different from that in normal human plasma—approximately 30 mg/100 ml. Their patient proved to have a normal concentration of ceruloplasmin— and Holmberg and Laurell concluded there was no further point in studying ceruloplasmin concentrations in these patients. Several years later they learned that the patient whom they had been given to study had been misdiagnosed and did not, in fact, have Wilson's disease!

II. Preparation

Holmberg and Laurell originally crystallized ceruloplasmin from purified fractions which they made from old serum. Chromatography on various substances has since greatly facilitated the large-scale preparation of this protein. Table I summarizes the more recent methods of preparing ceruloplasmin. Reports of the heterogeneity of this protein have led to questions as to whether the procedures involved in preparation and subsequent fractionation may not have produced degraded molecules which behaved differently from ceruloplasmin in its state in nature. A method reported by Broman and Kjellin (13) is of great significance in this regard since it did not involve the use of denaturing agents, such as alcohol, acetone, or chloroform, and was carried out at a pH only 0.5 units below the physiological.

III. Properties

Although ceruloplasmins from different mammals show some cross reactivity (14), they also show distinct differences in immunochemical behavior and in the one chemical property most widely studied, oxidase activity (15, 16, 17). The protein does not bind its copper atoms irreversibly since they can be exchanged for radioactive copper under suitable reducing conditions (18). Apoceruloplasmin, free of copper and capable

TABLE II

SIZE AND SHAPE OF THE CERULOPLASMIN MOLECULE

Molecular weight	151,000 (Sed.–Diff.)	(2)
	160,000 (Sed.–Diff.)	(23)
	155,000 (Approach to eq.)	(23)
Sedimentation coefficient	$7.08\ S$	(23)
Diffusion coefficient	$3.76 \times 10^{-7}\ cm^2\ sec^{-1}$	(23)
Partial specific volume	0.713	(23)
Axial ratio $(a:b)$	11	(23)

TABLE III

ELECTROPHORETIC PROPERTIES OF CERULOPLASMIN[a]

Buffer	$\Gamma/2$	pH	Mobility (cm² volt⁻¹ sec⁻¹ × 10⁵)	Ref.
Barbital	0.1	8.60	5.20	(23)
Tris	0.1	8.41	5.26	(23)
Phosphate	0.1	7.01	4.72	(23)
Acetate	0.1	5.48	2.74	(23)
Acetate	0.2	5.40	3.50	(24)

[a] Moving boundary electrophoresis (single peak). Two or more oxidase-active components are separated by starch gel electrophoresis (19); paper electrophoresis (25); microimmunoelectrophoresis (26).

TABLE IV

OPTICAL PROPERTIES OF CERULOPLASMIN[a]

Wavelength (mμ) of absorption line centers	Gram atomic[b] absorption coefficient
794	850
610	4400
459	460
332	1600

[a] $E_{1cm}^{1\%}$ at 610 mμ, 0.680–0.740; $E_{1cm}^{1\%}$ at 280 mμ, 14.9–16.2.
[b] Assuming that Cu^{2+} ions only contribute to all absorptions (20).

TABLE V

PROSTHETIC COPPER IN CERULOPLASMIN

Atoms per mole	8
Cu^{2+}:total Cu	
EPR (20)	0.29
EPR (27)	0.43–0.48
EPR (28)	0.40
Magnetic Susceptibility (29)	0.40
$g_\perp$ (30)	2.048
$g_\parallel$ (30)	2.214
A (30)	0.008 cm⁻¹

TABLE VI

CARBOHYDRATE COMPOSITION OF CERULOPLASMIN (31)

Carbohydrate M.W. of ceruloplasmin	12,200
Number of heterosaccharide chains	9–10
Sialic acid	9
N-Acetylglucosamine	18
Fucose	2
Hexose	36
Mannose:galactose	3:2

of recombining with it to reconstitute native ceruloplasmin, has been made (19). The blue color of ceruloplasmin is associated with the cupric atoms of the molecule which, unlike the cuprous atoms of hemocyanin, do not combine with molecular oxygen (20–22). The eight copper atoms are not identical (41).

Several other physicochemical properties of human ceruloplasmin are summarized in Tables II to VII.

TABLE VII

AMINO ACID COMPOSITION OF CERULOPLASMIN

	Residues per 160,000 M. W. (23)	Residues per 151,000 M. W. (32)
Aspartic acid	135	143
Threonine	86	89
Serine	69	73
Glutamic acid	130	132
Proline	57	60
Glycine	85	89
Alanine	56	58
½ Cystine	14	10
Cysteine	1	—
Valine	67	73
Methionine	26	19
Isoleucine	56	61
Leucine	79	80
Tyrosine	71	57
Phenylalanine	54	66
Lysine	68	77
Histidine	43	50
Arginine	46	44
Tryptophan	27	23

IV. Biological Activity

In the past 13 years four aspects of the possible biological activity of ceruloplasmin have occupied investigators: its enzymatic activity; the possibility that it is of significance in psychiatric disorders; the question of its identity with erythropoietin; and its possible role in the regulation of copper balance.

A. Enzymatic Activity

Ceruloplasmin, in serum and in purified form, has a moderate amount of oxidase activity toward a variety of polyamines and polyphenols. There has been, furthermore, a rather lively argument as to whether it may not also be an oxidase toward ascorbic acid (11, 33, 34). Considerable work has been published relating to ceruloplasmin's substrates and inhibitors (25, 35–44), on the fact that ceruloplasmins from different species tend to have different oxidase activities (15–17), and on the intimate details of the enzymatic reactions.

An interesting example of the last—and of controversy—began with Curzon and O'Reilly's finding that ceruloplasmin could oxidize DPD directly and also via the mediation of a ferrous–ferric couple. In accord with this they found that ferrous ion enhanced the activity of ceruloplasmin in its oxidase activity toward DPD although ferric ion, which should have been equally stimulatory, was considerably less so (36). Levine and Peisach (44) using PPD as substrate, also found that ferrous ion enhanced ceruloplasmin oxidase activity but found no enhancement whatever with ferric ion. There is a noteworthy difference, however, in the oxidation of PPD and DPD: PPD's oxidation is complex and involves many products whereas DPD's apparently involves only two (36, 42). Although Levine and Peisach (44) found no enhancement by ferric ion when they bubbled oxygen through the ferric solution for 30 minutes prior to assay, they did find considerable stimulation in the absence of oxygen bubbling which they attributed to ferrous impurities in the ferric salt. Both groups concluded that the inhibition of ceruloplasmin's oxidase activity by EDTA is caused in major part by chelation of trace amounts of iron.

Despite this large amount of work on the enzymatic properties of ceruloplasmin the physiological significance of this activity remains completely obscure. One can even ask whether the oxidase activity of ceruloplasmin has any greater relation to the physiologic function of this protein than the peroxidase activity of hemoglobin toward benzidine bears to the physiologic role of hemoglobin. A number of children, who have been studied for as long as 10 years with careful clinical and chemical observations, are known never to have had detectable ceruloplasmin in their plasma. Although these children seem to accumulate large excesses of copper in their livers and ultimately develop copper toxicity (Wilson's disease) if they are untreated, they exhibit no other abnormality. These observations make it difficult to believe that ceruloplasmin has an important function, connected either with its oxidase activity or with its other properties, which is *not* related to the maintenance of normal zero copper balance.

B. Relation to Psychiatric Disorders

In 1957 Akerfeldt suggested that an excess of ceruloplasmin might be associated with severe mental disease (45). Investigations similar to his, by other workers, did not substantiate his finding, and it appeared that the increased activity of ceruloplasmin found in Akerfeldt's psychotic patients may have been the consequence of a diminished concentration of substances which increase the lag period of ceruloplasmin's oxidase activity. The serum of a psychiatric in-patient is likely to be deficient in ascorbic acid, which is such a compound (46, 47).

Nevertheless the belief persisted, with some investigators, that qualitative or quantitative abnormalities in copper metabolism, or in the metabolism of ceruloplasmin, might have some fundamental connection with mental disease. This belief died hard (if indeed it can be considered stone-dead yet!) because of two sets of findings. First, there was, and still is, no doubt that *in vitro* ceruloplasmin can catalyze the oxidation of many amines which are associated with the central nervous system (6, 25, 35, 37–39). Second, there did, and does, appear to be some fraction of plasma which can influence animal behavior (48), and some earlier observations indicated that this fraction might be ceruloplasmin (49) though the proponents of the latter idea no longer hold this view (50). As of the present, I believe the state of affairs with respect to this lengthy and complicated controversy is as follows: perhaps half of the patients with Wilson's disease, the hereditary form of abnormal copper metabolism discussed by Dr. Walshe at this symposium, exhibit a variety of psychiatric disturbances. These disorders represent, wholly or partly, one of the effects of copper toxicity on the brain. However, when deficiency of ceruloplasmin, which is a biochemical hallmark not only of Wilson's disease but also of copper deficiency (51), was looked for in about 8000 patients in five mental institutions, only 20 were found with ceruloplasmin deficiency (52). This is evidence that neither an abnormal, positive copper balance nor ceruloplasmin deficiency plays any role in psychiatric patients except when the underlying disorder is Wilson's disease. Nor is there other evidence suggesting that there is any other abnormality in copper or ceruloplasmin metabolism in the vast majority of mentally ill patients.

C. Erythropoietic Activity

In 1962, Hatta, Yamaguchi, and their collaborators reported that apoceruloplasmin exhibited erythropoietic activity in rats and in rabbits (53, 54). In 1963, Hatta and collaborators (55) modified these conclusions to state that erythropoietin was a thermostable derivative of the ceruloplasmin molecule, which could be precipitated at pH 4.5 or separated by chromatography. At about the same time, furthermore, Rambach, Shaw, and Alt (56) could find no copper and no "copper oxidase" activity in erythropoietin.

D. Ceruloplasmin and Copper Balance

In the face of these negative, or inconclusive, studies is there any evidence—beyond teleological arguments—that ceruloplasmin has *any* physiological role? I believe that ceruloplasmin plays some role in the maintenance of the zero copper balance which appears to be the normal state of affairs in human beings. The luckless investigation of Wilson's disease which Holmberg and Laurell had carried out was repeated in 1952 (57) on a patient who did have the disorder. The conclusion drawn from the study was that the disease was characterized by a lifelong deficiency, or absence, of ceruloplasmin, and that this deficiency was autosomal recessive in origin. Two or three acquired conditions appeared to be associated with deficiency of the protein but such deficiency was always transient. Further evidence for this hypothesis follows:

(a) Wilson's disease is the only condition known in which human chronic copper toxicity is found (58).

(b) Wilson's disease is *almost always* associated with a lifelong deficiency or absence of ceruloplasmin (57, 59).

(c) Not only is there no other known form of significant human copper toxicity, but no other condition is known in which there is lifelong deficiency of ceruloplasmin except for occasional heterozygous carriers of the abnormal "copper balance," or Wilson's disease, gene (58, 60).

(d) The daily turnover of ceruloplasmin copper, in normal human beings, amounts to roughly ½ mg of copper which is probably very close to the amount of copper absorbed from the diet daily (61, 62).

(e) Considerable experimental evidence indicates that ceruloplasmin copper is incorporated into the protein only at the time of its synthesis in hepatic microsomes (63) and that exchange of this copper with ionic copper loosely bound to albumin does not occur *in vivo* (62). Ceruloplasmin's relation to copper in this respect, incidentally, is quite similar to the relationship of hemoglobin to iron and distinctly different from the relationship of transferrin to iron.

(f) Complete absence of ceruloplasmin, from early infancy on, is associated with no known biochemical or clinical abnormality—except abnormal, positive copper balance (64) and its consequences.

There is, however, some evidence, negative and positive, which is difficult to reconcile with the hypothesis that ceruloplasmin is involved in the control of normal, zero copper balance:

(a) Some patients with Wilson's disease possess normal concentrations of serum ceruloplasmin for some periods of their lives (59, 65). Further, most patients with Wilson's disease have *some* ceruloplasmin amounting on the average to about 25% of the normal concentration (64).

(b) A few heterozygous carriers of one "Wilson's disease" gene have almost zero plasma concentration of ceruloplasmin, and yet there is evidence, including that derived from quantitative analysis of hepatic biopsy samples, that their concentrations of tissue copper are normal (64, 66).

(c) No significant effect has been observed in patients with Wilson's disease whose ceruloplasmin levels were made normal by the infusion of purified human ceruloplasmin (67, 68). The infusion of apoceruloplasmin, in a state in which it can be readily reconstituted to native ceruloplasmin *in vitro*, resulted in no such reconstitution, and no significant effect, in patients with Wilson's disease or in normal individuals (66).

(d) Insufficient ceruloplasmin copper is excreted in the bile to account for excretion of enough copper to maintain zero copper balance normally and there is no evidence for its excretion via the intestinal wall or kidney (69).

Were it not for these four disturbing pieces of evidence, one could draw a pretty picture of the role of ceruloplasmin. Ingested copper, absorbed perhaps to the extent of 25% of the dietary supply, reaches the liver and is incorporated into ceruloplasmin only during the synthesis of this protein in microsomes (63). Although there is no doubt that *in vitro* all eight of ceruloplasmin's copper atoms can be removed (70) reversibly and are exchangeable for radioactive copper (71, 72), this does not appear to occur *in vivo* (60). Wilson's disease could, in this fantasy world, be the logical result of an inability to synthesize sufficient ceruloplasmin to insure the excretion, via this protein, of all of the copper which had been absorbed from the diet. Even a small net positive copper balance—50 micrograms daily maintained for years—could ultimately result in the retention by brain, liver, and almost all tissues of the body of the amounts found.

Of course, even if we could accept such a picture of the role of ceruloplasmin we would still be left with several facts—beyond the four above—for which we could not account. Thus, what significance is to be attached to the heterogeneity of ceruloplasmin described by several groups of workers (73–78)? What is the significance of the oxidase activity of ceruloplasmin directed toward so many substrates? What is the significance of the carbohydrate content of ceruloplasmin, which Jamieson (31) finds amounts to 8% of the protein in 9 or 10 carbohydrate chains? These questions, regretfully, I cannot answer.

V. Summary

Knowledge of the properties and methods of the preparation of ceruloplasmin is reviewed. The possible physiological roles of this protein which have been considered in the past are critically evaluated.

ACKNOWLEDGMENTS

I am greatly indebted to Professor Anatol G. Morell and Dr. C. J. A. Van den Hamer for critical help and advice in preparing this manuscript.

REFERENCES

1. Holmberg, C. G., and Laurell, C.-B., *Acta Chem. Scand.*, **1**, 944 (1947).
2. Holmberg, C. G., and Laurell, C.-B., *Acta Chem. Scand.*, **2**, 550 (1948).
3. Holmberg, C. G., and Laurell, C.-B., *Acta Chem. Scand.*, **5**, 476 (1951).
4. Holmberg, C. G., and Laurell, C.-B., *Acta Chem. Scand.*, **5**, 921 (1951).
5. Holmberg, C. G., and Laurell, C.-B., *Scand. J. Clin. and Lab. Invest.*, **3**, 103 (1951).
6. Sanders, B. E., Miller, O. P., and Richard, M. N., *Arch. Biochim. Biophys.*, **84**, 62 (1959).
7. Curzon, G., and Vallet, L., *Nature*, **183**, 751 (1959).
8. Curzon, G., and Vallet, L., *Biochem. J.*, **74**, 279 (1961).
9. Deutsch, H. F., *Arch. Biochem. Biophys.*, **89**, 225 (1960).
10. Deutsch, H. F., Kasper, C. B., and Welsch, D., *Arch. Biochem. Biophys.*, **99**, 132 (1962).
11. Morell, A. G., Aisen, P., and Scheinberg, I. H., *J. Biol. Chem.*, **237**, 3455 (1962).
12. Sgouris, J. T., Coryell, F. C., Gallick, H., Storey, R. W., McCall, K. B., and Anderson, H. D., *Vox Sang.*, **7**, 394 (1962).
13. Broman, L., and Kjellin, K., *Biochim. Biophys. Acta*, **82**, 101 (1964).
14. Kasper, E. B., and Deutsch, H. F., *J. Biol. Chem.*, **238**, 2343 (1963).
15. Garattini, S., Giachetti, A., and Pieri, L., *Arch. Biochem. Biophys.*, **91**, 83 (1960).
16. Seal, U. S., *Comp. Biochem.*, *Physiol.*, **13**, 143 (1964).
17. Van den Hamer, C. J. A., Buyze, G., and Van der Heyden, M. C. M., *Protides of the Biological Fluids*, **11**, 382 (1964).
18. Scheinberg, I. H., and Morell, A. G., *J. Clin. Invest.*, **36**, 1193 (1957).
19. Morell, A. G., and Scheinberg, I. H., *Science*, **127**, 588 (1958).

20. Blumberg, W. E., Eisinger, J., Aisen, P., Morell, A. G., and Scheinberg, I. H., *J. Biol. Chem.*, **238**, 1675 (1963).
21. Morell, A. G., Aisen, P., Blumberg, W. E., and Scheinberg, I. H., *J. Biol. Chem.*, **239**, 1042 (1964).
22. Malmström, B. G., and Vänngård, T., *J. Mol. Biol.*, **2**, 118 (1960).
23. Kasper, E. B., and Deutsch, H. F., *J. Biol. Chem.*, **238**, 2325 (1963).
24. Aisen, P., and Morell, A. G., *J. Biol. Chem.*, **240**, 1974 (1965).
25. Siva Sankar, D. V., *Fed. Proc.*, **18**, 441 (1959).
26. Uriel, J., Gotz, H., and Grabar, P., *J. Suisse de Med.*, **87**, 431 (1957).
27. Broman, L., Malmström, B. G., Aasa, R., and Vänngård, T., *J. Mol. Biol.*, **5**, 301 (1962).
28. Kasper, E. B., Deutsch, H. F., and Beinert, H., *J. Biol. Chem.*, **238**, 2338 (1963).
29. Ehrenberg, A., Malmström, B. G., Broman, L., and Mosbach, R., *J. Mol. Biol.*, **5**, 450 (1962).
30. Vänngård, T., and Aasa, R., *in* W. Low (ed.), "Paramagnetic resonance," Academic Press Inc., New York, 1963, p. 509.
31. Jamieson, G. A., *J. Biol. Chem.*, **240**, 2019 (1965).
32. Edsall, J. T., and Spahr, P. F., personal communication, 1960.
33. Osaki, S., *J. Biochem.*, **50**, 29 (1961).
34. Humoller, F. L., Mockler, M., Haltaus, J. M., and Mahler, D. I., *J. Lab. Clin. Med.*, **222**, 56 (1960).
35. Aprison, M. H., Hanson, K. M., and Austin, D. C., *J. Nerv. and Mental Dis.*, **128**, 249 (1959).
36. Curzon, G., and O'Reilly, S., *Biochem. Biophys. Res. Communs.*, **2**, 284 (1960).
37. Kalas, J. P., *Am. J. Med. Sci.*, **239**, 203 (1960).
38. Geller, E., Eiduson, S., and Yuwiler, A., *J. Neurochem.*, **5**, 73 (1959).
39. Levine, W. G., and Peisach, J., *Biochim. Biophys. Acta*, **63**, 528 (1962).
40. Walshe, J. M., *J. Clin. Invest.*, **42**, 1048 (1963).
41. Osaki, S., McDermott, J. A., and Frieden, E., *J. Biol. Chem.*, **239**, pc 364 (1964).
42. Peisach, J., and Levine, W. G., *Biochim. Biophys. Acta*, **77**, 615 (1963).
43. Curzon, G., and Cumings, J. N., this symposium.
44. Levine, W. G., and Peisach, J., *Biochim. Biophys. Acta*, **77**, 602 (1963).
45. Akerfeldt, S., *Science*, **125**, 119 (1957).
46. Kety, S. S., *Science*, **129**, 1528 (1959).
47. Scheinberg, I. H., Morell, A. G., Harris, R. S., and Berger, A., *Science*, **126**, 925 (1957).
48. Pennell, R. B., Pawlus, C., Saravis, C. A., and Scrimshaw, G., paper presented at NATO Advance Study Institute, Drammen, Norway, August 1965.
49. Leach, B. E., Cohen, M., Heath, R. G., and Martens, G., *Arch. Neurol. Psychiat.*, **76**, 635 (1956).
50. Heath, R. G., paper presented at NATO Advance Study Institute, Drammen, Norway, August 1965.
51. Sternlieb, I., and Janowitz, H. D., *J. Clin. Invest.*, **43**, 1049 (1964).
52. Scheinberg, I. H., paper presented at NATO Advance Study Institute, Drammen, Norway, August 1965.
53. Hatta, Y., Maruyama, Y., Tsuruoka, N., Yamaguchi, A., Kukita, M., Sugata, F., and Shimizu, M., *Acta Haemat. Japonica*, **25**, 682 (1962).
54. Yamaguchi, A., Tsuruoka, N., Maruyama, Y., Yamamoto, M., Ando, M., Veno. T., Hatta, Y., and Shimizu, M., *Acta Haemat. Japonica*, **25**, 773 (1962).

55. Hatta, Y., Maruyama, Y., Tsoruoka, N., Yamaguchi, A., Ando, M., Veno, T., and Shimizu, M., *Acta Haemat. Japonica*, **26,** 174 (1963).
56. Rambach, W. A., Shaw, R. A., and Alt, H. L., *in* L. O. Jacobson and Margot Doyle (eds.), "Erythropoiesis," Grune and Stratton Publishers, New York, 1962, p. 52.
57. Scheinberg, I. H., and Gitlin, D., *Science*, **116,** 484 (1952).
58. Scheinberg, I. H., and Sternlieb, I., *Ann. Rev. Med.*, **16,** 119 (1965).
59. Scheinberg, I. H., and Sternlieb, I., *The Lancet*, **i,** 1420 (1963).
60. Scheinberg, I. H., and Sternlieb, I., *Pharmacol. Rev.*, **12,** 355 (1960).
61. Gitlin, D., and Janeway, C. A., *Nature*, **185,** 693 (1960).
62. Sternlieb, I., Morell, A. G., Tucker, W. D., Green, M. W., and Scheinberg, I. H., *J. Clin. Invest.*, **40,** 1834 (1961).
63. Sternlieb, I., Morell, A. G., and Scheinberg, I. H., *Trans. Assoc. Am. Physicians*, **75,** 228 (1962).
64. Sternlieb, I., and Scheinberg, I. H., *J. Am. Med. Assoc.*, **183,** 747 (1963).
65. Sass-Kortsak, A., Cherniak, M., Geiger, D. W., and Slater, R. J., *J. Clin. Invest.*, **38,** 1672 (1959).
66. Scheinberg, I. H., unpublished observations.
67. Bickel, H., Neale, F. C., and Hall, G., *Quart. J. Med.*, **26,** 527 (1957).
68. Scheinberg, I. H., and Sternlieb, I., *Ann. Int. Med.*, **52,** 115 (1960).
69. Aisen, P., Morell, A. G., Alpert, S., and Sternlieb, I., *Nature*, **203,** 873 (1964).
70. Morell, A. G., and Scheinberg, I. H., *Science*, **127,** 588 (1958).
71. Scheinberg, I. H., and Morell, A. G., *J. Clin. Invest.*, **36,** 1193 (1957).
72. Morell, A. G., and van den Hamer, C. J. A., unpublished observations.
73. Broman, L., *Nature*, **182,** 1655 (1958).
74. Morell, A. G., and Scheinberg, I. H., *Science*, **131,** 930 (1960).
75. Richterich, R., Gautier, E., Stillhart, H., and Rossi, E., *Helv. Paediatria Acta*, **15,** 424 (1960).
76. McAllister, R., Martin, G. M., and Benditt, E. P., *Nature*, **190,** 927 (1961).
77. Poulik, M. D., *Nature*, **194,** 842 (1962).
78. Poulik, M. D., *Protides of the Biological Fluids*, **10,** 170 (1963).

The Subunit Structure of Human Ceruloplasmin*

WILLIAM N. POILLON† AND ALEXANDER G. BEARN

The Rockefeller University,
New York, New York

I. Heterogeneity of Ceruloplasmin

Since first described by Holmberg and Laurell (1), ceruloplasmin, a serum α_2-globulin, has been thoroughly characterized in recent studies with respect to its physicochemical properties (2), the nature of its prosthetic copper (3–5), and the role played by this copper in its intense blue color and oxidase activity toward aromatic diamines (6–8). However, the question whether the heterogeneity observed in ceruloplasmin purified from pooled sera represents a real genetic polymorphism has never been satisfactorily resolved. Several workers (9–11) have been able to separate at least two chromatographically distinct components which differed in electrophoretic mobility on starch gel and seemed to be distinct molecular species. Others (12, 13) have suggested that this observed heterogeneity has no genetic significance.

A problem closely related to the heterogeneity of ceruloplasmin is that of its subunit composition. Poulik (13, 14) and Deutsch (2) have both presented ultracentrifugal evidence for a molecular species smaller than the native protein after treatment with 8 M urea alone or 8 M urea plus mercaptoethanol. The molecular weight of this smaller species has not yet been reported. The same authors further showed that electrophoretic patterns of reduced and alkylated ceruloplasmin in starch gel made with urea–formate buffers were extremely complex and suggested that the native protein was composed of several nonidentical subunits.

In view of the uncertainty regarding the state of aggregation of native ceruloplasmin and its subunit composition, the present study was undertaken. The initial simplifying assumption was made that the native, globular form of ceruloplasmin was stabilized only by noncovalent interactions among its constituent polypeptide chains [i.e., the disulfide bridges of the seven cystine residues in native ceruloplasmin (2) were considered to be all intrachain].

* This investigation was supported (in part) by Public Health Service Grant No. GM–577 from the Institute of General Medical Sciences and by Public Health Service Grant AM 01542.

† Present address: Department of Medicine, College of Physicians and Surgeons, Columbia University, New York, New York.

The experimental approach adopted was to expose the native protein to conditions which would increase its net negative charge. The covalent modification achieved by reaction with succinic anhydride results principally in the conversion of the positively charged free amino groups to negatively charged succinyl residues. An increase in negative charge can also be achieved by increasing the pH above 7. At highly alkaline pH, the amino acid side chains ionize, and if the increase in net charge so induced is large enough, disruption of the quaternary structure would be expected to occur.

The present paper reports the dissociation of human ceruloplasmin into subunits by either treatment with alkali or succinylation at pH 7–8, or a combination of the two methods. The subunits obtained in each case were examined by a variety of physical and chemical techniques.

II. Experimental

Ceruloplasmin assay: The purified ceruloplasmin used in this study was a gift from Dr. James A. Pert, American Red Cross, Washington, D. C., and was obtained as an intensely blue solution. Protein content was estimated with the Folin-Ciocalteau phenol reagent. Oxidase activity was measured according to the procedure of Broman (9). Analysis for prosthetic copper was performed with BCS, according to the procedure of Poillon and Dawson (15). The assay of the ceruloplasmin used in this study is shown in Table I. As estimated by the absorbance ratio A_{610}/A_{280}, this material is about 93% pure.

TABLE I

ASSAY OF PURIFIED HUMAN CERULOPLASMIN

Protein content	18.9 mg/ml
Oxidase activity	75 units/mg[a]
Copper content	55.6 μg/ml
Percentage Cu	0.30%
A_{610}	1.29
A_{280}	31.4
A_{610}/A_{280}	0.041
Estimated purity[b]	93%

[a] One unit corresponds to that amount of ceruloplasmin which gives an A_{552} of 0.100 under standard conditions of incubation (9).

[b] Based on $A_{610}/A_{280} = 0.044$ for ceruloplasmin of 100% purity (10).

Buffers: All the experiments to be subsequently described utilized one of three basic buffers, whose compositions were as follows: phosphate, pH 7.1 (0.072 M Na_2HPO_4–0.028 M NaH_2PO_4); carbonate-bicarbonate, pH 10.2 (0.07 M Na_2CO_3–0.03 M $NaHCO_3$); borate-NaCl-NaOH, pH 12.5 (0.05 M H_3BO_3–0.05 M NaCl–0.1 M NaOH).

Alkali treatment: Ceruloplasmin was dialyzed at 4° against one liter of either the pH 10.2 or pH 12.5 buffer, for 2–5 days, with at least two changes. In one experiment at each pH the buffer was made 0.012 M in EDTA after dialysis for one day. Dialysis was then continued for one week through 5–6 further buffer changes. This exhaustive dialysis against EDTA was designed to remove completely any prosthetic copper dissociated as a result of the alkali treatment.

Reaction with succinic anhydride: A 1.0 ml portion (18.9 mg) of the stock ceruloplasmin solution was dialyzed overnight against 1 M phosphate buffer, pH 7.6. Solid succinic anhydride was added in 50 mg increments at room temperature, with stirring. As each increment of solid anhydride slowly dissolved, the pH gradually decreased to about 6. The pH was adjusted to 7–8 by dropwise addition of 1 M NaOH, before the addition of another anhydride increment. A gradual bleaching of the blue color was observed as each increment was added, and a colorless solution resulted when the milligram ratio of succinic anhydride to protein was 10:1. After dialysis to remove excess anhydride, the degree of succinylation achieved was estimated with the ninhydrin reagent (16).

Analytical ultracentrifugation: Sedimentation velocity and equilibrium experiments were performed in a Spinco Model E ultracentrifuge equipped with phase plate schlieren optics and a rotor temperature control unit, using standard methods. Sedimentation velocity experiments were performed at 52,640 rpm at 20°. The sedimentation coefficients (s_{20}) were determined at three protein concentrations and extrapolated to infinite dilution. These $s°_{20}$ values were then corrected to the viscosity and density of water in the usual manner, so as to obtain $s°_{20,w}$ values. Sedimentation equilibrium experiments were performed at speeds of either 12,590 rpm or 20,410 rpm at 20°. The anhydrous molecular weight was estimated by an extension of the Archibald principle, as developed by Trautman (17). For the partial specific volume, the value of 0.713 cm^3/g reported by Kasper and Deutsch (2) was used in all cases.

Polyacrylamide gel electrophoresis: These experiments were performed according to the procedure of Raymond (18). Vertical electrophoresis was carried out at 4° for 4–6 hours at 60 mA/120 V. The gel was stained for protein with Amido Black 10B and for oxidase activity with *p*-phenylenediamine at pH 5.6 and 37°.

III. Results

A. Aggregation of Native Ceruloplasmin

Sedimentation velocity analysis of purified ceruloplasmin in the ultra-centrifuge disclosed two distinct components (Fig. 1A, lower pattern). The sedimentation coefficients ($s_{20,w}$) for the major, slow component and

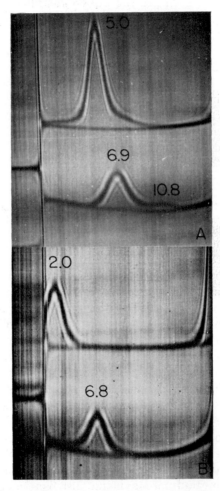

FIG. 1. Sedimentation velocity patterns for native and alkali-treated ceruloplasmin at 20°. A. Patterns at 64 minutes and phase-plate angle of 60° for pH 10.2 (upper) and pH 7.1 (lower) samples. B. Patterns at 48 minutes and phase-plate angle of 50° for pH 12.5 (upper) and pH 7.1 (lower) samples. The rotor speed was 52,640 rpm. Numerals refer to $s_{20,w}$ values.

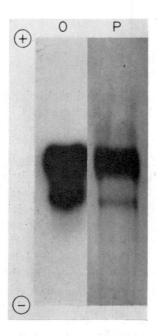

FIG. 2. Polyacrylamide gel electrophoresis of native ceruloplasmin in borate buffer, pH 8.5. The direction of migration was toward the anode. Left frame: oxidase stain (PPD at pH 5.6). Right frame: protein stain (Amido Black 10B).

the minor, fast component were calculated to be 6.9 S and 10.8 S, respectively. The major component was estimated to comprise about 90% of the sedimenting material and the minor component, 10%. If one assumes that the two species observed have the same frictional properties and differ only in molecular size, then the sedimentation coefficient varies as $M^{2/3}$ (19). From this relationship the ratio 1:1.96 was calculated for the molecular weights corresponding to the major and the minor peaks, respectively. Thus, it would appear that the faster sedimenting species (10.8 S) may represent a dimer of the slower (6.9 S), native ceruloplasmin molecule. Further support for a dimer of ceruloplasmin was obtained by polyacrylamide gel electrophoresis. Figure 2 shows the pattern obtained from a gel made up in borate buffer, pH 8.5, after staining for protein and oxidase activity. Two distinct bands, a fast, major band and a slow, minor one, are disclosed by both stains. If the fast band corresponds to native ceruloplasmin, then the slow band should correspond to the presumed dimer, present to the extent of 10% of the total protein material in this case. In light of these findings, reports of ceruloplasmin "heterogeneity" should be reexamined to exclude the possibility that aggregation of the native protein has produced electrophoretically and chromatographically separable components.

B. Alkali-Treated Ceruloplasmin

The sedimentation coefficient and molecular weight of native ceruloplasmin were determined to provide a standard of reference for the alkali-treated ceruloplasmin (Table II). The value of $s^{\circ}_{20,w} = 7.11$ S obtained agrees well with the value of 7.08 S previously reported by Kasper and Deutsch (3). The value of $M_w = 143,100 \pm 2900$ is also in reasonable agreement with the values reported in the literature (148,000–160,000).

(a) *pH 10.2:* After dialysis against EDTA at pH 10.2, a colorless solution was obtained which was devoid of oxidase activity and in which no prosthetic copper was detectable by bathocuproine assay. The molecular weight and sedimentation coefficient determined on this sample are summarized in Table II. The slope of the line obtained by plotting the Trautman coordinates, q_a versus $(c_a - c^{\circ})$, is proportional to the reduced molecular weight $M(1 - V\rho)$. The weight average molecular weight, M_w, was found to be $82,500 \pm 11,500$. Within the experimental error of the determination, this value corresponds approximately to one-half the molecular weight of native ceruloplasmin (71,600). The value of $s^{\circ}_{20,w} = 5.48$ S was obtained by sedimentation velocity experiments and a representative schlieren pattern is shown in Fig. 1A (upper pattern). It should be noted that the boundary is not completely symmetrical above the baseline, but instead shows a sharp "break" before the descending limb returns to the baseline. This skewness suggests the presence of a small amount of faster sedimenting material and probably represents inactive, undissociated ceruloplasmin. Its presence introduces an error which would make the calculated sedimentation rate for the slower, major component too high. Hence, the true

TABLE II

SEDIMENTATION COEFFICIENT AND MOLECULAR WEIGHT OF NATIVE, ALKALI-TREATED, AND SUCCINYLATED CERULOPLASMIN

Ceruloplasmin	pH	$s^{\circ}_{20,w}$ (10^{-13} sec)	M_w
Native	7.1	7.11	$143,100 \pm 2,900$
Alkali-treated	10.2	5.48	$82,500 \pm 11,500$
Alkali-treated	12.5	2.63	$37,700 \pm 750$
Succinylated	7.1	4.06	$87,890 \pm 6,150$
Succinylated and alkali-treated	12.5	$(1.22)^a$	$17,190 \pm 1,030$

[a] This value represents $s_{20,w}$ calculated at a single protein concentration of 2.3 mg/ml.

value of $s^{\circ}_{20,w}$ for the pH 10.2 species is probably somewhat lower than 5.48 S (20). Under the conditions described, native ceruloplasmin apparently undergoes an incomplete dissociation into half-molecules.

(b) *pH 12.5*: Although the blue color was rapidly bleached by dialysis at pH 12.5, the final solution was pale pink in color and was devoid of oxidase activity. This phenomenon has been reported by Kasper *et al.* (4) and attributed to the classical biuret reaction, with ceruloplasmin as the source of copper. Following two consecutive exhaustive dialyses against EDTA, the copper content was still essentially identical to a control ceruloplasmin dialyzed against EDTA at pH 7.1 (0.24% versus 0.27%). However, when the pH was lowered below 11 (0.1 M carbonate–bicarbonate, pH 10.6), the pink color disappeared and the copper became readily dialyzable against EDTA. It is apparent that the biuret complex is destroyed below pH 11. The molecular weight and sedimentation coefficient determined on this sample are summarized in Table II. The calculated values of $s^{\circ}_{20,w} = 2.63$ S and $M_w = 37,700 \pm 750$ were obtained. The latter value agrees well with one-quarter of the molecular weight of native ceruloplasmin (35,800). Hence it would appear that native ceruloplasmin dissociates into quarter-molecules at pH 12.5.

C. Succinylation Studies

(a) *Reaction with succinic anhydride*: The colorless, succinylated ceruloplasmin sample obtained at the anhydride-to-protein ratio of 10:1 was devoid of oxidase activity, and its prosthetic copper was readily dialyzable against EDTA at pH 7.1. The ninhydrin color yield was 9% of an unmodified control. Hence, one may assume that about 91% of the available amino groups in native ceruloplasmin were succinylated under these conditions. The calculated sedimentation coefficient at infinite dilution and the molecular weight, determined during the approach to sedimentation equilibrium, are summarized in Table II. A value of $s^{\circ}_{20,w} = 4.06$ S was found for this sample and a typical schlieren pattern is shown in Fig. 3D (upper pattern). A calculated M_w of $87,890 \pm 6150$ was obtained, which corresponds approximately to one-half the molecular weight of completely succinylated ceruloplasmin (74,900). Thus, it would appear that succinylation of native ceruloplasmin at pH 7–8 results in dissociation into half-molecules.

(b) *Alkali treatment of succinylated ceruloplasmin*: The succinylated ceruloplasmin species described above was subsequently redialyzed against the pH 12.5 buffer for one week at 4°, with several changes. The sedimentation coefficient and molecular weight were determined in the usual manner and the results are summarized in Table II. It should be noted that the

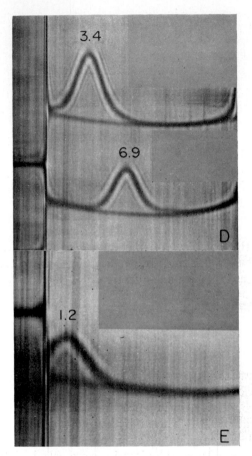

FIG. 3. Sedimentation velocity patterns for native and succinylated ceruloplasmin at 20°. D. Patterns at 64 minutes and phase-plate angle of 60° for succinylated (upper) and native (lower) ceruloplasmin, both at pH 7.1. E. Pattern at 80 minutes and phase-plate angle of 50° for succinylated ceruloplasmin at pH 12.5. The rotor speed was 52,640 rpm. Numerals refer to $s_{20,w}$ values.

value of $s_{20,w}$ of 1.2 S found is distinctly lower than the corresponding value (2.3 S) for the alkali-treated ceruloplasmin at the same protein concentration. A calculated molecular weight of 17,190 $\pm$ 1,030 was obtained. This value corresponds approximately to one-eighth the molecular weight of fully succinylated, native ceruloplasmin (18,700). To ensure that the decrease in molecular weight was not due to random hydrolytic cleavage of peptide bonds, the succinylated, pH 12.5 species was assayed for ninhydrin color yield. No free amino groups were detectable in this sample, and it was presumed that the decrease in M_w observed was due to further dissociation into discrete subunits and not to random peptide-bond cleavage. Additional supporting evidence was provided by the sedimentation velocity experiment. The schlieren pattern for this sample was sharp and symmetrical (Fig. 3E) suggesting a relatively homogeneous species. Furthermore, the schlieren pattern remained so throughout the experiment (about 3 hours). A system in which peptide bonds had been randomly cleaved would be expected to show a broad schlieren pattern increasing with time, indicative of heterogeneity. Thus, it would appear that the smallest subunit of human ceruloplasmin which can be obtained under the conditions employed is an eighth-molecule. Furthermore, the combined treatment of succinylation plus alkali is required to effect the dissociation into this eighth-molecule subunit. These treatments alone result in dissociation into either half- or quarter-molecules, respectively.

D. Polyacrylamide Gel Electrophoresis

A sample of the succinylated plus alkali-treated eighth-molecule system, pH 12.5, was run in a polyacrylamide gel made with borate buffer, pH 12.0 (Fig. 4). The eighth-molecules were clearly resolved into two bands.

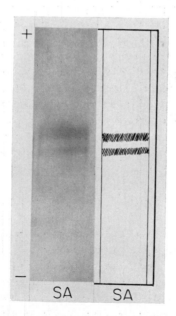

Fig. 4. Polyacrylamide gel electrophoresis of succinylated plus alkali-treated (SA) ceruloplasmin eighth-molecule subunits in borate buffer, pH 12.0. The direction of migration was toward the anode.

This finding suggests that ceruloplasmin may be composed of two kinds of eighth-molecule subunits, which differ by at least one charge unit.

IV. Discussion

The analytical ultracentrifuge results reported here indicate that native ceruloplasmin may be composed of eight polypeptide chains. The complex array of noncovalent interactions which stabilize the globular form of the native protein can be irreversibly disrupted to produce a variety of discrete subunits. Either of two kinds of treatment, which lead to an increase in negative charge density, result in disruption of the quaternary structure of the native protein. By increasing the pH from 7.1 to 10.2, stable half-molecules are produced, while an increase in pH from 7.1 to 12.5 results in the production of stable quarter-molecules. In each case, the characteristic blue color and oxidase activity are lost and the prosthetic copper becomes dialyzable against EDTA. When native ceruloplasmin is reacted with succinic anhydride at pH 7–8 to modify the free amino groups present, stable half-molecules are produced. Again, loss of blue color and oxidase activity result and the prosthetic copper becomes dialyzable against EDTA. If the pH of this succinylated half-molecules system is subsequently raised from 7.1 to 12.5, a further dissociation into stable eighth-molecules results. Hence, the eighth-molecule subunit species can be obtained only by the *combined* treatment of succinylation at pH 7–8, followed by an increase in pH to 12.5. This behavior raises the possibility that the interchain forces may be disrupted sequentially in such a way that stable intermediate species representing half-molecules and quarter-molecules can occur. A similar effect has been reported by Hass (21) for rabbit muscle aldolase. The reaction of that protein with succinic anhydride at neutral pH caused dissociation into third-molecules, which further dissociated into subunits representing sixth-molecules after the pH was increased to 12.5.

The polyacrylamide gel electrophoresis results suggest the possibility that the octameric form of native ceruloplasmin is composed of two kinds of polypeptide chains, identical with respect to molecular weight (ca. 18,000), but differing slightly in net charge. Such electrophoretic evidence cannot be considered definitive, however, and further investigation along other lines will be required before this point can be considered established.

From what is known concerning the nature of the prosthetic copper in native ceruloplasmin, one may tentatively suggest that an eighth-molecule is the ultimate subunit species for this protein. Various authors (3–5) have reported that of the eight copper atoms per mole, approximately four are cuprous and four are cupric and that only the cupric fraction can be enzymatically and chromophorically active. Such a heterogeneity among the eight copper atoms would indirectly support the evidence presented here for two kinds of eighth-molecule subunits. Presumably, the ligand groups which bind the metal in the intact molecule are different for each type of copper, and one can envisage a biosynthetic requirement for two kinds of polypeptide chains, each with a specific binding capacity for cuprous or cupric ion, respectively.

V. Summary

The quaternary structure of human ceruloplasmin has been disrupted by either of two kinds of treatment which lead to an increase in negative charge density on the molecule. Discrete subunits representing half-molecules, quarter-molecules, and eighth-molecules were obtained, depending on the treatment. The occurrence of such stable intermediate species indicates a complex array of stabilizing, noncovalent interactions in the globular form of the native protein. After polyacrylamide gel electrophoresis, the eighth-molecule subunit system resolved into two closely spaced, protein-positive bands. This finding raises the possibility that the native protein is composed of two kinds of polypeptide chains, identical with respect to molecular weight, but differing slightly in net charge.

REFERENCES

1. Holmberg, C. G., and Laurell, C.-B., *Acta Chem. Scand.*, **2**, 550 (1948).
2. Kasper, C. B., and Deutsch, H. F., *J. Biol. Chem.*, **238**, 2325 (1963).
3. Broman, L., Malmström, B. G., Aasa, R., and Vänngård, T., *J. Mol. Biol.*, **5**, 301 (1962).
4. Kasper, C. B., Deutsch, H. F., and Beinert, H., *J. Biol. Chem.*, **238**, 2338 (1963).
5. Blumberg, W. E., Eisinger, J., Aisen, P., Morell, A. G., and Scheinberg, I. H., *J. Biol. Chem.*, **238**, 1675 (1963).
6. Broman, L., Malmström, B. G., Aasa, R. and Vänngård, T., *Biochim. Biophys. Acta*, **75**, 365 (1963).
7. Peisach, J., and Levine, W., *Biochim. Biophys. Acta*, **77**, 615 (1963).
8. Morell, A. G., Aisen, P., Blumberg, W. E., and Scheinberg, I. H., *J. Biol. Chem.*, **239**, 1042 (1964).
9. Broman, L., *Nature*, **182**, 1655 (1958).
10. Hirschman, S. Z., Morell, A. G., and Scheinberg, I. H., *Ann. N. Y. Acad. Sci.*, **94**, 960 (1961).
11. Richterich, R., Temperli, A., and Aebi, H., *Biochim. Biophys. Acta*, **56**, 240 (1962).
12. Poulik, M. D., and Bearn, A. G., *Clin. Chim. Acta*, **7**, 374 (1962).
13. Poulik, M. D., *Protides of the Biological Fluids*, **10**, 170 (1963).
14. Poulik, M. D., *Nature*, **194**, 838 (1962).
15. Poillon, W. N., and Dawson, C. R., *Biochim. Biophys. Acta*, **77**, 37 (1963).
16. Fraenkel-Conrat, H., *in* S. P. Colowick and N. O. Kaplan (eds.), "Methods in enzymology," Vol. IV, Academic Press Inc., New York, 1957, p. 252.

17. Trautman, R., and Crampton, C. F., *J. Am. Chem. Soc.*, **81,** 4036 (1959).
18. Raymond, S., *Ann. N. Y. Acad. Sci.*, **121,** 350 (1964).
19. Schachman, H. K., "Ultracentrifugation in biochemistry," Academic Press Inc., New York 1959.
20. Kawahara, K., Kirshner, A. G., and Tanford, C., *Biochemistry*, **4,** 1203 (1965).
21. Hass, L. F., *Biochemistry*, **3,** 535 (1964).

The Interaction of Ceruloplasmin with Catecholamines[*]

E. WALAAS, O. WALAAS, AND R. LØVSTAD[†]

Institute for Medical Biochemistry,
University of Oslo,
Oslo, Norway

In previous studies (1, 2) it has been reported that catecholamines can serve as substrates for ceruloplasmin, although the reaction rates are somewhat slower than for the oxidation of p-phenylenediamines. The difference has been attributed to a more rapid rate of reduction of the cupric centers of ceruloplasmin by p-phenylenediamines (3). The purpose of the present work is to characterize the mechanism of reaction when ceruloplasmin is subjected to reduction by substrates of the catecholamine group.

This paper is concerned with the kinetic data obtained by spectrophotometric and EPR techniques. Additional observations have been made by the exclusion of oxygen in the system. Since the first oxidation product of catecholamines functions as an electron acceptor for reduced pyridine nucleotides (1), the influence of nucleotides as modifiers of enzyme activity has been studied.

I. Experimental Procedure

Ceruloplasmin, purified on DEAE–Sephadex according to the method of Bjørling (4), was obtained from AB Kabi, Stockholm. Spectrophotometric measurements were done on a Beckman DK spectrophotometer at 25°. The procedures used for spectrophotometric and EPR measurements, as well as the enzymatic assays, have been described previously (1, 3). Spectrofluorometric investigations were made on a Farrand spectrofluorometer.

II. Results

The reduction of ceruloplasmin Cu^{2+} by catecholamines in air is increased by increasing the concentration of substrate, as shown in Fig. 1 for dopamine. There is a close parallelism between the decrease of the EPR signal and the decrease of the blue color (605 mμ absorption). At the higher concentrations of dopamine used in these experiments where steady state reoxidation of the enzyme takes place, maximal reduction occurs

[*] The work has been supported by grants from the Norwegian Research Council for Science and the Humanities, from the Nordic Insulin Fund, and from Forskningsfondet av 1919.

[†] Not at meeting.

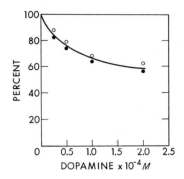

FIG. 1. The reduction of ceruloplasmin Cu^{2+} by dopamine. Conditions: $6.25 \times 10^{-5} M$ ceruloplasmin, 0.05 M acetate buffer, pH 5.9. The values are expressed in percent of the initial concentration and represent the levels at maximal reduction (obtained after 30 seconds reaction time). EPR absorption determined in liquid air (77°K). ●, A_{605}; ○, integrated EPR absorption.

after 30 seconds of incubation and approaches 50% of the ceruloplasmin Cu^{2+}. In these studies it was essential to avoid the formation of oxidation products of catecholamines which might interfere with the absorption spectrum of ceruloplasmin. This was accomplished by adding reduced pyridine nucleotide (NADH, NADPH) to the incubation mixture. NADH (NADPH) keeps the concentration of catecholamines constant by reducing the initial oxidation product formed. An experiment using a high concentration of norepinephrine is shown in Fig. 2. During the initial phase the ceruloplasmin Cu^{2+} is partly reduced to the steady state level and NADH

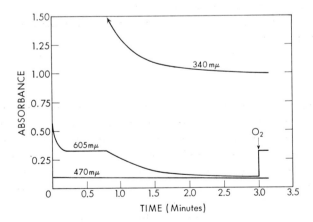

FIG. 2. Spectrophotometric recording of the reduction of ceruloplasmin by dopamine in the presence of NADH. Conditions: $5.35 \times 10^{-5} M$ ceruloplasmin, $1.0 \times 10^{-3} M$ dopamine, $8.0 \times 10^{-4} M$ NADH, pH 5.9.

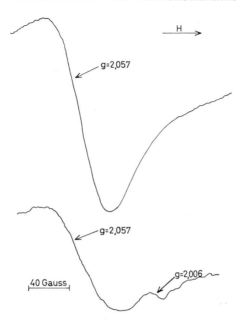

Fig. 3. EPR absorption spectra of ceruloplasmin in the presence of dopamine. A. Resting enzyme at a concentration of $6.65 \times 10^{-5} M$. B. 30 seconds after addition of $4.3 \times 10^{-3} M$ dopamine at 25° pH 5.9. EPR absorption spectra recorded at 77°K.

is oxidized. The duration of the steady state level is limited by the oxygen supply. When the oxygen tension decreases, the decolorization of the enzyme proceeds to a very low level. Readmission of oxygen rapidly re-oxidizes ceruloplasmin Cu⁺ to a steady state level as shown by optical absorption measurements. The rate constants for the initial reduction of ceruloplasmin by different catecholamines have been determined in the presence of NADH and correspond to those reported earlier without NADH in the system (3).

It has previously been postulated that free radicals of catecholamines occur as initial oxidation products by the action of ceruloplasmin (1). Frozen samples of the reaction mixture containing ceruloplasmin and catecholamine have therefore been studied by EPR. As shown in Fig. 3, with dopamine as substrate, a small signal with $g = 2.006$ appeared simultaneously with a pronounced reduction of the ceruloplasmin Cu²⁺ EPR absorption. Further experiments have indicated that the free radical has a very short lifetime and probably is converted rapidly to a biradical and quinone before indolization of the catecholamine takes place.

In order to study in detail the influence of the reduction of the copper catalytic center on the optical properties experiments have been performed with oxygen excluded from the system. In Fig. 4 the reduction of cerulo-

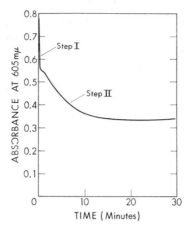

Fig. 4. The decolorization of ceruloplasmin by norepinephrine under anaerobic conditions. Experimental: $7.0 \times 10^{-5} M$ ceruloplasmin, $8.4 \times 10^{-5} M$ norepinephrine, pH 5.9, in N_2.

plasmin by norepinephrine under anaerobic conditions is shown. The curve is characterized by an initial rapid decolorization (step I), followed by a somewhat slower reduction curve (step II). This type of curve has been found at concentrations of norepinephrine and other catecholamines above $5 \times 10^{-5} M$. The extent of reduction during step I only slightly increases with the concentration of substrate until approximately one half of the cupric ions of ceruloplasmin are reduced. The slow reduction step II approaches a level corresponding to the reduction of two cupric ions in ceruloplasmin by a molecule of catecholamine.

The second-order rate constants for step I, $430 \ M^{-1} \sec^{-1}$, and for step II, $127 \ M^{-1} \sec^{-1}$, differ by a factor of 4. It should be pointed out that a short steady level appears after the reduction step I has been completed. The reduction of ceruloplasmin under these conditions is reversible. Admission of oxygen completely restores the blue color indicating that no denaturation has occurred.

By combined studies involving Michaelis kinetics and spectrophotometric and EPR measurements some kinetic constants have been obtained for the catecholamines. These constants, which are shown in Table I, should be considered as "apparent" constants representing over-all reactions of several processes.

The second-order rate constant (k_{+1}) for the association reaction between ceruloplasmin and substrates is somewhat faster for dopamine than for norepinephrine and epinephrine, although considerably slower than the rate of association of PPD with ceruloplasmin. The lowest value of the Michaelis constant has been observed with dopamine as the substrate.

TABLE I

KINETIC CONSTANTS FOR THE INTERACTION OF CATECHOLAMINES WITH CERULOPLASMIN
DETERMINED BY SPECTROPHOTOMETRIC MEASUREMENTS[a]

	k_{+1} $(M^{-1}\ sec^{-1})$ [b]		Apparent K_M [c]	
	Method A	Method B	Method A	Method B
Dopamine	405	380	$2.5 \times 10^{-4}\ M$	$2.1 \times 10^{-4}\ M$
Norepinephrine	300	360	$4.1 \times 10^{-4}\ M$	$4.0 \times 10^{-4}\ M$
Epinephrine	142	130	$5.8 \times 10^{-4}\ M$	—

[a] 0.05 M acetate buffer, pH 5.9, 25°.

[b] k_{+1} represents the rate of association of catecholamines with ceruloplasmin determined by two independent methods. Method A: The slope of the decrease of A_{605} at zero time was calculated. Method B: The concentration of catecholamines were kept constant by the presence of NADH. k_{+1} determined by measuring the time for half reduction of A_{605} to the steady state level. The absolute values are higher than those previsouly reported (3). This is due to a more purified and more active preparation of ceruloplasmin. However, the ratio between k_{+1}'s for different catecholamines are of the same order for all ceruloplasmin preparations studied.

[c] Method A: Enzyme activity determined by measuring the formation of colored oxidation products of catecholamines ("direct method"). Method B: Enzyme activity determined by adding NADH and measuring the decrease of A_{340} ("indirect method ")

In determining K_m good correspondence exists between the "direct" method and the "indirect" method, showing that electron transfer from NADH to the primary oxidation product of the substrates is not rate limiting.

It has previously been postulated that NADH is bound to the protein surface durings its oxidation by catecholamines in the presence of ceruloplasmin (1). To test this hypothesis the influence of NADH on the fluoresence of ceruloplasmin has been studied. As shown in Fig. 5 NADH (NADPH) exerts a quenching effect on the fluorescence of ceruloplasmin (max. at 340 mμ). By addition of dopamine to the system the quenching effect gradually disappears simultaneously with the oxidation of NADH to NAD$^+$, which has no quenching effect on the fluorescence. The quenching of fluorescence of ceruloplasmin by NADH does not itself indicate that NADH is bound near the active copper centers, but may be due to a less specific binding to aromatic amino acid residues of the protein. A clue in discriminating between these two possibilities was suggested in experiments where GMP was added. GMP, but not adenine nucleotides, including adenosine diphosphate ribose, exerts a quenching effect on the fluorescence of ceruloplasmin.

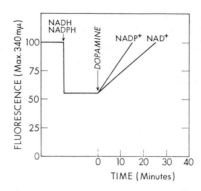

FIG. 5. Quenching of the fluorescence of ceruloplasmin by NADH (NADPH). The quenching effect was released by oxidation of NADH to NAD$^+$ when dopamine was added. Conditions: 1×10^{-6} M ceruloplasmin, 3×10^{-5} M NADH, 5×10^{-5} M dopamine, 0.05 M acetate buffer, pH 5.9.

When enzyme activity was measured in the presence of NADH, inhibition by GMP at a concentration range of $1–5 \times 10^{-4}$ M was observed. However, no effect by GMP was observed without NADH in the system. These results indicate binding of NADH to aromatic residues of the polypeptide chains near the active copper centers, and that GMP competes with NADH for binding to these sites. However, the observations that neither NADH nor GMP influenced the optical or EPR absorption spectra of ceruloplasmin indicate that a binding to the copper centers itself does not occur.

III. Discussion

Recent studies have shown (5–10) that ceruloplasmin is built as a very complex and labile protein molecule, where copper plays an important role both in maintaining the structure and conferring upon the protein flexible catalytic sites for oxidase activity. Disaggregation of the protein has been achieved by treatment with ascorbic acid, Tris, or barbital buffer, as well as by chromatographic procedures. In light of these findings it would be expected that the interaction of ceruloplasmin with substrates would be complex and differ with different types of substrates.

The present results obtained with catecholamines support the generally accepted view that ceruloplasmin contains active sites for special groups of electron donor molecules. The catecholamines, however, differ from the commonly used p-phenylenediamines in several respects. The decolorization process occurs in two separate stages, probably because of different accessibility of the copper centers to this group of substrates. These results support the suggestion made by Humoller (11) and by Frieden (12) that two different active sites, both involving cupric ions are present.

The common feature to all substrates would be the formation of charge-transfer complexes between substrates and ceruloplasmin Cu^{2+}. A subsequent stepwise reduction of the flexible active sites and a change in conformation may, however, differ among the groups of substrates tested.

The kinetic studies have shown that the structure of the side chain of catecholamines influences the association of these substrates with ceruloplasmin. Alkylation of the nitrogen atom and hydroxylation of the β-carbon atom decrease the rate of association.

It is important to stress that unsubstituted *ortho*-diphenol groups are essential for binding. No electron transfer has been obtained from the methoxy derivatives, normetanephrine and metanephrine. In this connection it is of interest to point out that *p*-phenylenediamines, according to Levine and Peisach (13), contribute to electron transfer by the π-electrons of the aromatic ring. The present experiments indicate that such a mechanism for binding is not essential for catecholamines. The blockage of interaction of catecholamines with ceruloplasmin Cu^{2+} by O-methylation indicates that coordination of the phenol groups with copper centers in the protein takes place. This different type of binding to the enzyme may explain the differences between the two groups of substrates as far as kinetic behavior and conformational changes in the protein are concerned.

It is of interest that ceruloplasmin reacts with guanosine nucleotides at sites on the protein apparently in the neighborhood of the active copper centers. The significance of this observation may be related to the widely observed regulatory influence of nucleotides on enzyme activity.

IV. Summary

(a) The interaction of ceruloplasmin with catecholamines has been studied by spectrophotometric and EPR absorption technique.

(b) During reduction of ceruloplasmin Cu^{2+} by dopamine a short-lived free radical appeared with $g = 2.006$.

(c) The reduction of the ceruloplasmin copper catalytic site has been investigated under anaerobic conditions. A two-step reaction has been recorded. In the first, fast step half of the copper centers are reduced, indicating that these centers are more accessible to the catecholamines than the remaining copper sites.

(d) The kinetic constants obtained show the influence of substitutions, in the side chain, on enzyme-substrate complex formation. An unsubstituted *ortho*-diphenol structure is essential, as no binding has been recorded by the O-methyl substituted amines.

(e) The resting ceruloplasmin is subjected to modification in its fluorescence properties by nucleotides. A quenching of fluorescence has been observed by reduced pyridine nucleotides (NADH, NADPH) and by guanosine nucleotides (GMP), while the oxidized pyridine nucleotides and the adenine nucleotides, including adenine diphosphate ribose are without effect. The quenching of fluorescence does not affect the rate of the electron transfer process from catecholamines to the catalytic copper center. However, the electron transfer between reduced pyridine nucleotides and catecholamines in the presence of ceruloplasmin is inhibited by GMP.

ACKNOWLEDGMENT

We are indebted to Dr. H. Bjørling, AB Kabi, for a generous supply of ceruloplasmin and to Dr. T. Brustad, Biophysical Department, Norsk Hydro's Institute for Cancer Research, for kind permission to perform EPR measurements with him.

REFERENCES

1. Walaas, E., and Walaas, O., *Arch. Biochem. Biophys.*, **95,** 151 (1961).
2. Walaas, E., Walaas, O., Haavaldsen, S., and Pedersen, B., *Arch. Biochem. Biophys.*, **100,** 97 (1963).
3. Walaas, O., Walaas, E., Henriksen, T., and Løvstad R., *Acta Chem. Scand.*, **17,** 263 (1963).
4. Bjørling, H., *Vox Sang.*, **8,** 641 (1963).
5. Kasper, C. B., and Deutsch, H. F., *J. Biol. Chem.*, **238,** 2325 (1963).
6. Blumberg, W. E., Eisinger, J., Aisen, P., Morell, A. G., and Scheinberg, I. H., *J. Biol. Chem.*, **238,** 1675 (1963).
7. Broman, L., Malmström, B. G., Aasa, R., and Vänngård, T., *Biochim. Biophys. Acta*, **75,** 365 (1963).
8. Poulik, M. D., *Protides of the Biological Fluids*, **10,** 170 (1963)
9. Deutsch, H. F., and Fisher, G. B., *J. Biol. Chem.*, **239,** 3325 (1964).
10. Jamieson, G. A., *J. Biol. Chem.*, **240,** 2019 (1965).
11. Humoller, P. L., Mockler, M., Haltaus, J. M., and Mahler, D. I., *J. Lab. Clin. Med.*, **222, 56** (1960).
12. Frieden, E., *in* M. Kasha and B. Pullman (eds.), "Horizons in biochemistry," Academic Press Inc., New York, 1962, p. 461.
13. Levine, W. G., and Peisach, J., *Biochim. Biophys. Acta*, **63,** 528 (1962).

Some Interactions of Ceruloplasmin with Inhibitors

G. CURZON AND J. N. CUMINGS

Department of Chemical Pathology,
Institute of Neurology, The National Hospital,
London, England

I. Introduction

The deep blue color, the unusual electron spin resonance spectrum, and the oxidase activity of ceruloplasmin are all considered as being related to the manner in which copper is bound within the ceruloplasmin molecule. Therefore, the investigation of any changes of these properties should lead to information on the ceruloplasmin copper atoms. It is striking that although many substances have been claimed to inhibit the oxidase activity of ceruloplasmin little increase in our understanding of the structure of the molecule has resulted. There are two main reasons for this. First, owing to attempts made some years ago to implicate ceruloplasmin in the regulation of mental health, many substances were selected for study as potential inhibitors not because they might reasonably have been expected to

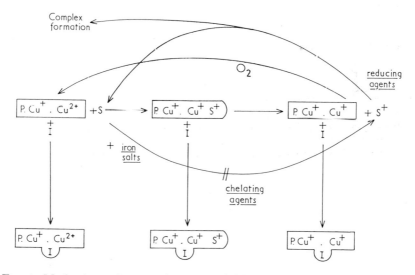

FIG. 1. Mechanisms of true and apparent inhibition of ceruloplasmin. PCu⁺Cu²⁺, native ceruloplasmin; S, substrate; S⁺, product; I, inhibitor. The enzyme–product complex PCu⁺Cu⁺S⁺ is shown but the enzyme–substrate complex PCu⁺Cu²⁺S has been omitted for the sake of simplicity.

TABLE 1

REPORTED INHIBITORS OF CERULOPLASMIN[a]

Inhibitors	Possible mechanism involved
A. Inorganic anions	
F⁻, Br⁻ [5, 6]	—
Cl⁻ [5, 6]	Anticompetitive [6]
NO_3^-, HPO_4^{2-}, $H_2PO_4^-$ [5]	—
$B_4O_7^{2-}$ [7]	Noncompetitive [7]
N_3^- [8, 9]	—
CN⁻ [2, 8, 9, 10]	—
SCN⁻ [6, 8]	—
OCN⁻ [8]	—
B. Carboxylate anions	
Formate [5]	—
Acetate [5, 6, 11]	Anticompetitive [6]
Salicylate, fumarate [12]	—
3-Hydroxyanthranilate [13]	—
5-Hydroxyanthranilate [13]	Decolorization of product [13]
Oxalate [5, 6, 12, 14]	—
Malonate [6]	—
Maleate [6, 12]	—
Citrate [5, 14]	Competitive [14]
Isocitrate, oxaloacetate [14]	—
C. Sulfhydryl compounds	
Cysteine, penicillamine [15]	Decolorization of product [15]
Glutathione, BAL [10]	—
Dithiocarbamate [5]	—
D. Nonsulfhydryl chelating agents	
EDTA [3, 4, 6, 10, 16]	Binds iron [4]
8-Hydroxyquinoline, 2,2′-bipyridine, 4,5-dihydroxy-1,3-benzenedisulfonic acid [4]	Bind iron [4]
1,10-Phenanthroline [4, 17]	Binds iron [4]
E. Hydrazines	
Methylhydrazine [2]	Decolorization of product [2]
Semicarbazide [2, 10]	Decolorization of product [2]
Iproniazid [2, 10, 15, 16, 18]	Competitive [15, 18]
Isoniazid [10, 19]	—
Miscellaneous [10]	—
F. 5-Hydroxyindoles	
5-Hydroxytryptamine [13]	Competitive [13]
5-Hydroxyindoleacetic acid [13]	Noncompetitive [13]
5-Hydroxytryptophan, bufotenine [13]	—

TABLE I (*Continued*)

REPORTED INHIBITORS OF CERULOPLASMIN

Inhibitors	Possible mechanism involved
G. Miscellaneous	
Ascorbate [2, 10, 15, 20]	Decolorization of product [2, 15]
Hydroxylamine, chlorpromazine,	
rescinnamine [2]	Decolorization of product [2]
DOPA [15]	Competitive [15]
Metals [6]	—
Hydrosulfite [10]	Binds metal [3]
Protein [3, 21]	Decolorization of product [21]

 a Conditions of activity determination: The following data are given in the order: ceruloplasmin, CP; buffer; substrate; temperature; activity method. Pre = incubation of enzyme with inhibitor before addition of substrate. Where not specifically stated, ceruloplasmin was purified human material, substrate was DPD, and activity was determined colorimetrically. [2] Human serum, pH 6.8 Tris, PPD, 37°; [3] 0.08 M pH 5.5 acetate, 25°. [4] pig CP, 0.1 M pH 5.5 acetate, PPD, 37°. [5] PPD, 37°, O_2 uptake; [6] as [3] but 37°; [7] pig CP, 0.04 M pH 6.0 acetate, PPD, 30°, pre; [8] as [5]; [9] as [3] but 37°; [10] 0.14 M pH 7.5 phosphate, 5-hydroxytryptamine, residual substrate, pre; [11] human serum, 0.66 M pH 6.0 acetate, 30°; [12] pH 5.3 trimethylamine-acetate-EDTA, 37°, pre; [13] human and rabbit serum, pH 6.2, 25°; [14] 0.2 M pH 5.2 acetate, ascorbic acid or DPD, 30°; [15] as [13]; [16] 0.2 M pH 5.2 acetate, 37°, pre; [18] human serum, pH 6.0 phosphate, 5-hydroxytryptamine, O_2 uptake; [19] as [10]; [20] human serum; [21] as [11].

interact with a copper protein but because of their psychopharmacological interest. Very many of these substances have been pointed out by Szent-Györgyi to be electron donors (1) and it had previously been suggested that some apparent inhibitions may have been due to electron transfer to the reaction product rather than to an enzyme-inhibitor interaction (2).

Second, ceruloplasmin oxidase activity is sensitive to iron, being enhanced by trace amounts which may be present even after careful purification of reagents (3, 4). Any claim that a substance with metal-binding properties is an inhibitor of ceruloplasmin is suspect if the incubation mixture used did not contain a chelating agent to bind iron, preferably EDTA which has only a slight direct effect on ceruloplasmin (4). Figure 1 indicates some ways in which true and apparent inhibition of ceruloplasmin may occur and Table I summarizes the majority of the substances previously reported to inhibit ceruloplasmin. Few of these have been systematically investigated and many require restudy in the light of present knowledge.

This paper describes a critical study of potential inhibitors of ceruloplasmin in use in our laboratory and indicates some recent results obtained thereby.

II. Materials and Experimental Procedure

A. Ceruloplasmin

Human ceruloplasmin from the American Red Cross (Batch No. 1995) was dialyzed against 0.01 M NaCl. Any nonceruloplasmin copper was removed by passing through a column of 100–200 mesh Chelex 100 chelating resin. The absorbance at 605 mμ was about 1.5. This was diluted with water for use in the oxidase activity determination.

B. Oxidase Activity Determination

DPD was oxidized by ceruloplasmin at 25° and the extinction of the red reaction product measured at 550 mμ. The incubation mixture contained 10 mM pH 5.5 acetate, 4 μM EDTA, 1 mM DPD dihydrochloride, and about 3×10^{-6} M ceruloplasmin copper. The ceruloplasmin was added last.

The conditions of ceruloplasmin activity determination used are such that the results are capable of clear interpretation. The first oxidation product of PPD is a yellow free radical, PPD$^+$, which changes to a purple or blue material during bromine (22) or ceruloplasmin (23) oxidation. The formation of a purple product has frequently been used in the determination of oxidase activity. DPD$^+$ is much more stable and further transformation does not occur during either bromine oxidation (22) or oxidation by ceruloplasmin (24) until almost all the DPD is oxidized to it. As under the assay conditions used here there is always a large excess of DPD over DPD$^+$, decreased formation of DPD$^+$ provides better evidence of enzyme inhibition than does decreased formation of purple PPD product.

Because EDTA was routinely present in the incubation mixture any complications due to enhancement of activity by contaminant iron (3, 4) may be disregarded.

1. Time Course of Inhibition

The red color was allowed to develop at 25° in a thermostated spectrophotometer cell housing and absorbance at 550 mμ measured at 30 seconds or 1 minute intervals against a suitable blank. Three effects of inhibitors may be distinguished as indicated in Fig. 2:

(a) A linear development of color at a lower rate than in its absence. This indicates the likelihood of true inhibition in the particular incubation system used in which EDTA is present.

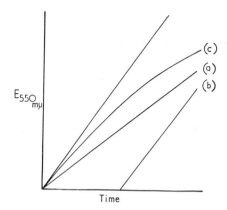

Fig. 2. Effects of inhibitors and apparent inhibitors on the time course of formation of DPD$^+$ by ceruloplasmin. The three types of time course, a, b, c are discussed in the text.

(b) A lag period followed by the development of color at the same rate as in its absence. This indicates apparent inhibition due to decolorization of DPD$^+$ at a rate at least as rapid as that at which it is formed (21). The lag period is proportional to the amount of apparent inhibitor (15).

(c) A progressively decreasing rate of development of color. This indicates as one possibility an apparent inhibition due to decolorization of DPD$^+$ at a rate lower than that at which it is formed. This has been discussed by Humoller *et al.* (21). The rate of decolorization is a function of the concentrations of both the apparent inhibitor and DPD$^+$. The latter increases as the enzyme reaction proceeds and hence so does the rate of its decolorization as indicated in Fig. 2. Alternatively an inhibition curve of this kind may indicate a true inhibitor which only equilibrates with the enzyme after some time has elapsed. Here, the rate of color formation should decrease with time, eventually becoming linear.

2. Decolorization of DPD$^+$

Although it may be easy to demonstrate qualitatively that DPD$^+$ is decolorized by a substance, the decision whether this observation accounts quantitatively for an apparent inhibition of oxidase activity is not so simple in those cases when the rate of decolorization is dependent on DPD$^+$ concentration. The following procedure is therefore used and is illustrated in Fig. 3.

DPD is oxidized by bromine solution and the effects of inhibitors on the red color measured at 1 minute intervals. The time course of development of color using the ceruloplasmin incubation mixture was also followed under similar conditions until the same extinction as that obtained by Br$_2$ oxida-

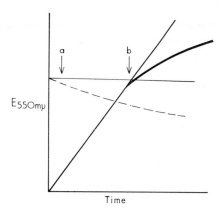

Fɪɢ. 3. Comparison of apparent inhibition of ceruloplasmin with the decolorization of DPD⁺ by the inhibitor. ——, Effect of time on DPD⁺ prepared by partial Br₂ oxidation of DPD. – – – –, Effect of adding inhibitor at arrow a. ——, Time course of DPD⁺ formation from DPD by ceruloplasmin. ▬▬, Subsequent DPD⁺ formation after adding inhibitor at arrow b.

tion of DPD had developed, inhibitor solution was now added, and the further development of color followed; a similar experiment was performed in the absence of inhibitor.

Thus the total inhibition may be separated into two components resulting from reaction of inhibitor with ceruloplasmin and with DPD⁺ respectively.

III. Results and Discussion

A selection of the inhibitors recorded in Table I were studied further.

A. Inorganic Anions

Holmberg and Laurell (5) showed that low concentrations of inorganic anions activated ceruloplasmin while higher concentrations caused inhibition. Chloride has been shown to inhibit by an apparent anticompetitive mechanism, Lineweaver–Burk plots being parallel (6). Borate has been claimed by Osaki (7) to cause noncompetitive inhibition, which was suggested to indicate the necessity of the carbohydrate residues of ceruloplasmin for its oxidase properties. Osaki found about 40% inhibition with 10^{-2} M borate. We have found 60% inhibition under our conditions when the pH of the borate solution was adjusted with hydrochloric acid following Osaki, but only 11% inhibition when sulfuric acid was used. Preincubation

TABLE II

EFFECT OF INORGANIC ANIONS ON CERULOPLASMIN ACTIVITY

Anion[a]	Concentration for 50% inhibition (M)
CN^-	3×10^{-6}
N_3^-	4×10^{-6}
CNO^-	1×10^{-4}
SCN^-	6×10^{-4}
$SeCN^-$	8×10^{-4}
F^-	6×10^{-3}
Cl^-	2×10^{-2}

[a] N_3^-, F^-, and Cl^- were as Na salts and other anions as K salts.

of borate with the enzyme did not significantly alter the inhibition. The concentrations of chloride and sulfate present caused 53% and 4% inhibition, respectively, in the absence of borate. Therefore under our conditions borate is only weakly inhibitory.

We find that azide and cyanide are powerful inhibitors, being significantly inhibitory at molar concentrations not much greater than that of ceruloplasmin itself (Table II). Neither these nor the other anions referred to in Table II caused any decolorization of DPD^+ at inhibitory concentrations and are therefore true inhibitors.

B. Carboxylate Ions

Maleic acid was reported by Broman (12) to inhibit strongly at 10^{-5} M in triethylamine–acetic acid buffer with EDTA but not in an acetate buffer with EDTA. Curzon (6) found some inhibition at this concentration in acetate buffer without EDTA. In the present study (in which EDTA was used) inhibition did not occur at 10^{-5} or 10^{-4} M. Holmberg and Laurell (5) found citrate to be a weak inhibitor while Osaki, McDermott, and Frieden (14) reported strong competitive inhibition below 10^{-6} M in the absence of EDTA. This was not confirmed. In the absence of EDTA, 10^{-4} M citrate gave only 18% inhibition which decreased to 6% when one-tenth the usual substrate concentration was used. In the presence of EDTA there was only 5% inhibition with a citrate concentration as high as 10^{-3} M.

C. Hydrazines

Abood, Gibbs, and Smith (2) suggested that methyl hydrazine, semicarbazide, and iproniazid caused an apparent inhibition of ceruloplasmin

TABLE III

TRUE AND APPARENT INHIBITION OF CERULOPLASMIN BY
HYDRAZINES AND HYDROXYLAMINE[a]

Inhibitor concentration (M)	Inhibition (apparent) (%)	Inhibition corrected for DPD+ decolorization (%)
Hydrazine 2.5 × 10⁻³	55	25
Methylhydrazine 2.5 × 10⁻³	38	12
Semicarbazide 2.5 × 10⁻³	34	13
Iproniazid 8 × 10⁻⁴	99	30
Isoniazid 8 × 10⁻⁴	0	0
Hydroxylamine 2.5 × 10⁻³	45	11

[a] Hydrazine and methylhydrazine were as sulfates, semicarbazide and hydroxylamine as hydrochlorides, and iproniazid as the phosphate. Results have, where necessary been corrected for the inhibitory effects of the anion.

by reaction with DPD+ while Hanson, Austin, and Aprison (15) and Martin, Eriksen, and Benditt (18) claimed that iproniazid was a competitive inhibitor of DPD and 5-hydroxytryptamine oxidation, respectively. We find that hydrazines in general cause a gradually increasing apparent inhibition if present in the initial incubation mixture and this is largely explicable by their reaction with DPD+. When this was corrected for, evidence of relatively weak true inhibition could be obtained (Table III). Iproniazid was a somewhat stronger true inhibitor than the other hydrazines tested while isoniazid was found to be without inhibitory power at the same concentration as iproniazid.

D. 5-Hydroxyindoles

Aprison, Hanson, and Austin (13) obtained inhibition by various 5-hydroxyindoles. 5-Hydroxytryptamine and 5-hydroxyindoleacetic acid were claimed to inhibit competitively and noncompetitively, respectively. Inhibition by 5-hydroxyindoleacetic acid has now been reinvestigated. Using 4 × 10⁻⁵ M inhibitor the slope of the red color against time curve decreased over the first 20 minutes to 20% of that observed in its absence and then *increased* continuously over the next 20 minutes toward its value in the absence of inhibitor. This concentration of 5-hydroxyindoleacetic acid caused marked decrease of extinction of DPD+ at 550 mμ with the gradual development of a deep blue color which disappeared on addition of more 5-hydroxyindoleacetic acid. It was also noted that in the presence of inhibitor, the oxidation of DPD by ceruloplasmin resulted in a color which was purple rather than red and which after prolonged incubation became deep blue. Because of this interfering color investigations were not pursued further. However, it is clear that apparent inhibition by 5-hydroxyindoleacetic acid is largely due to interaction with DPD⁺. Qualitatively similar results were obtained with 5-hydroxytryptamine.

E. Miscellaneous Inhibitors

Abood *et al.* (2) using a 1-hour incubation period suggested that inhibition by hydroxylamine and chlorpromazine was due to decolorization of DPD⁺. We confirmed this for hydroxylamine (Table III). It was also found that chlorpromazine at a concentration as high as 10^{-2} M had no effect on activity. This is in agreement with Hanson *et al.* (15). DOPA, which these authors found to produce an inhibition increasing with time, was found by us to be an apparent inhibitor at 10^{-3} M, acting somewhat similarly to the 5-hydroxyindoles, causing DPD⁺ decolorization and eventual development of a grayish-purple color.

Apart from the inorganic anions, the inhibitors so far discussed have been shown to have either a considerably slighter effect than in previous reports or to have such complex effects that true inhibitory mechanisms cannot readily be determined.

F. Further Studies on Azide Inhibition

The powerful inhibitory effect of azide prompted more detailed study (25). The inhibition may be reversed either by dilution of the incubation

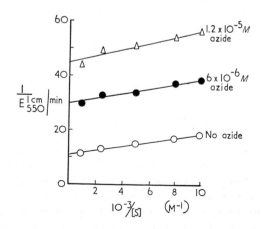

Fig. 4. Lineweaver–Burk plot. Effect of azide on ceruloplasmin activity at 25°.

mixture or by removal of azide, DPD, and DPD⁺ on Sephadex. This suggests that inhibition is due to the formation of a ceruloplasmin–copper–azide complex rather than to free copper azide being split off as in the latter case reversal on Sephadex treatment would not occur. Lineweaver–Burk graphs at various inhibitor concentrations were parallel (Fig. 4). Such parallel Lineweaver–Burk graphs may be explained by anticompetitive inhibition, in which enzyme-substrate interaction is necessary before the inhibited complex can be formed (26). It is possible to obtain parallel Lineweaver-Burk plots not only if the inhibitor reacts with the enzyme-substrate but also if it reacts with any subsequently formed intermediate. In these circumstances the inhibition may reasonably be referred to as anticompetitive, as enzyme-substrate complex formation is necessary before it can occur. It is known that 4 of the 8 copper atoms of ceruloplasmin are made accessible in the presence of substrate, being then exchangeable with ionic Cu (27). Therefore it would seem reasonable that substrate may also make them accessible to an *inhibitor* and that it is the four valence-changing copper atoms (28) which interact both with azide and with ionic copper.

An azide concentration not much greater than that of ceruloplasmin itself is required for inhibition to occur at 25°. This suggests that if the inhibition was studied at rather higher enzyme concentration, a significant

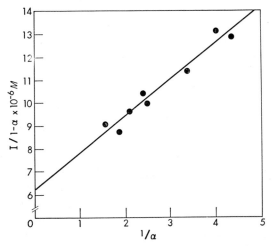

Fɪɢ. 5. Determination of number of inhibitory azide binding sites per ceruloplasmin molecules. *I*, total inhibitor concentration; α, fractional oxidase activity in the presence of inhibitor. The temperature was 7.5°. The intercept gives the concentration of azide binding sites, 6.3×10^{-6} *M*. The concentration of ceruloplasmin was 6.7×10^{-6} *M* (assuming 8 copper atoms per molecule); therefore there is one inhibitory azide binding site per molecule.

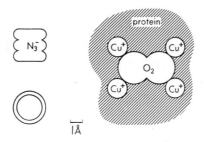

Fɪɢ. 6. Possible arrangement of the four valence-changing copper atoms of reduced ceruloplasmin allowing inhibition by a single azide group shown in plan and elevation.

fraction of the inhibitor would be bound to the enzyme and the Michaelis–Menten assumption that total inhibitor concentration equals free inhibitor concentration would not hold. In the latter circumstances the graphical method of Straus and Goldstein (29) can be used to determine the number of inhibitor-binding sites per enzyme molecule. Accordingly inhibition at lower temperature was investigated so that a higher enzyme concentration could conveniently be used. At 7.5° it was found that the amount of azide needed to cause inhibition was comparable to the amount of enzyme and from Fig. 5 it can therefore be seen that there is one azide-binding site per enzyme molecule. The assumption is made that at saturation with substrate all the ceruloplasmin molecules are available to azide.

Thus though each ceruloplasmin molecule has four valence-changing copper atoms (28), only one azide ion is needed to form the inhibited complex. The simplest explanation of this finding is that the four valence-changing copper atoms are in a group together so that binding of an azide to one copper atom prevents reoxidation of the reduced ceruloplasmin. The reoxidation probably occurs according to the formal equation (28):

$$PCu^+ + \tfrac{1}{4} O_2 + H^+ \rightarrow PCu^{2+} + \tfrac{1}{2} H_2O$$

where PCu^+, PCu^{2+} are the reduced and the oxidized forms of the enzyme, respectively. Broman (30) has suggested that the four valence-changing copper atoms are probably so close together that they are capable of being simultaneously reoxidized by an O_2 molecule. Figure 6 shows a model for the relative positions of the valence-changing copper atoms of ceruloplasmin consistent both with our findings and Broman's suggestion.

IV. Summary

Various previously reported inhibitors of ceruloplasmin were investigated. Particular attention was paid to the dangers of erroneous interpretation of results because of interaction of the inhibitor with the product of the enzyme-substrate reaction or with contaminant trace metals. In general the substances studied were shown either to have slighter inhibitory effects on ceruloplasmin than had previously been reported or to have such complex effects as to put previously proposed inhibition mechanisms in some doubt.

The inhibitory effect of various inorganic anions was confirmed, azide and cyanide being shown to be powerful inhibitors. Kinetic studies of the action of azide showed an anticompetitive inhibition mechanism. The relationship between degree of inhibition and azide concentration indicates that one azide molecule interacted with each ceruloplasmin molecule. This is explicable in terms of a structure in which the four valence-changing copper atoms of ceruloplasmin are grouped together.

ACKNOWLEDGMENTS

We thank the American Red Cross for supplies of ceruloplasmin, the Upjohn Co. for 5-hydroxyindoleacetic acid, Roche Products Ltd. for iproniazid and isoniazid, and May & Baker Ltd. for chlorpromazine.

REFERENCES

1. Szent-Györgyi, A., "Introduction to a submolecular biology," Academic Press Inc., New York, 1960.
2. Abood, L. G., Gibbs, F. A., and Gibbs, E., *Arch. Neurol. Psychiat.*, **77**, 643 (1957).
3. Curzon, G., *Biochem. J.*, **79**, 656 (1961).
4. Levine, W. G., and Peisach, J., *Biochim. Biophys. Acta*, **77**, 602 (1963).
5. Holmberg, C. G., and Laurell, C.-B., *Acta Chem. Scand.*, **5**, 921 (1951).
6. Curzon, G., *Biochem. J.*, **77**, 66 (1960).
7. Osaki, S., *J. Biochem.*, **50**, 29 (1961).
8. Holmberg, C. G., and Laurell, C.-B., *Acta Chem. Scand.*, **5**, 476 (1951).
9. Curzon, G., and Vallet, L., *Biochem. J.*, **74**, 279 (1960).
10. Zarafonetis, C. J. D., and Kalas, J. P., *Proc. Soc. Exp. Biol.*, **105**, 560 (1961).
11. Humoller, F. L., Mockler, M. P., Holthaus, J. M., and Mahler, D. J., *J. Lab. Clin. Med.*, **56**, 222 (1960).
12. Broman, L., *Nature*, **182**, 1655 (1958).
13. Aprison, M. H., Hanson, K. M., and Austin, D. C., *J. Nerv. Ment. Dis.*, **128**, 249 (1959).
14. Osaki, S., McDermott, J. A., and Frieden, E., *J. Biol. Chem.*, **239**, PC 364 (1964).
15. Hanson, K. M., Austin, D. C., and Aprison, M. H., *J. Appl. Physiol.*, **14**, 363 (1959).
16. Nakajima, H., *Encéphale*, **48**, 313 (1959).
17. Malmström, B. G., *in* T. S. King, H. S. Mason, and M. Morrison (eds.), "Oxidases and related redox systems," John Wiley and Sons, Inc., New York, 1965, p. 107.
18. Martin, G., Eriksen, N., and Benditt, E. P., *Fed. Proc.*, **17**, 447 (1958).
19. Zarafonetis, C. J. D., and Kalas, J. P., *Am. J. Med. Sci.*, **239**, 203 (1960).
20. Akerfeldt, S., *Science*, **125**, 117 (1957).
21. Humoller, F. L., Majka, F. A., Barak, A. J., Stevens, J. D., and Holthaus, J. M., *Clin. Chem.*, **4**, 1 (1958).
22. Michaelis, L., Schubert, M. P., and Granick, S., *J. Am. Chem. Soc.*, **61**, 1981 (1939).

23. Peisach, J., and Levine, W. G., *Biochim. Biophys. Acta*, **77,** 615 (1963).
24. Curzon, G., and Speyer, B., unpublished observations.
25. Curzon, G., *Biochem. J.*, **96,** 14P (1965).
26. Burk, D., quoted by Ebersole, E. R., Guttentag, C., and Wilson, P. W., *Arch. Biochem.*, **3,** 399 (1944).
27. Scheinberg, I. H., and Morell, A. G., *J. Clin. Invest.*, **36,** 1193 (1957).
28. Broman, L., Malmström, B. G., Aasa, R., and Vänngård, T., *Biochim. Biophys. Acta*, **75,** 365 (1963).
29. Straus, O. H., and Goldstein, A., *J. Gen. Physiol.*, **26,** 559 (1943).
30. Broman, L., *Acta Soc. Med. Upsalien.*, **69,** Supp. 7 (1964).

The Inhibition of the Ascorbate Oxidizing Activity of Serum Ceruloplasmin by Citrate and Apotransferrin*

SHIGEMASA OSAKI, JAMES A. McDERMOTT, DONALD A. JOHNSON,† AND EARL FRIEDEN

Department of Chemistry and the Institute of Molecular Biophysics,
Florida State University,
Tallahassee, Florida

Ceruloplasmin is a fascinating protein not only because of its beautiful blue color and the fact that it comprises one out of every 300 serum protein molecules, but also because in its role as a biocatalyst, its substrate range includes a spectrum of important biological compounds, e.g., ascorbic acid, epinephrine, norepinephrine, and serotonin, etc. (1–7). Its relatively low molecular activity, particularly at pH 7.4, has led to the assumption that the catalytic activity of ceruloplasmin is incidental to its other primary function, or functions, such as copper transport or other unrecognized duties. We believe that this idea requires further attention. First of all, the concentration of this protein in normal serum is relatively high, averaging about 2 μM (8, 9), which is considerably higher than the typical enzyme, even many extracellular ones. Thus the net catalytic activity of ceruloplasmin towards a substrate which has a molecular activity of 10–100 will obviously be the same as an enzyme with a molecular activity of 1000–10,000 but at a concentration of 0.02 μM.

We accept the possibility that the enzymatic activity of ceruloplasmin could be accidental or coincidental. Any oxidation of ascorbate to dehydroascorbate which is not coupled to phosphorylation or terminal oxidation might be regarded as biochemically wasteful. Under certain conditions, however, it may be desirable to have a convenient serum mechanism for this reaction. Martin and Mecca (10) have shown that dehydroascorbate penetrates the brain, the eye, and erythrocytes more rapidly and to a greater extent than ascorbate. Niedermeier and associates (11) have shown that ceruloplasmin prevents ascorbate (and trace metal ion) promoted depolymerization of hyaluronic acid. Recently, in our laboratory a dramatic increase (10- to 100-fold as measured by its catalytic activity) in serum ceruloplasmin level has been observed during anuran metamorphosis (12, 13). This increase begins very early in metamorphosis

* The research in this paper was supported in part by Grant HE–08344, United States Public Health Service, and by Contract AT–(40–1)–2690, Division of Biology and Medicine, United States Atomic Energy Commission.

† Not at meeting.

and may precede many of the significant changes in other blood proteins including hemoglobins and serum albumin (14–16). The enzyme activity of the serum is masked by dialyzable inhibitors as reported earlier by Osaki, McDermott, and Frieden (17). This observation may portend an important role for ceruloplasmin in blood changes observed during this impressive biological differentiation.

I. The Catalytic Range of Ceruloplasmin

The catalytic activity of ceruloplasmin was recently summarized in a review paper by Frieden, McDermott, and Osaki (2). Several valuable papers relevant to the catalytic activity of ceruloplasmin have appeared since then (18–22). Only the facts relevant to our present discussion will be outlined here.

The substrates of ceruloplasmin, all of which are reducing agents, fall into three different classes:

(a) Aromatic polyamines and polyphenols or a combination of these, e.g., epinephrine, serotonin, p-phenylenediamine.

(b) Enediols, e.g., ascorbic acid.

(c) A miscellaneous group of selected reducing agents, e.g., Fe^{2+}, $Na_2S_2O_4$, NH_2OH, $HSCH_2CO_2H$, $K_4Fe(CN)_6$.

In addition Walaas et al. (23, 24) have shown that NADH will provide electrons for the oxidative reactions of numerous aryl compounds in the presence of ceruloplasmin. Ceruloplasmin also accepts electrons from the enzymes of the respiratory chain with NADH, reduced cytochrome c, and succinate serving as substrates under anaerobic conditions (25). The oxidative reaction catalyzed by ceruloplasmin follows the over-all equation:

$$AH_2 + \tfrac{1}{2} O_2 \longrightarrow A + H_2O$$

where AH_2 is a substrate.

A careful comparison of the reaction characteristics of human ceruloplasmin, squash ascorbate oxidase, and the Cu^{2+}-catalyzed oxidation of ascorbate (7, 18) is shown in Table I. We need merely note here that the copper ion catalysis of ascorbate oxidation is unique in producing H_2O_2. The pH optima of these reactions are clearly different. The K_m with respect to oxygen for ceruloplasmin is surprisingly low, 4×10^{-6} M, whereas the protein of ascorbate oxidase does not contribute significantly to the ability of copper ion to interact with oxygen. Both enzymes have much smaller K_m's with respect to ascorbate. Obviously ascorbate oxidase is a much more specific and effective catalyst for the oxidation of a limited

TABLE I

COMPARISON OF THE CATALYSIS OF ASCORBATE OXIDATION BY Cu²⁺, SQUASH
ASCORBATE OXIDASE, AND HUMAN CERULOPLASMIN

Property	Ceruloplasmin	Plant ascorbate oxidase	Cu²⁺
pH optimum	6.0	5.6	>7.5
Moles H_2O_2/moles dehydroascorbate	0	0	1
K_m for ascorbate (M)	1.3×10^{-5}	2.4×10^{-4}	7×10^{-3}
K_m for O_2 (M)	3.9×10^{-6}	2.2×10^{-4}	2×10^{-4}
Molecular activity	12	$>10^5$	150
Activation energy (Kcal/mole)	12.5	—	16.5
Inhibition by			
10 μM citrate	94	—	3
16 μM neocuproine	0	—	100
0.2% albumin	0	0	99

group of substrates (26). Also included in this table are data establishing the differences in other reaction parameters, particularly between Cu²⁺ and ceruloplasmin catalysis. Perhaps the most important difference is the specific sensitivity of ceruloplasmin to inhibition by citrate and the inhibition of the Cu²⁺ reactions by neocuproine, serum albumin, and other copper ion chelators (18).

How quantitatively significant are these catalytic activities? Table II summarizes estimates of the molecular activity of human ceruloplasmin toward a variety of substrates. It should be emphasized that these values are dependent on temperature, pH, ionic strength, and the nature of the buffer anion. The frequently used synthetic substrates, PPD and DPD, have the greatest molecular activity. Smaller but significant values are observed for several naturally occurring substrates. Additional data are reported for those substrates which have some biological significance along with serum levels and hypothetical half survival times, assuming that ceruloplasmin is fully active. It is quite clear that despite the relatively small molecular activities, ceruloplasmin's enzymatic activity could appreciably affect the serum levels of several important biological substrates including ascorbate, the epinephrine series, and the serotonin group. Since ascorbate is the most prevalent of the ceruloplasmin substrates in serum, a calculation of its half survival time may be of interest. In a relatively inert buffer, 0.2 M acetate, pH 7.4, 0.27 μM crystalline ceruloplasmin catalyzes ascorbate oxidation at a rate of about 0.8 μM per minute at 30°. At an average serum ceruloplasmin concentration of 2.0 μM, 6μM ascorbate is

TABLE II

MOLECULAR ACTIVITY OF HUMAN CERULOPLASMIN[a]

Substrate	No NADH	With NADH	Serum concentration[b] (μM)	Est. $t_{\frac{1}{2}}$ (min)
p-Phenylenediamine	74[c]	45[d]	—	—
N, N-Dimethyl-p-phenylenediamine	67[e]	57[d]	—	—
Ascorbate	12[f], (276)[h]	1[g]	40 (10 mg/l)	3–4
Epinephrine	25[e]	14[d]	0.001 (0.15 μg/l)	<1
Norepinephrine	30[e], 14[g]	50[d]	0.0015 (0.2 μg/l)	<1
Serotonin	4[i]	6[d]	1 (0.13 mg/l)	<1
Dopamine	36[e]	54[d]	—	—
Dihydroxyphenylalanine	2[e]	30[d]	—	—
Fe^{2+}	550[j] (pH 6.5)	—	—	—

[a] Molecular activity is defined as the number of molecules of substrate transformed per minute by one molecule of enzyme. Data using optimum substrate concentration were used where possible. Porcine ceruloplasmin has considerably greater catalytic activity than the human enzyme. Estimations of the molecular activity of porcine ceruloplasmin toward typical substrates as reported recently by Peisach and Levine (22) are p-phenylenediamine–395; N,N-dimethyl-p-phenylenediamine–246, hydroquinone–108, psilocin (N,N-dimethyl-4-hydroxytryptamine)–50. Conditions: 37°, pH 5.5 in 0.1 M acetate buffer.

[b] Most of the serum concentrations are taken from "Blood and other Body Fluids," P. L. Altman and D. S. Dittmer (eds.), Fed. Am. Soc. Exptl. Biol. Washington, D.C., 1961.

[c] (27) Conditions: 17°, pH 5.5, 0.1 M triethylamine–acetic acid buffer.

[d] (23) Conditions: 38°, pH 5.9, 0.05 M acetate buffer, 10^{-4} M NADH.

[e] (24) Conditions: 5°, pH 5.9, 0.03 M acetate buffer.

[f] (18) Conditions: 30°, pH 5.2, 0.2 M acetate buffer.

[g] (28) Conditions: 30°, pH 5.2, 0.10 M acetate buffer, 10^{-4} M NADH.

[h] Unpublished data from this laboratory. Conditions: 30°, pH 6.3, 0.20 M acetate buffer, $Fe^{2+} = 2 \times 10^{-4}$ M.

[i] (23) Conditions: 20°, pH 5.9, 0.05 M acetate buffer.

[j] Unpublished data from this laboratory. Conditions: 30° pH 6.5, 0.20 M acetate buffer, 55 μM apotransferrin.

oxidized per minute. Therefore at an average serum ascorbate level of 40 μM about half will be oxidized in 3 minutes.

II. Inhibition of Ceruloplasmin Activity

The predicted rapid destruction of ascorbate and other serum substrates appears to be inconsistent with the stability of ascorbate in normal human serum. The ascorbate oxidizing activity of ceruloplasmin appears to be under the control of two normal serum components: citrate and apo-transferrin (transferrin also inhibits). This biochemical regulation is the main subject of this paper. It will be convenient to treat separately the low molecular weight and dialyzable modifiers from those that are nondialyz-able and probably macromolecular.

The modification of the catalytic activity of ceruloplasmin by numerous low molecular weight compounds was evident in the early studies of Holmberg and Laurell (3). Further studies on the intense sensitivity of the catalytic activity of ceruloplasmin to a variety of simple anions, certain polyacid anions, metal ions, copper chelators, and certain substrate isosteres have been noted by many authors (8, 22, 29–31). We shall discuss in detail only those substances which seem to be involved in the serum regulation of ceruloplasmin ascorbate oxidase activity.

The dialyzable constituents of serum, principally metal cations, anions, and organic acid anions, have been studied for their effect on the ascorbate oxidase activity of ceruloplasmin at pH 7.4. The only compound in this group which significantly inhibits ceruloplasmin activity at this pH at prevailing serum concentrations is citrate. The inhibition by chloride noted in several laboratories (8, 22, 28) is significant only at pH's below 7.0. We have confirmed these chloride effects but have also found that the inhibitory activity of 0.10 M Cl$^-$ is not appreciable at pH 7.0 or above. Appreciable inhibition of ceruloplasmin by chloride at pH 7.0 occurs so that 1.0 M chloride inhibits ceruloplasmin activity about 50%. Except for several metal ions the other anions and cations of serum produce only slight effects at serum concentrations. Metal ions such as Cu^{2+}, Fe^{2+}, and Zn^{2+}, would produce a variety of effects if they were not protein-bound in serum. Many of their inhibiting effects are reduced or eliminated in the presence of moderate amounts of serum albumin or other serum proteins. O'Reilly (32) reported that 20 μM Fe^{2+} doubled serum PPD oxidase activity since it stimulates and serves as a substrate for ceruloplasmin (30, 35), but it is unlikely that free Fe^{2+} ion ever reaches this concentration in normal serum. Thus we conclude that the principal dialyzable serum inhibitor of the ascorbate oxidizing activity of ceruloplasmin at pH 7.0–7.4 is citrate as reported in an earlier paper (17).

III. Citrate as an Inhibitor of Ceruloplasmin

The presence of a dialyzable serum inhibitor of ceruloplasmin can be discerned from experiments in which undialyzed serum was shown to inhibit the rate of oxidation of added ceruloplasmin. After dialysis the ceruloplasmin of the serum becomes more active. This dialyzable inhibitor was identified by concentrating the serum ultrafiltrate from freshly clotted normal blood, passing the concentrate through an Amberlite CG-120 column, and absorption on an Amberlite CG-4B column. The eluate from the latter resin was further purified by paper chromatography so that the eluted inhibitor gave a single spot on paper chromatography with R_f's identical with citrate using four different solvent mixtures. The inhibitor was also identified as citrate in the pentabromoacetone and ammonium citrazinate tests. The amount of citrate necessary to restore the inhibitory effect in dialyzed serum was shown to correspond to the original concentration of citrate in serum, $1.2 \times 10^{-4} M$ (17). An unidentified dialyzable serum inhibitor of ceruloplasmin was also reported by Walshe (33).

Among the common naturally occurring organic acids, citrate alone is sufficiently inhibitory and in sufficient concentration to account for the inhibition of ceruloplasmin by serum. Only isocitrate approaches citrate in inhibitory activity but it is barely detectable ($10^{-8} M$) in serum. Certain earlier studies on the inhibition of ceruloplasmin by other organic acids did not reveal any inhibitors effective in the same range as these tribasic acids (17).

Kinetic studies on the citrate inhibition of the oxidase activity of ceruloplasmin were reported earlier (2, 17, 28) and suggested that citrate was a competitive inhibitor of the ceruloplasmin-catalyzed oxidation of at least three substrates, ascorbate, PPD, and DPD with estimated K_i's in the range of $6 \pm 2 \times 10^{-7} M$. Since the average citrate concentration in normal human serum is 50–100 μM, oxidation of any of these substrates should be strongly affected in serum. Greater concentrations of citrate are required to inhibit ceruloplasmin activity when determined by oxygen uptake, because the ascorbate concentration used is 100 times greater than in the spectrophotometric method (17). As mentioned subsequently for apotransferrin, it is likely that the mechanism of citrate inhibition involves the elimination of the stimulating effects of Fe^{2+} on ceruloplasmin ascorbate oxidizing activity.

IV. Apotransferrin and Transferrin as Inhibitors of Ceruloplasmin

A. Identification as the Nondialyzable Serum Inhibitor

When human serum was exhaustively dialyzed to remove citrate and other low molecular weight species the resulting mixture did not reveal the catalytic activity anticipated from the known ceruloplasmin content, particularly at a pH of 7.4. The addition of dialyzed human serum to homogeneous ceruloplasmin produced an inhibition of the expected ascorbate oxidase activity at pH 7.0–7.4. The inhibitory activity of human serum proteins was eventually traced to Cohn fraction IV-4 and its subfraction IV-7 (34). Since two of the principal components of this fraction are transferrin and apotransferrin these proteins were tested for their effect on the catalytic activity of ceruloplasmin. Both apotransferrin and transferrin proved to be extremely strong inhibitors of ceruloplasmin and they account for most, if not all, the inhibitory activity of dialyzed normal human serum. Apoceruloplasmin, when added in a molar ratio of 50 times the amount of ceruloplasmin present, did not inhibit the catalysis of the oxidation of PPD or ascorbate.

A comparison of the inhibition of the ascorbate oxidase activity of ceruloplasmin by the two principal serum inhibitors, apotransferrin and citrate is shown in Fig. 1. The powerful and apparently stoichiometric range of inhibition of ceruloplasmin by apotransferrin and transferrin appears to be competitive and reversible. The concentrations used in these experiments, in the 10^{-7} M range, are even less than their typical serum concentrations, i.e., ceruloplasmin 2 μM, apotransferrin plus transferrin, 20 μM. We have examined the possibility that a low molecular weight compound associated with apotransferrin might be involved. But experiments designed to prove this have been consistently negative. Apotransferrin also partially inhibits the PPD oxidase activity of ceruloplasmin confirming an earlier observation of Curzon (35) who reported that 1 μM

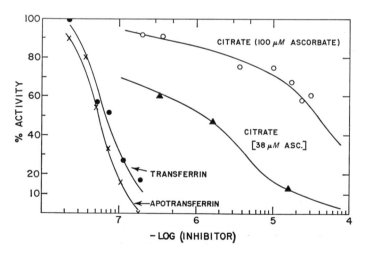

Fig. 1. The effect of different concentrations of the three serum inhibitors on the ascorbate oxidase activity of 0.22 μM ceruloplasmin. The test conditions were 30°, 0.20 M acetate buffer, pH 7.1. The concentration of ascorbate was 100 μM except for one citrate series at 0.38 μM ascorbate.

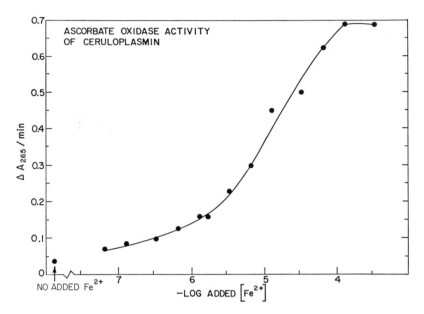

FIG. 2. The stimulation by Fe^{2+} on the rate of ascorbate oxidation by 170 nM cerulo-plasmin. Other test conditions were 30°, 0.20 M acetate buffer, pH 6.3, and 100 μM ascorbate.

human transferrin inhibited DPD oxidation up to 50%. It has not been possible to find evidence for a direct interaction between apotransferrin and ceruloplasmin. Therefore we must consider the possibility that the strong ceruloplasmin inhibition by apotransferrin and citrate may involve the removal of the activating effects of Fe^{2+} on the ascorbate oxidase activity of ceruloplasmin. As shown in Fig. 2, the stimulation of Fe^{2+} on ascorbate oxidation leads to a 20 fold increase in ceruloplasmin activity. This is a greater effect than the enhancing effect (2–4 fold) of Fe^{2+} on the aryldiamine oxidase activity of ceruloplasmin first noted by Curzon (30) and studied extensively by Levine and Peisach (22, 36). At a maximum stimulating level of Fe^{2+}, 2×10^{-4} M, the molecular activity of ascorbate as a substrate for ceruloplasmin is increased to 276. However, both apo-transferrin and citrate can inhibit ascorbate oxidation with ceruloplasmin even when the catalytic activity has not been stimulated by added Fe^{2+}. Further experiments in this area are in progress.

B. Effect of pH on Apotransferrin Inhibition

The effect of apotransferrin and transferrin on ceruloplasmin catalysis is extremely pH sensitive and was best revealed by testing the effect of

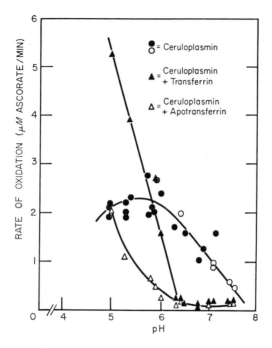

FIG. 3. The effect of pH on the rate of ascorbate oxidation by ceruloplasmin with and without apotransferrin and transferrin. The rate with 0.17 μM ceruloplasmin at 30° and 100 μM ascorbate in 0.2 M acetate buffer is indicated by ● and in 0.02 M imidazole–0.20 M acetate buffer by ○; with 0.076 μM transferrin, ▲; and with 0.073 μM apotransferrin, △. The same buffers were used at the corresponding pH's in all experiments.

serum on ceruloplasmin activity at pH 7.0–7.4. A typical pH-activity curve for ceruloplasmin with ascorbate as substrate is shown in Fig. 3 by the curve denoted by the open and filled circles. The inhibition of ceruloplasmin by apotransferrin is virtually complete above pH 6.0 and declines rapidly until no inhibition can be observed at pH 5.0. The behavior of (iron-containing) transferrin is similar to apotransferrin from pH 7.5 to 6.3, but consistently more transferrin is required for equivalent inhibition than apotransferrin. At lower pH's an apparent marked reduction in ceruloplasmin inhibition is noted until an activation begins below pH 5.8. We believe that this activation is due to the release of Fe, which has been reported to occur with transferrin at a pH of less than 6.0. This reaction and its ultimate effect on ceruloplasmin activity is obviously complex and will have to be studied more completely to separate activation from inhibition effects.

The striking pH sensitivity of these various effects on ceruloplasmin deserves comment. Three different types of pH effects from pH 5 to 7 have been observed as follows: (a) no significant effect of pH on inhibition as illustrated by citrate, (b) significant inhibition above pH 6 and no effect at pH 5 as shown by a apotransferrin, (c) inhibition at pH 5.0 with virtually no effect at pH 7, e.g., chloride ion. These drastically different responses suggest an intense specificity of interaction and (or) pH-induced conformation changes of ceruloplasmin.

An additional ceruloplasmin inhibitor has also been found in serum from Wilson's disease patients. This inhibitor also appears to be a protein. Its identity and its possible relation to a Wilson's disease serum inhibitor of ceruloplasmin suggested by Walshe (33) is being studied further.

V. Summary

Two components of normal human serum appear to exert a major inhibitory control over the ascorbate oxidizing activity of ceruloplasmin. Probably the more significant of these components comprises the transferrins, especially apotransferrin, which inhibits ceruloplasmin at pH 6.0 to 7.5 at very low concentrations. The other influential component is citrate, which inhibits ceruloplasmin over the entire pH 5.0 to 7.5 range.

ACKNOWLEDGMENTS

We are grateful to the Blood Program of the American National Red Cross, Washington, D.C., for various blood fractions and for some purified ceruloplasmin. We should like to thank Professor Anatol G. Morell for a generous gift of apoceruloplasmin and Dr. Gerard A. Fleischer for serum from a patient with Wilson's disease.

REFERENCES

1. Holmberg, C. G., and Laurell, C.-B., *Acta Chem. Scand.*, **1,** 944 (1947).
2. Holmberg, C. G., and Laurell, C.-B., *Acta Chem. Scand.*, **2,** 550 (1948).
3. Holmberg, C. G., and Laurell, C.-B., *Acta Chem. Scand.*, **5,** 476, 921 (1951).
4. Humoller, F. L., Mockler, M., Holtaus, J. M., and Mahler, D. J., *J. Lab. Clin. Med.*, **56,** 222 (1960).
5. Frieden, E., *in* M. Kasha and B. Pullman (eds.), "Horizons in biochemistry," Academic Press Inc., New York, 1962, p. 461.
6. Frieden, E., McDermott, J. A., and Osaki, S., *in* T. E. King, H. S. Mason, and M. Morrison (eds.), "Oxidases and related redox systems," John Wiley & Sons, Inc., New York, 1965, p. 240.
7. Frieden, E., Osaki, S., and Kobayashi, H., *J. Gen. Physiol.*, **49,** 213 (1965).
8. Scheinberg, I. H., and Sternlieb, I., *Pharmacol. Rev.*, **12,** 355 (1960).
9. Adelstein, S. J., and Vallee, B. L., *New Eng. J. Med.*, **265,** 892, 941 (1961).
10. Martin, G. R., and Mecca, C. E., *Arch. Biochem. Biophys.*, **93,** 110 (1961).
11. Niedermeier, W., private communication.
12. Trader, C. D., Frieden, E., and Inaba, T., *Fed. Proc.*, **24,** 222 (1965).
13. Inaba, T., and Frieden, E., unpublished observations.
14. Herner, A. E., and Frieden, E., *J. Biol. Chem.*, **235,** 2845 (1960).

15. Herner, A. E., and Frieden, E., *Arch. Biochem. Biophys.*, **95**, 25 (1961).
16. Trader, C. D., Wortham, J. S., and Frieden, E., *Science*, **139**, 918 (1963).
17. Osaki, S., McDermott, J. A., and Frieden, E., *J. Biol. Chem.*, **239**, PC364 (1964).
18. Osaki, S., McDermott, J. A., and Frieden, E., *J. Biol. Chem.*, **239**, 3570 (1964).
19. Horer, O., Thomas, E., Mira, M., and Nicolau, C., *Rev. Roumaine Chim.*, **9**, 871 (1964).
20. Aisen, P., and Morell, A. G., *J. Biol. Chem.*, **240**, 1974 (1965).
21. Jamieson, G. A., *J. Biol. Chem.*, **240**, 2019 (1965).
22. Peisach, J., and Levine, W. G., *J. Biol. Chem.*, **240**, 2284 (1965).
23. Walaas, E., and Walaas, O., *Arch. Biochem. Biophys.*, **95**, 151 (1961).
24. Walaas, O., Walaas, E., Henriksen, F., and Løvstad, R., *Acta Chem. Scand.*, **17**, S263 (1963).
25. Brown, F. C., and White, J. B., *J. Biol. Chem.*, **236**, 911 (1961).
26. Stark, G. R., and Dawson, C. R., *in* P. O. Boyer, H. Lardy, and K. Myrbach (eds.), "The enzymes," 2nd ed., Vol. VIII, Academic Press Inc., New York, 1963, p. 297.
27. Broman, L., Malmström, B. G., Aasa, R., and Vänngård, T., *Biochim. Biophys. Acta*, **75**, 365 (1963).
28. McDermott, J. A., M. S. thesis, Florida State University, (1963).
29. Broman, L., *Nature*, **182**, 1655 (1958).
30. Curzon, G., *Biochem. J.*, **77**, 66 (1960).
31. Aprison, M. H., Hanson, K. M., and Austin, D. C., *J. Nerv. Ment. Dis.*, **128**, 249 (1959).
32. O'Reilly, S., *Neurology*, **12**, 460 (1962).
33. Walshe, J. M., *J. Clin. Invest.*, **42**, 1048 (1963).
34. Surgenor, D. M., Strong, L. E., Taylor, H. C., Gordon, R. S. Jr., and Gibson, D. M., *J. Am. Chem. Soc.*, **71**, 1223 (1949).
35. Curzon, G., *Biochem. J.*, **79**, 656 (1961).
36. Levine, W., G. and Peisach, J., *Biochim. Biophys. Acta*, **77**, 602 (1963).

Ceruloplasmin Discussion

DR. FRIEDEN: Dr. Scheinberg said that the turnover of ceruloplasmin in serum might be proportional to the amount of absorbed copper.

DR. SCHEINBERG: Equal.

DR. FRIEDEN: I think that is a hypothesis that could be tested, and I wondered if it had been.

DR. SCHEINBERG: No, that is a fact. If you take the known amount of copper in the diet, and if you take the best available figures for the fraction absorbed as 10 to 20% [Gitlin, D., and Janeway, C. A., *Nature*, **185**, 693 (1960)], in the mouse—and we have some similar indications in man—about half a milligram of copper a day is absorbed. The turnover of ceruloplasmin (ceruloplasmin copper does not exchange *in vivo*) gives a turnover of about half a milligram of ceruloplasmin copper a day. The copper absorbed consequently goes into ceruloplasmin, and not into the brain or the liver. The details, nobody knows. The attempts of Dr. Aisen and his collaborators to determine whether copper ultimately is excreted via the bile, the intestinal wall or the urine all have been negative.

DR. FRIEDEN: Can you modify that by modifying the amount of copper absorbed in some experimental way?

DR. SCHEINBERG: That is what Dr. Bearn referred to earlier in the experiment involving feeding copper.

DR. FRIEDEN: Lethal doses, I gather.

DR. SCHEINBERG: No, no—to himself. He's very much alive.

DR. MASON: Dr. Scheinberg has suggested that because ceruloplasmin exists it must have a function. I would like to point out that "that ain't necessarily so." An enzyme which has been known for over 100 years and is very widely distributed and very highly characterized—namely, catalase—has no known physiological function, and in fact in those cases of acatalasia there is no significant pathology except perhaps slightly greater susceptibility to infection.

DR. SCHEINBERG: I agree with you, Doctor.

DR. MASON: In his very interesting chapter on catalase in "The enzymes" [2nd ed., Vol. 8, P. D. Boyer, H. Lardy, and K. Myrbäck (eds.), Academic Press Inc., New York, 1963, p. 147] Nicholls points out that such a protein could conceivably be an evolutionary vestige. While it may very well be that ceruloplasmin plays a very important role and that in its absence Wilson's disease ensues, it could also be that it is merely a vestige.

DR. SCHEINBERG: I certainly agree that it "ain't necessarily so." I'm only saying that it's quite likely to be; but beyond the teleology I think the second thing that you said is much more impressive.

Wilson's disease is the only condition in which there is a lifelong deficiency of ceruloplasmin. There is a marked associated abnormality resulting, which is progressive and fatal, and nothing else happens. And if you put both of these facts together you can forget the teleology—it's quite different from acatalasia.

DR. HOLTZMAN: In reference to Dr. Poillon's paper, we also tried to separate ceruloplasmin into subunits. In preliminary experiments, we incubated ceruloplasmin in 8 M urea in the presence of mercaptoethanol, pH 7 to 8, then passed the treated ceruloplasmin though a column of Sephadex G-100 equilibrated with 8 M urea and mercaptoethanol. We got two peaks, and the fingerprints of the tryptic digests are quite different. There are 114 arginine and lysine residues per molecule of ceruloplasmin. The tryptic peptide map of the molecule has only 50 spots, and that would suggest that there is a repeating unit, as one would strongly suspect, rather than one long polypeptide chain. The fingerprints of the subunits are different from each other, and each has about half the number of spots of the total. From this we would calculate that there probably are subunits, each of which is repeated twice. This disagrees with Dr. Poillon's data. Our separation on Sephadex G-100 suggests a molecular weight difference. It is possible even under the conditions of gel filtration in 8 M urea that the so-called heavy subunit is really a polymer itself.

DR. PEISACH: A comment on Professor Walaas' paper. When we first examined concentrated solutions of ceruloplasmin we noted that the addition of aryl substrates always produced a flash of green color [Peisach, J., and Levine, W. G., Biochim. Biophys. Acta, **77**, 615 (1963)]. Now, it seems reasonable that the addition of catecholamine to ceruloplasmin (Walaas, Fig. 4) represents a decrease of ceruloplasmin absorption at 605 mμ and, at the first break in the curve (plateau), the formation of a green intermediate added to the decrease at 605 mμ leads to a situation where there is no change of optical absorption. This is followed by a falloff at 605 mμ. I think your findings give support to the charge-transfer phenomenon that we originally postulated.

DR. MORELL: But this would not explain the difference in rates between that first portion of the curve and the second portion of the curve.

DR. WALAAS: No, Dr. Peisach, during reduction of ceruloplasmin by catecholamines anaerobically we have definitely not been able to detect any given oxidation product of the substrates interfering with the 605 mμ absorption curve. After the first reduction step we have recorded the visible absorption spectrum, and have not been able to detect any shift in the ceruloplasmin absorption band with a maximum at 605 mμ. However, we have also observed that the interpretation of 605 mμ absorption curves of ceruloplasmin during reduction by PPD is much more difficult due to the formation of colored oxidation products of these substrates.

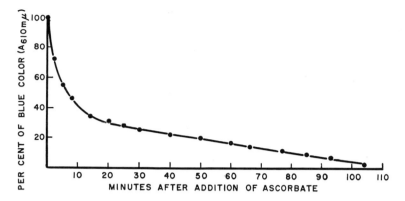

FIG. 1. Decolorization of ceruloplasmin by ascorbate sufficient to reduce 50% of total copper from Cu^{2+} to Cu^+. Phosphate buffer, pH 7.4, 37°.

DR. MORELL: I would like also to confirm results of Dr. Walaas in a somewhat similar system. Dr. Aisen and I decolorized ceruloplasmin in a vacuum with ascorbic acid, and consistently observed that there were two phases in the reaction. We added four electrons per eight atoms of copper, and we always found an initial fast decolorization until about 50% of the color was gone, and then a slow reaction for the rest of the decolorization (Fig. 1).

DR. CURZON: With regard to the difference between O'Reilly and myself [*Biochem. Biophys. Res. Communs*, **2**, 284 (1960)] and Peisach and Levine [*J. Biol. Chem.*, **240**, 2284 (1965)] on the mechanism by which iron increases the activity of ceruloplasmin, we explained it as a cyclic coupled iron oxidation system in which ceruloplasmin oxidizes Fe^{2+} to Fe^{3+}, and then Fe^{3+} oxidizes substrate and is reduced to Fe^{2+}. These stages definitely work individually. However, we found much less activation with Fe^{3+} than with the same amount of Fe^{2+}, which does not fit with a cyclic mechanism. So far we have never gotten that. We have only obtained 20% of the Fe^{2+} effect when we use Fe^{3+}. Perhaps the dilute Fe^{3+} in solution is in an unavailable, hydrolyzed, and aggregated state. Another possibility is that putting all the iron into the system as Fe^{3+} might result in much of it being bound by some site in the ceruloplasmin molecule before substrate is able to react with it. I think that both Levine and Peisach's mechanism and ours are possibilities. We need kinetic data on individual stages to decide.

Just one other point. I see from the last paper by Peisach and Levine [*J. Biol. Chem.*, **240**, 2284 (1965)] on laccase that although this is similar to ceruloplasmin, iron does not increase activity. Our mechanism implies that with ceruloplasmin the PPD and iron are competing substrates.

As PPD and DPD are much better substrates for laccase than for ceruloplasmin they perhaps compete for the enzyme very successfully with the iron so that enhancement of activity by iron may only occur here at very low DPD concentrations.

DR. PEISACH: In answer to your first point concerning the ferrous effect, if you take a solution of Fe^{3+} and bubble oxygen through it to remove all the Fe^{2+} contaminant, you will see *no* stimulation, not 20%. You completely obviate the effect by removing Fe^{2+} contaminants from Fe^{3+} solutions.

There is something bothering me about the assay procedure for ceruloplasmin commonly used by clinicians. I have always felt that clinicians were not really getting back in their ceruloplasmin purification procedures the quantities equal to those they originally assumed to be present. The general technique in the measurement of ceruloplasmin levels in serum is to add PPD and to observe the rate of purple color formation. Also they isolate and purify the ceruloplasmin and assay for this with a PPD oxidation assay and relate ceruloplasmin concentrations to the amount of oxidase activity in both systems.

Well, these are two totally different systems. Iron will not stimulate ceruloplasmin oxidation in serum as much as in a purified system. Therefore, instead of using a PPD assay, where the role of iron is complex, I suggest

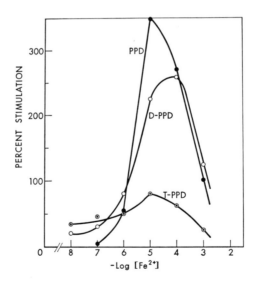

FIG. 2. Effect of Fe^{2+} on the ceruloplasmin-catalyzed oxidation of aromatic diamines. PPD, *p*-phenylenediamine; D-PPD, *N*,*N*-diethyl-*p*-phenylenediamine; T-PPD, *N*,*N*,*N'*,*N'*-tetramethyl-*p*-phenylenediamine. After Levine, W. G., and Peisach, J., *Nature*, **207**, 406 (1965).

that clinical chemists should use DPD, where the iron stimulation is much less; or, better still, use N,N,N',N'-tetramethyl-p-phenylenediamine, where iron stimulation is negligible (see Fig. 2).

DR. SCHEINBERG: Perhaps one of the products of the PPD reaction ties up ferrous ions. This may well explain some of the controversy involving iron stimulation.

DR. MORELL: I want to point out that our purified preparations of ceruloplasmin are enhanced in their enzymatic activity with PPD upon their addition to the plasma system. When they are in a plasma system they are more active than in a buffer.

DR. FRIEDEN: But you don't need much Fe^{2+} for stimulation.

DR. WALSHE: We find that adding ferrous ion to serum will greatly potentiate the oxidase activity of ceruloplasmin.

DR. MORELL: Dr. Frieden, you cautioned against this iron contamination, but if you actually eliminate iron, would you ever find an ascorbic acid oxidase activity of ceruloplasmin?

DR. FRIEDEN: I think the data are headed in that direction, and I think what we may have to say in the future is that Fe^{2+} is a co-factor for the ascorbate oxidase activity, but the protein is required and the iron is required. I think that fits the definition of most enzymes and catalytic activity.

DR. MORELL: It would be fair, then, to say that ceruloplasmin functions as an ascorbic acid oxidase only in conjunction with a co-factor, and the co-factor is iron.

DR. FRIEDEN: Well, we haven't been able to knock all the activity out by eliminating Fe^{2+} insofar as possible. There is always a residual activity.

DR. WALAAS: The rate of reduction of ceruloplasmin under anaerobic conditions decreases in the order: p-phenylenediamines > catecholamines ≫ ascorbic acid. The ascorbic acid reduction of ceruloplasmin is very slow. I wonder to what extent the cupric-cuprous cycle is really operating in this activity. Perhaps it is a different kind of catalytic activity involving the iron more than the copper.

DR. WALSHE: We have done a lot of work on the effect of the ability of iproniazid to inhibit the oxidation activity of ceruloplasmin in whole serum, using DPD as substrate. In normal people a concentration of iproniazid (10^{-3} M) will produce about 80% inhibition, but it only produces about 30 to 40% inhibition when added to Wilson's disease serum. Now, if this is simply a decolorization effect, it should be exactly the same in both sera. There must be in part at least an inhibition action on the enzyme activity, too.

We have tried oxidizing DPD either with peroxide or by simply allowing the solution to stand on the bench in the sunlight, so you don't have the embarrassment of getting rid of your bromine, and then adding iproniazid to reduce it. It will certainly produce some reduction, but nothing like the percentage of inhibition it will produce. What is more interesting—if you add your iproniazid and ceruloplasmin together, you will then increase your rate of disappearance of color. This suggests to me that we produced a system where you are actually using ceruloplasmin as a reducing agent instead of an oxidizing one.

DR. HOLTZMAN: Dr. Frieden and Dr. Walshe mentioned that there was a possible inhibitor of ceruloplasmin in serum of patients with Wilson's disease. In the two patients from whom we purified ceruloplasmin, the yield of ceruloplasmin was not higher than we expected. One cannot say therefore that in patients with low ceruloplasmin, there are simply inhibitors and that ceruloplasmin is there but we are not seeing it. I don't think such an inhibitor is significant in changing the measured levels of ceruloplasmin.

DR. WALAAS: I would like to make a comment on Dr. Curzon's model. Apparently it is in disagreement with our conclusion that we have two different kinds of copper centers in ceruloplasmin. Dr. Curzon now thinks that all four are sitting in one cluster. I would ask the question: "What happens to the ceruloplasmin when you add substrate?"

Our idea can be illustrated by (Fig. 3, top) showing two pairs of 2 Cu^{2+} differently bound to the peptide chains. When you add substrate two of the copper atoms easily interact and are reduced. This brings about conformation changes of the polypeptide chains. I think there is good evidence from the work by Yankeelow and Koshland, [*J. Biol. Chem.*, **240**, 1593 (1965)] that the binding of substrates induces conformation changes in the flexible polypeptide chains of enzymes. As shown (Fig. 3, bottom) these conformation changes bring together the second pair of Cu^{2+} with the substrate in a complex, and the whole cluster may now be able to interact with one molecule of azide.

I think this fits in with Dr. Curzon's observation that ceruloplasmin must first react with substrate to get the azide inhibition.

DR. SCHEINBERG: Regarding Dr. Curzon's comment about the well in the ceruloplasmin molecule I want to ask Dr. Blumberg whether if the copper atoms were as close as this you would expect some interaction in the EPR spectrum.

DR. BLUMBERG: Dr. Curzon has given us a scale drawing with an Ångstrom unit marked clearly on it, but the drawing concerns the configuration when all four of those atoms were cuprous. What we have said from the EPR data is that, when we look at the atoms which are cupric, each one appears to be at least six Ångstroms from other cupric copper atoms. But both points of view could be correct, because on the change of oxidation state the configuration could change in such a clever way that the coppers

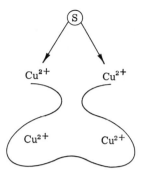

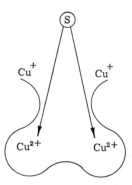

FIG. 3. Possible arrangement of copper ions in ceruloplasmin.

are brought into such a proximity that they can indeed fit on to a single oxygen molecule, and upon transfer of electrons spring back again.

DR. MASON: Now, on the point of azide inhibition I'd like to ask Dr. Curzon specifically: Do you think that the azide combines with the cupric form of the protein, or the cuprous?

DR. CURZON: I think the kinetics show that the azide combines with something in the protein that is changed by the interaction with substrate, and this very much suggests to me that the azide is combining with valence-changing copper when it is cuprous.

DR. JØRGENSEN: With respect to Dr. Curzon's most remarkable finding of inhibition by one azide ion on four Cu's at a time, may I mention the fact that a Swedish crystallographer, Hesse, [*Arkiv för Kemi*, **20,** 481 (1963)] found that Cu⁺ diethyldithiocarbamate exists as a tetramer and contains a tetrahedron of four copper atoms. This seems to be a very specific thing for Cu⁺, because, for example, Hesse finds a similar Au⁺

compound is a dimer. I must also emphasize that the distances in this tetrahedron are slightly shorter than in the metallic element.

So one could have the slightly heterodox opinion that in a few cases one could find metallic clusters, such as those studied by Dr. Nyholm in London [C. K. Jørgensen, "Inorganic Complexes," Academic Press Inc., 1963]. One of the things happening here might simply be that the eight copper atoms occur in two tetrahedral clusters, one of the atoms sticking its neck sufficiently out of the protein bulk to be inhibited by just one azide.

DR. BLUMBERG: The gross change of protein configuration suggested by Dr. Walaas, where many coppers move a long way back and forth during enzyme activity, violates my intuition a little in regard to entropy. The ultraviolet optical rotatory dispersion of oxidized and reduced ceruloplasmin does not, in fact, differ very much, so no enormous changes are taking place.

I would like to try to synthesize some remarks made by Drs. Jørgensen, Williams, Curzon, and Freeman into a single operating model for the ceruloplasmin molecule (see Fig. 4).

First we write down Dr. Curzon's suggestion for the four Cu$^+$, arranged perhaps as Dr. Jørgensen has suggested. These are the center group in this Fig. 4. Then out from these we have the four copper atoms which rest in the cupric state. These are not necessarily very close to each other. The line represents a coupling such that when the outer group is oxidized, reduced, or changed in configuration, the inner group immediately knows about it and changes its configuration such that oxygen (or azide) will or will not go on. So when substrate comes along, it binds to the outer Cu^{2+} and, as suggested by Dr. Freeman, changes its configuration. Perhaps

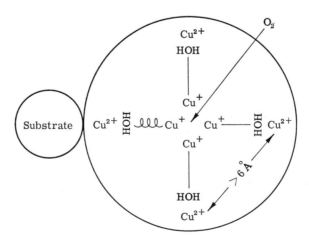

FIG. 4. A suggested model of the oxidative apparatus of the ceruloplasmin molecule.

a water molecule moves away from the Cu^{2+} to give the signal. When that happens in all four cases, the group in the middle is then in a position to accept an oxygen molecule, which it does. Immediately the four electrons go back via one of Dr. William's conduction mechanisms to reestablish the initial configuration.

DR. CAUGHEY: How many coppers are reacting with a given oxygen molecule?

DR. BLUMBERG: Well, in a certain sense all of them are.

DR. CAUGHEY: No. I mean, the ones that atoms of the oxygen molecule have to come in closest (or direct) contact with.

DR. BLUMBERG: I'm referring to Dr. Curzon's Figure for this; that configuration requires four.

DR. CURZON: But these are the four valence-changing coppers.

DR. BLUMBERG: Everybody has been assuming that some, but not all, of the coppers are changing valence. In this model all of the coppers change valence. However, there is an intermediate state where it is waiting for the reaction to proceed sufficiently so that it can restore itself to the resting state.

DR. CURZON: What is the advantage of this new assumption?

DR. BLUMBERG: It avoids any large configuration change in the protein and is compatible with the EPR data that the ones that rest as Cu^{2+} are separated from each other and your data that the ones that are going to latch on to the oxygen are in close proximity to each other.

DR. FRIEDEN: Doesn't that imply a movement of electrons from the center out? Dr. Williams would frown on that, I think. As I recall, he said that electrons don't move through peptide chains. Are you implying that they would?

DR. BLUMBERG: He proposed several mechanisms of conduction in his paper as to how this could be implemented in a protein.

DR. SCHEINBERG: How does the conformation change?

DR. BLUMBERG: The conformation change only has to be minuscule. It only has to change so that an oxygen molecule does or does not like to sit in this hole that Dr. Curzon drew.

DR. SCHEINBERG: But that change has to be signaled by the Cu^{2+}.

DR. BLUMBERG: Of course the Cu^{2+}'s are attached mechanically and electronically on the outer side.

DR. CAUGHEY: At the Oxidase Symposium at Amherst last summer we discussed the possibility of a linear array, or at least a sequential array, of copper atoms where a terminal copper atom was the only one presented for reaction. I wondered if you have evidence that can eliminate the possibility for such a structure or why you would prefer the model you presented.

DR. CURZON: Was this a structure in which the four copper atoms were close together, and electrons jumping along from one to the other?

DR. CAUGHEY: We discussed several possibilities. There is the possibility, I believe, of metal-metal bonding as well as of bridging ligands between the copper atoms. This arrangement would work in the following way. In the fully reduced protein with all four coppers as Cu^+, one copper atom (the terminal one) reacts with oxygen; the oxygen is reduced to the level of water and each copper atom is oxidized to Cu^{2+} as a consequence of electron transfer from and through internal copper atoms to the terminal copper atom. Subsequently the terminal copper of the fully oxidized protein could then receive electrons from reducing substrate molecules until all four copper atoms were reduced back to Cu^+. Thus the electrons reach all four copper atoms via a pathway through bridging groups or possibly via metal–metal bonds. One could envision sulfide bridging groups between these copper atoms.

DR. BLUMBERG: In order to separate them by more than 6 Ångstroms?

DR. CAUGHEY: Yes. Now, what evidence really eliminates such a possibility as this, which is a rather simple arrangement and is consistent with reduction of all four and subsequent oxidation of all four?

DR. BLUMBERG: I have no evidence to confirm or deny such a suggestion. I only drew my diagram in order to incorporate suggestions by Dr. Curzon and others.

DR. AISEN: If the coppers are so clustered, I wonder if crystallographic techniques shouldn't pick them up fairly clearly.

DR. FREEMAN: Copper atoms are not "heavy" enough (do not have enough electrons) to be picked out of such a complex structure as a protein, until the structure is on the way to a complete solution. The answer to Dr. Aisen's question is therefore that you must find (a) somebody who can grow crystals of the pure protein and of several isomorphously substituted heavy-atom derivatives, and (b) a crystallographer with a well-equipped laboratory, lots of patience, and a corresponding research grant. The crystallographer may ultimately determine the whole structure, not just part of it.

The reason for this is that the mathematical solutions of crystal structures are systematically overdetermined. A very large number of data (diffraction measurements) are used to find a much smaller number of parameters (atomic positions). Every observation is linked mathematically to every parameter, so that you cannot determine the positions of some atoms and not others. (An exception arises when you have a derivative of such a "heavy" atom that, for a first approximation, you can forget about the rest of the structure.)

This is the respect in which crystallography differs from the other methods whose results have been discussed at this symposium. Some of these methods do measure something specific about a small part of a protein. At the same time, reduced to physical terms, many biochemical problems still involve extrapolations to many more parameters than there are measurements.

To return to Dr. Aisen's question: Pending complete crystal structure analyses of copper proteins, our information is limited to what we can learn from precise structure determinations of simpler compounds. I should like to suggest that there is now enough of this information for it to begin being useful in restricting one's speculations on problems of copper protein biochemistry.

For instance, it is certain that where copper forms chelate rings with part of a protein or peptide, these rings have a well defined geometry which is strainless as long as the copper is cupric. If the Cu^{2+} is reduced to Cu^{+}, four bonds which lie at angles between 84°and 90° from one another have to be rearranged to point at 100° to 120° from one another toward the corners of an approximate tetrahedron. This requires a small shift in the protein structure. If the Cu^{2+} is part of a chelate ring, the ring will be broken; its geometry will simply not be suitable for Cu^{+}.

There have been suggestions that Cu^{2+} can be reduced to Cu^{+}, or Cu^{+} oxidized to Cu^{2+}, without protein rearrangement. The structural evidence shows that some local rearrangement *must* take place, but it may not be significant enough to be detected by the methods used to measure protein configuration.

We should therefore consider whether there is any way of binding a copper atom to the protein flexibly enough so that the different steric requirements of both Cu^{+} and Cu^{2+} can be accommodated by minor local changes without major disturbances of the surrounding protein. Now, among the 15 cupric complexes reviewed in my paper at this symposium, there is only one Cu^{2+} atom whose four closest ligand atoms are *not* at the corners of an approximate square: In bisimidazolato-Cu^{2+}, one of the two types of copper is bonded to four different ligand molecules whose mutual repulsions cause gross distortions from a square-planar environment. The geometrical conditions here are much less rigid than in chelate ring formation.

This leads to the idea that oxidation-reduction may take place without a drastic rearrangement of the protein near the copper-binding site provided that (a) no chelate ring is involved, and (b) the copper is attached to at most one site on the main peptide chain and is otherwise bound only by the functional groups of flexible side-chains.

As far as the specific question of the mechanism in ceruloplasmin is concerned, Dr. Blumberg has said two things which are almost too good to be true (and which may, therefore, just be true). His first suggestion is that the cuprous atoms *move* at the instant when they become cupric. When the Cu^+ atoms lose an electron, their bond angles must simultaneously change from 109° to near 90°. It is not unlikely that this pushes the copper atoms some distance relative to the rest of the protein, although 6 Å seems a rather larger distance.

Second, the proposed reduction mechanism seems to be explicable in terms of a suggestion made in my paper. The copper proteins about which we are talking are blue. Blue Cu^{2+}–peptide complexes generally have copper atoms with total coordination number 5. Imagine that such a copper atom is bonded to the protein by four strong bonds, and to a water molecule or other group by a weaker bond normal to the other four. If a potential ligand, such as a substrate molecule, now collides with the copper, the bond to the fifth ligand may break and the substrate become bonded to the copper. The breaking of the bond to the fifth ligand may provide the signal that is needed to trigger the proposed reaction a few atoms away.

It is important that such a process should be reversible: unless it is, the substrate will stay bonded to the copper. It has been one of the fundamental difficulties in biological coordination chemistry that there has been no reason why a protein–Cu^{2+}–substrate complex, once formed, should ever come apart. Dr. Blumberg's model is a complex which *will* come apart. If our imaginations have stretched so far, then it is not impossible to see that the displaced water molecule (or other apical group) may bounce back, reform its bond to the copper atom and displace the substrate.

If these comments appear far-fetched, they at least illustrate the way in which the facts of structural chemistry can be used as criteria for the workability of biochemical hypotheses. In view of the lateness of the hour, this may be a suitably interdisciplinary note on which to end this Symposium.

DR. PETERS: I should like to say a word especially on behalf of those from overseas. We do want to thank you, all of those who have made this possible, especially Dr. Peisach, Dr. Aisen, and Dr. Blumberg and all their staff who have been so devoted in helping us and who have put up with us as well as with our manuscripts. I'm sure we are all very grateful to them. We are entranced by these excellent surroundings. We are very grateful for the financial side of this. I think we can say that we have all learned something. Sometimes, as in my case, we learn of our ignorance, but at any rate we have enjoyed the intellectual treat. Of course, this sort of true blue is rather near the center of my interest as it is the Oxford blue and we all hope, and I personally feel sure, that this conference will bear much fruit in the future. There will be, as it were, personal ligands which will go on, and I hope lead to an even better conference in the future.

Thank you very much indeed, those of you who made this possible.

Index